Stanley Gibbo
Commonwealth Stamp

Cyprus, Gibraltar & Malta

5th edition 2019

STANLEY GIBBONS LTD
London and Ringwood

By Appointment to
Her Majesty The Queen
Philatelists
Stanley Gibbons Ltd
London

Published by Stanley Gibbons Ltd
Editorial, Publication and Sales Offices:
7 Parkside, Christchurch Road, Ringwood,
Hants BH24 3SH

British Library Cataloguing in Publication Data.
A catalogue record for this book is available from the
British Library.

1st Edition - 2004
2nd Edition - 2008
3rd Edition - 2011
4th Edition - 2014
5th Edition - 2019

Errors and omissions excepted
the colour reproduction of stamps is only as
accurate as the printing process will allow.

ISBN-13: 978-1-911304-24-1

Item No. R2976-19

Printed by
Cambrian Printers, Wales

Contents

Stanley Gibbons Holdings Plc

Stanley Gibbons Limited,
Stanley Gibbons Auctions
399 Strand, London WC2R 0LX
Tel: +44 (0)207 836 8444
Fax: +44 (0)207 836 7342
E-mail: help@stanleygibbons.com
Website: www.stanleygibbons.com
for all departments, Auction and
Specialist Stamp Departments.

Open Monday–Friday 9.30 am to 5 pm
Shop. Open Monday–Friday 9 am
to 5.30 pm and Saturday 9.30 am
to 5.30 pm

Stanley Gibbons Publications
Gibbons Stamp Monthly and
Philatelic Exporter
7 Parkside, Christchurch Road,
Ringwood, Hampshire BH24 3SH.
Tel: +44 (0)1425 472363
Fax: +44 (0)1425 470247
E-mail: help@stanleygibbons.com
Publications Mail Order.
FREEPHONE 0800 611622

Monday–Friday 8.30 am to 5 pm

Stanley Gibbons Publications Overseas Representation
Stanley Gibbons Publications are represented overseas by the following:

Australia
Renniks Publications PTY LTD
Unit 3 37-39 Green Street,
Banksmeadow, NSW 2019, Australia
Tel: +612 9695 7055
Website: www.renniks.com

Canada
Unitrade Associates
99 Floral Parkway, Toronto,
Ontario M6L 2C4, Canada
Tel: +1 416 242 5900
Website: www.unitradeassoc.com

Germany
Schaubek Verlag Leipzig
Am Glaeschen 23, D-04420
Markranstaedt, Germany
Tel: +49 34 205 67823
Website: www.schaubek.de

Italy
Ernesto Marini S.R.L.
V. Struppa, 300, Genova, 16165, Italy
Tel: +3901 0247-3530
Website: www.ernestomarini.it

Japan
Japan Philatelic
PO Box 2, Suginami-Minami,
Tokyo 168-8081, Japan
Tel: +81 3330 41641
Website: www.yushu.co.jp

Netherlands – also covers Belgium
Denmark, Finland & France
Uitgeverij Davo BV
PO Box 411, Ak Deventer, 7400
Netherlands
Tel: +315 7050 2700
Website: www.davo.nl

New Zealand
House of Stamps
PO Box 12, Paraparaumu,
New Zealand
Tel: +61 6364 8270
Website: www.houseofstamps.co.nz

Philatelic Distributors
PO Box 863
15 Mount Edgecumbe Street
New Plymouth 4615, New Zealand
Tel: +6 46 758 65 68
Website: www.stampcollecta.com

Norway
SKANFIL A/S
SPANAV. 52 / BOKS 2030
N-5504 HAUGESUND, Norway
Tel: +47-52703940
E-mail: magne@skanfil.no

Singapore
C S Philatelic Agency
Peninsula Shopping Centre #04-29
3 Coleman Street, 179804, Singapore
Tel: +65 6337-1859
Website: www.cs.com.sg

South Africa
Peter Bale Philatelics
PO Box 3719, Honeydew,
2040, South Africa
Tel: +27 11 462 2463
Tel: +27 82 330 3925
E-mail: balep@iafrica.com

Sweden
Chr Winther Sorensen AB
Box 43, S-310 20 Knaered, Sweden
Tel: +46 43050743
Website: www.collectia.se

Stanley Gibbons
Stamp Catalogues

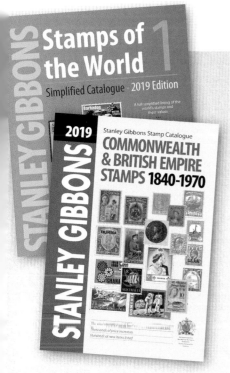

We have catalogues
to suit every aspect of
stamp collecting

Our catalogues cover stamps issued
from across the globe - from the
Penny Black to the latest issues.
Whether you're a specialist in a
certain reign or a thematic collector,
we should have something to suit
your needs. All catalogues include
the famous SG numbering system,
making it as easy as possible to find
the stamp you're looking for.

**Commonwealth & British Empire Stamps
1840–1970** (121st edition, 2019)

King George VI (9th edition, 2018)

Commonwealth Country Catalogues
Australia & Dependencies
(11th Edition, 2018)
Bangladesh, Pakistan & Sri Lanka
(3rd edition, 2015)
Belize, Guyana, Trinidad & Tobago
(2nd edition, 2013)
Brunei, Malaysia & Singapore
(5th edition, 2017)
Canada (6th edition, 2016)
Cyprus, Gibraltar & Malta
(5th edition, 2019)
East Africa with Egypt & Sudan
(4th edition, 2018)
Eastern Pacific (3rd edition, 2015)
Falkland Islands (7th edition, 2016)
Hong Kong (6th edition, 2018)
**India (including Convention &
Feudatory States)** (5th edition, 2018)
Indian Ocean (3rd edition, 2016)
Ireland (6th edition, 2015)
Leeward Islands (3rd edition, 2017)
New Zealand (6th edition, 2016)
Northern Caribbean, Bahamas & Bermuda
(4th edition, 2016)
St. Helena & Dependencies
(6th edition, 2017)
Southern & Central Africa
(2nd edition, 2014)
West Africa (2nd edition, 2012)
Western Pacific (4th edition, 2017)
Windward Islands & Barbados
(3rd edition, 2015)

Stamps of the World 2019
Volume 1	Abu Dhabi – Charkhari
Volume 2	Chile – Georgia
Volume 3	German Commands – Jasdan
Volume 4	Jersey – New Republic
Volume 5	New South Wales – Singapore
Volume 6	Sirmoor – Zululand

Great Britain Catalogues
2019 Collect British Stamps
(70th edition, 2019)
Collect Channel Islands & Isle of Man
(30th edition, 2016)
2018 GB Concise
(33rd edition, 2018)

Great Britain Specialised
Volume 1	Queen Victoria
	(16th edition, 2012)
Volume 2	King Edward VII to
	King George VI
	(14th edition, 2015)
Volume 3*	Queen Elizabeth II
	Pre-decimal issues
	(12th edition, 2011)
Volume 4	Queen Elizabeth II Decimal
	Definitive Issues – Part 1
	(10th edition, 2008)
	Queen Elizabeth II Decimal
	Definitive Issues – Part 2
	(10th edition, 2010)

Foreign Countries
Antarctica (2nd edition, 2012)
Arabia (1st edition, 2016)
Austria and Hungary (8th Edition 2014)
Belgium & Luxembourg
(1st edition, 2015)
Central America (3rd edition, 2007)
China (12th edition, 2018)
Czech Republic and Slovakia
(1st edition, 2017)
Denmark and Norway
(1st edition, 2018)
Finland and Sweden
(1st edition, 2017)
France, Andorra and Monaco
(1st edition, 2015)
French Colonies (1st edition, 2016)
Germany (12th edition, 2018)
Japan & Korea (5th edition, 2008)
Middle East (1st Edition, 2018)
Netherlands & Colonies
(1st edition, 2017)
North East Africa (2nd edition 2017)
Poland (1st edition, 2015)
Russia (7th edition, 2014)
South-East Asia (5th edition, 2012)
United States of America
(8th edition, 2015)

*Currently out of stock.

General Philatelic Information and Guidelines to the Scope of Stanley Gibbons Commonwealth Catalogues

These notes reflect current practice in compiling the Stanley Gibbons Commonwealth Catalogues.

The Stanley Gibbons Stamp Catalogue has a very long history and the vast quantity of information it contains has been carefully built up by successive generations through the work of countless individuals. Philately is never static and the Catalogue has evolved and developed over the years. These notes relate to the current criteria upon which a stamp may be listed or priced. These criteria have developed over time and may have differed somewhat in the early years of this catalogue. These notes are not intended to suggest that we plan to make wholesale changes to the listing of classic issues in order to bring them into line with today's listing policy, they are designed to inform catalogue users as to the policies currently in operation.

PRICES

The prices quoted in this Catalogue are the estimated selling prices of Stanley Gibbons Ltd at the time of publication. They are, unless it is specifically stated otherwise, for examples in fine condition for the issue concerned. Superb examples are worth more; those of a lower quality considerably less.

All prices are subject to change without prior notice and Stanley Gibbons Ltd may from time to time offer stamps below catalogue price. Individual low value stamps sold at 399 Strand are liable to an additional handling charge. Purchasers of new issues should note the prices charged for them contain an element for the service rendered and so may exceed the prices shown when the stamps are subsequently catalogued. Postage and handling charges are extra.

No guarantee is given to supply all stamps priced, since it is not possible to keep every catalogued item in stock. Commemorative issues may, at times, only be available in complete sets and not as individual values.

Quotation of prices. The prices in the left-hand column are for unused stamps and those in the right-hand column are for used.

A dagger (†) denotes that the item listed does not exist in that condition and a blank, or dash, that it exists, or may exist, but we are unable to quote a price.

We welcome information concerning items which are currently unpriced; such assistance may lead to them being priced in future editions.

Prices are expressed in pounds and pence sterling. One pound comprises 100 pence (£1 = 100p).

The method of notation is as follows: pence in numerals (e.g. 10 denotes ten pence); pounds and pence, up to £100, in numerals (e.g. 4·25 denotes four pounds and twenty-five pence); prices above £100 are expressed in whole pounds with the '£' sign shown.

Unused stamps. Great Britain and Commonwealth: the prices for unused stamps of Queen Victoria to King George V are for lightly hinged examples. Unused prices for King Edward VIII, King George VI and Queen Elizabeth issues are for unmounted mint or 'mint never hinged' (MNH).

Some stamps from the King George VI period are often difficult to find in unmounted mint condition. In such instances we would expect that collectors would need to pay a high proportion of the price quoted to obtain mounted mint examples. Generally speaking lightly mounted mint stamps from this reign, issued before 1945, are in considerable demand.

Used stamps. The used prices are normally for stamps fine postally used, which for the vast majority of those issued since 1900 refers to cancellation with a clear circular or oval dated postmark. It may also include stamps cancelled to order, where this practice exists, or with commemorative or 'first day' postmarks.

A pen-cancellation on early issues can sometimes correctly denote postal use. Instances are individually noted in the Catalogue in explanation of the used price given.

Prices quoted for bisects on cover or large piece are for those dated during the period officially authorised.

Stamps not sold unused to the public (e.g. some official stamps) are priced used only.

The use of 'unified' designs, that is stamps inscribed for both postal and fiscal purposes, results in a number of stamps of very high face value. In some instances these may not have been primarily intended for postal purposes, but if they are so inscribed we include them. The used prices shown refer to postally used examples, although prices for fiscally used may be shown within brackets. Collectors should be careful to avoid stamps with fiscal cancellations being offered as 'postal fiscals' and also fiscally used stamps that have had their cancellations removed and fraudulent postmarks applied.

Cover prices. To assist collectors, cover prices are quoted for issues up to 1945 at the beginning of each country.

The system gives a general guide in the form of a factor by which the corresponding used price of the basic loose stamp should be multiplied when found in fine average condition on cover.

Care is needed in applying the factors and they relate to a cover which bears a single of the denomination listed; if more than one denomination is present the most highly priced attracts the multiplier and the remainder are priced at the simple figure for used singles in arriving at a total.

The cover should be of non-philatelic origin; bearing the correct postal rate for the period and distance involved and cancelled with the markings normal to the offices concerned. Purely philatelic items have a cover value only slightly greater than the catalogue value for the corresponding used stamps. This applies generally to those high-value stamps used philatelically rather than in the normal course of commerce. Low-value stamps, e.g. ¼d. and ½d., are desirable when used as a single rate on cover and merit an increase in 'multiplier' value.

First day covers in the period up to 1945 are not within the scope of the system and the multiplier should not be used. As a special category of philatelic usage, with wide variations in valuation according to scarcity, they require separate treatment.

Oversized covers, difficult to accommodate on an album page, should be reckoned as worth little more than the corresponding value of the used stamps. The condition of a cover also affects its value. Except for 'wreck covers', serious damage or soiling reduce the value where the postal markings and stamps are ordinary ones. Conversely, visual appeal adds to the value and this can include freshness of appearance, important addresses, old-fashioned but legible hand-writing, historic town-names, etc.

The multipliers are a base on which further value would be added to take account of the cover's postal historical importance in demonstrating such things as unusual, scarce or emergency cancels, interesting routes, significant postal markings, combination usage, the development of postal rates, and so on.

Minimum price. The minimum catalogue price quoted is 10p. For individual stamps prices between 10p. and 95p. are provided as a guide for catalogue users. The lowest price charged for individual stamps or sets purchased from Stanley Gibbons Ltd is £1.

Set prices. Set prices are generally for one of each value, excluding shades and varieties, but including major colour changes. Where there are alternative shades, etc., the cheapest is usually included. The number of stamps in the set is always stated for clarity. The prices for sets containing *se-tenant* pieces are based on the prices quoted for such combinations, and not on those for the individual stamps.

Varieties. Where plate or cylinder varieties are priced in used condition the price quoted is for a fine used example with the cancellation well clear of the listed flaw.

Specimen stamps. The pricing of these items is explained under that heading.

Stamp booklets. Prices are for complete assembled booklets in fine condition with those issued before 1945 showing normal wear and tear. Incomplete booklets and those which have been 'exploded' will, in general, be worth less than the figure quoted.

Repricing. Collectors will be aware that the market factors of supply and demand directly influence the prices quoted in this Catalogue. Whatever the scarcity of a particular stamp, if there is no one in the market who wishes to buy, it cannot be expected to achieve a high price. Conversely, the same item actively sought by numerous potential buyers may cause the price to rise.

All the prices in this Catalogue are examined during the preparation of each new edition by the expert staff of Stanley Gibbons and repriced as necessary. They take many factors into account, including supply and demand, and are in close touch with the international stamp market and the auction world.

Commonwealth cover prices and advice on postal history material originally provided by Edward B Proud.

GUARANTEE

All stamps are guaranteed originals in the following terms:

If not as described, and returned by the purchaser, we undertake to refund the price paid to us in the original transaction. If any stamp is certified as genuine by the Expert Committee of the Royal Philatelic Society, London, or by BPA Expertising Ltd, the purchaser shall not be entitled to make any claim against us for any error, omission or mistake in such certificate.

Consumers' statutory rights are not affected by the above guarantee.

The recognised Expert Committees in this country are those of the Royal Philatelic Society, 41 Devonshire Place, London W1G, 6JY, and BPA Expertising Ltd, PO Box 1141, Guildford, Surrey GU5 0WR. They do not undertake valuations under any circumstances and fees are payable for their services.

MARGINS ON IMPERFORATE STAMPS

| Superb | Very fine | Fine | Average | Poor |

GUM

| Unmounted | Very lightly mounted | Lightly mounted | Mounted/ large part original gum (o.g.). | Heavily mounted small part o.g. |

CENTRING

| Superb | Very fine | Fine | Average | Poor |

CANCELLATIONS

| Superb | Very fine | Fine | Average | Poor |

| Superb | Very fine |

| Fine | Average | Poor |

CONDITION GUIDE

To assist collectors in assessing the true value of items they are considering buying or in reviewing stamps already in their collections, we now offer a more detailed guide to the condition of stamps on which this catalogue's prices are based.

For a stamp to be described as 'Fine', it should be sound in all respects, without creases, bends, wrinkles, pin holes, thins or tears. If perforated, all perforation 'teeth' should be intact, it should not suffer from fading, rubbing or toning and it should be of clean, fresh appearance.

Margins on imperforate stamps: These should be even on all sides and should be at least as wide as half the distance between that stamp and the next. To have one or more margins of less than this width, would normally preclude a stamp from being described as 'Fine'. Some early stamps were positioned very close together on the printing plate and in such cases 'Fine' margins would necessarily be narrow. On the other hand, some plates were laid down to give a substantial gap between individual stamps and in such cases margins would be expected to be much wider.

An 'average' four-margin example would have a narrower margin on one or more sides and should be priced accordingly, while a stamp with wider, yet even, margins than 'Fine' would merit the description 'Very Fine' or 'Superb' and, if available, would command a price in excess of that quoted in the catalogue.

Gum: Since the prices for stamps of King Edward VIII, King George VI and Queen Elizabeth are for 'unmounted' or 'never hinged' mint, even stamps from these reigns which have been very lightly mounted should be available at a discount from catalogue price, the more obvious the hinge marks, the greater the discount.

Catalogue prices for stamps issued prior to King Edward VIII's reign are for mounted mint, so unmounted examples would be worth a premium. Hinge marks on 20th century stamps should not be too obtrusive, and should be at least in the lightly mounted category. For 19th century stamps more obvious hinging would be acceptable, but stamps should still carry a large part of their original gum—'Large part o.g.'—in order to be described as 'Fine'.

Centring: Ideally, the stamp's image should appear in the exact centre of the perforated area, giving equal margins on all sides. 'Fine' centring would be close to this ideal with any deviation having an effect on the value of the stamp. As in the case of the margins on imperforate stamps, it should be borne in mind that the space between some early stamps was very narrow, so it was very difficult to achieve accurate perforation, especially when the technology was in its infancy. Thus, poor centring would have a less damaging effect on the value of a 19th century stamp than on a 20th century example, but the premium put on a perfectly centred specimen would be greater.

Cancellations: Early cancellation devices were designed to 'obliterate' the stamp in order to prevent it being reused and this is still an important objective for today's postal administrations. Stamp collectors, on the other hand, prefer postmarks to be lightly applied, clear, and to leave as much as possible of the design visible. Dated, circular cancellations have long been 'the postmark of choice', but the definition of a 'Fine' cancellation will depend upon the types of cancellation in use at the time a stamp was current—it is clearly illogical to seek a circular datestamp on a Penny Black.

'Fine', by definition, will be superior to 'Average', so, in terms of cancellation quality, if one begins by identifying what 'Average' looks like, then one will be half way to identifying 'Fine'. The illustrations will give some guidance on mid-19th century and mid-20th century cancellations of Great Britain, but types of cancellation in general use in each country and in each period will determine the appearance of 'Fine'.

As for the factors discussed above, anything less than 'Fine' will result in a downgrading of the stamp concerned, while a very fine or superb cancellation will be worth a premium.

Self-adhesive stamps: The majority of used self-adhesive stamps cannot easily be removed from postal items and are therefore best collected intact or 'on-piece'. In the latter case, we recommend that stamps are carefully trimmed from envelopes with straight, even margins all round, taking care not to cut into the stamp itself. A margin of 2mm all round is ideal.

Combining the factors: To merit the description 'Fine', a stamp should be fine in every respect, but a small deficiency in one area might be made up for in another by a factor meriting an 'Extremely Fine' description.

Some early issues are so seldom found in what would normally be considered to be 'Fine' condition, the catalogue prices are for a slightly lower grade, with 'Fine' examples being worth a premium. In such cases a note to this effect is given in the catalogue, while elsewhere premiums are given for well-centred, lightly cancelled examples.

In the 21st century many postal administrations seem to feel that there is little need for stamps to be legibly cancelled and ink-jet markings, heavy obliterations and pen cancellations are very much the order of the day, while a large proportion of stamps are left without a postal marking of any kind. Used stamps of this type are of very little value and the prices shown in this catalogue are for clear circular operational date stamps or appropriate commemorative cancellations, although the latter are also frowned upon by many collectors.

Stamps graded at less than fine remain collectable and, in the case of more highly priced stamps, will continue to hold a value. Nevertheless, buyers should always bear condition in mind.

The Catalogue in General

Contents. The Catalogue is confined to adhesive postage stamps, including miniature sheets. For particular categories the rules are:

(a) Revenue (fiscal) stamps are listed only where they have been expressly authorised for postal duty.

(b) Stamps issued only precancelled are included, but normally issued stamps available additionally with precancel have no separate precancel listing unless the face value is changed.

(c) Stamps prepared for use but not issued, hitherto accorded full listing, are nowadays foot-noted with a price (where possible).

(d) Bisects (trisects, etc.) are only listed where such usage was officially authorised.

(e) Stamps issued only on first day covers or in presentation packs and not available separately are not listed but may be priced in a footnote.

(f) New printings are only included in this Catalogue where they show a major philatelic variety, such as a change in shade, watermark or paper. Stamps which exist with or without imprint dates are listed separately; changes in imprint dates are mentioned in footnotes.

(g) Official and unofficial reprints are dealt with by footnote.

(h) Stamps from imperforate printings of modern issues which occur perforated are covered by footnotes, but are listed where widely available for postal use.

Exclusions. The following are excluded:

(a) non-postal revenue or fiscal stamps;

(b) postage stamps used fiscally (although prices are now given for some fiscally used high values);

(c) local carriage labels and private local issues;

(d) bogus or phantom stamps;

(e) railway or airline letter fee stamps, bus or road transport company labels or the stamps of private postal companies operating under licence from the national authority;

(f) cut-outs;

(g) all types of non-postal labels and souvenirs;

(h) documentary labels for the postal service, e.g. registration, recorded delivery, air-mail etiquettes, etc.;

(i) privately applied embellishments to official issues and privately commissioned items generally;

(j) stamps for training postal officers.

Full listing. 'Full listing' confers our recognition and implies allotting a catalogue number and (wherever possible) a price quotation.

In judging status for inclusion in the catalogue broad considerations are applied to stamps. They must be issued by a legitimate postal authority, recognised by the government concerned, and must be adhesives valid for proper postal use in the class of service for which they are inscribed. Stamps, with the exception of such categories as postage dues and officials, must be available to the general public, at face value, in reasonable quantities without any artificial restrictions being imposed on their distribution.

For errors and varieties the criterion is legitimate (albeit inadvertent) sale through a postal administration in the normal course of business. Details of provenance are always important; printers' waste and deliberately manufactured material are excluded.

Certificates. In assessing unlisted items due weight is given to Certificates from recognised Expert Committees and, where appropriate, we will usually ask to see them.

Date of issue. Where local issue dates differ from dates of release by agencies, 'date of issue' is the local date. Fortuitous stray usage before the officially intended date is disregarded in listing.

Catalogue numbers. Stamps of each country are catalogued chronologically by date of issue. Subsidiary classes are placed at the end of the country, as separate lists, with a distinguishing letter prefix to the catalogue number, e.g. D for postage due, O for official and E for express delivery stamps.

The catalogue number appears in the extreme left-column. The boldface Type numbers in the next column are merely cross-references to illustrations.

A catalogue number with a suffix will normally relate to the main number, so 137a will be a variant of No. 137, unless the suffix appears as part of the number in the left-hand column such as Great Britain No. 20a, in which case it should be treated as the main number. A number with multiple suffixes will relate to the first letter or letters of that suffix, so 137ab will be a variant of 137a and 137aba a variant of 137ab. The exception is an 'aa' suffix, which will precede an 'a' and always refers to the main number, so 137aa relates to 137, not 137a.

Once published in the Catalogue, numbers are changed as little as possible; really serious renumbering is reserved for the occasions when a complete country or an entire issue is being rewritten. The edition first affected includes cross-reference tables of old and new numbers.

Our catalogue numbers are universally recognised in specifying stamps and as a hallmark of status.

Illustrations. Stamps are illustrated at three-quarters linear size. Stamps not illustrated are the same size and format as the value shown, unless otherwise indicated. Stamps issued only as miniature sheets have the stamp alone illustrated but sheet size is also quoted. Overprints, surcharges, watermarks and postmarks are normally actual size. Illustrations of varieties are often enlarged to show the detail. Stamp booklet covers are illustrated half-size, unless otherwise indicated.

The colour illustrations of stamps are intended as a guide only, they may differ in shade from the originals.

Designers. Designers' names are quoted where known, though space precludes naming every individual concerned in the production of a set. In particular, photographers supplying material are usually named only where they also make an active contribution in the design stage; posed photographs of reigning monarchs are, however, an exception to this rule.

CONTACTING THE CATALOGUE EDITOR

The editor is always interested in hearing from people who have new information which will improve or correct the Catalogue. As a general rule he must see and examine the actual stamps before they can be considered for listing; scans, photographs or photocopies are insufficient evidence; although initial contact by email (hjefferies@ stanleygibbons.com) is welcome.

Submissions should be made in writing to the Catalogue Editor, Stanley Gibbons Publications at the Ringwood office. The cost of return postage for items submitted is appreciated, and this should include the registration fee if required.

Where information is solicited purely for the benefit of the enquirer, the editor cannot undertake to reply if the answer is already contained in these published notes or if return postage is omitted. Written communications are greatly preferred to enquiries by telephone or e-mail and the editor regrets that he or his staff cannot see personal callers without a prior appointment being made. Correspondence may be subject to delay during the production period of each new edition.

The editor welcomes close contact with study circles and is interested, too, in finding reliable local correspondents who will verify and supplement official information in countries where this is deficient.

We regret we do not give opinions as to the genuineness of stamps, nor do we identify stamps or number them by our Catalogue.

TECHNICAL MATTERS

The meanings of the technical terms used in the catalogue will be found in our *Philatelic Terms Illustrated*.

References below to (more specialised) listings are to be taken to indicate, as appropriate, the Stanley Gibbons *Great Britain Specialised Catalogue* in five volumes or the *Great Britain Concise Catalogue*.

1. Printing

Printing errors. Errors in printing are of major interest to the Catalogue. Authenticated items meriting consideration would include: background, centre or frame inverted or omitted; centre or subject transposed; error of colour; error or omission of value; double prints and impressions; printed both sides; and so on. Apparent 'double prints' including overprints, on stamps printed by offset litho arising from movement of the rubber 'blanket' involved in this process are however, outside the scope of this catalogue, although they may be included in more specialised listings. Designs *tête-bêche*, whether intentionally or by accident, are listable. *Se-tenant* arrangements of stamps are recognised in the listings or footnotes. Gutter pairs (a pair of stamps separated by blank margin) are not included in this volume. Colours only partially omitted are not listed. Stamps with embossing omitted are reserved for our more specialised listings.

Printing varieties. Listing is accorded to major changes in the printing base which lead to completely new types. In recess-printing this could be a design re-engraved; in photogravure or photolithography a screen altered in whole or in part. It can also encompass flat-bed and rotary printing if the results are readily distinguishable.

To be considered at all, varieties must be constant.

Early stamps, produced by primitive methods, were prone to numerous imperfections; the lists reflect this, recognising re-entries, retouches, broken frames, misshapen letters, and so on. Printing technology has, however, radically improved over the years, during which time photogravure and lithography have become predominant. Varieties nowadays are more in the nature of flaws and these, being too specialised for this general catalogue, are almost always outside the scope.

In no catalogue, however, do we list such items as: dry prints, kiss prints, doctor-blade flaws, colour shifts or registration flaws (unless they lead to the complete omission of a colour from an individual stamp), lithographic ring flaws, and so on. Neither do we recognise fortuitous happenings like paper creases or confetti flaws.

'Varieties of varieties'. We no longer provide individual listings for combinations of two or more varieties; thus a plate variety or overprinting error will not be listed for various watermark orientations.

Overprints (and surcharges). Overprints of different types qualify for separate listing. These include overprints in different colours; overprints from different printing processes such as litho and typo; overprints in totally different typefaces, etc. Major errors in machine-printed overprints are important and listable. They include: overprint inverted or omitted; overprint double (treble, etc.); overprint diagonal; overprint double, one inverted; pairs with one overprint omitted, e.g. from a radical shift to an adjoining stamp; error of colour; error of type fount; letters inverted or omitted, etc. If the overprint is hand-stamped, few of these would qualify and a distinction is drawn. We continue, however, to list pairs of stamps where one has a handstamped overprint and the other has not.

Albino prints or double prints, one of them being albino (i.e. showing an uninked impression of the printing plate) are listable unless they are particularly common in this form (see the note below Travancore No. 32fa, for example). We do not, however, normally list reversed albino overprints, caused by the accidental or deliberate folding of sheets prior to overprinting (British Levant Nos. 51/8).

Varieties occurring in overprints will often take the form of broken letters, slight differences in spacing, rising spaces, etc. Only the most important would be considered for listing or footnote mention.

Sheet positions. If space permits we quote sheet positions of listed varieties and authenticated data is solicited for this purpose.

De La Rue plates. The Catalogue classifies the general plates used by De La Rue for printing British Colonial stamps as follows:

VICTORIAN KEY TYPE

Die I

1. The ball of decoration on the second point of the crown appears as a dark mass of lines.
2. Dark vertical shading separates the front hair from the bun.
3. The vertical line of colour outlining the front of the throat stops at the sixth line of shading on the neck.
4. The white space in the coil of the hair above the curl is roughly the shape of a pin's head.

Die II

1. There are very few lines of colour in the ball and it appears almost white.
2. A white vertical strand of hair appears in place of the dark shading.
3. The line stops at the eighth line of shading.
4. The white space is oblong, with a line of colour partially dividing it at the left end.

Plates numbered 1 and 2 are both Die I. Plates 3 and 4 are Die II.

GEORGIAN KEY TYPE

Die I

A. The second (thick) line below the name of the country is cut slanting, conforming roughly to the shape of the crown on each side.
B. The labels of solid colour bearing the words 'POSTAGE' and '& REVENUE' are square at the inner top corners.
C. There is a projecting 'bud' on the outer spiral of the ornament in each of the lower corners.

Die II

A. The second line is cut vertically on each side of the crown.
B. The labels curve inwards at the top.
C. There is no 'bud' in this position.

Unless otherwise stated in the lists, all stamps with watermark Multiple Crown CA (w **8**) are Die I while those with watermark Multiple Crown Script CA (w **9**) are Die II. The Georgian Die II was introduced in April 1921 and was used for Plates 10 to 22 and 26 to 28. Plates 23 to 25 were made from Die I by mistake.

2. Paper

All stamps listed are deemed to be on (ordinary) paper of the wove type and white in colour; only departures from this are normally mentioned.

Types. Where classification so requires we distinguish such other types of paper as, for example, vertically and horizontally laid; wove and laid bâtonné; card(board); carton; cartridge; glazed; granite; native; pelure; porous; quadrillé; ribbed; rice; and silk thread.

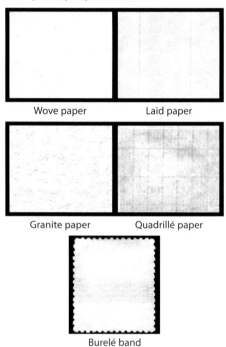

Wove paper   Laid paper

Granite paper   Quadrillé paper

Burelé band

The various makeshifts for normal paper are listed as appropriate. The varieties of double paper and joined paper are recognised. The security device of a printed burelé band on the back of a stamp, as in early Queensland, qualifies for listing.

Descriptive terms. The fact that a paper is handmade (and thus probably of uneven thickness) is mentioned where necessary. Such descriptive terms as 'hard' and 'soft'; 'smooth' and 'rough'; 'thick', 'medium' and 'thin' are applied where there is philatelic merit in classifying papers.

Coloured, very white and toned papers. A coloured paper is one that is coloured right through (front and back of the stamp). In the Catalogue the colour of the paper is given in italics, thus:

black/*rose* = black design on rose paper.

Papers have been made specially white in recent years by, for example, a very heavy coating of chalk. We do not classify shades of whiteness of paper as distinct varieties. There does exist, however, a type of paper from early days called toned. This is off-white, often brownish or buffish, but it cannot be assigned any definite colour. A toning effect brought on by climate, incorrect storage or gum staining is disregarded here, as this was not the state of the paper when issued.

'Ordinary' and 'Chalk-surfaced' papers. The availability of many postage stamps for revenue purposes made necessary some safeguard against the illegitimate re-use of stamps with removable cancellations. This was at first secured by using fugitive inks and later by printing on paper surfaced by coatings containing either chalk or china clay, both of which made it difficult to remove any form of obliteration without damaging the stamp design.

This catalogue lists these chalk-surfaced paper varieties from their introduction in 1905. Where no indication is given, the paper is 'ordinary'.

The 'traditional' method of indentifying chalk-surfaced papers has been that, when touched with a silver wire, a black mark is left on the paper, and the listings in this catalogue are based on that test. However, the test itself is now largely discredited, for, although the mark can be removed by a soft rubber, some damage to the stamp will result from its use.

The difference between chalk-surfaced and pre-war ordinary papers is fairly clear: chalk-surfaced papers being smoother to the touch and showing a characteristic sheen when light is reflected off their surface. Under good magnification tiny bubbles or pock marks can be seen on the surface of the stamp and at the tips of the perforations the surfacing appears 'broken'. Traces of paper fibres are evident on the surface of ordinary paper and the ink shows a degree of absorption into it.

Initial chalk-surfaced paper printings by De La Rue had a thinner coating than subsequently became the norm. The characteristics described above are less pronounced in these printings.

During and after the Second World War, substitute papers replaced the chalk-surfaced papers, these do not react to the silver test and are therefore classed as 'ordinary', although differentiating them without recourse to it is more difficult, for, although the characteristics of the chalk-surfaced paper remained the same, some of the ordinary papers appear much smoother than earlier papers and many do not show the watermark clearly. Experience is the only solution to identifying these, and comparison with stamps whose paper type is without question will be of great help.

Another type of paper, known as 'thin striated' was used only for the Bahamas 1s. and 5s. (Nos. 155a, 156a, 171 and 174) and for several stamps of the Malayan states. Hitherto these have been described as 'chalk-surfaced' since they gave some reaction to the silver test, but they are much thinner than usual chalk-surfaced papers, with the watermark showing clearly. Stamps on this paper show a slightly 'ribbed' effect when the stamp is held up to the light. Again, comparison with a known striated paper stamp, such as the 1941 Straits Settlements Die II 2c. orange (No. 294) will prove invaluable in separating these papers.

Glazed paper. In 1969 the Crown Agents introduced a new general-purpose paper for use in conjunction with all current printing processes. It generally has a marked glossy surface but the degree varies according to the process used, being more marked in recess-printing stamps. As it does not respond to the silver test this presents a further test where previous printings were on chalky paper. A change of paper to the glazed variety merits separate listing.

Green and yellow papers. Issues of the First World War and immediate postwar period occur on green and yellow papers and these are given separate Catalogue listing. The original coloured papers (coloured throughout) gave way to surface-coloured papers, the stamps having 'white backs'; other stamps show one colour on the front and a different one at the back. Because of the numerous variations a grouping of colours is adopted as follows:

Yellow papers

(1) The original *yellow* paper (throughout), usually bright in colour. The gum is often sparse, of harsh consistency and dull-looking. Used 1912–1920.

(2) The *white-backs*. Used 1913–1914.

(3) A bright lemon paper. The colour must have a pronounced greenish tinge, different from the 'yellow' in (1). As a rule, the gum on stamps using this lemon paper is plentiful, smooth and shiny, and the watermark shows distinctly. Care is needed with stamps printed in green on yellow paper (1) as it may appear that the paper is this lemon. Used 1914–1916.

(4) An experimental *orange-buff* paper. The colour must have a distinct brownish tinge. It is not to be confused with a muddy yellow (1) nor the misleading appearance (on the surface) of stamps printed in red on yellow paper where an engraved plate has been insufficiently wiped. Used 1918–1921.

(5) An experimental *buff* paper. This lacks the brownish tinge of (4) and the brightness of the yellow shades. The gum is shiny when compared with the matt type used on (4). Used 1919–1920.

(6) A *pale yellow* paper that has a creamy tone to the yellow. Used from 1920 onwards.

Green papers

(7) The original 'green' paper, varying considerably through shades of blue-green and yellow-green, the front and back sometimes differing. Used 1912–1916.

(8) The *white backs*. Used 1913–1914.

(9) A paper blue-green on the surface with *pale olive* back. The back must be markedly paler than the front and this and the pronounced olive tinge to the back distinguish it from (7). Used 1916–1920.

(10) Paper with a vivid green surface, commonly called *emerald-green*; it has the olive back of (9). Used 1920.

(11) Paper with *emerald-green* both back and front. Used from 1920 onwards.

3. Perforation and Rouletting

Perforation gauge. The gauge of a perforation is the number of holes in a length of 2 cm. For correct classification the size of the holes (large or small) may need to be distinguished; in a few cases the actual number of holes on each edge of the stamp needs to be quoted.

Measurement. The Gibbons *Instanta* gauge is the standard for measuring perforations. The stamp is viewed against a dark background with the transparent gauge put on top of it. Though the gauge measures to decimal accuracy, perforations read from it are generally quoted in the Catalogue to the nearest half. For example:

Just over perf 12¾ to just under 13¼	= perf 13
Perf 13¼ exactly, rounded up	= perf 13½
Just over perf 13¼ to just under 13¾	= perf 13½
Perf 13¾ exactly, rounded up	= perf 14

However, where classification depends on it, actual quarter-perforations are quoted.

Notation. Where no perforation is quoted for an issue it is imperforate. Perforations are usually abbreviated (and spoken) as follows, though sometimes they may be spelled out for clarity. This notation for rectangular stamps (the majority) applies to diamond shapes if 'top' is read as the edge to the top right.

P 14: perforated alike on all sides (read: 'perf 14').

P 14×15: the first figure refers to top and bottom, the second to left and right sides (read: 'perf 14 by 15'). This is a compound perforation. For an upright triangular stamp the first figure refers to the two sloping sides and second to the base. In inverted triangulars the base is first and the second figure to the sloping sides.

P 14–15: perforation measuring anything between 14 and 15: the holes are irregularly spaced, thus the gauge may vary along a single line or even along a single edge of the stamp (read: 'perf 14 to 15').

P 14 *irregular*: perforated 14 from a worn perforator, giving badly aligned holes irregularly spaced (read: 'irregular perf 14').

P *comp(ound)* 14×15: two gauges in use but not necessarily on opposite sides of the stamp. It could be one side in one gauge and three in the other; or two adjacent sides with the same gauge. (Read: 'perf compound of 14 and 15'.) For three gauges or more, abbreviated as 'P 12, 14½, 15 *or compound*' for example.

P 14, 14½: perforated approximately 14¼ (read: 'perf 14 or 14½'). It does *not* mean two stamps, one perf 14 and the other perf 14½. This obsolescent notation is gradually being replaced in the Catalogue.

Imperf: imperforate (not perforated)

Imperf×P 14: imperforate at top ad bottom and perf 14 at sides.

P 14×*imperf*: perf 14 at top and bottom and imperforate at sides.

Such headings as 'P 13×14 (*vert*) and P 14×13 (*horiz*)' indicate which perforations apply to which stamp format—vertical or horizontal.

Some stamps are additionally perforated so that a label or tab is detachable; others have been perforated for use as two halves. Listings are normally for whole stamps, unless stated otherwise.

Imperf×perf

Other terms. Perforation almost always gives circular holes; where other shapes have been used they are specified, e.g. square holes; lozenge perf. Interrupted perfs are brought about by the omission of pins at regular intervals. Perforations merely simulated by being printed as part of the design are of course ignored. With few exceptions, privately applied perforations are not listed.

In the 19th century perforations are often described as clean cut (clean, sharply incised holes), intermediate or rough (rough holes, imperfectly cut, often the result of blunt pins).

Perforation errors and varieties. Authenticated errors, where a stamp normally perforated is accidentally issued imperforate, are listed provided no traces of perforation (blind holes or indentations) remain. They must be provided as pairs, both stamps wholly imperforate, and are only priced in that form.

Note that several postal administrations and their agencies are now deliberately releasing imperforate versions of issued stamps in restricted quantities and at premium prices. These are not listable, but, where possible, thier existance will be noted.

Stamps imperforate between stamp and sheet margin are not listed in this catalogue, but such errors on Great Britain stamps will be found in the *Great Britain Specialised Catalogue*.

Pairs described as 'imperforate between' have the line of perforations between the two stamps omitted.

Imperf between (horiz pair): a horizontal pair of stamps with perfs all around the edges but none between the stamps.

Imperf between (vert pair): a vertical pair of stamps with perfs all around the edges but none between the stamps.

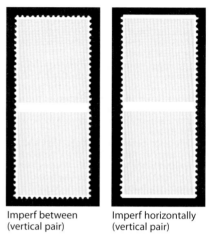

Imperf between   Imperf horizontally
(vertical pair)   (vertical pair)

Where several of the rows have escaped perforation the resulting varieties are listable. Thus:

Imperf vert (horiz pair): a horizontal pair of stamps perforated top and bottom; all three vertical directions are imperf—the two outer edges and between the stamps.

Imperf horiz (vert pair): a vertical pair perforated at left and right edges; all three horizontal directions are imperf—the top, bottom and between the stamps.

Straight edges. Large sheets cut up before issue to post offices can cause stamps with straight edges, i.e. imperf on one side or on two sides at right angles. They are not usually listable in this condition and are worth less than corresponding stamps properly perforated all round. This does not, however, apply to certain stamps, mainly from coils and booklets, where straight edges on various sides are the manufacturing norm affecting every stamp. The listings and notes make clear which sides are correctly imperf.

Malfunction. Varieties of double, misplaced or partial perforation caused by error or machine malfunction are not listable, neither are freaks, such as perforations placed diagonally from paper folds, nor missing holes caused by broken pins.

Types of perforating. Where necessary for classification, perforation types are distinguished.

These include:

Line perforation from one line of pins punching single rows of holes at a time.

Comb perforation from pins disposed across the sheet in comb formation, punching out holes at three sides of the stamp a row at a time.

Harrow perforation applied to a whole pane or sheet at one stroke.

Rotary perforation from toothed wheels operating across a sheet, then crosswise.

Sewing machine perforation. The resultant condition, clean-cut or rough, is distinguished where required.

Pin-perforation is the commonly applied term for pin-roulette in which, instead of being punched out, round holes are pricked by sharp-pointed pins and no paper is removed.

Mixed perforation occurs when stamps with defective perforations are re-perforated in a different gauge.

Die-cut. Self-adhesive stamps are not perforated in the traditional way, but are die-cut in order to facilitate their removal from the backing paper. Such die-cutting may be 'free-form', to match the design of the stamp, with straight edges, or, most frequently, with simulated 'perforations' or undulating edges. Such 'perforations' or undulations are measured in the same way as conventional perforations.

Punctured stamps. Perforation holes can be punched into the face of the stamp. Patterns of small holes, often in the shape of initial letters, are privately applied devices against pilferage. These (perfins) are outside the scope except for Australia, Canada, Cape of Good Hope, Papua and Sudan where they were used as official stamps by the national administration. Identification devices, when officially inspired, are listed or noted; they can be shapes, or letters or words formed from holes, sometimes converting one class of stamp into another.

Rouletting. In rouletting the paper is cut, for ease of separation, but none is removed. The gauge is measured, when needed, as for perforations. Traditional French terms descriptive of the type of cut are often used and types include:

Arc roulette (percé en arc). Cuts are minute, spaced arcs, each roughly a semicircle.

Cross roulette (percé en croix). Cuts are tiny diagonal crosses.

Line roulette (percé en ligne or en ligne droite). Short straight cuts parallel to the frame of the stamp. The commonest basic roulette. Where not further described, 'roulette' means this type.

Rouletted in colour or coloured roulette (percé en lignes colorées or en lignes de coleur). Cuts with coloured edges, arising from notched rule inked simultaneously with the printing plate.

Saw-tooth roulette (percé en scie). Cuts applied zigzag fashion to resemble the teeth of a saw.

Serpentine roulette (percé en serpentin). Cuts as sharply wavy lines.

Zigzag roulette (percé en zigzags). Short straight cuts at angles in alternate directions, producing sharp points on separation. US usage favours 'serrate(d) roulette' for this type.

Pin roulette (originally percé en points and now perforés trous d'epingle) is commonly called pin-perforation in English.

4. Gum

All stamps listed are assumed to have gum of some kind; if they were issued without gum this is stated. Original gum (o.g.) means that which was present on the stamp as issued to the public. Deleterious climates and the presence of certain chemicals can cause gum to crack and, with early stamps, even make the paper deteriorate. Unscrupulous fakers are adept in removing it and regumming the stamp to meet the unreasoning demand often made for 'full o.g.' in cases where such a thing is virtually impossible.

The gum normally used on stamps has been gum arabic until the late 1960s when synthetic adhesives were introduced. Harrison and Sons Ltd for instance use *polyvinyl alcohol, known to philatelists as PVA*. This is almost invisible except for a slight yellowish tinge which was incorporated to make it possible to see that the stamps have been gummed. It has advantages in hot countries, as stamps do not curl and sheets are less likely to stick together. Gum arabic and PVA are not distinguished in the lists except that where a stamp exists with both forms this is indicated in footnotes. Our more specialised catalogues provide separate listing of gums for Great Britain.

Self-adhesive stamps are issued on backing paper, from which they are peeled before affixing to mail. Unused examples are priced as for backing paper intact, in which condition they are recommended to be kept. Used examples are best collected on cover or on piece.

5. Watermarks

Stamps are on unwatermarked paper except where the heading to the set says otherwise.

Detection. Watermarks are detected for Catalogue description by one of four methods: (1) holding stamps to the light; (2) laying stamps face down on a dark background; (3) adding a few drops of petroleum ether 40/60 to the stamp laid face down in a watermark tray; (4) by use of the Stanley Gibbons Detectamark Spectrum, or other equipment, which work by revealing the thinning of the paper at the watermark. (Note that petroleum ether is highly inflammable in use and can damage photogravure stamps.)

Listable types. Stamps occurring on both watermarked and unwatermarked papers are different types and both receive full listing.

Single watermarks (devices occurring once on every stamp) can be modified in size and shape as between different issues; the types are noted but not usually separately listed. Fortuitous absence of watermark from a single stamp or its gross displacement would not be listable.

To overcome registration difficulties the device may be repeated at close intervals *(a multiple watermark)*, single stamps thus showing parts of several devices. Similarly, a *large sheet watermark* (or *all-over watermark*) covering numerous stamps can be used. We give informative notes and illustrations for them. The designs may be such that numbers of stamps in the sheet automatically lack watermark: this is not a listable variety. Multiple and all-over watermarks sometimes undergo modifications, but if the various types are difficult to distinguish from single stamps notes are given but not separate listings.

Papermakers' watermarks are noted where known but not listed separately, since most stamps in the sheet will lack them. Sheet watermarks which are nothing more than officially adopted papermakers' watermarks are, however, given normal listing.

Marginal watermarks, falling outside the pane of stamps, are ignored except where misplacement caused the adjoining row to be affected, in which case they may be footnoted. They usually consist of straight or angled lines and double-lined capital letters, they are particularly prevalent on some Crown CC and Crown CA watermark stamps.

Watermark errors and varieties. Watermark errors are recognised as of major importance. They comprise stamps intended to be on unwatermarked paper but issued watermarked by mistake, or stamps printed on paper with the wrong watermark. Varieties showing letters omitted from the watermark are also included, but broken or deformed bits on the dandy roll are not listed unless they represent repairs.

Watermark positions. The diagram shows how watermark position is described in the Catalogue. Paper has a side intended for printing and watermarks are usually impressed so that they read normally when looked through from that printed side. However, since philatelists customarily detect watermarks by looking at the back of the stamp the watermark diagram also makes clear what is actually seen.

Illustrations in the Catalogue are of watermarks in normal positions (from the front of the stamps) and are actual size where possible.

Differences in watermark position are collectable varieties.

This Catalogue now lists inverted, sideways inverted and reversed watermark varieties on Commonwealth stamps from the 1860s onwards except where the watermark position is completely haphazard.

Great Britain inverted and sideways inverted watermarks can be found in the *Great Britain Specialised Catalogue* and the *Great Britain Concise Catalogue*.

Where a watermark comes indiscriminately in various positions our policy is to cover this by a general note: we do not give separate listings because the watermark position in these circumstances has no particular philatelic importance.

AS DESCRIBED (Read through front of stamp)		AS SEEN DURING WATERMARK DETECTION (Stamp face down and back examined
GvR	Normal	ЯvƆ
ЯvƆ	Inverted	ɘʌЯ
ЯvƆ	Reversed	GvR
ɘʌЯ	Reversed and Inverted	Я^Ɔ
GvR (sideways, rotated)	Sideways	ɘʌЯ (sideways, rotated)
GvR (sideways, rotated)	Sideways Inverted	ЯvƆ (sideways, rotated)

As shown in the diagram, a watermark described as 'sideways' will normally show the top of the watermark (as shown in its illustration), pointing to the left of the stamp, as seen from the front and to the right as seen from the back.

For clarification, or in cases where the 'normal' watermark is 'sideways inverted' a note is generally provided at the foot of the relevant listing, particularly where sideways and sideways inverted varieties exist.

Standard types of watermark. Some watermarks have been used generally for various British possessions rather than exclusively for a single colony. To avoid repetition the Catalogue classifies 11 general types, as under, with references in the headings throughout the listings being given either in words or in the form ('W w 9') (meaning 'watermark type w 9'). In those cases where watermark illustrations appear in the listings themselves, the respective reference reads, for example, W 153, thus indicating that the watermark will be found in the normal sequence of illustrations as (type) 153.

The general types are as follows, with an example of each quoted.

W	Description	Example
w 1	Large Star	St Helena No. 1
w 2	Small Star	Turks Is. No. 4
w 2a	Small Truncated Star	Queensland No. 59
w 3	Broad (pointed) Star	Grenada No. 24
w 4	Crown (over) CC, small stamp	Antigua No. 13
w 5	Crown (over) CC, large stamp	Antigua No. 31
w 6	Crown (over) CA, small stamp	Antigua No. 21
w 7	Crown CA (CA over Crown), large stamp	Sierra Leone No. 54
w 8	Multiple Crown CA	Antigua No. 41
w 9	Multiple Script CA	Seychelles No. 158
w 9a	do. Error	Seychelles No. 158a
w 9b	do. Error	Seychelles No. 158b
w 10	V over Crown	N.S.W. No. 327
w 11	Crown over A	N.S.W. No. 347

CC in these watermarks is an abbreviation for 'Crown Colonies' and CA for 'Crown Agents'. Watermarks w **1**, w **2** and w **3** are on stamps printed by Perkins, Bacon; w **4** onwards on stamps from De La Rue and other printers.

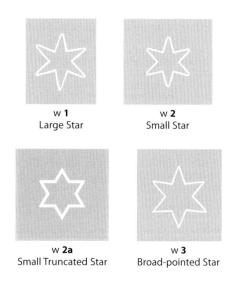

w **1**
Large Star

w **2**
Small Star

w **2a**
Small Truncated Star

w **3**
Broad-pointed Star

Watermark w **1**, *Large Star*, measures 15 to 16 mm across the star from point to point and about 27 mm from centre to centre vertically between stars in the sheet. It was made for long stamps like Ceylon 1857 and St Helena 1856.

Watermark w **2**, *Small Star* is of similar design but measures 12 to 13½mm from point to point and 24 mm from centre to centre vertically. It was for use with ordinary-size stamps.

When the Large Star watermark was used with the smaller stamps it only occasionally comes in the centre of the paper. It is frequently so misplaced as to show portions of two stars above and below and this eccentricity will very often help in determining the watermark.

Watermark w **2a**, *Small Truncated Star*, only used for Queensland stamps of 1868–1874.

Watermark w **3**, *Broad-pointed Star*, resembles w **1** but the points are broader.

w **4**
Crown (over) CC

w **5**
Crown (over) CC

Two *Crown (over) CC* watermarks were used:
w **4** was for stamps of ordinary size and w **5** for those of larger size.

w **6**
Crown (over) CA

w **7**
CA over Crown

Two watermarks of *Crown CA* type were used, w **6** being for stamps of ordinary size. The other, w **7**, is properly described as *CA over Crown*. It was specially made for paper on which it was intended to print long fiscal stamps: that some were used postally accounts for the appearance of w **7** in the Catalogue. The watermark occupies twice the space of the ordinary Crown CA watermark, w **6**. Stamps of normal size printed on paper with w **7** watermark show it *sideways*; it takes a horizontal pair of stamps to show the entire watermark.

w **8**
Multiple Crown CA

w **9**
Multiple Script CA

Multiple watermarks began in 1904 with w **8**, *Multiple Crown CA*, changed from 1921 to w **9**, *Multiple Script CA*. On stamps of ordinary size portions of two or three watermarks appear and on the large-sized stamps a greater number can be observed. The change to letters in script character with w **9** was accompanied by a Crown of distinctly different shape.

It seems likely that there were at least two dandy rolls for each Crown Agents watermark in use at any one time with a reserve roll being employed when the normal one was withdrawn for maintenance or repair.

Both the Mult Crown CA and the Mult Script CA types exist with one or other of the letters omitted from individual impressions. It is possible that most of these occur from the reserve rolls as they have only been found on certain issues. The MCA watermark experienced such problems during the early 1920s and the Script over a longer period from the early 1940s until 1951.

During the 1920s damage must also have occurred on one of the Crowns as a substituted Crown has been found on certain issues. This is smaller than the normal and consists of an oval base joined to two upright ovals with a circle positioned between their upper ends. The upper line of the Crown's base is omitted, as are the left and right-hand circles at the top and also the cross over the centre circle.

Substituted Crown

The *Multiple Script CA* watermark, w **9**, is known with two errors, recurring among the 1950–1952 printings of several territories. In the first a crown has fallen away from the dandy roll that impresses the watermark into the paper pulp. It gives w **9a**, *Crown missing*, but this omission has been found in both 'Crown only' (*illustrated*) and 'Crown CA' rows. The resulting faulty paper was used for Bahamas, Johore, Seychelles and the postage due stamps of nine colonies

w **9a**: Error, Crown missing

w **9b**: Error, St Edward's Crown

When the omission was noticed a second mishap occurred, which was to insert a wrong crown in the space, giving w **9b**, St Edward's Crown. This produced varieties in Bahamas, Perlis, St. Kitts-Nevis and Singapore and the incorrect crown likewise occurs in (Crown only) and (Crown CA) rows.

w **10**
V over Crown

w **11**
Crown over A

Resuming the general types, two watermarks found in issues of several Australian States are: w **10**, *V over Crown*, and w **11**, *Crown over A*.

w **12**
Multiple St Edward's
Crown Block CA

w **13**
Multiple PTM

The *Multiple St Edward's Crown Block CA* watermark, w **12**, was introduced in 1957 and besides the change in the Crown (from that used in Multiple Crown Script CA, w **9**) the letters reverted to block capitals. The new watermark began to appear sideways in 1966 and these stamps are generally listed as separate sets.

The watermark w **13**, *Multiple PTM*, was introduced for new Malaysian issues in November 1961.

w **14**
Multiple Crown CA Diagonal

By 1974 the two dandy-rolls the 'upright' and the 'sideways' for w **12** were wearing out; the Crown Agents therefore discontinued using the sideways watermark one and retained the other only as a stand-by. A new dandy-roll with the pattern of w **14**, *Multiple Crown CA Diagonal*, was introduced and first saw use with some Churchill Centenary issues.

The new watermark had the design arranged in gradually spiralling rows. It is improved in design to allow smooth passage over the paper (the gaps between letters and rows had caused jolts in previous dandy-rolls) and the sharp corners and angles, where fibres used to accumulate, have been eliminated by rounding.

This watermark had no 'normal' sideways position amongst the different printers using it. To avoid confusion our more specialised listings do not rely on such terms as 'sideways inverted' but describe the direction in which the watermark points.

w **15**
Multiple POST OFFICE

During 1981 w **15**, *Multiple POST OFFICE* was introduced for certain issues prepared by Philatelists Ltd, acting for various countries in the Indian Ocean, Pacific and West Indies.

w **16**
Multiple Crown Script CA Diagonal

A new Crown Agents watermark was introduced during 1985, w **16**, *Multiple Crown Script CA Diagonal*. This was very similar to the previous w **14**, but showed 'CA' in script rather than block letters. It was first used on the omnibus series of stamps commemorating the Life and Times of Queen Elizabeth the Queen Mother.

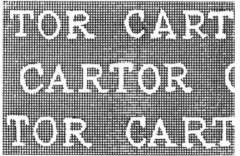

w **17**
Multiple CARTOR

Watermark w **17**, *Multiple CARTOR*, was used from 1985 for issues printed by this French firm for countries which did not normally use the Crown Agents watermark.

w **18**

In 2008, following the closure of the Crown Agents Stamp Bureau, a new Multiple Crowns watermark, w **18** was introduced

In recent years the use of watermarks has, to a small extent, been superseded by fluorescent security markings. These are often more visible from the reverse of the stamp (Cook Islands from 1970 onwards), but have occurred printed over the design (Hong Kong Nos. 415/430). In 1982 the Crown Agents introduced a new stock paper, without watermark, known as 'C-Kurity' on which a fluorescent pattern of blue rosettes is visible on the reverse, beneath the gum. This paper was used for issues from Gambia and Norfolk Island.

6. Colours

Stamps in two or three colours have these named in order of appearance, from the centre moving outwards. Four colours or more are usually listed as multicoloured.

In compound colour names the second is the predominant one, thus:

orange-red = a red tending towards orange,
red-orange = an orange containing more red
than usual.

Standard colours used. The 200 colours most used for stamp identification are given in the Stanley Gibbons Stamp Colour Key. The Catalogue has used the Stamp Colour Key as standard for describing new issues for some years. The names are also introduced as lists are rewritten, though exceptions are made for those early issues where traditional names have become universally established.

Determining colours. When comparing actual stamps with colour samples in the Stamp Colour Key, view in a good north daylight (or its best substitute; fluorescent 'colour matching' light). Sunshine is not recommended. Choose a solid portion of the stamp design; if available, marginal markings such as solid bars of colour or colour check dots are helpful. Shading lines in the design can be misleading as they appear lighter than solid colour. Postmarked portions of a stamp appear darker than normal. If more than one colour is present, mask off the extraneous ones as the eye tends to mix them.

Errors of colour. Major colour errors in stamps or overprints which qualify for listing are: wrong colours; one colour inverted in relation to the rest; albinos (colourless impressions), where these have Expert Committee certificates; colours completely omitted, but only on unused stamps (if found on used stamps the information is footnoted) and with good credentials, missing colours being frequently faked.

Colours only partially omitted are not recognised, Colour shifts, however spectacular, are not listed.

Shades. Shades in philately refer to variations in the intensity of a colour or the presence of differing amounts of other colours. They are particularly significant when they can be linked to specific printings. In general, shades need to be quite marked to fall within the scope of this Catalogue; it does not favour listing the often numerous shades of a stamp, but chooses a single applicable colour name which will indicate particular groups of outstanding shades. Furthermore, the listings refer to colours as issued; they may deteriorate into something different through the passage of time. Collectors are warned against according any significance to colours which may have been altered by immersion in water or exposure to sunlight, but time, alone will sometimes cause colours to change, notably some of the letterpress De la Rue stamps of the late 19th and early 20th centuries.

Modern colour printing by lithography is prone to marked differences of shade, even within a single run, and variations can occur within the same sheet. Such shades are not listed.

Aniline colours. An aniline colour meant originally one derived from coal-tar; it now refers more widely to colour of a particular brightness suffused on the surface of a stamp and showing through clearly on the back.

Colours of overprints and surcharges. All overprints and surcharges are in black unless stated otherwise in the heading or after the description of the stamp.

7. Specimen Stamps

Originally, stamps overprinted SPECIMEN were circulated to postmasters or kept in official records, but after the establishment of the Universal Postal Union supplies were sent to Berne for distribution to the postal administrations of member countries.

During the period 1884 to 1928 most of the stamps of British Crown Colonies required for this purpose were overprinted SPECIMEN in various shapes and sizes by their printers from typeset formes. Some locally produced provisionals were handstamped locally, as were sets prepared for presentation. From 1928 stamps were punched with holes forming the word SPECIMEN, each firm of printers using a different machine or machines. From 1948 the stamps supplied for UPU distribution were no longer punctured, although receiving authorities sometimes applied SPECIMEN markings of their own.

Stamps of some other Commonwealth territories were overprinted or handstamped locally, while stamps of Great Britain and those overprinted for use in overseas postal agencies (mostly of the higher denominations) bore SPECIMEN overprints and handstamps applied by the Inland Revenue or the Post Office.

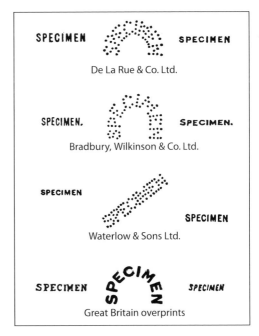

Some of the more common types of overprints or punctures are illustrated here. Collectors are warned that dangerous forgeries of the punctured type exist.

The *Stanley Gibbons Commonwealth Catalogues* record those Specimen overprints or perforations intended for distribution by the UPU to member countries and we are grateful to James Bendon, author and publisher of *UPU Specimen Stamps, 1878 - 1961*, a much expanded edition of which was published in 2015, for his assistance with these listings. The Specimen overprints of Australia and its dependent territories, which were sold to collectors by the Post Office, are also included.

Various Perkins Bacon issues exist obliterated with a 'CANCELLED' within an oval of bars handstamp.

Perkins Bacon 'CANCELLED'
Handstamp

This was applied to six examples of those issues available in 1861 which were then given to members of Sir Rowland Hill's family. 75 different stamps (including four from Chile) are recorded with this handstamp although others may possibly exist. The unauthorised gift of these 'CANCELLED' stamps to the Hill family was a major factor in the loss of the Agent General for the Crown Colonies (the forerunner of the Crown Agents) contracts by Perkins Bacon in the following year. Where examples of these scarce items are known to be in private hands the catalogue provides a price.

For full details of these stamps see *CANCELLED by Perkins Bacon* by Peter Jaffé (published by Spink in 1998).

All other Specimens are outside the scope of this volume.

In specifying type of specimen for individual high-value stamps, 'H/S' means handstamped, 'Optd' is overprinted and 'Perf' is punctured. Some sets occur mixed, e.g. 'Optd/Perf'. If unspecified, the type is apparent from the date or it is the same as for the lower values quoted as a set.

Prices. Prices for stamps up to £1 are quoted in sets; higher values are priced singly. Where specimens exist in more than one type the price quoted is for the cheapest. Specimen stamps have rarely survived even as pairs; these and strips of three, four or five are worth considerably more than singles.

8. Luminescence

Machines which sort mail electronically have been introduced in recent years. In consequence some countries have issued stamps on fluorescent or phosphorescent papers, while others have marked their stamps with phosphor bands.

The various papers can only be distinguished by ultraviolet lamps emitting particular wavelengths. They are separately listed only when the stamps have some other means of distinguishing them, visible without the use of these lamps. Where this is not so, the papers are recorded in footnotes or headings.

For this catalogue we do not consider it appropriate that collectors be compelled to have the use of an ultraviolet lamp before being able to identify stamps by our listings. Some experience will also be found necessary in interpreting the results given by ultraviolet. Collectors using the lamps, nevertheless, should exercise great care in their use as exposure to their light is potentially dangerous to the eyes.

Phosphor bands are listable, since they are visible to the naked eye (by holding stamps at an angle to the light and looking along them, the bands appear dark). Stamps existing with or without phosphor bands or with differing numbers of bands are given separate listings. Varieties such as double bands, bands omitted, misplaced or printed on the back are not listed.

Detailed descriptions appear at appropriate places in the listings in explanation of luminescent papers; see, for example, Australia above No. 363, Canada above Nos. 472 and 611, Cook Is. above 249, etc.

For Great Britain, where since 1959 phosphors have played a prominent and intricate part in stamp issues, the main notes above Nos. 599 and 723 should be studied, as well as the footnotes to individual listings where appropriate. In general the classification is as follows.

Stamps with phosphor bands are those where a separate cylinder applies the phosphor after the stamps are printed. Issues with 'all-over' phosphor have the 'band' covering the entire stamp. Parts of the stamp covered by phosphor bands, or the entire surface for 'all-over' phosphor versions, appear matt. Stamps on phosphorised paper have the phosphor added to the paper coating before the stamps are printed. Issues on this paper have a completely shiny surface.

Further particularisation of phosphor – their methods of printing and the colours they exhibit under ultraviolet – is outside the scope of this catalogue. The more specialised listings should be consulted for this information.

9. Coil Stamps

Stamps issued only in coil form are given full listing. If stamps are issued in both sheets and coils the coil stamps are listed separately only where there is some feature (e.g. perforation or watermark sideways) by which singles can be distinguished. Coil stamps containing different stamps *se-tenant* are also listed.

Coil join pairs are too random and too easily faked to permit of listing; similarly ignored are coil stamps which have accidentally suffered an extra row of perforations from the claw mechanism in a malfunctioning vending machine.

10. Stamp Booklets

Stamp booklets are now listed in this catalogue.

Single stamps from booklets are listed if they are distinguishable in some way (such as watermark or perforation) from similar sheet stamps.

Booklet panes are listed where they contain stamps of different denominations *se-tenant*, where stamp-size labels are included, or where such panes are otherwise identifiable. Booklet panes are placed in the listing under the lowest denomination present.

Particular perforations (straight edges) are covered by appropriate notes.

The majority of stamp booklets were made up from normal sheets and panes may be bound upright or inverted and booklets may be stapled or stitched at either the left or right-hand side. Unless specifically mentioned in the listings, such variations do not command a price premium.

11. Miniature Sheets and Sheetlets

We distinguish between 'miniature sheets' and 'sheetlets' and this affects the catalogue numbering. An item in sheet form that is postally valid, containing a single stamp, pair, block or set of stamps, with wide, inscribed and/or decorative margins, is a miniature sheet if it is sold at post offices as an indivisible entity. As such the Catalogue allots a single **MS** number and describes what stamps make it up. The sheetlet or small sheet differs in that the individual stamps are intended to be purchased separately for postal purposes. For sheetlets, all the component postage stamps are numbered individually and the composition explained in a footnote. Note that the definitions refer to post office sale—not how items may be subsequently offered by stamp dealers.

12. Forgeries and Fakes

Forgeries. Where space permits, notes are considered if they can give a concise description that will permit unequivocal detection of a forgery. Generalised warnings, lacking detail, are not nowadays inserted, since their value to the collector is problematic.

Forged cancellations have also been applied to genuine stamps. This catalogue includes notes regarding those manufactured by 'Madame Joseph', together with the cancellation dates known to exist. It should be remembered that these dates also exist as genuine cancellations.

For full details of these see *Madame Joseph Forged Postmarks* by Derek Worboys (published by the Royal Philatelic Society London and the British Philatelic Trust in 1994) or *Madame Joseph Revisited* by Brian Cartwright (published by the Royal Philatelic Society London in 2005).

Fakes. Unwitting fakes are numerous, particularly 'new shades' which are colour changelings brought about by exposure to sunlight, soaking in water contaminated with dyes from adherent paper, contact with oil and dirt from a pocketbook, and so on. Fraudulent operators, in addition, can offer to arrange: removal of hinge marks; repairs of thins on white or coloured papers; replacement of missing margins or perforations; reperforating in true or false gauges; removal of fiscal cancellations; rejoining of severed pairs, strips and blocks; and (a major hazard) regumming. Collectors can only be urged to purchase from reputable sources and to insist upon Expert Committee certification where there is any kind of doubt.

The Catalogue can consider footnotes about fakes where these are specific enough to assist in detection.

ACKNOWLEDGEMENTS

We are grateful to individual collectors, members of the philatelic trade and specialist societies and study circles for their assistance in improving and extending the Stanley Gibbons range of catalogues.

The addresses of societies and study circles relevant to this volume are:

Cyprus Study Circle
Secretary – Mr Robert Wheeler
47 Drayton Avenue, Ealing,
London W13 0LF

Gibraltar Study Circle
Membership Secretary – Mr Eric Holmes
29 Highgate Road, Woodley,
Reading RG5 3ND

Malta Study Group
Membership Secretary – Mr Colin Searle
4 Sunderland Place, Wellesbourne,
Warwick CV35 9LE

Abbreviations

Printers

A.B.N. Co.	American Bank Note Co, New York.
B.A.B.N.	British American Bank Note Co. Ottawa
B.D.T.	B.D.T. International Security Printing Ltd, Dublin, Ireland
B.W.	Bradbury Wilkinson & Co, Ltd.
Cartor	Cartor S.A., La Loupe, France
C.B.N.	Canadian Bank Note Co, Ottawa.
Continental	Continental Bank Note Co. B.N. Co.
Courvoisier	Imprimerie Courvoisier S.A., La-Chaux-de-Fonds, Switzerland.
D.L.R.	De La Rue & Co, Ltd, London.
Enschedé	Joh. Enschedé en Zonen, Haarlem, Netherlands.
Format	Format International Security Printers Ltd., London
Harrison	Harrison & Sons, Ltd. London
J.W.	John Waddington Security Print Ltd., Leeds
L.M.G.	Lowe Martin Group, Ottawa, Canada
P.B.	Perkins Bacon Ltd, London.
Questa	Questa Colour Security Printers Ltd, London
Walsall	Walsall Security Printers Ltd
Waterlow	Waterlow & Sons, Ltd, London.

General Abbreviations

Alph	Alphabet
Anniv	Anniversary
Comp	Compound (perforation)
Des	Designer; designed
Diag	Diagonal; diagonally
Eng	Engraver; engraved
F.C.	Fiscal Cancellation
H/S	Handstamped
Horiz	Horizontal; horizontally
Imp, Imperf	Imperforate
Inscr	Inscribed
L	Left
Litho	Lithographed
mm	Millimetres
MS	Miniature sheet
N.Y.	New York
Opt(d)	Overprint(ed)
P or P-c	Pen-cancelled
P, Pf or Perf	Perforated
Photo	Photogravure
Pl	Plate
Pr	Pair
Ptd	Printed
Ptg	Printing
R	Right

R.	Row
Recess	Recess-printed
Roto	Rotogravure
Roul	Rouletted
S	Specimen (overprint)
Surch	Surcharge(d)
T.C.	Telegraph Cancellation
T	Type
Typo	Typographed
Un	Unused
Us	Used
Vert	Vertical; vertically
W or wmk	Watermark
Wmk s	Watermark sideways

(†) = Does not exist

(–) (or blank price column) = Exists, or may exist, but no market price is known.

/ between colours means 'on' and the colour following is that of the paper on which the stamp is printed.

Colours of Stamps

Bl (blue); blk (black); brn (brown); car, carm (carmine); choc (chocolate); clar (claret); emer (emerald); grn (green); ind (indigo); mag (magenta); mar (maroon); mult (multicoloured); mve (mauve); ol (olive); orge (orange); pk (pink); pur (purple); scar (scarlet); sep (sepia); turq (turquoise); ultram (ultramarine); verm (vermilion); vio (violet); yell (yellow).

Colour of Overprints and Surcharges

(B.) = blue, (Blk.) = black, (Br.) = brown, (C.) = carmine, (G.) = green, (Mag.) = magenta, (Mve.) = mauve, (Ol.) = olive, (O.) = orange, (P.) = purple, (Pk.) = pink, (R.) = red, (Sil.) = silver, (V.) = violet, (Vm.) or (Verm.) = vermilion, (W.) = white, (Y.) = yellow.

Arabic Numerals

As in the case of European figures, the details of the Arabic numerals vary in different stamp designs, but they should be readily recognised with the aid of this illustration.

٠	١	٢	٣	٤	٥	٦	٧	٨	٩
0	1	2	3	4	5	6	7	8	9

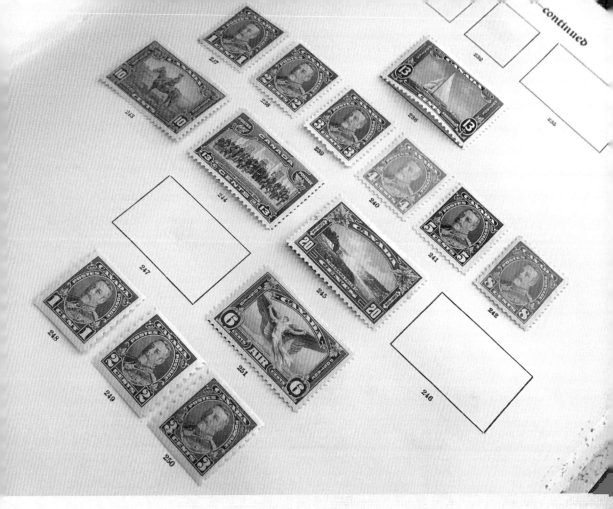

continued

Looking for that
Elusive Stamp?

Get in touch with our team

Great Britain Department: email **gb@stanleygibbons.com** or phone **020 7557 4413**
Commonwealth Department: email **amansi@stanleygibbons.com** or phone **020 7557 4415**

BY APPOINTMENT TO
HER MAJESTY THE QUEEN
PHILATELISTS
STANLEY GIBBONS LTD
LONDON

STANLEY GIBBONS
LONDON 1856

STANLEY GIBBONS 399 STRAND LONDON WC2R 0LX | WWW.STANLEYGIBBONS.COM

International Philatelic Glossary

English	French	German	Spanish	Italian
Agate	Agate	Achat	Agata	Agata
Air stamp	Timbre de la poste aérienne	Flugpostmarke	Sello de correo aéreo	Francobollo per posta aerea
Apple Green	Vert-pomme	Apfelgrün	Verde manzana	Verde mela
Barred	Annulé par barres	Balkenentwertung	Anulado con barras	Sbarrato
Bisected	Timbre coupé	Halbiert	Partido en dos	Frazionato
Bistre	Bistre	Bister	Bistre	Bistro
Bistre-brown	Brun-bistre	Bisterbraun	Castaño bistre	Bruno-bistro
Black	Noir	Schwarz	Negro	Nero
Blackish Brown	Brun-noir	Schwärzlichbraun	Castaño negruzco	Bruno nerastro
Blackish Green	Vert foncé	Schwärzlichgrün	Verde negruzco	Verde nerastro
Blackish Olive	Olive foncé	Schwärzlicholiv	Oliva negruzco	Oliva nerastro
Block of four	Bloc de quatre	Viererblock	Bloque de cuatro	Bloco di quattro
Blue	Bleu	Blau	Azul	Azzurro
Blue-green	Vert-bleu	Blaugrün	Verde azul	Verde azzuro
Bluish Violet	Violet bleuâtre	Bläulichviolett	Violeta azulado	Violtto azzurrastro
Booklet	Carnet	Heft	Cuadernillo	Libretto
Bright Blue	Bleu vif	Lebhaftblau	Azul vivo	Azzurro vivo
Bright Green	Vert vif	Lebhaftgrün	Verde vivo	Verde vivo
Bright Purple	Mauve vif	Lebhaftpurpur	Púrpura vivo	Porpora vivo
Bronze Green	Vert-bronze	Bronzegrün	Verde bronce	Verde bronzo
Brown	Brun	Braun	Castaño	Bruno
Brown-lake	Carmin-brun	Braunlack	Laca castaño	Lacca bruno
Brown-purple	Pourpre-brun	Braunpurpur	Púrpura castaño	Porpora bruno
Brown-red	Rouge-brun	Braunrot	Rojo castaño	Rosso bruno
Buff	Chamois	Sämisch	Anteado	Camoscio
Cancellation	Oblitération	Entwertung	Cancelación	Annullamento
Cancelled	Annulé	Gestempelt	Cancelado	Annullato
Carmine	Carmin	Karmin	Carmín	Carminio
Carmine-red	Rouge-carmin	Karminrot	Rojo carmín	Rosso carminio
Centred	Centré	Zentriert	Centrado	Centrato
Cerise	Rouge-cerise	Kirschrot	Color de ceresa	Color Ciliegia
Chalk-surfaced paper	Papier couché	Kreidepapier	Papel estucado	Carta gessata
Chalky Blue	Bleu terne	Kreideblau	Azul turbio	Azzurro smorto
Charity stamp	Timbre de bienfaisance	Wohltätigkeitsmarke	Sello de beneficenza	Francobollo di beneficenza
Chestnut	Marron	Kastanienbraun	Castaño rojo	Marrone
Chocolate	Chocolat	Schokolade	Chocolate	Cioccolato
Cinnamon	Cannelle	Zimtbraun	Canela	Cannella
Claret	Grenat	Weinrot	Rojo vinoso	Vinaccia
Cobalt	Cobalt	Kobalt	Cobalto	Cobalto
Colour	Couleur	Farbe	Color	Colore
Comb-perforation	Dentelure en peigne	Kammzähnung, Reihenzähnung	Dentado de peine	Dentellatura e pettine
Commemorative stamp	Timbre commémoratif	Gedenkmarke	Sello conmemorativo	Francobollo commemorativo
Crimson	Cramoisi	Karmesin	Carmesí	Cremisi
Deep Blue	Blue foncé	Dunkelblau	Azul oscuro	Azzurro scuro
Deep bluish Green	Vert-bleu foncé	Dunkelbläulichgrün	Verde azulado oscuro	Verde azzurro scuro
Design	Dessin	Markenbild	Diseño	Disegno

English	French	German	Spanish	Italian
Die	Matrice	Urstempel. Type, Platte	Cuño	Conio, Matrice
Double	Double	Doppelt	Doble	Doppio
Drab	Olive terne	Trüboliv	Oliva turbio	Oliva smorto
Dull Green	Vert terne	Trübgrün	Verde turbio	Verde smorto
Dull purple	Mauve terne	Trübpurpur	Púrpura turbio	Porpora smorto
Embossing	Impression en relief	Prägedruck	Impresión en relieve	Impressione a relievo
Emerald	Vert-eméraude	Smaragdgrün	Esmeralda	Smeraldo
Engraved	Gravé	Graviert	Grabado	Inciso
Error	Erreur	Fehler, Fehldruck	Error	Errore
Essay	Essai	Probedruck	Ensayo	Saggio
Express letter stamp	Timbre pour lettres par exprès	Eilmarke	Sello de urgencia	Francobollo per espresso
Fiscal stamp	Timbre fiscal	Stempelmarke	Sello fiscal	Francobollo fiscale
Flesh	Chair	Fleischfarben	Carne	Carnicino
Forgery	Faux, Falsification	Fälschung	Falsificación	Falso, Falsificazione
Frame	Cadre	Rahmen	Marco	Cornice
Granite paper	Papier avec fragments de fils de soie	Faserpapier	Papel con filamentos	Carto con fili di seta
Green	Vert	Grün	Verde	Verde
Greenish Blue	Bleu verdâtre	Grünlichblau	Azul verdoso	Azzurro verdastro
Greenish Yellow	Jaune-vert	Grünlichgelb	Amarillo verdoso	Giallo verdastro
Grey	Gris	Grau	Gris	Grigio
Grey-blue	Bleu-gris	Graublau	Azul gris	Azzurro grigio
Grey-green	Vert gris	Graugrün	Verde gris	Verde grigio
Gum	Gomme	Gummi	Goma	Gomma
Gutter	Interpanneau	Zwischensteg	Espacio blanco entre dos grupos	Ponte
Imperforate	Non-dentelé	Geschnitten	Sin dentar	Non dentellato
Indigo	Indigo	Indigo	Azul indigo	Indaco
Inscription	Inscription	Inschrift	Inscripción	Dicitura
Inverted	Renversé	Kopfstehend	Invertido	Capovolto
Issue	Émission	Ausgabe	Emisión	Emissione
Laid	Vergé	Gestreift	Listado	Vergato
Lake	Lie de vin	Lackfarbe	Laca	Lacca
Lake-brown	Brun-carmin	Lackbraun	Castaño laca	Bruno lacca
Lavender	Bleu-lavande	Lavendel	Color de alhucema	Lavanda
Lemon	Jaune-citron	Zitrongelb	Limón	Limone
Light Blue	Bleu clair	Hellblau	Azul claro	Azzurro chiaro
Lilac	Lilas	Lila	Lila	Lilla
Line perforation	Dentelure en lignes	Linienzähnung	Dentado en linea	Dentellatura lineare
Lithography	Lithographie	Steindruck	Litografía	Litografia
Local	Timbre de poste locale	Lokalpostmarke	Emisión local	Emissione locale
Lozenge roulette	Percé en losanges	Rautenförmiger Durchstich	Picadura en rombos	Perforazione a losanghe
Magenta	Magenta	Magentarot	Magenta	Magenta
Margin	Marge	Rand	Borde	Margine
Maroon	Marron pourpré	Dunkelrotpurpur	Púrpura rojo oscuro	Marrone rossastro
Mauve	Mauve	Malvenfarbe	Malva	Malva
Multicoloured	Polychrome	Mehrfarbig	Multicolores	Policromo
Myrtle Green	Vert myrte	Myrtengrün	Verde mirto	Verde mirto
New Blue	Bleu ciel vif	Neublau	Azul nuevo	Azzurro nuovo
Newspaper stamp	Timbre pour journaux	Zeitungsmarke	Sello para periódicos	Francobollo per giornali
Obliteration	Oblitération	Abstempelung	Matasello	Annullamento
Obsolete	Hors (de) cours	Ausser Kurs	Fuera de curso	Fuori corso
Ochre	Ocre	Ocker	Ocre	Ocra

English	French	German	Spanish	Italian
Official stamp	Timbre de service	Dienstmarke	Sello de servicio	Francobollo di
Olive-brown	Brun-olive	Olivbraun	Castaño oliva	Bruno oliva
Olive-green	Vert-olive	Olivgrün	Verde oliva	Verde oliva
Olive-grey	Gris-olive	Olivgrau	Gris oliva	Grigio oliva
Olive-yellow	Jaune-olive	Olivgelb	Amarillo oliva	Giallo oliva
Orange	Orange	Orange	Naranja	Arancio
Orange-brown	Brun-orange	Orangebraun	Castaño naranja	Bruno arancio
Orange-red	Rouge-orange	Orangerot	Rojo naranja	Rosso arancio
Orange-yellow	Jaune-orange	Orangegelb	Amarillo naranja	Giallo arancio
Overprint	Surcharge	Aufdruck	Sobrecarga	Soprastampa
Pair	Paire	Paar	Pareja	Coppia
Pale	Pâle	Blass	Pálido	Pallido
Pane	Panneau	Gruppe	Grupo	Gruppo
Paper	Papier	Papier	Papel	Carta
Parcel post stamp	Timbre pour colis postaux	Paketmarke	Sello para paquete postal	Francobollo per pacchi postali
Pen-cancelled	Oblitéré à plume	Federzugentwertung	Cancelado a pluma	Annullato a penna
Percé en arc	Percé en arc	Bogenförmiger Durchstich	Picadura en forma de arco	Perforazione ad arco
Percé en scie	Percé en scie	Bogenförmiger Durchstich	Picado en sierra	Foratura a sega
Perforated	Dentelé	Gezähnt	Dentado	Dentellato
Perforation	Dentelure	Zähnung	Dentar	Dentellatura
Photogravure	Photogravure, Heliogravure	Rastertiefdruck	Fotograbado	Rotocalco
Pin perforation	Percé en points	In Punkten durchstochen	Horadado con alfileres	Perforato a punti
Plate	Planche	Platte	Plancha	Lastra, Tavola
Plum	Prune	Pflaumenfarbe	Color de ciruela	Prugna
Postage Due stamp	Timbre-taxe	Portomarke	Sello de tasa	Segnatasse
Postage stamp	Timbre-poste	Briefmarke, Freimarke, Postmarke	Sello de correos	Francobollo postale
Postal fiscal stamp	Timbre fiscal-postal	Stempelmarke als Postmarke verwendet	Sello fiscal-postal	Fiscale postale
Postmark	Oblitération postale	Poststempel	Matasello	Bollo
Printing	Impression, Tirage	Druck	Impresión	Stampa, Tiratura
Proof	Épreuve	Druckprobe	Prueba de impresión	Prova
Provisionals	Timbres provisoires	Provisorische Marken. Provisorien	Provisionales	Provvisori
Prussian Blue	Bleu de Prusse	Preussischblau	Azul de Prusia	Azzurro di Prussia
Purple	Pourpre	Purpur	Púrpura	Porpora
Purple-brown	Brun-pourpre	Purpurbraun	Castaño púrpura	Bruno porpora
Recess-printing	Impression en taille-douce	Tiefdruck	Grabado	Incisione
Red	Rouge	Rot	Rojo	Rosso
Red-brown	Brun-rouge	Rotbraun	Castaño rojizo	Bruno rosso
Reddish Lilac	Lilas rougeâtre	Rötlichlila	Lila rojizo	Lilla rossastro
Reddish Purple	Poupre-rouge	Rötlichpurpur	Púrpura rojizo	Porpora rossastro
Reddish Violet	Violet rougeâtre	Rötlichviolett	Violeta rojizo	Violetto rossastro
Red-orange	Orange rougeâtre	Rotorange	Naranja rojizo	Arancio rosso
Registration stamp	Timbre pour lettre chargée (recommandée)	Einschreibemarke	Sello de certificado lettere	Francobollo per raccomandate
Reprint	Réimpression	Neudruck	Reimpresión	Ristampa
Reversed	Retourné	Umgekehrt	Invertido	Rovesciato
Rose	Rose	Rosa	Rosa	Rosa
Rose-red	Rouge rosé	Rosarot	Rojo rosado	Rosso rosa
Rosine	Rose vif	Lebhaftrosa	Rosa vivo	Rosa vivo
Roulette	Percage	Durchstich	Picadura	Foratura
Rouletted	Percé	Durchstochen	Picado	Forato
Royal Blue	Bleu-roi	Königblau	Azul real	Azzurro reale
Sage green	Vert-sauge	Salbeigrün	Verde salvia	Verde salvia
Salmon	Saumon	Lachs	Salmón	Salmone

English	French	German	Spanish	Italian
Scarlet	Écarlate	Scharlach	Escarlata	Scarlatto
Sepia	Sépia	Sepia	Sepia	Seppia
Serpentine roulette	Percé en serpentin	Schlangenliniger Durchstich	Picado a serpentina	Perforazione a serpentina
Shade	Nuance	Tönung	Tono	Gradazione de colore
Sheet	Feuille	Bogen	Hoja	Foglio
Slate	Ardoise	Schiefer	Pizarra	Ardesia
Slate-blue	Bleu-ardoise	Schieferblau	Azul pizarra	Azzurro ardesia
Slate-green	Vert-ardoise	Schiefergrün	Verde pizarra	Verde ardesia
Slate-lilac	Lilas-gris	Schierferlila	Lila pizarra	Lilla ardesia
Slate-purple	Mauve-gris	Schieferpurpur	Púrpura pizarra	Porpora ardesia
Slate-violet	Violet-gris	Schieferviolett	Violeta pizarra	Violetto ardesia
Special delivery stamp	Timbre pour exprès	Eilmarke	Sello de urgencia	Francobollo per espressi
Specimen	Spécimen	Muster	Muestra	Saggio
Steel Blue	Bleu acier	Stahlblau	Azul acero	Azzurro acciaio
Strip	Bande	Streifen	Tira	Striscia
Surcharge	Surcharge	Aufdruck	Sobrecarga	Soprastampa
Tête-bêche	Tête-bêche	Kehrdruck	Tête-bêche	Tête-bêche
Tinted paper	Papier teinté	Getöntes Papier	Papel coloreado	Carta tinta
Too-late stamp	Timbre pour lettres en retard	Verspätungsmarke	Sello para cartas retardadas	Francobollo per le lettere in ritardo
Turquoise-blue	Bleu-turquoise	Türkisblau	Azul turquesa	Azzurro turchese
Turquoise-green	Vert-turquoise	Türkisgrün	Verde turquesa	Verde turchese
Typography	Typographie	Buchdruck	Tipografia	Tipografia
Ultramarine	Outremer	Ultramarin	Ultramar	Oltremare
Unused	Neuf	Ungebraucht	Nuevo	Nuovo
Used	Oblitéré, Usé	Gebraucht	Usado	Usato
Venetian Red	Rouge-brun terne	Venezianischrot	Rojo veneciano	Rosso veneziano
Vermilion	Vermillon	Zinnober	Cinabrio	Vermiglione
Violet	Violet	Violett	Violeta	Violetto
Violet-blue	Bleu-violet	Violettblau	Azul violeta	Azzurro violetto
Watermark	Filigrane	Wasserzeichen	Filigrana	Filigrana
Watermark sideways	Filigrane couché	Wasserzeichen liegend	Filigrana acostado	Filigrana coricata
Wove paper	Papier ordinaire, Papier uni	Einfaches Papier	Papel avitelado	Carta unita
Yellow	Jaune	Gelb	Amarillo	Giallo
Yellow-brown	Brun-jaune	Gelbbraun	Castaño amarillo	Bruno giallo
Yellow-green	Vert-jaune	Gelbgrün	Verde amarillo	Verde giallo
Yellow-olive	Olive-jaunâtre	Gelboliv	Oliva amarillo	Oliva giallastro
Yellow-orange	Orange jaunâtre	Gelborange	Naranja amarillo	Arancio giallastro
Zig-zag roulette	Percé en zigzag	Sägezahnartiger Durchstich	Picado en zigzag	Perforazione a zigzag

Guide to Entries

(A) Country of Issue – When a country changes its name, the catalogue listing changes to reflect the name change, for example Namibia was formerly known as South West Africa, the stamps in Southern Africa are all listed under Namibia, but split into South West Africa and then Namibia.

(B) Country Information – Brief geographical and historical details for the issuing country.

(C) Currency – Details of the currency, and dates of earliest use where applicable, on the face value of the stamps.

(D) Illustration – Generally, the first stamp in the set. Stamp illustrations are reduced to 75%, with overprints and surcharges shown actual size.

(E) Illustration or Type Number – These numbers are used to help identify stamps, either in the listing, type column, design line or footnote, usually the first value in a set. These type numbers are in a bold type face – **123**; when bracketed (**123**) an overprint or a surcharge is indicated. Some type numbers include a lower-case letter – **123a**, this indicates they have been added to an existing set.

(F) Date of issue – This is the date that the stamp/set of stamps was issued by the post office and was available for purchase. When a set of definitive stamps has been issued over several years the Year Date given is for the earliest issue. Commemorative sets are listed in chronological order. Stamps of the same design, or issue are usually grouped together, for example some of the New Zealand landscapes definitive series were first issued in 2003 but the set includes stamps issued to May 2007.

(G) Number Prefix – Stamps other than definitives and commemoratives have a prefix letter before the catalogue number.
Their use is explained in the text: some examples are A for airmail, D for postage due and O for official stamps.

(H) Footnote – Further information on background or key facts on issues.

(I) Stanley Gibbons Catalogue number – This is a unique number for each stamp to help the collector identify stamps in the listing. The Stanley Gibbons numbering system is universally recognised as definitive.
Where insufficient numbers have been left to provide for additional stamps to a listing, some stamps will have a suffix letter after the catalogue number (for example 214a). If numbers have been left for additions to a set and not used they will be left vacant.
The separate type numbers (in bold) refer to illustrations (see **E**).

(J) Colour – If a stamp is printed in three or fewer colours then the colours are listed, working from the centre of the stamp outwards (see **R**).

(K) Design line – Further details on design variations

(L) Key Type – Indicates a design type on which the stamp is based. These are the bold figures found below each illustration, for example listed in Cameroon, in the West Africa catalogue, is the Key type A and B showing the ex-Kaiser's yacht *Hohenzollern*. The type numbers are also given in bold in the second column of figures alongside the stamp description to indicate the design of each stamp. Where an issue comprises stamps of similar design, the corresponding type number should be taken as indicating the general design. Where there are blanks in the type number column it means that the type of the corresponding stamp

is that shown by the number in the type column of the same issue. A dash (–) in the type column means that the stamp is not illustrated. Where type numbers refer to stamps of another country, e.g. where stamps of one country are overprinted for use in another, this is always made clear in the text.

(M) Coloured Papers – Stamps printed on coloured paper are shown – e.g. 'brown/*yellow*' indicates brown printed on yellow paper.

(N) Surcharges and Overprints – Usually described in the headings. Any actual wordings are shown in bold type. Descriptions clarify words and figures used in the overprint. Stamps with the same overprints in different colours are not listed separately. Numbers in brackets after the descriptions are the catalogue numbers of the non-overprinted stamps. The words 'inscribed' or 'inscription' refer to the wording incorporated in the design of a stamp and not surcharges or overprints.

(O) Face value – This refers to the value of each stamp and is the price it was sold for at the Post Office when issued. Some modern stamps do not have their values in figures but instead it is shown as a letter, for example Great Britain use 1st or 2nd on their stamps as opposed to the actual value.

(P) Catalogue Value – Mint/Unused. Prices quoted for Queen Victoria to King George V stamps are for lightly hinged examples.

(Q) Catalogue Value – Used. Prices generally refer to fine postally used examples. For certain issues they are for cancelled-to-order.

Prices
Prices are given in pence and pounds. Stamps worth £100 and over are shown in whole pounds:

Shown in Catalogue as	Explanation
10	10 pence
1·75	£1·75
15.00	£15
£150	£150
£2300	£2300

Prices assume stamps are in 'fine condition'; we may ask more for superb and less for those of lower quality. The minimum catalogue price quoted is 10p and is intended as a guide for catalogue users. The lowest price for individual stamps purchased from Stanley Gibbons is £1.
Prices quoted are for the cheapest variety of that particular stamp. Differences of watermark, perforation, or other details, often increase the value. Prices quoted for mint issues are for single examples, unless otherwise stated. Those in *se-tenant* pairs, strips, blocks or sheets may be worth more. Where no prices are listed it is either because the stamps are not known to exist (usually shown by a †) in that particular condition, or, more usually, because there is no reliable information on which to base their value.
All prices are subject to change without prior notice and we cannot guarantee to supply all stamps as priced. Prices quoted in advertisements are also subject to change without prior notice.

(R) Multicoloured – Nearly all modern stamps are multicoloured (more than three colours); this is indicated in the heading, with a description of the stamp given in the listing.

(S) Perforations – Please see page xiii for a detailed explanation of perforations.

(A) Country of issue →

Bangladesh

In elections during December 1970 the Awami League party won all but two of the seats in the East Pakistan province and, in consequence, held a majority in the National Assembly. On 1 March 1971 the Federal Government postponed the sitting of the Assembly with the result that unrest spread throughout the eastern province. Pakistan army operations against the dissidents forced the leaders of the League to flee to India from where East Pakistan was proclaimed independent as Bangladesh. In early December the Indian army moved against Pakistan troops in Bangladesh and civilian government was re-established on 22 December 1971. ← **(B) Country Information**

From 20 December 1971 various Pakistan issues were overprinted by local postmasters, mainly using handstamps. Their use was permitted until 30 April 1973. These are of philatelic interest, but are outside the scope of the catalogue.

(C) Currency ——— **(Currency. 100 paisa = 1 rupee)**

← **(D) Illustration**

L 17 ← **(E) Illustration or Type number**

(F) Date of issue — **1978** (8 Mar). No. L 57 surch with Type L **16**. Chalky paper.

L63	L **14**	25c. on 2½c. ultramarine, green and buff	75	1·75

(Des A. G. Mitchell. Litho Harrison)

1981 (3 June). P 14½

(G) Number prefix —

L64	L **17**	5c. multicoloured	10	10
L65		10c. multicoloured	10	10
L66		20c. multicoloured	15	15
L67		30c. multicoloured	25	25
L68		40c. multicoloured	30	30
L69		50c. multicoloured	30	45
L64/9	Set of 6		1·00	1·25

(H) Footnote — Issues for the Government Life Insurance Department were withdrawn on 1 December 1989 when it became the privatised Tower Corporation.

(Des G. R. Bull and G. R. Smith. Photo Harrison)

1959 (2 Mar). Centenary of Marlborough Province. T **198** and similar horiz designs. W **98** (sideways). P 14½×14.

(I) Stanley Gibbons catalogue number —

772		2d. green	30	10
773		3d. deep blue	30	10
774		8d. light brown	1·25	2·25	← **(J) Colour**
772/4	Set of 3		1·60	2·25

(K) Design line — Designs:—3d. Shipping wool, Wairau Bar, 1857; 8d. Salt industry, Grassmere.

1915 (12 July). Stamps of German Kamerun. Types A and B, surch as T **1** (Nos. B1/9) or **2**. (Nos. B10/13) in black or blue.

(L) Key type column —

B1	A	1½d. on 3pf. (No. k7) (B.)	13·00	42·00
		a. Different fount "d"	£150	£350

340	**41**	2d. purple (1903)	£350	£325
341	**28**	3d. bistre-brown (1906)	£700	£600
342	**37**	4d. blue and chestnut/*bluish* (1904)	£300	£350	← **(M) Coloured papers**
		a. Blue and yellow-brown/*bluish*	£300	£350

(N) Surcharges and overprints — **1913** (1 Dec). Auckland Industrial Exhibition. Nos. 387aa, 389, 392 and 405 optd with T **59** by Govt Printer, Wellington.

412	**51**	½d. deep green	20·00	55·00	← **(P) Catalogue value – Mint**
413	**53**	1d. carmine	25·00	48·00
		a. "Feather" flaw	£225	
414	**52**	3d. chestnut	£130	£250
415		6d. carmine	£160	£300	← **(Q) Catalogue value – Used**
412/15	Set of 4		£300	£600

(O) Face value —

These overprinted stamps were only available for letters in New Zealand and to Australia.

(Des Martin Bailey. Litho Southern Colour Print)

2008 (2 July). Olympic Games, Beijing. T **685** and similar diamond-shaped designs. Multicoloured. Phosphorised paper. P 14½. ← **(S) Perforations**

(R) Multicoloured stamp —

3056	50c. Type **685**	1·00	85

BY APPOINTMENT TO
HER MAJESTY THE QUEEN
PHILATELISTS
STANLEY GIBBONS LTD
LONDON

STANLEY GIBBONS
LONDON 1856

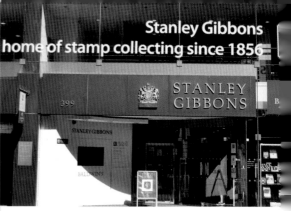

STANLEY GIBBONS - THE HOME OF STAMP COLLECTING FOR OVER 160 YEARS.

Visit our store at 399 Strand for all your philatelic needs.

EVERYTHING FOR THE STAMP COLLECTOR.

· Great Britain Stamps
· Commonwealth Stamps
· Publications and Accessories
· Auctions

WHERE TO FIND US

STANLEY GIBBONS
399 STRAND
LONDON, WC2R 0LX
UNITED KINGDOM

0207 557 4436

SHOP@STANLEYGIBBONS.COM

OPENING HOURS

Mon - Fri: 9am - 5:30pm | Sat: 9:30 - 5:30pm | Sun: Closed

British POs in Crete

BRITISH ADMINISTRATION OF CANDIA PROVINCE (HERAKLEION)

Crete, formerly part of the Turkish Empire, was made autonomous, under Turkish suzerainty, in November 1898 with British, French, Italian and Russian troops stationed in separate zones to keep the peace.

Overseas mail franked with Nos. B1/B5 was forwarded through the Austrian post office at Canea, being additionally franked with stamps of the Austro-Hungarian Post Offices in the Turkish Empire.

(Currency. 40 paras = 1 piastre)

PRICES FOR STAMPS ON COVER TO 1945	
No. B1	from × 8
Nos. B2/B5	—

B **1**   B **2**

1898 (25 Nov). Handstruck locally. Imperf.
B1	B **1**	20pa. bright violet	£450	£225

1898 (3 Dec). Litho by M. Grundmann, Athens. P 11½.
B2	B **2**	10pa. blue	11·00	25·00
		a. Imperf (pair)	£250	
B3		20pa. green	20·00	23·00
		a. Imperf (pair)	£250	

1899. P 11½.
B4	B **2**	10pa. brown	11·00	35·00
		a. Imperf (pair)	£250	
B5		20pa. rose	20·00	19·00
		a. Imperf (pair)	£250	

Forgeries exist of Nos. B1/B5. Note that genuine examples of T B **2** show a full circle in the ornament above the figures of value. Forgeries with a broken circle in this position are frequently met with.

The British postal service closed at the end of 1899.

Cyprus

Cyprus was part of the Turkish Ottoman Empire from 1571.

The first records of an organised postal service date from 1871 when a post office was opened at Nicosia (Lefkosa) under the jurisdiction of the Damascus Head Post Office. Various stamps of Turkey from the 1868 issue onwards are known used from this office, cancelled 'KIBRIS', in Arabic, within a double-lined oblong. Manuscript cancellations have also been reported. The records report the opening of a further office at Larnaca (Tuzla) in 1873, but no cancellation for this office has been identified.

To provide an overseas postal service the Austrian Empire opened a post office in Larnaca during 1845. Stamps of the Austrian Post Offices in the Turkish Empire were placed on sale there from 1 June 1864 and were cancelled with an unframed straight-line mark or circular date stamp. This Austrian post office closed on 6 August 1878.

BRITISH ADMINISTRATION

Following the convention with Turkey, Great Britain assumed the administration of Cyprus on 11 July 1878 and the first post office, as part of the British GPO system, was opened at Larnaca on 27 July 1878. Further offices at Famagusta, Kyrenia, Limassol, Nicosia and Paphos followed in September 1878.

The stamps of Great Britain were supplied to the various offices as they opened and continued to be used until the Cyprus Administration assumed responsibility for the postal service on 1 April 1880. With the exception of '969' (Nicosia) similar numeral cancellations had previously been used at offices in Great Britain.

Numeral postmarks for Headquarters Camp, Nicosia ('D48') and Polymedia (Polemidhia) Camp, Limassol ('D47') were supplied by the GPO in London during January 1881. These cancellations had three bars above and three bars below the numeral. Similar marks, but with four bars above and below, had previously been used in London on newspapers and bulk mail.

Although both three bar cancellations subsequently occur on Cyprus issues only, isolated examples have been found on loose Great Britain stamps and there are no known covers or pieces which confirm such usage in Cyprus.

(9)

FAMAGUSTA

Stamps of GREAT BRITAIN cancelled '982' as T **9**.
1878–80.
Z1	½d. rose-red (1870–1879) (Plate Nos. 11, 13)		£750
Z2	1d. rose-red (1864–1879)		£600
	Plate Nos. 145, 174, 181, 193, 202, 204, 206, 215, 217.		
Z3	2d. blue (1858–1869) (Plate Nos. 13, 14, 15)		£1200
Z4	2½d. rosy mauve (1876) (Plate Nos. 13, 16)		£1300
Z5	6d. grey (1874–1880) (Plate No. 15)		£3250
Z6	1s. green (1873–1877) (Plate No. 12)		

KYRENIA

Stamps of GREAT BRITAIN cancelled '974' as T **9**.
1878–80.
Z8	½d. rose-red (1870–1879) (Plate No. 13)		£1100
Z9	1d. rose-red (1864–1879)	From	£700
	Plate Nos. 168, 171, 193, 196, 206, 207, 209, 220. .		
Z10	2d. blue (1858–1869) (Plate Nos. 13, 15)	From	£1200
Z11	2½d. rosy mauve (1876–1879) (Plate Nos. 12, 13, 14, 15)	From	£1200
Z12	4d. sage-green (1877) (Plate No. 16)		
Z13	6d. grey (1874–1880) (Plate No. 16)		

LARNACA

Stamps of GREAT BRITAIN cancelled '942' as T **9**.
1878–80.
Z14	½d. rose-red (1870–1879)	From	£250
	Plate Nos. 11, 12, 13, 14, 15, 19, 20.		

Z15		1d. rose-red (1864–1879).................................*From*	£180
		Plate Nos. 129, 131, 146, 154, 170, 171, 174, 175,	
		176, 177, 178, 179, 181, 182, 183, 184, 187, 188,	
		190, 191, 192, 193, 194, 195, 196, 197, 198, 199,	
		200, 201, 202, 203, 204, 205, 206, 207, 208, 209,	
		210, 212, 213, 214, 215, 216, 217, 218, 220, 221,	
		222, 225..	
Z16		1½d. lake-red (1870) (Plate No. 3)........................	£2250
Z17		2d. blue (1858–1869) (Plate Nos. 9, 13, 14, 15)...........	£300
Z18		2½d. rosy mauve (1876–1879)........................*From*	75·00
		Plate Nos. 4, 5, 6, 8, 9, 10, 11, 12, 13, 14, 15, 16, 17.	
Z19		2½d. blue (1880) (Plate Nos. 17, 18)......................	£500
Z21		4d. sage-green (1877) (Plate Nos. 15, 16)..................	£550
Z22		6d. grey (1874–1876) (Plate Nos. 15, 16, 17)..............	£600
Z23		6d. pale buff (1872–1873) (Plate No. 11)..................	£3750
Z24		8d. orange (1876)..	£8500
Z25		1s. green (1873–1877) (Plate Nos. 12, 13).................	£1000
Z27		5s. rose (1874) (Plate No. 2)............................	£8500

LIMASSOL

Stamps of GREAT BRITAIN cancelled '975' as T **9**.

1878–80.

Z28		½d. rose-red (1870–1879) (Plate Nos. 11, 13, 15, 19) ...	£450
Z29		1d. rose-red (1864–1879)...........................*From*	£300
		Plate Nos. 159, 160, 171, 173, 174, 177, 179, 184,	
		187, 190, 193, 195, 196, 197, 198, 200, 202, 206,	
		207, 208, 209, 210, 213, 215, 216, 218, 220, 221,	
		222, 225.	
Z30		1½d. lake-red (1870–1874) (Plate No. 3)..................	£2750
Z31		2d. blue (1858–1869) (Plate Nos. 14, 15)............*From*	£550
Z32		2½d. rosy-mauve (1876–1880)........................*From*	£250
		Plate Nos. 11, 12, 13, 14, 15, 16.	
Z33		2½d. blue (1880) (Plate No. 17)..........................	£1200
Z34		4d. sage-green (Plate No. 16)............................	£1100

NICOSIA

Stamps of GREAT BRITAIN cancelled '969' as T **9**.

1878–80.

Z35		½d. rose-red (1870–1879)................................	£475
		Plate Nos. 12, 13, 14, 15, 20.	
Z36		1d. rose-red (1864–1879)...........................*From*	£300
		Plate Nos. 170, 171, 174, 189, 190, 192, 193, 195,	
		196, 198, 200, 202, 203, 205, 206, 207, 210, 212,	
		214, 215, 218, 221, 222, 225.	
Z36a		1½d. lake red (1870) (Plate No. 3).......................	£3250
Z37		2d. blue (1858–1869) (Plate Nos. 14, 15).................	£550
Z38		2½d. rosy mauve (1876–1879).......................*From*	£200
		Plate Nos. 10, 11, 12, 13, 14, 15, 16.	
Z39		2½d. blue (1880) (Plate No. 17)..........................	£800
Z42		4d. sage-green (1877) (Plate No. 16).....................	£850
Z43		6d. grey (1873) (Plate No. 16)..........................	£1000

PAPHOS

Stamps of GREAT BRITAIN cancelled '981' as T **9**.

1878–80.

Z44		½d. rose-red (1870–1879) (Plate Nos. 13, 15).............	
Z45		1d. rose-red (1864–1879)...........................*From*	£700
		Plate Nos. 196, 201, 202, 204, 206, 213, 217.	
Z46		2d. blue (1858–1869) (Plate No. 15).....................	£1200
Z47		2½d. rosy mauve (1876–1879)........................*From*	£650
		Plate Nos. 13, 14, 15, 16.	

PRICES FOR STAMPS ON COVER TO 1945	
Nos. 1/4	*from* × 50
Nos. 5/6	—
Nos. 7/10	*from* × 100
Nos. 11/15	*from* × 12
No. 16	—
Nos. 16a/22	*from* × 20
Nos. 23/25	*from* × 100
No. 26	—
No. 27	*from* × 25
No. 28	—
No. 29	*from* × 200
Nos. 31/35a	*from* × 10
Nos. 36/37	—
Nos. 40/49	*from* × 8
Nos. 50/71	*from* × 5
Nos. 74/99	*from* × 4
Nos. 100/102	—
Nos. 103/117	*from* × 4
No. 117a	—
Nos. 118/131	*from* × 8
No. 132	—
Nos. 133/143	*from* × 5
Nos. 144/147	*from* × 6
Nos. 148/163	*from* × 5

PERFORATION. Nos. 1/122 are perf 14.

Stamps of Great Britain overprinted

CYPRUS   CYPRUS
(1)   (2)

(Optd by D.L.R.)

1880 (1 Apr).

| 1 | 1 | ½d. rose.. | £120 | £110 |
| | | a. Opt double (Plate 15).............................. | † | £45000 |

Plate No.	Un.	Used.	Plate No.	Un.	Used
12.	£225	£250	19.	£5000	£700
15.	£120	£110			

2	2	1d. red..	23·00	48·00
		a. Opt double (Plate 208).............................	£7000	†
		aa. Opt double (Plate 218)............................	£4250	†
		b. Vert pair, top stamp without opt		
		(Plate 208)..	£27000	†

Plate No.	Un.	Used.	Plate No.	Un.	Used
174.	£1400	£1400	208.	£130	55·00
181.	£500	£190	215.	23·00	60·00
184.	£20000	£3500	216.	24·00	48·00
193.	£800	†	217.	24·00	65·00
196.	£700	†	218.	30·00	70·00
201.	27·00	55·00	220.	£350	£375
205.	90·00	55·00			

3	2	2½d. rosy mauve....................................	4·50	18·00
		a. Large thin 'C' (Plate 14) (BK, JK).................	£110	£375
		b. Large thin 'C' (Plate 15) (BK, JK).................	£225	£1000
		w. Wmk inverted (Plate 15)............................	£650	

Plate No.	Un.	Used.	Plate No.	Un.	Used
14.	4·50	18·00	15.	8·00	50·00

4	2	4d. sage-green (Plate 16)..........................	£140	£225
		a. Opt double, one albino.............................	£1500	
5		6d. grey (Plate 16).................................	£500	£650
6		1s. green (Plate 13)................................	£850	£475

HALF-PENNY   HALF-PENNY
(3) 18 mm   (4) 16 or 16½ mm

HALF-PENNY   HALF-PENNY   30 PARAS
(4a) 17 mm   (5) 13 mm   (6)

(Optd by Govt Ptg Office, Nicosia)

1881 (Feb–June). No. 2 surch.

7	3	½d. on 1d. red (2.81)..............................	80·00	90·00
		a. 'HALFPENN' (BG, LG)		
		(all plates).................................*From*	£3000	£2750
		b. Surch double (Plate 220)..........................	£2750	

Plate No.	Un.	Used.	Plate No.	Un.	Used
174.	£250	£375	215.	£800	£950
181.	£225	£250	216.	80·00	95·00
201.	£110	£130	217.	£900	£850
205.	80·00	90·00	218.	£500	£650
208.	£200	£350	220.	£325	£400

| 8 | 4 | ½d. on 1d. red (2.81).............................. | £130 | £160 |
| | | a. Surch double (Plates 201 and 216) . | £3750 | £2500 |

Plate No.	Un.	Used.	Plate No.	Un.	Used
201.	£130	£160	218.	—	£15000
216.	£350	£425			

| 8b | 4a | ½d. on 1d. red (2.81).............................. | — | £800 |

Plate No.	Un.	Used.	Plate No.	Un.	Used
201.	—	£800	216.	—	£1100

The most noticeable difference between T **4** (16½ mm) and T **4a** (17 mm) is the space between the 'F' of 'HALF' and the 'P' of 'PENNY'. This measures 1 mm on T **4**, but 2 mm on T **4a**.

9	5	½d. on 1d. red (1.6)...............................	50·00	70·00
		aa. Surch double (Plate 205).........................	£800	
		ab. Surch double (Plate 215).........................	£450	£650
		b. Surch treble (Plate 205)..........................	£4500	
		ba. Surch treble (Plate 215).........................	£800	
		bc. Surch treble (Plate 218).........................	£4500	
		c. Surch quadruple (Plate 205).......................	£7000	
		ca. Surch quadruple (Plate 215)......................	£7000	

Plate No.	Un.	Used.	Plate No.	Un.	Used
205.	£400	—	217.	£160	£110
215.	50·00	70·00	218.	90·00	£120

The surcharges on Nos. 8 and 8b were handstamped; the others were applied by lithography.

(New Currency: 40 paras = 1 piastre, 180 piastres = £1)

1881 (June). No. 2 surch with T **6** by lithography.

10	**6**	30 paras on 1d. red	£150	90·00
		a. Surch double, one inverted (Plate 216)	£7500	
		aa. Surch double, one inverted (Plate 220)	£1900	£1400

Plate No.	*Un.*	*Used.*	*Plate No.*	*Un.*	*Used*
201.	£180	£110	217.	£200	£200
216.	£150	90·00	220.	£170	£180

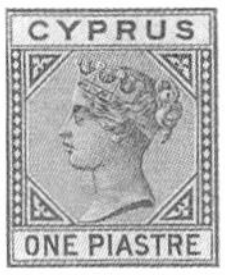

7

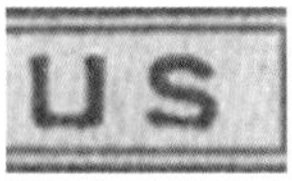

'US' damaged at foot (R. 5/5 of both panes)

(Typo D.L.R.)

1881 (1 July). Die I. Wmk Crown CC.

11	**7**	½pi. emerald-green	£180	45·00
		w. Wmk inverted	£1200	£650
12		1pi. rose	£375	32·00
13		2pi. blue	£450	35·00
		w. Wmk inverted	—	£1800
14		4pi. pale olive-green	£950	£275
15		6pi. olive-grey	£1800	£475

Stamps of Queen Victoria initialled 'J.A.B.' or overprinted 'POSTAL SURCHARGE' with or without the same initials were employed for accounting purposes between the Chief Post Office and sub-offices, the initials are those of the then Postmaster, Mr. J. A. Bulmer.

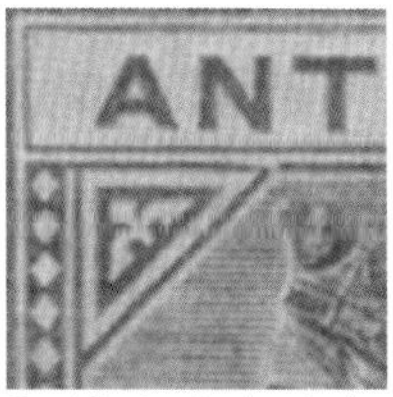

Top left triangle detached (Pl 2 R. 3/3 of right pane)

1882 (May)–**86**. Die I*. Wmk Crown CA.

16	**7**	½pi. emerald-green (5.82)	£5000	£500
		a. Dull green (4.83)	25·00	3·00
		ab. Top left triangle detached	£1400	£275
17		30pa. pale mauve (7.6.82)	80·00	28·00
		a. Top left triangle detached	£2500	£1000
		b. Damaged 'US'	£1300	£500
18		1pi. rose (3.83)	£110	4·25
		a. Top left triangle detached	—	£325
19		2pi. blue (4.83)	£160	3·75
		a. Top left triangle detached	—	£375
20		4pi. pale olive-green (10.83)	£350	38·00
		a. Deep olive-green	£550	50·00
		b. Top left triangle detached	£5000	£1200
21		6pi. olive-grey (7.82)	75·00	17·00
		a. Top left triangle detached	—	£1200
22		12pi. orange-brown (1886)	£200	42·00
		s. Optd 'SPECIMEN'	£2250	
16*a*/22 *Set of 7*			£900	£120

* For description and illustrations of Dies I and II see Introduction.

No. 21 with manuscript 'Specimen' endorsement is known with 'CYPRUS' and value double.

See also Nos. 31/37.

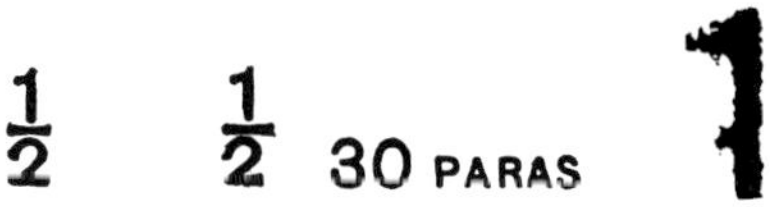

(**8**) (**9**)

Spur on '1' (position 3 in setting)

(Surch litho by Govt Ptg Office, Nicosia)

1882. Surch with Types **8**/**9**.

(a) Wmk Crown CC

23	**7**	½ on ½pi. emerald-green (6.82)	£700	75·00
		c. Spur on '1'	£1500	£140
		w. Wmk inverted		
24		30pa. on 1pi. rose (22.5.82)	£1600	£110

(b) Wmk Crown CA

25	**7**	½ on ½pi. emerald-green (22.5.82)	£170	9·00
		a. Surch double	†	£2750
		b. '½' inserted by hand	†	£5000
		c. Spur on '1'	£325	16·00

Nos. 23 and 25 were surcharged by a setting of six arranged as a horizontal row.

No. 25b shows an additional handstamped '½' applied to examples on which the surcharge was so misplaced as to almost omit one of the original '½'s.

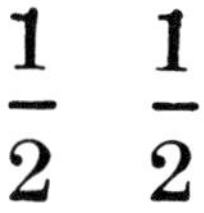

(**10**)

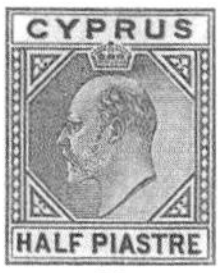

11

Varieties of numerals:

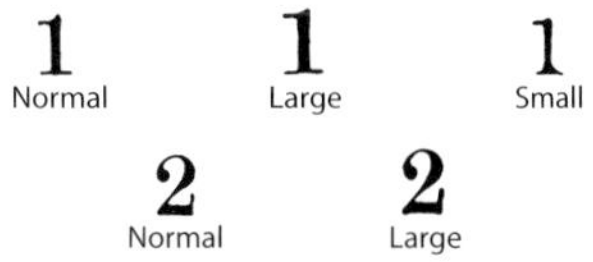

1886 (Apr). Surch with T **10** (fractions approx 6 *mm* apart) in typography.

(a) Wmk Crown CC

26	**7**	½ on ½pi. emerald-green	£22000	†

(b) Wmk Crown CA

27	**7**	½ on ½pi. emerald-green	£300	70·00
		a. Large '2' at right	£3000	£750

No. 27a occured at R. 10/1 and another unknown position in the setting of 60.

1886 (27 May–June). Surch with T **10** (fractions approx 8 *mm* apart) in typography.

(a) Wmk Crown CC

28	**7**	½ on ½pi. emerald-green	£8000	£425
		a. Large '1' at left	—	£1900
		b. Small '1' at right	£16000	£2250
		c. Large '2' at left	—	£2250
		d. Large '2' at right	†	£2250

(b) Wmk Crown CA

29	**7**	½ on ½pi. emerald-green (1.6)	£550	17·00
		a. Large '1' at left	£4000	£275
		b. Small '1' at right	£3500	£275
		c. Large '2' at left	£4000	£350
		d. Large '2' at right	£4000	£350

Nos. 28/29 were surcharged in a setting of 60. The large '1' at left occurs at R. 4/4, the large '2' at left at R. 2/5 and the large '2' at right at R. 3/4. The position of the small '1' at right (as illustrated) may be R. 1/2, but this awaits confirmation.

A third type of this surcharge is known with the fractions spaced approximately 10 mm apart on CA paper with postmarks from August 1886. This may be due to the shifting of type.

1892–**94**. Die II. Wmk Crown CA.

31	**7**	½pi. dull green	16·00	2·75
		w. Wmk inverted		
32		30pa. mauve	12·00	14·00
		a. Damaged 'US'	£350	£350
33		1pi. carmine	15·00	10·00
34		2pi. ultramarine	14·00	2·00
35		4pi. olive-green	50·00	50·00
		a. Pale olive-green	18·00	42·00
36		6pi. olive-grey (1894)	£250	£750
37		12pi. orange brown (1893)	£190	£450
31/37 *Set of 7*			£450	£1100

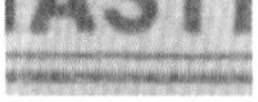

Large 'S' in 'PIASTRE'

1894 (14 Aug)–**96**. Colours changed and new values. Die II. Wmk Crown CA.

40	**7**	½pi. green and carmine (1896)	4·25	1·25
		a. Large 'S' in 'PIASTRE'	£190	90·00
		w. Wmk inverted	†	£2500
41		30pa. bright mauve and green (1896)	5·00	5·50
		a. Damaged 'US'	£200	£200
42		1pi. carmine and blue (1896)	8·50	2·00
43		2pi. blue and purple (1896)	18·00	1·50

44		4pi. sage-green and purple (1896)	22·00	17·00
45		6pi. sepia and green (1896)	22·00	40·00
46		9pi. brown and carmine	29·00	40·00
47		12pi. orange-brown and black (1896)	24·00	70·00
48		18pi. greyish slate and brown	55·00	65·00
49		45pi. grey-purple and blue	£120	£160
40/49 Set of 10			£250	£325
40s/49s Optd 'SPECIMEN' Set of 10			£350	

The large 'S' in 'PIASTRE' was a retouch to correct a damaged letter (R. 1/4, both panes). It was corrected when a new duty plate (120-set) was introduced in 1905.

LIMASSOL FLOOD HANDSTAMP. Following a flood on 14 November 1894, which destroyed the local stamp stocks, the postmaster of Limassol produced a temporary handstamp showing '½C.P.' which was applied to local letters with the usual c.d.s.

(Typo D.L.R.)

1902–04. Wmk Crown CA.

50	**11**	½pi. green and carmine (12.02)	15·00	1·25
		a. Large 'S' in 'PIASTRE'	£225	60·00
		w. Wmk inverted	£170	90·00
51		30pa. violet and green (2.03)	26·00	5·00
		a. Mauve and green	30·00	10·00
		b. Damaged 'US'	£450	£160
52		1pi. carmine and blue (9.03)	42·00	7·50
53		2pi. blue and purple (2.03)	85·00	17·00
54		4pi. olive-green and purple (9.03)	60·00	26·00
55		6pi. sepia and green (9.03)	50·00	£150
56		9pi. brown and carmine (5.04)	£120	£275
57		12pi. chestnut and black (4.03)	25·00	85·00
58		18pi. black and brown (5.04)	90·00	£170
59		45pi. dull purple and ultramarine (10.03)	£200	£500
50/59 Set of 10			£600	£1100
50sw/59s Optd 'SPECIMEN' Set of 10			£450	

The ½pi 'SPECIMEN' is only known with watermark inverted.

Broken top left triangle
(Left pane R. 7/5)

1904–10. Wmk Mult Crown CA.

60	**11**	5pa. bistre and black (14.1.08)	1·00	2·00
		a. Broken top left triangle	95·00	£150
		w. Wmk inverted	£1900	
61		10pa. orange and green (12.06)	6·00	1·75
		aw. Wmk inverted	—	£160
		b. Orange-yellow and green	45·00	5·50
		bw. Wmk inverted	—	£180
		c. Broken top left triangle	£170	80·00
62		½pi. green and carmine (1.7.04)	12·00	1·50
		a. Broken top left triangle	£225	60·00
		b. Large 'S' in 'PIASTRE'	£275	75·00
		w. Wmk inverted	£225	£150
		y. Wmk inverted and reversed	†	£1700
63		30pa. purple and green (1.7.04)	21·00	2·50
		a. Violet and green (1910)	28·00	2·50
		b. Broken top left triangle	£400	£120
		c. Damaged 'US'	£325	90·00
		w. Wmk inverted	†	£1800
64		1pi. carmine and blue (11.04)	17·00	1·00
		a. Broken top left triangle	£300	85·00
65		2pi. blue and purple (11.04)	22·00	1·75
		a. Broken top left triangle	£375	£110
		w. Wmk inverted	†	£2500
66		4pi. olive-green and purple (2.05)	32·00	20·00
		a. Broken top left triangle	£475	£325
67		6pi. sepia and green (17.7.04)	32·00	15·00
		a. Broken top left triangle	£475	£375
68		9pi. brown and carmine (30.5.04)	50·00	9·50
		a. Yellow-brown and carmine	60·00	24·00
		aw. Wmk inverted	£325	£120
		b. Broken top left triangle	£750	£325
69		12pi. chestnut and black (4.06)	38·00	65·00
		a. Broken top left triangle	£750	£950
70		18pi. black and brown (16.6.04)	55·00	14·00
		a. Broken top left triangle	£850	£375
71		45pi. dull purple and ultramarine (15.6.04)	£120	£160
		a. Broken top left triangle	£1800	
60/71 Set of 12			£350	£250
60s/61s Optd 'SPECIMEN' Set of 2			£130	

12   13

Broken bottom left triangle
(Right pane R. 10/6)

(Typo D.L.R.)

1912 (July)–15. Wmk Mult Crown CA.

74	**12**	10pa. orange and green (11.12)	7·50	2·50
		a. Wmk sideways	†	£3500
		b. Broken bottom left triangle	£200	85·00
		c. Orange-yellow and bright green (8.15)	2·25	1·25
		ca. Broken bottom left triangle	£130	65·00
75		½pi. green and carmine	4·50	30
		a. Broken bottom left triangle	£160	75·00
		b. Yellow-green and carmine	7·50	1·90
		ba. Broken bottom left triangle	£200	90·00
		w. Wmk inverted	†	£2000
76		30pa. violet and green (12.12)	3·00	2·25
		a. Broken bottom left triangle	£150	75·00
		w. Wmk inverted		
77		1pi. rose-red and blue (9.12)	8·50	1·75
		a. Broken bottom left triangle	£225	80·00
		b. Carmine and blue (1.15?)	15·00	4·25
		ba. Broken bottom left triangle	£375	£120
78		2pi. blue and purple (7.13)	6·50	2·00
		a. Broken bottom left triangle	£225	85·00
79		4pi. olive-green and purple	4·50	6·00
		a. Broken bottom left triangle	£190	£225
80		6pi. sepia and green	8·50	11·00
		a. Broken bottom left triangle	£275	£325
81		9pi. brown and carmine (3.15)	42·00	27·00
		a. Yellow-brown and carmine	48·00	38·00
		b. Broken bottom left triangle	£750	£600
82		12pi. chestnut and black (7.13)	25·00	55·00
		b. Broken bottom left triangle	£450	£750
83		18pi. black and brown (12.14)	50·00	50·00
		a. Broken bottom left triangle	£750	£750
84		45pi. dull purple and ultramarine (3.15)	£130	£160
		a. Broken bottom left triangle	£1800	£2000
74/84 Set of 11			£250	£275
74s/84s Optd 'SPECIMEN' Set of 11			£550	

1921–23.

(a) Wmk Mult Script CA

85	**12**	10pa. orange and green	15·00	19·00
		a. Broken bottom left triangle	£300	£350
		w. Wmk inverted	£3250	£3250
86		10pa. grey and yellow (1923)	15·00	11·00
		a. Broken bottom left triangle	£275	£190
87		30pa. violet and green	4·00	2·75
		a. Broken bottom left triangle	£160	85·00
		w. Wmk inverted	£3000	£3000
		y. Wmk inverted and reversed	†	£2750
88		30pa. green (1923)	7·50	1·75
		a. Broken bottom left triangle	£200	75·00
		w. Wmk inverted	†	£2500
89		1pi. carmine and blue	25·00	50·00
		a. Broken bottom left triangle	£375	
90		1pi. violet and red (1922)	3·75	4·00
		a. Broken bottom left triangle	£160	£180
91		1½pi. yellow and black (1922)	13·00	11·00
		a. Broken bottom left triangle	£250	£200
92		2pi. blue and purple	32·00	30·00
		a. Broken bottom left triangle	£475	£425
93		2pi. carmine and blue (1922)	15·00	27·00
		a. Broken bottom left triangle	£325	£550
94		2¾pi. blue and purple (1922)	12·00	9·00
		a. Broken bottom left triangle	£250	£275
95		4pi. olive-green and purple	18·00	25·00
		a. Broken bottom left triangle	£350	£450
		w. Wmk inverted	†	£2750
96		6pi. sepia and green (1923)	38·00	95·00
		a. Broken bottom left triangle	£475	
97		9pi. brown and carmine (1922)	50·00	95·00
		a. Yellow-brown and carmine	£120	£160
		b. Broken bottom left triangle	£650	£950

98		18pi. black and brown (1923)	90·00	£180
		a. Broken bottom left triangle	£1000	
99		45pi. dull purple and ultramarine (1923).	£275	£275
		a. Broken bottom left triangle	£2500	£2750
85/99 *Set of* 15			£550	£750
85s/99s Optd 'SPECIMEN' *Set of* 15			£700	

A ½pi. black was prepared for use but not issued. One example exists, opt 'SPECIMEN'.

(b) Wmk Mult Crown CA (1923)

100	**12**	10s. green and red/*pale yellow*	£400	£900
		a. Broken bottom left triangle	£4750	
101		£1 purple and black/*red*	£1400	£3500
		a. Broken bottom left triangle	£8500	£14000
100s/101s Optd 'SPECIMEN' *Set of* 2			£600	

Examples of Nos. 96/101 are known showing a forged Limassol postmark dated '14 MR 25'.

1924–28. Chalk-surfaced paper.

(a) Wmk Mult Crown CA

102	**13**	£1 purple and black/*red*	£300	£850

(b) Wmk Mult Script CA

103	**13**	¼pi. grey and chestnut	2·00	50
		w. Wmk inverted	†	£2500
104		½pi. brownish black and black	6·00	14·00
105		¾pi. green	4·00	1·00
106		1pi. purple and chestnut	3·25	1·00
107		1½pi. orange and black	6·50	18·00
108		2pi. carmine and green	6·50	23·00
109		2¾pi. bright blue and purple	3·25	5·00
110		4pi. sage-green and purple	5·00	5·00
111		4½pi. black and orange/*emerald*	3·50	5·00
112		6pi. olive-brown and green	5·00	12·00
113		9pi. brown and purple	9·00	5·50
114		12pi. chestnut and black	18·00	65·00
115		18pi. black and orange	32·00	5·00
116		45pi. olive-brown and green	70·00	50·00
117		90pi. green and red/*yellow*	£130	£275
117*a*		£5 black/*yellow* (1928) (F.C. £350)	£3750	£8000
		as. Optd 'SPECIMEN'	£1000	

Examples of No. 102 are known showing a forged Limassol postmark dated '14 MR 25' and of No. 117*a* showing a forged Registered Nicosia postmark dated '6 MAY 35'.

CROWN COLONY

1925. Wmk Mult Script CA. Chalk-surfaced paper (½, ¾ and 2pi.).

118	**13**	½pi. green	5·00	1·00
119		¾pi. brownish black and black	6·50	1·00
120		1½pi. scarlet	10·00	1·50
121		2pi. yellow and black	15·00	3·25
122		2½pi. bright blue	11·00	1·75
102/122 (*ex* £5) *Set of* 21			£550	£1200
102s/122s (*ex* £5) Optd 'SPECIMEN' *Set of* 21			£1100	

In the above set the fraction bar in the value is horizontal. In Nos. 91, 94, 107 and 109 it is diagonal.

14 Silver Coin of Amathus, 6th-cent BC

15 Zeno (philosopher)

16 Map of Cyprus

17 Discovery of body of St Barnabas

18 Cloister, Abbey of Bellapaise

19 Badge of Cyprus

20 Tekke of Umm Haram

21 Statue of Richard I, Westminster

22 St Nicholas Cathedral (now Lala Mustafa Pasha Mosque), Famagusta

23 King George V

(Recess B.W.)

1928 (1 Feb). 50th Anniversary of British Rule. Types **14/23**. Wmk Mult Script CA. P 12.

123	**14**	¾pi. deep dull purple	3·75	1·50
124	**15**	1pi. black and greenish blue	4·00	1·50
125	**16**	1½pi. scarlet	8·50	2·00
126	**17**	2½pi. light blue	4·25	2·25
127	**18**	4pi. deep brown	11·00	11·00
128	**19**	6pi. blue	14·00	40·00
129	**20**	9pi. maroon	11·00	19·00
130	**21**	18pi. black and brown	30·00	45·00
131	**22**	45pi. violet and blue	42·00	50·00
132	**23**	£1 blue and bistre-brown	£225	£300
123/132 *Set of* 10			£300	£400
123s/132s Optd 'SPECIMEN' *Set of* 10			£700	

24 Ruins of Vouni Palace

25 Small Marble Forum, Salamis

26 Church of St Barnabas and St Hilarion, Peristerona

27 Roman Theatre, Soli

28 Kyrenia Harbour

29 Kolossi Castle

30 St Sophia Cathedral, Nicosia (now Selimiye Mosque)

31 Bayraktar Mosque, Nicosia

32 Queen's window, St Hilarion Castle

33 Buyuk Khan, Nicosia

34 Forest scene, Troodos

(Recess Waterlow)

1934 (1 Dec). Types 24/34. Wmk Mult Script CA (sideways on ½pi., 1½pi., 2½pi., 4½pi., 6pi., 9pi. and 18pi.). P 12½.

133	24	¼pi. ultramarine and orange-brown	2·00	1·00
		a. Imperf between (vert pair)	£55000	£32000
134	25	½pi. green	3·75	1·00
		a. Imperf between (vert pair)	£18000	£20000
135	26	¾pi. black and violet	4·00	40
		a. Imperf between (vert pair)	£60000	
136	27	1pi. black and red-brown	5·00	2·25
		a. Imperf between (vert pair)	£25000	£25000
		b. Imperf between (horiz pair)	£21000	
137	28	1½pi. carmine	6·00	2·00
138	29	2½pi. ultramarine	7·00	1·75
139	30	4½pi. black and crimson	8·50	6·50
140	31	6pi. black and blue	12·00	24·00
141	32	9pi. sepia and violet	22·00	8·50
142	33	18pi. black and olive-green	55·00	55·00
143	34	45pi. green and black	£120	90·00
133/143 *Set of 11*			£200	£170
133s/143s Perf 'SPECIMEN' *Set of 11*			£650	

34a Windsor Castle

Kite and horizontal log (Plate "2B" R. 10/6)

(Recess Waterlow & Sons)

1935 (6 May). Silver Jubilee. Wmk Mult Script CA. P11×12.

144	34a	¾pi. ultramarine and grey	4·00	1·50
145		1½pi. deep blue and scarlet	6·00	2·75
		l. Kite and horizontal log	£950	£750
146		2½pi. brown and deep blue	5·00	2·25
147		9pi. slate and purple	23·00	30·00
144/147 *Set of 4*			35·00	32·00
144s/147s Perf 'SPECIMEN' *Set of 4*			£200	

34b King George VI and Queen Elizabeth

(Des D.L.R. Recess B.W.)

1937 (12 May). Coronation. Wmk Mult Script CA. P 11×11½.

148	34b	¾pi. grey	3·00	1·00
149		1½pi. carmine	3·50	3·00
150		2½pi. blue	3·50	3·25
148/150 *Set of 3*			9·00	6·50
148s/150s Perf 'SPECIMEN' *Set of 3*			£225	

35 Vouni Palace

36 Map of Cyprus

37 Othello's Tower, Famagusta

38 King George VI

(Recess Waterlow)

1938 (12 May)–**51**. Types **35** to **38** and other designs as 1934, but with portrait of King George VI. Wmk Mult Script CA. P 12½.

151	35	¼pi. ultramarine and orange-brown	1·75	60
152	25	½pi. green	2·75	50
152a		½pi. violet (2.7.51)	4·50	75
153	26	¾pi. black and violet	22·00	1·75
154	27	1pi. orange	3·25	40
		a. Perf 13½×12½ (4.44)	£550	27·00
155	28	1½pi. carmine	6·00	1·50
155a		1½pi. violet (15.3.43)	3·00	75
155ab		1½pi. green (2.7.51)	7·00	1·25
155b	26	2pi. black and carmine (2.2.42)	3·25	40
		c. Perf 12½×13½ (10.44)	4·25	17·00
156	29	2½pi. ultramarine	45·00	2·50
156a		3pi. ultramarine (2.2.42)	3·50	60
156b		4pi. ultramarine (2.7.51)	7·00	1·25
157	36	4½pi. grey	3·00	40
158	31	6pi. black and blue	4·50	1·00
159	37	9pi. black and purple	3·75	75
160	33	18pi. black and olive-green	16·00	1·75
		a. Black and sage-green (19.8.47)	24·00	2·50
161	34	45pi. green and black	55·00	4·75
162	38	90pi. mauve and black	38·00	8·50
163		£1 scarlet and indigo	65·00	32·00
151/163 *Set of 19*			£250	55·00
151s/163s Perf 'SPECIMEN' *Set of 16*			£800	

38a Houses of Parliament, London

Dot between '1' and '½' in right-hand value tablet (PI B1 R. 7/1)

1946 (21 Oct). Victory. Wmk Mult Script CA. P 13½×14.

164	38a	1½pi. deep violet	50	10
		a. Dot between '1' and '½'	70·00	65·00
165		3pi. blue	50	40
164s/165s Perf 'SPECIMEN' *Set of 2*			£190	

38b King George VI and Queen Elizabeth

38c

Extra decoration (R. 3/5)

(Des and photo Waterlow (T **38b**). Design recess, name typo B.W. (T **38c**))

1948 (20 Dec). Royal Silver Wedding. Wmk Mult Script CA.

166		1½pi. violet	1·50	50
		a. Extra decoration	55·00	65·00
167		£1 indigo	60·00	75·00

38d Hermes, Globe and Forms of Transport

38e Hemispheres, Jet powered Vickers Viking Airliner, Steamer

38f Hermes and Globe

38g UPU Monument

(Recess Waterlow (T **38d**, **38g**) or B.W. (T **38e**, **38f**))

1949 (10 Oct). 75th Anniversary of Universal Postal Union. Wmk Mult Script CA. P 13½-14 (Nos. 168 and 171) or 11×11½ (Nos. 169/170).

168	**38d**	1½pi. violet	60	1·50
169	**38e**	2pi. carmine-red	1·50	1·50
		a. 'C' of 'CA' missing from wmk	£1600	
170	**38f**	3pi. deep blue	1·00	1·50
171	**38g**	9pi. purple	1·00	6·50
168/171		Set of 4	3·50	10·00

38h Queen Elizabeth II

(Des and eng B.W. Recess D.L.R.)

1953 (2 June). Coronation. Wmk Mult Script CA. P 13½×13.

172	**38h**	1½pi. black and emerald	2·00	10

(New Currency = 1000 mils = £1)

39 Carobs

40 Grapes

41 Oranges

42 Mavrovouni Copper Pyrites Mine

43 Troodos Forest

44 Beach of Aphrodite

45 5th-century BC coin of Paphos

46 Kyrenia

47 Harvest in Mesaoria

48 Famagusta Harbour

49 St Hilarion Castle

50 Hala Sultan Tekke

51 Kanakaria Church

52 Coins of Salamis, Paphos, Citium and Idalium

53 Arms of Byzantium, Lusignan, Ottoman Empire and Venice

1955 (1 Aug)–**60**. Types **39**/**53**. Wmk Mult Script CA. P 13½ (Nos. 183/185) or 11½ (others).

173	**39**	2m. blackish brown	1·00	40
174	**40**	3m. blue-violet	65	15
175	**41**	5m. brown-orange	3·25	10
		a. Orange-brown (17.9.58)	13·00	1·00
176	**42**	10m. deep brown and deep green	3·25	10
177	**43**	15m. olive-green and indigo	5·50	45
		aa. Yellow-olive and indigo (17.9.58)	42·00	6·00
		a. Bistre and indigo (14.6.60)	35·00	17·00
178	**44**	20m. brown and deep bright blue	2·50	15
179	**45**	25m. deep turquoise-blue	5·00	60
		a. Greenish blue (17.9.58)	29·00	5·50
180	**46**	30m. black and carmine-lake	3·75	10
181	**47**	35m. orange-brown and deep turquoise-blue	3·25	40
182	**48**	40m. deep green and sepia	3·25	60
183	**49**	50m. turquoise-blue and reddish brown	3·25	30
184	**50**	100m. mauve and bluish green	14·00	60
185	**51**	250m. deep grey-blue and brown	17·00	13·00
186	**52**	500m. slate and purple	38·00	15·00
187	**53**	£1 brown-lake and slate	30·00	55·00
173/187		Set of 15	£110	75·00

(**54** 'Cyprus Republic')

55 Map of Cyprus

(Recess B.W.)

1960 (16 Aug)–**61**. Nos. 173/187 optd as T **54** in blue by B.W. Opt larger on Nos. 191/197 and in two lines on Nos 198/202.

188		2m. blackish brown	20	75
189		3m. blue-violet	20	15
190		5m. brown-orange	2·25	10
		a. Orange-brown (15.8.61)	10·00	1·00

191		10m. deep brown and deep green	1·00	10
192		15m. yellow-bistre and indigo	3·50	40
	a.	Olive-green and indigo	£160	85·00
	b.	Brownish bistre and deep indigo (10.10.61)	22·00	5·50
193		20m. brown and deep bright blue	1·75	1·50
	a.	Opt double	†	£12000
194		25m. deep turquoise-blue	1·75	1·75
	a.	Greenish blue (7.2.61)	50·00	16·00
195		30m. black and carmine-lake	1·75	30
	a.	Opt double	†	£45000
196		35m. orange-brown and deep turquoise-blue	1·75	70
197		40m. deep green and sepia	2·00	2·50
198		50m. turquoise-blue and reddish brown	2·00	60
199		100m. mauve and bluish green	9·00	2·50
200		250m. deep grey-blue and brown	30·00	5·50
201		500m. slate and purple	45·00	27·00
202		£1 brown-lake and slate	48·00	65·00
188/202 *Set of 15*			£130	95·00

Only three used examples of No. 195a are known.

(Recess B.W.)

1960 (16 Aug). Constitution of Republic. W w **12**. P 11½.

203	**55**	10m. sepia and deep green	25	10
204		30m. ultramarine and deep brown	50	10
205		100m. purple and deep slate	1·75	2·00
203/205 *Set of 3*			2·25	2·00

PRINTERS. All the following stamps were designed by A. Tassos and lithographed by Aspioti-Elka, Athens, *unless otherwise stated.*

56 Doves

57 Campaign Emblem

(Des T. Kurpershoek)

1962 (19 Mar). Europa. P 14×13.

206	**56**	10m. purple and mauve	10	10
207		40m. ultramarine and cobalt	20	15
208		100m. emerald and pale green	20	20
206/208 *Set of 3*			45	40

1962 (14 May). Malaria. Eradication. P 14×13½.

209	**57**	10m. black and olive-green	15	15
210		30m. black and brown	30	15

58 Mult K C K Δ and Map

WATERMARK VARIETIES. The issues printed by Aspioti-Elka with W **58** are known with the vertical stamps having the watermark normal or inverted and the horizontal stamps with the watermark reading upwards or downwards. Such varieties are not given separate listing.

59 Iron Age Jug   **60** Grapes   **61** Bronze head of Apollo

62 Selimiye Mosque, Nicosia   **63** St Barnabas's Church

64 Temple of Apollo, Hylates   **65** Head of Aphrodite

66 Skiing, Troodos   **67** Salamis Gymnasium

68 Hala Sultan Tekke   **69** Bellapaise Abbey

70 Mouflon   **71** St Hilarion Castle

1962 (17 Sept). Types **59/71**. W **58** (sideways) on 25, 30, 40, 50, 250m., £1). P 13½×14 (vert) or 14×13½ (horiz).

211	**59**	3m. deep brown and orange-brown	10	30
212	**60**	5m. purple and grey-green	10	10
213	**61**	10m. black and yellow-green	15	10
214	**62**	15m. black and reddish purple	50	15
215	**63**	25m. deep brown and chestnut	60	20
216	**64**	30m. deep blue and light blue	20	10
217	**65**	35m. light green and blue	35	10
218	**66**	40m. black and violet-blue	1·25	1·75
219	**67**	50m. bronze-green and bistre	50	10
220	**68**	100m. deep brown and yellow-brown	3·50	30
221	**69**	250m. black and cinnamon	17·00	1·75
222	**70**	500m. deep brown and light green	22·00	9·00
223	**71**	£1 bronze-green and grey	15·00	28·00
211/223 *Set of 13*			55·00	38·00

72 Europa 'Tree'

(Des L. Weyer)

1963 (28 Jan). Europa. W **58** (sideways). P 14×13½.

224	**72**	10m. bright blue and black		1·50	20
225		40m. carmine-red and black		4·50	1·50
226		150m. emerald-green and black		15·00	5·00
224/226 *Set of 3*				19·00	6·00

73 Harvester   **75** Wolf Cub in Camp

1963 (21 Mar). Freedom from Hunger. T **73** and similar vert design. W **58**. P 13½×14.

227	25m. ochre, sepia and bright blue		1·00	25
228	75m. grey, black and lake		2·75	2·50

Designs: 25m, T **73**; 75m. Demeter, Goddess of Corn.

1963 (21 Aug). 50th Anniversary of Cyprus Scout Movement and Third Commonwealth Scout Conference, Platres. T **75** and similar vert designs. Multicoloured. W **58**. P 13½×14.

229	3m. Type **75**		10	20
230	20m. Sea Scout		35	10
231	150m. Scout with Mouflon		1·00	2·50
229/231 *Set of 3*			1·25	2·50
MS231*a* 110×90 mm. Nos. 229/231 (*sold at* 250m.).				
Imperf			£110	£180

78 Nurse tending Child   **79** Children's Centre, Kyrenia

1963 (9 Sept). Centenary of Red Cross. W **58** (sideways on 100m.). P 13½×14 (10m.) or 14×13½ (100m.).

232	**78**	10m. red, blue, grey-blue, chestnut and black	50	15
233	**79**	100m. red, green, black and blue	3·00	4·50

80 'Co-operation' (emblem)   (**81**)

(Des A. Holm)

1963 (4 Nov). Europa. W **58** (sideways). P 14×13½.

234	**80**	20m. buff, blue and violet	1·75	40
235		30m. grey, yellow and blue	1·75	40
236		150m. buff, blue and orange-brown	15·00	9·00
234/236 *Set of 3*			17·00	9·00

1964 (5 May). UN Security Council's Cyprus Resolutions, March, 1964. Nos. 213, 216, 218/220 optd with T **81** in blue by Government Printing Office, Nicosia.

237	**61**	10m. black and yellow-green	15	10
238	**64**	30m. deep blue and light blue	20	10
239	**66**	40m. black and violet-blue	25	30
240	**67**	50m. bronze-green and bistre	25	10
241	**68**	100m. deep brown and yellow-brown	25	50
237/241 *Set of 5*			1·00	1·00

82 Soli Theatre

1964 (15 June). 400th Birth Anniversary of Shakespeare. T **82** and similar horiz designs. Multicoloured. W **58**. P 13½×13.

242	15m. Type **82**		90	15
243	35m. Curium Theatre		90	15
244	50m. Salamis Theatre		90	15
245	100m. Othello Tower and scene from *Othello*		1·50	2·25
242/245 *Set of 4*			3·75	2·50

86 Running   **89** Europa 'Flower'

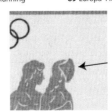

10m. Brown flaw covering face of right-hand runner gives the appearance of a mask (R. 9/2).

As these stamps were printed in sheets of 400, divided into four post office sheets of 100, the variety was only constant on one sheet in four. Moreover, it was quickly discovered and many were removed from the sheets by post office clerks.

1964 (6 July). Olympic Games, Tokyo. T **86** and similar designs. W **50** (sideways, 25m., 75m.). P 13½×14 (10m.) or 14×13½ (others).

246	10m. brown, black and yellow		10	10
	a. Blind runner		£900	
247	25m. brown, blue and blue-grey		20	10
248	75m. brown, black and orange-red		35	65
246/248 *Set of 3*			60	75
MS248*a* 110×90 mm. Nos. 246/248 (*sold at* 250m.). Imperf			4·75	15·00

Designs: Vert—10m. T **86**. Horiz—25m. Boxing; 75m. Charioteers.

(Des G. Bétemps)

1964 (14 Sept). Europa. W **58**. P 13½×14.

249	**89**	20m. chestnut and light ochre	1·25	10
250		30m. ultramarine and light blue	1·25	10
251		150m. olive and light blue-green	9·00	4·75
249/251 *Set of 3*			10·00	4·75

90 Dionysus and Acme   **91** Silenus (satyr)

1964 (26 Oct). Cyprus Wines. Types **90/91** and similar multicoloured designs. W **58** (sideways, 10m. or 100m.). P 14×13½ (horiz) or 13½×14 (vert).

252	10m. Type **90**		25	10
253	40m. Type **91**		55	75

254		50m. Commandaria Wine (*vert*)	55	10
255		100m. Wine factory (*horiz*)	1·10	1·50
252/255 *Set of 4*			2·25	2·00

94 President Kennedy

1965 (16 Feb). President Kennedy Commemoration. W **58** (sideways). P 14×13½.

256	**94**	10m. ultramarine	10	10
257		40m. green	25	35
258		100m. carmine-lake	30	35
256/258 *Set of 3*			60	70
MS258*a* 110×90 mm. Nos. 256/258 (*sold at 250m.*). Imperf			2·25	7·00

95 'Old Age' **96** 'Maternity'

1965 (12 Apr). Introduction of Social Insurance Law. Types **95**/**96** and similar design. W **58**. P 13½×12 (75m.) or 13½×14 (others).

259		30m. drab and dull green	15	10
260		45m. light grey-green, blue and deep ultramarine	20	10
261		75m. red-brown and flesh	1·25	1·50
259/261 *Set of 3*			1·40	1·50

Designs: 30m. T **95**. Vert as T **95**—45m. 'Accident'. 75m. T **96**.

98 ITU Emblem and Symbols

1965 (17 May). ITU Centenary. W **58** (sideways). P 14×13½.

262	**98**	15m. black, brown and yellow	75	20
263		60m. black, green and light green	6·50	3·25
264		75m. black, indigo and light blue	7·50	4·75
262/264 *Set of 3*			13·00	7·25

99 ICY Emblem

1965 (17 May). International Co-operation Year. W **58** (sideways). P 14×13½.

265	**99**	50m. brown, deep green and light yellow-brown	75	10
266		100m. purple, deep green and light purple	1·25	50

100 Europa 'Sprig'

U. N. Resolution on Cyprus 18 Dec. 1965

(101)

(Des H. Karlsson)

1965 (27 Sept). Europa. W **58** (sideways). P 14×13½.

267	**100**	5m. black, orange-brown and orange	50	10
268		45m. black, orange-brown and light emerald	3·00	2·00
269		150m. black, orange-brown and light grey	7·50	4·50
267/269 *Set of 3*			10·00	6·00

1966 (31 Jan). UN General Assembly's Cyprus Resolution, 18 December 1965. Nos. 211, 213, 216 and 221 optd with T **101** in blue by Government Printing Office, Nicosia.

270	**59**	3m. deep brown and orange-brown	10	50
271	**61**	10m. black and yellow-green	10	10
272	**64**	30m. deep blue and light blue	15	15
273	**69**	250m. black and cinnamon	80	2·25
270/273 *Set of 4*			1·00	2·75

102 Discovery of St Barnabas's Body   **104** St Barnabas (icon)

103 St Barnabas's Chapel

105 Privileges of Cyprus Church (*Actual size 102×82 mm*)

1966 (25 Apr). 1900th Death Anniversary of St Barnabas. W **58** (sideways on 15m., 100m., 250m.). P 14×13 (25m.) or 13×14 (others).

274	**102**	15m. multicoloured	10	10
275	**103**	25m. drab, black and blue	15	10
276	**104**	100m. multicoloured	45	2·00
274/276 *Set of 3*			60	2·00
MS277 110×91 mm. Type **105** 250m. mult. Imperf			2·25	10·00

5 M

Ξ

(106)

107 General K. S. Thimayya and UN Emblem

1966 (30 May). No. 211 surch with T **106** by Government Printing Office, Nicosia.

278		5m. on 3m. deep brown and orange-brown	10	10

1966 (6 June). General Thimayya Commemoration. W **58** (sideways). P 14×13.

279	**107**	50m. black and light orange-brown	30	10

108 Europa 'Ship'

(Des G. and J. Bender)

1966 (26 Sept). Europa. W **58**. P 13½×14.

280	**108**	20m. green and blue	30	10
281		30m. bright purple and blue	30	10
282		150m. bistre and blue	2·25	2·50
280/282 *Set of 3*..........................			2·50	2·50

110 Church of **119** Vase of **120** Bronze Ingot-stand
St James, Trikomo 7th-century BC

1966 (21 Nov)–**69**. Types **110**, **119/120** and similar designs. W **58** (sideways on 3, 15, 25, 50, 250, 500m., £1. P 12×13 (3m.), 13×12 (5, 10m.), 14×13½ (15, 25, 50m.), 13½×14 (20, 30, 35, 40, 100m.) or 13×14 (others).

283	3m. grey-green, buff, black and light blue......	40	10
284	5m. bistre, black and steel blue	10	10
	a. Brownish bistre, black and steel-blue		
	(18.4.69)	75	20
285	10m. black and bistre	15	10
286	15m. black, chestnut and light orange-		
	brown	15	10
287	20m. black, slate and brown....................	1·25	1·00
288	25m. black, drab and lake-brown..............	30	10
289	30m. black, yellow-ochre and turquoise	50	20
290	35m. yellow, black and carmine-red..........	50	30
291	40m. black, grey and new blue..................	70	30
	a. Grey (background) omitted....................		
292	50m. black, slate and brown....................	90	10
293	100m. black, red, pale buff and grey....................	4·00	15
294	250m. olive-green, black and light yellow-		
	ochre	1·00	40
295	500m. multicoloured	2·75	70
296	£1 black, drab and slate	2·25	6·50
283/296 *Set of 14*........................		13·00	8·50

Designs: Horiz (as T **110**)—3m. Stavrovouni Monastery. (As T **119**)—15m. *Minoan wine ship of 700 BC* (painting); 25m. *Sleeping Eros* (marble statue); 50m. Silver coin of Alexander the Great. Vert 5m. T **110**. (As T **110**)—10m. *Zeno of Cibium* (marble bust). (As T **119**)—20m. Silver coin of Evagoras I; 30m. St Nicholas Cathedral, Famagusta; 35m. Gold sceptre from Curium; 40m. Silver dish from 7th-century. 100m. T **119**. 250m. T **120**. (As T **120**)—500m. *The Rape of Ganymede* (mosaic); £1 Aphrodite (marble statue).

123 Power Station, **124** Cogwheels
Limassol

1967 (10 Apr). First Development Programme. T **123** and similar designs but horiz. Multicoloured. W **58** (sideways on 15 to 100m.). P 13½×14 (10m.) or 14×13½ (others).

297	10m. Type **123**	10	10
298	15m. Arghaka-Maghounda Dam..............	15	10
299	35m. Troodos Highway	30	10
300	50m. Hilton Hotel, Nicosia......................	20	10
301	100m. Famagusta Harbour........................	35	1·10
297/301 *Set of 5*........................		1·00	1·25

(Des O. Bonnevalle)

1967 (2 May). Europa. W **58**. P 13½×14.

302	**124**	20m. olive-green, green and pale		
		yellow-green	25	10
303		30m. reddish violet, lilac and pale lilac........	25	10
304		150m. brown, light reddish brown and		
		pale yellow-brown	1·75	2·25
302/304 *Set of 3*....................			2·00	2·25

125 Throwing the Javelin

126 Running (amphora) and Map of Eastern Mediterranean (*Actual size 97×77 mm*)

1967 (4 Sept). Athletic Games, Nicosia. T **125** and similar designs and T **126**. Multicoloured. W **58**. P 13½×13.

305	15m. Type **125**..........................	20	10
306	35m. Running	20	35
307	100m. High jumping	30	1·00
305/307 *Set of 3*..........................		60	1·25
MS308 110×90 mm. Type **126**. 250m. (wmk sideways).			
Imperf..........................		1·25	6·50

127 Ancient Monuments **128** St Andrew Mosaic

1967 (16 Oct). International Tourist Year. T **127** and similar horiz designs. Multicoloured. W **58**. P 13×13½.

309	10m. Type **127**..........................	10	10
310	40m. Famagusta Beach	20	90
311	50m. Hawker Siddeley Comet 4 at Nicosia		
	Airport..........................	40	10
312	100m. Skier and youth hostel....................	45	95
309/312 *Set of 4*..........................		1·00	1·75

1967 (8 Nov). Centenary of St Andrew's Monastery. W **58** (sideways). P 13×13½.

313	**128**	25m. multicoloured	10	10

129 *The Crucifixion* (icon) **130** The Three Magi

(Photo French Govt Ptg Wks, Paris)
1967 (8 Nov). Cyprus Art Exhibition, Paris. P 12½×13½.
314   **129** 50m. multicoloured 10 10

1967 (8 Nov). 20th Anniversary of UNESCO. W **58** (sideways). P 13×13½.
315   **130** 75m. multicoloured 35 35

131 Human Rights   **132** Human Rights
Emblem over Stars   and UN Emblems

133 Scroll of Declaration (*Actual size 95×75½ mm*)

1968 (18 Mar). Human Rights Year. W **58**. P 13×14.
316   **131** 50m. multicoloured 10 10
317   **132** 90m. multicoloured 30 70
MS318 95×75½ mm. Type **133** 250m. multicoloured.
   W **58** (sideways). Imperf .... 60 4·75

134 Europa 'Key'   **135** UN Children's Fund Symbol
                     and Boy drinking Milk

(Des H. Schwarzenbach)
1968 (29 Apr). Europa. W **58** (sideways). P 14×13.
319   **134** 20m. multicoloured 25 10
320   30m. multicoloured 25 10
321   150m. multicoloured .... 1·00 2·25
319/321 *Set of 3* .... 1·40 2·25

1968 (2 Sept). 21st Anniversary of UNICEF. W **58** (sideways). P 14×13.
322   **135** 35m. yellow-brown, carmine-red and
                black 10 10

136 Aesculapius   **137** Throwing the   **138** ILO Emblem
                  Discus

1968 (2 Sept). 20th Anniversary of WHO. W **58**. P 13×14.
323   **136** 50m. black, green and light olive 10 10

1968 (24 Oct). Olympic Games, Mexico. T **137** and similar designs.
   Multicoloured. W **58** (sideways on 100m.). P 14×13 (100m.) or 13×14
   (others).
324   10m. Type **137** 10 10

325   25m. Sprint finish 10 10
326   100m. Olympic Stadium (*horiz*) .... 20 1·25
324/326 *Set of 3* .... 35 1·25

1969 (3 Mar). 50th Anniversary of International Labour Organisation. W **58**.
   P 12×13½.
327   **138** 50m. yellow-brown, blue and light blue .. 15 10
328   90m. yellow-brown, black and pale grey. 15 55

139 Mercator's Map of Cyprus, 1554

140 Blaeu's Map of Cyprus, 1635

1969 (7 Apr). First International Congress of Cypriot Studies. W **58**
   (sideways). P 14×14½.
329   **139** 35m. multicoloured 20 30
330   **140** 50m. multicoloured 20 10
         a. Wmk upright .... 5·00 2·75
         ab. Grey (shading on boats and
             cartouche) omitted £450

141 Europa Emblem

(Des L. Gasbarra and G. Belli)
1969 (28 Apr). Europa. W **58** (sideways). P 14×13½.
331   **141** 20m. multicoloured 30 10
332   30m. multicoloured 30 10
333   150m. multicoloured .... 1·00 2·00
331/333 *Set of 3* .... 1·40 2·00

142 European Roller

1969 (7 July). Birds of Cyprus. T **142** and similar designs. Multicoloured.
   W **58** (sideways on horiz designs). P 13½×12 (horiz designs) or
   12×13½ (vert designs).
334   5m. Type **142** 35 15
335   15m. Audouin's Gull 40 15
336   20m. Cyprus Warbler 40 15
337   30m. Jay (*vert*) 40 15
338   40m. Hoopoe (*vert*) 45 30
339   90m. Eleanora's Falcon (*vert*) .... 80 3·50
334/339 *Set of 6* .... 2·50 4·00
   The above were printed on glazed Samuel Jones paper with very faint
watermark.

143 *The Nativity* (12th-century
Wall Painting)

145 *Virgin and Child between Archangels Michael and Gabriel* (6th/7th-century Mosaic) (*Actual size 102×81 mm*)

1969 (24 Nov). Christmas. T **143** and similar horiz design, and T **145**. Multicoloured. W **58** (sideways). P 13½×13.

340	20m. Type **143**		15	10
341	45m. *The Nativity* (14th-century wall painting)		15	20
MS342	110×90 mm. Type **145**. 250m. Imperf		3·00	12·00
	a. Grey and light brown omitted	£3500		

146 Mahatma Gandhi

1970 (26 Jan). Birth Centenary of Mahatma Gandhi. W **58** (sideways). P 14×13½.

343	**146**	25m. ultramarine, drab and black	50	10
344		75m. yellow-brown, drab and black	75	65

147 'Flaming Sun'

148 Gladioli

(Des L. le Brocquy)

1970 (4 May). Europa. W **58** (sideways). P 14×13.

345	**147**	20m. brown, greenish yellow and orange	30	10
346		30m. new blue, greenish yellow and orange	30	10
347		150m. bright purple, greenish yellow and orange	1·00	2·50
345/347	*Set of 3*		1·40	2·50

1970 (3 Aug). European Conservation Year. T **148** and similar vert designs. Multicoloured. W **58**. P 13×13½.

348	10m. Type **148**		10	10
349	50m. Poppies		15	10
350	90m. Giant Fennel		50	1·10
348/350	*Set of 3*		65	1·10

149 IEY Emblem

150 Mosaic

151 Globe, Dove and UN Emblem

(Des G. Simonis (75m.))

1970 (7 Sept). Anniversaries and Events. W **58** (sideways on horiz designs). P 13×14 (5m.) or 14×13 (others).

351	**149**	5m. black, red-brown and light yellow-brown	10	10
352	**150**	15m. multicoloured	10	10
353	**151**	75m. multicoloured	15	75
351/353	*Set of 3*		30	85

Events: 5m. International Education Year; 15m. 50th General Assembly of International Vine and Wine Office; 75m. 25th anniversary of United Nations.

152 Virgin and Child

153 Cotton Napkin

(Photo Harrison)

1970 (23 Nov). Christmas. Wall-painting from Church of Panayia Podhythou, Galata. T **152** and similar multicoloured designs. P 14×14½.

354	25m. Archangel (facing right)		15	20
	a. Horiz strip of 3. Nos. 354/356		40	55
355	25m. Type **152**		15	20
356	25m. Archangel (facing left)		15	20
357	75m. Virgin and Child between Archangels		15	30
354/357	*Set of 4*		55	80

The 75m. is horiz, size 42×30 mm, and the 25m. values are vert, size as T **152**.

Nos. 354/356 were issued in *se-tenant* strips of three, throughout the sheet. The triptych thus formed is depicted in its entirety on the 75m. value.

1971 (22 Feb). Multicoloured designs as T **153**. W **58** (sideways on horiz designs).

(a) Vert designs 23×33 mm. P 12×13½

358	3m. Type **153**		30	35
359	5m. St George and Dragon (19th-century bas-relief)		10	10

(b) Vert (10, 20, 25, 40, 50, 75m.) or horiz (15, 30, 90m.) designs, each 24×37 mm or 37×24 mm. P 13×14 (15, 30, 90m.) or 14×13 (others)

360	10m. Woman in festival costume		15	50
361	15m. Archaic Bichrome Kylix (cup)		20	10
	a. Vert laid paper		1·50	
362	20m. A pair of donors (St Mamas Church)		35	65
363	25m. *The Creation* (6th-century mosaic)		30	10
364	30m. Athena and horse-drawn chariot (4th-century BC terracotta)		30	10
365	40m. Shepherd playing pipe (14th-century fresco)		1·00	1·00
366	50m. Hellenistic head (3rd-century BC)		80	10
367	75m. Angel (mosaic detail), Kanakaria Church		2·00	1·00
368	90m. Mycenaean silver bowl		2·00	2·25

(c) Horiz (250, 500m.) or vert (£1) designs, each 41×28 mm or 28×41 mm. P 13½×13 (250, 500m. or 13×13½ (£1)

369	250m. Mouflon (detail of 3rd-century mosaic) (shades)		1·50	30
370	500m. Ladies and sacred tree (detail, 6th-century amphora)		1·00	30
371	£1 Horned god from Enkomi (12th-century bronze statue)		1·75	45
358/371	*Set of 14*		10·00	5·50

See also No. 410, 430, 431/434 and 451.

154 Europa Chain

155 Archbishop Kyprianos

(Des H. Haflidason)

1971 (3 May). Europa. W **58** (sideways). P 14 ×13.

372	**154**	20m. pale blue, ultramarine and black.....	25	10
373		30m. apple green, myrtle-green and black....................................	25	10
374		150m. lemon, bright green and black........	1·10	3·00
372/374 *Set of 3*...			1·40	3·00

The above were printed on glazed paper with very faint watermark.

1971 (9 July). 150th Anniversary of Greek War of Independence. T **155** and similar multicoloured designs. W **58** (sideways on 30m.). P 13½×12½ (30m.) or 12½×13½ (others).

375	15m. Type **155**..	10	10
376	30m. Taking the Oath (*horiz*)................................	10	10
377	100m. Bishop Germanos, flag and freedom fighters....................................	20	50
375/377 *Set of 3*..		30	55

156 Kyrenia Castle

157 Madonna and Child in Stable

1971 (20 Sept). Tourism. T **156** and similar multicoloured designs. W **58** (sideways on 15 and 100m.). P 13½×13 (15 and 100m.) or 13×13½ (others).

378	15m. Type **156**..	10	10
379	25m. Gourd on sunny beach (*vert*)......................	10	10
380	60m. Mountain scenery (*vert*)................................	20	60
381	100m. Church of St Evlalios, Lambousa...............	20	65
378/381 *Set of 4*...		45	1·25

1971 (22 Nov). Christmas. T **157** and similar vert designs. Multicoloured. W **58**. P 13×14.

382	10m. Type **157**..	10	10
	a. Horiz strip of 3. Nos. 382/384......................	35	70
383	50m. The Three Wise Men...................................	15	35
384	100m. The Shepherds..	20	35
382/384 *Set of 3*...		35	70

The 10m. was issued in sheets of 100, and all three values were printed horizontally *se-tenant* in sheets of 36, the order being 50, 10 and 100m.

158 Heart

159 Communications

1972 (11 Apr). World Heart Month. W **58** (sideways). P 13½×12.

385	**158**	15m. multicoloured....................................	10	10
386		50m. multicoloured....................................	20	45

(Des P. Huovinen)

1972 (22 May). Europa. W **58**. P 12½×13½.

387	**159**	20m. yellow-orange, sepia and pale grey-brown......................................	30	15

388	30m. yellow-orange, bright deep ultramarine and cobalt..............................	30	15
389	150m. yellow-orange, myrtle-green and pale turquoise-green...........................	1·60	3·50
387/389 *Set of 3*..		2·00	3·50

160 Archery

1972 (24 July). Olympic Games, Munich. T **160** and similar horiz designs. Multicoloured. W **58** (sideways). P 14×13.

390	10m. Type **160**..	25	10
391	40m. Wrestling..	35	15
392	100m. Football...	50	1·75
390/392 *Set of 3*...		1·00	1·75

161 Stater of Marion

162 Bathing the Child Jesus

1972 (25 Sept). Ancient Coins of Cyprus (1st series), T **161** and similar horiz designs. W **58** (sideways). P 14×13.

393	20m. pale turquoise-blue, black and silver.......	20	10
394	30m. pale violet-blue, black and silver.............	20	10
395	40m. brownish stone, black and silver..............	20	20
396	100m. light salmon-pink, black and silver.........	60	1·00
393/396 *Set of 4*...		1·10	1·25

Coins: 20m. T **161**; 30m. Stater of Paphos; 40m. Stater of Lapithos; 100m. Stater of Idalion.

See also Nos. 486/489.

1972 (20 Nov). Christmas. T **162** and similar vert designs showing portions of a mural in the Church of the Holy Cross of Agiasmati. Multicoloured. W **58** (sideways on No. **MS**400). P 13×14.

397	10m. Type **162**..	10	10
398	20m. The Magi..	10	10
399	100m. The Nativity...	15	30
397/399 *Set of 3*...		30	35
MS400 100×90 mm. 250m. Showing the mural in full. Imperf..		1·10	4·50

163 Mount Olympus, Troodos

1973 (13 Mar). 29th International Ski Federation Congress. T **163** and similar horiz design. Multicoloured. W **58** (sideways). P 14×13.

401	20m. Type **163**..	10	10
402	100m. Congress emblem...................................	25	35

164 Europa Posthorn

(Des I. Anisdahl)

1973 (7 May). Europa. W **58** (sideways). P 14×13.

403	**164**	20m. multicoloured....................................	25	10
404		30m. multicoloured....................................	25	10
405		150m. multicoloured..................................	1·10	2·75
403/405 *Set of 3*...			1·50	2·75

165 Archbishop's Palace, Nicosia   **(166)**

1973 (23 July). Traditional Architecture. T **165** and similar multicoloured designs. W **58** (sideways on 20 and 100m.). P 14×13 (20 and 100m.) or 13×14 (others).

406	20m. Type **165**	10	10
407	30m. House of Hajigeorgajis Cornessios, Nicosia (*vert*)	10	10
408	50m. House at Gourri, 1850 (*vert*)	15	10
409	100m. House at Rizokarpaso, 1772	40	85
406/409 *Set of 4*		65	1·00

1973 (24 Sept). No. 361 surch with T **166**.

410	20m. on 15m. Archaic Bichrome Kylix (cup)	15	15
	a. Vert laid paper	1·00	
	b. Surch inverted		

167 Scout Emblem   **168** Archangel Gabriel

1973 (24 Sept). Anniversaries and Events. T **167** and similar designs. W **58** (sideways on 25 and 35m.). P 13×14 (10, 50 and 100m.) or 14×13 (others).

411	10m. yellow-olive and deep brown	70	10
412	25m. deep blue and slate-lilac	20	10
413	35m. light brown-olive, stone and sage-green	20	25
414	50m. dull blue and indigo	20	10
415	100m. brown and sepia	50	80
411/415 *Set of 5*		1·10	1·10

Designs and Events: Vert—10m. T **167** (60th Anniversary of Cyprus Boy Scouts); 50m. Airline emblem (25th Anniversary of Cyprus Airways); 100m. Interpol emblem (50th Anniversary of Interpol). Horiz—25m. Outline of Cyprus and EEC nations (Association of Cyprus with the EEC); 35m. FAO emblem (Tenth Anniversary of FAO).

1973 (26 Nov). Christmas. Murals from Araka Church. T **168** and similar multicoloured designs. W **58** (sideways on 100m.). P 14×13 (100m.) or 13×14 (others).

416	10m. Type **168**	10	10
417	20m. Madonna and Child	10	10
418	100m. Araka Church (*horiz*)	40	75
416/418 *Set of 3*		45	75

169 Grapes   **170** The Rape of Europa (Silver Stater of Marion)

1974 (18 Mar). Products of Cyprus. T **169** and similar vert designs. Multicoloured. W **58**. P 13×14.

419	25m. Type **169**	10	15
420	50m. Grapefruit	20	50
	a. Horiz strip of 3. Nos. 420/422	55	1·50
421	50m. Oranges	20	50
422	50m. Lemons	20	50
419/422 *Set of 4*		65	1·50

Nos. 420/422 were printed together, horizontally *se-tenant* throughout the sheet.

1974 (29 Apr). Europa. W **58**. P 13½×14.

423	**170** 10m. multicoloured	15	10
424	40m. multicoloured	40	30
425	150m. multicoloured	1·10	2·75
423/425 *Set of 3*		1·50	2·75

171 Title Page of   **(172)**
A. Kyprianos' *History of Cyprus* (1788)

REFUGEE
FUND
ΤΑΜΕΙΟΝ
ΠΡΟΣΦΥΓΩΝ
GÖÇMENLER
FONU

1974 (22 July*). Second International Congress of Cypriot Studies. T **171** and similar multicoloured designs. W **58** (sideways on 25m. and No. **MS**429). P 14×13½ (25m.) or 13½×14 (others).

426	10m. Type **171**	10	10
427	25m. Solon (philosopher) in mosaic (*horiz*)	15	10
428	100m. *St Neophytos* (wall painting)	60	75
426/428 *Set of 3*		70	80
MS429 111×90 mm. 250m. Ortelius' map of Cyprus and Greek Islands, 1584. Imperf.		1·25	5·00

* Although this is the date appearing on first day covers, the stamps were not put on sale until the 24th.

1974 (1 Oct). Obligatory Tax. Refugee Fund. No. 359 surch with T **172**.

430	10m. on 5m. St George and Dragon	10	10

SECURITY COUNCIL RESOLUTION 353 20 JULY 1974

(173)

1974 (14 Oct). UN Security Council Resolution 353. Nos. 360, 365, 366 and 369 optd as T **173**.

431	10m. Woman in festival costume	20	10
432	40m. Shepherd playing pipe	25	85
433	50m. Hellenistic head	25	10
434	250m. Mouflon (*shades*)	60	2·75
431/434 *Set of 4*		1·10	3·50

174 Refugees

1974 (2 Dec). Obligatory Tax. Refugee Fund. W **58** (sideways). P 12×12½.

435	**174** 10m. black and light grey	10	10

175 Virgin and Child between Two Angels, Stavros Church

1974 (2 Dec). Christmas. T **175** and similar multicoloured designs showing wall-paintings. W **58** (sideways on 10m. and 100m.). P 13×14 (50m.) or 14×13 (others).

436	10m. Type **175**	10	10
437	50m. *Adoration of the Magi*, Ayios Neophytos Monastery (*vert*)	20	10
438	100m. *Flight into Egypt*, Ayios Neophytos Monastery	25	45
436/468 *Set of 3*		45	50

176 Larnaca–Nicosia Mail-coach, 1878

177 *The Distaff* (M. Kashalos)

(Photo Harrison)

1975 (17 Feb). Anniversaries and Events. T **176** and similar designs. No wmk. P 14.

439	**176**	20m. multicoloured	25	10
440	–	30m. ultramarine, slate-black and dull orange	25	60
441	**176**	50m. multicoloured	25	10
442	–	100m. multicoloured	40	1·40
439/442 *Set of 4*			1·00	2·00

Designs and Events: 20m., 50m. T **176** (Centenary of Universal Postal Union). Vert—30m. Disabled Persons (Eighth European Meeting of International Society for the Rehabilitation of Disabled Persons); 100m. Council flag (25th Anniversary of Council of Europe).

(Photo Harrison)

1975 (28 Apr). Europa. T **177** and similar vert designs. Multicoloured. P 13½×14½.

443	20m. Type **177**		25	40
	a. Horiz strip of 3. Nos. 443/445		80	1·50
444	30m. *Nature Morte* (C. Savva)		25	50
445	150m. *Virgin and Child of Liopetri* (G. P. Georghiou)		40	80
443/445 *Set of 3*			80	1·50

Nos. 443/445 were printed horizontally *se-tenant* throughout the sheet.

178 Red Cross Flag over Map

179 Submarine Cable Links

1975 (4 Aug). Anniversaries and Events. T **178** and similar horiz designs. P 12½×13½ (25m.) or 13½×12½ (others).

446	25m. multicoloured	20	10
447	30m. turquoise-green and greenish blue	20	10
448	75m. red-brown, orange-brown and pale blue-grey	20	90
446/448 *Set of 3*		55	1·00

Designs and Events: Vert—25m. T **178** (25th anniversary of Cyprus Red Cross). Horiz—30m. Nurse and lamp (International Nurses' Day); 75m. Woman's Steatite Idol (International Women's Year).

1975 (13 Oct). Telecommunications Achievements. T **179** and similar design. W **58** (sideways on 100m.). P 12×13½ (50m.) or 13½×12 (100m.).

449	50m. multicoloured	30	10
450	100m. orange-yellow, dull violet and lilac	35	90

Designs: Vert—50m. T **179**. Horiz—100m. International subscriber dialling.

(180)

181 Human-figured Vessel, 19th-century

1976 (5 Jan). No. 358 surch with T **180**.

451	10m. on 3m. Cotton napkin	20	1·00

1976 (3 May). Europa. Ceramics. T **181** and similar vert designs. Multicoloured. W **58**. P 13×14.

452	20m. Type **181**	20	10
453	60m. Composite vessel, 2100–2000 BC	50	80
454	100m. Byzantine goblet	90	1·75
452/454 *Set of 3*		1·40	2·40

182 Self-help Housing

183 Terracotta Statue of Youth

1976 (3 May). Economic Reactivation. T **182** and similar horiz designs. Multicoloured. W **58** (sideways). P 14×13.

455	10m. Type **182**	10	10
456	25m. Handicrafts	15	20
457	30m. Reafforestation	15	20
458	60m. Air Communications	30	55
455/458 *Set of 4*		55	90

1976 (7 June). Cypriot Treasures. T **183** and similar designs. W **58** (sideways on horiz designs, upright on vert designs). Ordinary cream paper. P 12×13½ (5, 10m.), 13×14 (20 25, 30m.), 14×13 (40, 50, 60m.), 13½×12 (100m.) or 13×13½ (250m. to £1).

459	5m. multicoloured	10	80
460	10m. multicoloured	10	60
461	20m. red, yellow and black	20	60
462	25m. multicoloured	20	10
463	30m. multicoloured	20	10
464	40m. grey-green, light olive-bistre and black	30	55
465	50m. buff, brown and black	30	10
466	60m. multicoloured	30	20
467	100m. multicoloured	40	40
468	250m. deep dull blue, grey and black	50	1·40
469	500m. black, stone and deep blue-green	60	1·50
470	£1 multicoloured	1·00	1·75
459/470 *Set of 12*		3·75	7·00

Sizes: 23×34 mm, 5m., 10m.; 34×23 mm, 100m.; 24×37 mm, 20, 25, 30m.; 37×24 mm, 40, 50, 60m.; 28×41 mm, others.

Designs: 5m. T **183**; 10m. Limestone head; 20m. Gold necklace from Lambousa; 25m. Terracotta warrior; 30m. Statue of a priest of Aphrodite; 40m. Bronze tablet; 50m. Mycenaean crater; 60m. Limestone sarcophagus; 100m. Gold bracelet from Lambousa; 250m. Silver dish from Lambousa; 500m. Bronze stand; £1 Statue of Artemis.

184 Olympic Symbol

185 *George Washington* (G. Stuart)

(Litho Harrison)

1976 (5 July). Olympic Games, Montreal. T **184** and similar designs. P 14.

471	20m. carmine-red, black and yellow	10	10
472	60m. multicoloured	20	30
473	100m. multicoloured	30	35
471/473 *Set of 3*		55	65

Designs: Vert—20m. T **184**. Horiz—60, 100m. Olympic symbols (*different*).

1976 (5 July). Bicentenary of American Revolution. W **58**. P 13×13½.

474	**185**	100m. multicoloured	40	30

186 Children in Library

187 Archangel Michael

1976 (27 Sept). Anniversaries and Events. T **186** and similar vert designs. W **58**. P 13½×12½ (50m.) or 13½ (others).

475	40m. multicoloured	15	15
476	50m. yellow-brown and black	15	10
477	80m. multicoloured	30	60
475/477	Set of 3	55	75

Designs and Events: 40m. T **186** (Promotion of Children's Books); 50m. Low-cost housing (HABITAT Conference, Vancouver); 80m. Eye protected by hands (World Health Day).

(Litho Harrison)

1976 (15 Nov). Christmas. T **187** and similar vert designs showing icons from Ayios Neophytis Monastery. Multicoloured. P 12½.

478	10m. Type **187**	10	10
479	15m. Archangel Gabriel	10	10
480	150m. The Nativity	60	80
478/480	Set of 3	70	80

188 *Cyprus 74* (wood-engraving by A. Taesos)

189 *View of Prodhromos* (A. Diamantis)

1977 (10 Jan*)–**82**. Obligatory Tax. Refugee Fund. W **58**. Ordinary cream paper. P 13×12½.

481	**188**	10m. grey-black	20	10
		a. Chalk-surfaced cream paper	20	10

* Earliest known date of use.
For 1c. value, see Nos. 634/634*b*, 729 and 747.

1977 (2 May). Europa. Paintings. T **189** and similar horiz designs. Multicoloured. No wmk. P 13½×13.

482	20m. Type **189**	20	10
483	60m. *Springtime at Monagroulli* (T. Kanthos)	30	55
484	120m. *Old Port, Limassol* (V. Ioannides)	60	2·40
482/484	Set of 3	1·00	2·75

190 Overprinted 500m. Stamp of 1960

191 Bronze Coin of Emperor Trajan

1977 (13 June). Silver Jubilee. W **58**. P 13×13½.

485	**190** 120m. multicoloured	30	30

(Litho Harrison)

1977 (13 June). Ancient Coins of Cyprus (2nd series). T **191** and similar horiz designs. P 14.

486	10m. brownish black, gold and ultramarine	15	10
487	40m. brownish black, silver and pale blue	30	30
488	60m. brownish black, silver and dull orange	35	35
489	100m. brownish black, gold and blue-green	50	95
486/489	Set of 4	1·10	1·50

Designs: 10m. T **191**; 40m. Silver tetradrachm of Demetrios Poliorcetes; 60m. Silver tetradrachm of Ptolemy VIII; 100m. Gold Octadrachm of Arsinoe II.

192 Archbishop Makarios in Ceremonial Robes

193 Embroidery, Pottery and Weaving

1977 (10 Sept). Death of Archbishop Makarios. T **192** and similar vert designs. Multicoloured. P 13×13½.

490	20m. Type **192**	15	10
491	60m. Archbishop and doorway	20	10
492	250m. Head and shoulders portrait	50	1·10
490/492	Set of 3	75	1·10

1977 (17 Oct). Anniversaries and Events. T **193** and similar horiz designs. Multicoloured. W **58** (sideways). P 13½×13.

493	20m. Type **193**	10	10
494	40m. Map of Mediterranean	15	20
495	60m. Gold medals	20	20
496	80m. *Sputnik*	20	85
493/496	Set of 4	60	1·25

Events: 20m. Revitalisation of handicrafts; 40m. Man and the Biosphere Programme in the Mediterranean region; 60m. Gold medals won by Cypriot students in the Orleans Gymnasiade; 80m. 60th anniversary of Russian October Revolution.

194 *Nativity*

(Litho Harrison)

1977 (21 Nov). Christmas. T **194** and similar horiz designs showing children's paintings. Multicoloured. P 14×13½.

497	10m. Type **194**	10	10
498	40m. *The Three Kings*	10	10
499	150m. *Flight into Egypt*	25	80
497/499	Set of 3	35	90

195 Demetrios Libertis

(Des A. Ioannides)

1978 (6 Mar). Cypriot Poets. T **195** and similar horiz design. W **58** (sideways). P 14×13.

500	40m. dull brown and olive-bistre	10	10
501	150m. grey, grey-black and light red	30	80

Designs: 40m. T **195**; 150m. Vasilis Michaelides.

196 Chrysorrhogiatissa Monastery Courtyard

(Litho Harrison)

1978 (24 Apr). Europa. Architecture. T **196** and similar horiz designs. Multicoloured. P 14×13½.

502	25m. Type **196**	15	10
503	75m. Kolossi Castle	25	35
504	125m. Municipal Library, Paphos	45	1·50
502/504	Set of 3	75	1·75

197 Archbishop of Cyprus, 1950–1977

198 Affected Blood Corpuscles (Prevention of Thalassaemia)

199 Icon Stand

(Des A. Ioannides (300m.). Photo Harrison)

1978 (3 Aug). Archbishop Makarios Commemoration. T **197** and similar vert designs. Multicoloured. P 14×15.

505	15m. Type **197**	15	20
	a. Silver (inscr and emblem) omitted		
	b. Horiz strip of 5. Nos. 505/509	85	
	ba. Imperf (horiz strip of 5)	£1000	
	bb. Silver omitted (horiz strip of 5)	£750	
506	25m. Exiled in Seychelles, 9 March 1956–1928 March 1957	15	20
507	50m. President of the Republic, 1960–1977	20	25
508	75m. Soldier of Christ	20	30
509	100m. Fighter for Freedom	25	35
505/509 Set of 5		85	1·10
MS510 110×80 mm. 300m. The Great Leader. Imperf		1·00	2·50

Nos. 505/509 were printed together, *se-tenant*, in horizontal strips of five throughout the sheet.

Sheets of this issue are known with the silver omitted completely or only from the first or last vertical rows.

(Des A. Ioannides)

1978 (23 Oct). Anniversaries and Events. T **198** and similar designs. P 13½×14 (15, 35m.) or 14×13½ (others).

511	15m. multicoloured	10	10
512	35m. multicoloured	15	10
513	75m. black and grey	20	30
514	125m. multicoloured	35	80
511/514 Set of 4		70	

Designs and Events. Vert—15m. T **198**; 35m. *Aristotle* (sculpture) (2300th death anniversary). Horiz—75m. 'Heads' (Human Rights); 125m. Wright brothers and *Wright Flyer I* (75th anniversary of powered flight).

(Litho Harrison)

1978 (4 Dec). Christmas. T **199** and similar vert designs showing icon stands. P 14×14½.

515	15m. multicoloured	10	10
516	35m. multicoloured	15	10
517	150m. multicoloured	40	60
515/517 Set of 3		60	65

200 *Aphrodite* (statue from Soli)

(Des G. Simonis. Litho Harrison)

1979 (12 Mar). Aphrodite (Greek goddess of love and beauty) Commemoration (1st issue). T **200** and similar horiz design showing Aphrodite emerging from the sea at Paphos (legendary birthplace). Multicoloured. P 14×13½.

518	75m. Type **200**	25	10
519	125m. Aphrodite on a shell (detail from *Birth of Venus* by Botticelli)	35	25

See also Nos. 584/585.

201 Van, Larnaca–Nicosia Post van and Envelope

202 Peacock Wrasse (*Thalassoma pavo*)

(Des G. Simonis)

1979 (30 Apr). Europa. Communications. T **201** and similar horiz designs. Multicoloured. W **58** (sideways). P 14×13.

520	25m. Type **201**	20	10
521	75m. Radar, satellite and early telephone	30	20
522	125m. Aircraft, ship and envelopes	85	1·50
520/522 Set of 3		1·25	1·60

1979 (25 June). Flora and Fauna. T **202** and similar multicoloured designs. W **58** (sideways on 25 and 125m.). P 13½×12 (25 and 125m.) or 12×13½ (others).

523	25m. Type **202**	15	10
524	50m. Black Partridge (*Francolinus francolintus*) (*vert*)	70	60
525	75m. Cedar (*Cedar brevifolia*) (*vert*)	45	30
526	125m. Mule (*Equus mulus*)	50	1·25
523/526 Set of 4		1·60	2·00

203 IBE and UNESCO Emblems

204 Jesus (from Church of the Virgin Mary of Arakas, Lagoudhera)

(Des Mrs. A. Kalathia (25m.), A. Ioannides (others). Litho Harrison)

1979 (1 Oct). Anniversaries and Events. T **203** and similar designs in black, yellow-brown and yellow-ochre (50m.) or multicoloured (others). P 12½.

527	15m. Type **203**	10	10
528	25m. Graphic design of Dove and stamp album (*horiz*)	10	10
529	50m. Lord Kitchener and map of Cyprus (*horiz*)	20	15
530	75m. Child's face (*horiz*)	25	10
531	100m. Graphic design of footballers (*horiz*)	30	20
532	125m. Rotary International emblem and '75'.	30	75
527/532 Set of 6		1·10	1·25

Events: 15m. 50th anniversary of International Bureau of Education; 25m. T **203**, 20th anniversary of Cyprus Philatelic Society; 50m. Centenary of Cyprus Survey; 75m. International Year of the Child; 100m. 25th anniversary of UEFA (European Football Association); 125m. 75th anniversary of Rotary International.

1979 (5 Nov). Christmas. Icons. T **204** and similar vert designs. Multicoloured. W **58**. P 13½×13 (35m.) or 13½×14 (others).

533	15m. Type **204**	10	10
534	35m. Nativity (from the Iconostasis of the Church of St Nicholas, Famagusta District) (29×41 *mm*)	10	10
535	150m. Holy Mary (from Church of the Virgin Mary of Arakas, Lagoudhera)	25	45
533/535 Set of 3		35	55

205 1880 ½d. Stamp with '969' (Nicosia) Postmark

206 St Barnabas (Patron Saint of Cyprus)

1980 (17 Mar). Cyprus Stamp Centenary. T **205** and similar horiz designs. Multicoloured. W **58** (sideways). P 13½×13.

536	40m. Type **205**	10	10
537	125m. 1880 2½d. stamp with '974' (Kyrenia) postmark	15	20
538	175m. 1880 1s. stamp with '942' (Larnaca) postmark	15	25
536/538 Set of 3		30	45
MS539 105×85 mm. 500m. 1880 1d., ½d., 2½d., 4d., 6d. and 1s. stamps (90×75 *mm*). Imperf		70	85

(Photo Harrison)

1980 (28 Apr). Europa. Personalities. T **206** and similar vert design. Multicoloured. P 12½.

540	40m. Type **206**	15	10
541	125m. Zeno of Citium (founder of the Stoic		
	philosophy)	30	20
	a. Pale Venetian red omitted	£130	

The pale Venetian red colour on No. 541 appears as an overlay on the bust On No. 541a the bust is pure grey.

207 Sailing

(Des A. Ioannides)

1980 (23 June). Olympic Games, Moscow. T **207** and similar horiz designs. Multicoloured. W **58** (sideways). P 13½×13.

542	40m. Type **207**	10	10
543	125m. Swimming	20	20
544	200m. Gymnastics	25	25
542/544 Set of 3		50	50

208 Gold Necklace, Arsos (7th-century BC)

209 Cyprus Flag

1980 (15 Sept). Archaeological Treasures. Multicoloured designs as T **208**. W **58** (sideways on 15, 40, 150 and 500m.). Chalk-surfaced cream paper. P 14×13 (15, 40, 150 and 500m.) or 13×14 (others).

545	10m. Type **208**	30	1·00
546	15m. Bronze Cow, Vouni Palace (5th-century		
	BC) (horiz)	30	1·00
547	25m. Amphora, Salamis (6th-century BC)	30	30
548	40m. Gold finger-ring, Enkomi (13th-century		
	BC) (horiz)	40	75
549	50m. Bronze cauldron, Salamis (8th-century BC)	40	10
550	75m. Funerary stele, Marion (5th-century BC).	1·25	1·50
551	100m. Jug (5/14th-century BC)	65	15
552	125m. Warrior (Terracotta) (6/5th-century BC) ..	65	1·00
553	150m. Lions attacking Bull (bronze relief),		
	Vouni Palace (5th-century BC) (horiz)	75	15
554	175m. Faience rhyton, Kition (13th-century BC)	75	1·25
555	200m. Bronze statue of Ingot God, Enkomi		
	(12th-century BC)	75	30
556	500m. Stone bowl, Khirokitia (6th-millennium		
	BC) (horiz)	75	1·50
557	£1 Ivory plaque, Salamis (7th-century BC) ...	1·00	1·25
558	£2 Leda and the Swan (mosaic), Kouklia		
	(3rd-century AD)	1·75	2·00
545/558 Set of 14		9·00	11·00

See also Nos. 607/618.

1980 (1 Oct). 20th Anniversary of Republic. T **209** and similar multicoloured designs. P 13½×13 (125m.) or 13×14 (others).

559	40m. Type **209**	20	10
560	125m. Signing Treaty of Establishment		
	(41×29 mm)	25	15
561	175m. Archbishop Makarios	35	25
559/561 Set of 3		70	45

210 Peace Dove and Head Silhouettes

(Des A. Ioannides)

1980 (29 Nov). International Palestinian Solidarity Day. T **210** and similar horiz design showing Peace Dove and head silhouettes. W **58** (sideways). P 13½×13.

562	40m. grey and black	20	20
	a. Horiz pair. Nos. 562/563	55	55
563	125m. grey and black	35	35

Nos. 562/563 were printed together, se-tenant, in horizontal pairs throughout the sheet.

211 Pulpit, Tripiotis Church, Nicosia

212 Folk-dancing

1980 (29 Nov). Christmas. T **211** and similar vert designs. Multicoloured. W **58**. P 13×14.

564	25m. Type **211**	10	10
565	100m. Holy Doors, Panayia Church, Paralimni		
	(24×37 mm)	15	20
566	125m. Pulpit, Ayios Lazaros Church, Larnaca	15	20
564/566 Set of 3		30	40

(Litho Harrison)

1981 (4 May). Europa. Folklore. T **212** and similar vert design showing folk-dancing from paintings by T. Photiades. P 14.

567	40m. multicoloured	30	10
568	175m. multicoloured	60	50

213 Self-portrait

214 Ophrys kotschyi

1981 (15 June). 500th Anniversary of Leonardo da Vinci's Visit. T **213** and similar multicoloured designs. W **58** (sideways on 125m.). P 12×14 (125m.) or 13½×14 (others).

569	50m. Type **213**	40	10
570	125m. The Last Supper (50×25 mm)	70	40
571	175m. Cyprus lace and Milan Cathedral	95	60
569/571 Set of 3		1·90	1·00

(Des A. Tassos)

1981 (6 July). Cypriot Wild Orchids. T **214** and similar vert designs. Multicoloured. W **58**. P 13½×14.

572	25m. Type **214**	40	60
	a. Block of 4. Nos. 572/575	1·90	2·75
573	50m. Orchis punctulata	50	70
574	75m. Ophrys argolica elegans	55	80
575	150m. Epipactis veratrifolia	65	90
572/575 Set of 4		1·90	2·75

Nos. 572/575 were printed together, se-tenant, in blocks of four throughout the sheet.

215 Heinrich von Stephan

216 The Lady of the Angels (from Church of the Transfiguration of Christ, Palekhori)

(Des A. Tassos (200m.), A. Ioannides (others))

1981 (28 Sept). Anniversaries and Events. T **215** and similar horiz designs. W **58** (sideways). P 12½×13.

576	25m. brown-olive, deep yellow-green and bright blue	15	10
577	40m. multicoloured	15	10
578	125m. black, vermilion and deep yellow-green	30	25
579	150m. multicoloured	35	30
580	200m. multicoloured	70	80
576/580 *Set of 5*		1·50	1·40

Designs and Events: 25m. T **215** (150th birth anniversary of Heinrich von Stephan (founder of UPU); 40m. Stylised man holding dish of food (World Food Day); 125m. Stylised hands (International Year for Disabled Persons); 150m. Stylised building and flower (European Campaign for Urban Renaissance); 200m. Prince Charles, Lady Diana Spencer and St Paul's Cathedral (Royal Wedding).

1981 (16 Nov). Christmas. Murals from Nicosia District Churches. T **216** and similar multicoloured designs. W **58** (sideways on 25 and 125m.). P 12½.

581	25m. Type **216**	20	10
582	100m. *Christ Pantokrator* (from Church of Madonna of Arakas, Lagoudera) (*vert*)	60	20
583	125m. *Baptism of Christ* (from Church of Our Lady of Assinou, Nikitari)	70	30
581/583 *Set of 3*		1·25	50

217 *Louomene* (statue of Aphrodite bathing, 250 BC)

218 Naval Battle with Greek Fire, 985 AD

1982 (12 Apr). Aphrodite (Greek goddess of love and beauty) Commemoration (2nd issue). T **217** and similar vert design. Multicoloured. W **58**. P 13½×14.

584	125m. Type **217**	55	45
585	175m. *Anadyomene* (Aphrodite emerging from the waters) (Titian)	70	65

(Des G. Simonis. Photo Harrison)

1982 (3 May). Europa. Historical Events. T **218** and similar horiz design. Multicoloured. P 12½.

586	40m. Type **218**	60	10
587	175m. Conversion of Roman Proconsul Sergius Paulus to Christianity, Paphos, 45 AD	80	2·00

219 Monogram of Christ (mosaic)

100

(220)

1982 (5 July). World Cultural Heritage. T **219** and similar multicoloured designs. W **58** (sideways on 50 and 225m.). P 13½×14 (125m.) or 12½ (others).

588	50m. Type **219**	20	10
589	125m. Head of priest-king of Paphos (sculpture) (24×37 *mm*)	40	25
590	225m. Theseus (Greek god) (mosaic)	60	95
588/590 *Set of 3*		1·10	1·10

1982 (6 Sept). No. 550 surch with T **220** by Government Ptg Office, Nicosia.

591	100m. on 75m. Funerary stele, Marion (5th-century BC)	50	50

221 Cyprus and Stylised '75'

222 Holy Communion–The Bread

1982 (8 Nov). 75th Anniversary of Boy Scout Movement. T **221** and similar multicoloured designs. W **58** (sideways on 100m. and 175m.). P 12½×13½ (125m.) or 13½×12½ (others).

592	100m. Type **221**	35	20
593	125m. Lord Baden-Powell (*vert*)	40	40
594	175m. Camp-site	40	90
592/594 *Set of 3*		1·00	1·40

1982 (6 Dec). Christmas. T **222** and similar designs. W **58** (sideways on 25 and 250m.). P 12½×12 (25 and 250m.) or 13½×14 (100m.).

595	25m. multicoloured	10	10
596	100m. gold and black	30	15
597	250m. multicoloured	70	1·50
595/597 *Set of 3*		1·00	1·60

Designs: Vert—100m. Holy Chalice. Horiz—25m. T **222**; 250m. Holy Communion–The Wine.

223 Cyprus Forest Industries' Sawmill

1983 (14 Mar). Commonwealth Day. T **223** and similar horiz designs. Multicoloured. W **58** (sideways). P 14×13½.

598	50m. Type **223**	10	10
599	125m. Ikarios and the Discovery of Wine (3rd-century mosaic)	20	25
600	150m. Folk-dancers, Commonwealth Film and Television Festival, 1980	25	35
601	175m. Royal Exhibition Building, Melbourne (Commonwealth Heads of Government Meeting, 1981)	25	40
598/601 *Set of 4*		70	1·00

224 Cyprosyllabic Inscription (6th-century BC)

(Des G. Simonis. Photo Harrison)

1983 (3 May). Europa. T **224** and similar horiz design. Multicoloured. P 14½×14.

602	50m. Type **224**	30	10
603	200m. Copper ore, ingot (Enkomi 1400–1250 BC) and bronze jug (2nd-century AD)	80	2·00

225 *Pararge aegeria*

1983 (28 June). Butterflies. T **225** and similar horiz designs. Multicoloured. W w **58**. P 12½.

604	60m. Type **225**	25	20
605	130m. *Aricia agestis*	45	25
606	250m. *Glaucopsyche melanops*	85	2·00
604/606 *Set of 3*		1·40	2·25

(New Currency: 100 cents = £1 (Cyprus))

1c

=

(226)

1983 (3 Oct). Nos. 545/556 surch as T **226** by Government Printing Office, Nicosia.

607	1c. on 10m. Type **208**	35	1·00
608	2c. on 15m. Bronze Cow, Vouni Palace (5th-century BC)	35	1·25

609	3c. on 25m. Amphora, Salamis (6th-century BC)	35	1·00
610	4c. on 40m. Gold finger-ring, Enkomi (13th-century BC)	40	1·00
611	5c. on 50m. Bronze cauldron, Salamis (8th-century BC)	50	50
612	6c. on 75m. Funerary stele, Marion (5th-century BC)	50	1·00
613	10c. on 100m. Lion (15/14th-century BC)	50	40
614	13c. on 125m. Warrior (Terracotta) (6/5th-century BC)	50	50
615	15c. on 150m. Lions attacking Bull (bronze relief), Vouni Palace (5th-century BC)	50	55
616	20c. on 200m. Bronze statue of Ingot God, Enkomi (12th-century BC)	50	65
617	25c. on 175m. Faience rhyton, Kition (13th-century BC)	55	1·10
618	50c. on 500m. Stone bowl, Khirokitia (6th-millennium BC)	75	2·00
607/618 Set of 12		5·25	9·75

227 View of Power Station

228 St Lazarus Church, Larnaca

1983 (27 Oct). Anniversaries and Events. T **227** and similar vert designs. Multicoloured. W **58**. P 13×14.

619	3c. Type **227**	10	20
620	6c. WCY logo	15	15
621	13c. *Sol Olympia* (liner) and *Polys* (tanker)	30	35
622	15c. Human Rights emblem and map of Europe	20	25
623	20c. Nicos Kazantzakis (poet)	20	75
624	25c. Archbishop Makarios in church	25	75
619/624 Set of 6		1·00	2·25

Events: 3c. 30th Anniversary of the Cyprus Electricity Authority; 6c. World Communications Year; 13c. 25th Anniversary of International Maritime Organisation; 15c. 35th Anniversary of Universal Declaration of Human Rights; 20c. Birth centenary; 25c. 70th birth anniversary.

1983 (12 Dec). Christmas. Church Towers. T **228** and similar vert designs. Multicoloured. W **58**. P 12×13½.

625	4c. Type **228**	15	10
626	13c. St Varvara Church, Kaimakli, Nicosia	40	35
627	20c. St Ioannis Church, Larnaca	70	1·50
625/627 Set of 3		1·10	1·75

229 Waterside Cafe, Larnaca

(Litho Harrison)

1984 (6 Mar). Old Engravings. T **229** and similar horiz designs. Each pale stone and black. P 14½×14 (6c.) or 14 (others).

628	6c. Type **229**	15	15
629	20c. Bazaar at Larnaca (30×25 *mm*)	40	85
630	30c. Famagusta Gate, Nicosia (30×25 *mm*)	65	1·50
628/630 Set of 3		1·10	2·25
MS631 110×85 mm. 75c. *The Confession* (St Lazarus Church, Larnaca)		1·50	2·00

230 CEPT 25th Anniversary Logo

(Des J. Larrivière. Litho Harrison)

1984 (30 Apr). Europa. W **58**. P 12½.

632	**230**	6c. apple-green, deep blue-green and black	40	10
633		15c. light blue, dull ultramarine and black	70	2·00

A. Waddington ptgs (Nos. 634/634a)

B. Aspioti-Elka ptg (No. 634b)

(Des A. Tassos)

1984 (18 June)–87. Obligatory Tax. Refugee Fund. Design as T **188** but new value and '1984' date. P 13×12½.

*(a) Litho J.W. W **58**. Chalk-surfaced cream paper*

634	1c. grey-black (A.)	10	10
	a. Wmk sideways. Ordinary paper (21.2.87)*	1·00	70

*(b) Litho Aspioti-Elka. W **58**. Chalk-surfaced cream paper*

634b	1c. grey-black (B.) (3.11.87)*	1·00	65

* Earliest known date of use.

In addition to the redrawn inscriptions there are other minor differences between the work of the two printers.

For a further version of this design, showing '1974' at top right, see Nos. 729, 747, 807 and 892.

231 Running

(Des. K. Haine. Litho Harrison)

1984 (18 June). Olympic Games, Los Angeles. T **231** and similar horiz designs. Multicoloured. W **58** (sideways). P 14.

635	3c. Type **231**	15	10
636	4c. Olympic column	15	20
637	13c. Swimming	35	75
638	20c. Gymnastics	45	1·50
635/638 Set of 4		1·00	2·25

232 Prisoners-of-War

233 Open Stamp Album (25th Anniversary of Cyprus Philatelic Society)

1984 (20 July). Tenth Anniversary of Turkish Landings in Cyprus. T **232** and similar horiz design. Multicoloured. P 14×13½.

639	15c. Type **232**	40	45
640	20c. Map and burning buildings	50	55

(Des P. St Antoniades (6c.), A. Ioannides (10c.), Harrison (others). Litho Harrison)

1984 (15 Oct). Anniversaries and Events. T **233** and similar multicoloured designs. W **58** (sideways on horiz designs). P 12½.

641	6c. Type **233**	30	20
642	10c. Football in motion (*horiz*) (50th Anniversary of Cyprus Football Association)	45	30
643	15c. *Dr. George Papanicolaou* (medical scientist–birth centenary)	75	50
644	25c. Antique map of Cyprus and ikon (*horiz*) (International Symposia on Cartography and Medieval Paleography)	1·10	2·00
641/644 Set of 4		2·40	2·75

234 St Mark
(miniature from
11th-century Gospel)

235 Autumn at Platania,
Troodos Mountains

(Des and litho Harrison)

1984 (26 Nov). Christmas. Illuminated Gospels. T **234** and similar vert designs. Multicoloured. W **58**. P 12½.

645	4c. Type **234**	25	10
646	13c. Beginning of St Mark's Gospel	45	50
647	20c. St Luke (miniature from 11th-century Gospel)	70	2·00
645/647 Set of 3		1·25	2·40

(Des and litho Harrison)

1985 (18 Mar). Cyprus Scenes and Landscapes. T **235** and similar multicoloured designs. Ordinary white paper. P 14×15 (6c., 20c., 25c., £1, £5) or 15×14 (others).

648	1c. Type **235**	20	60
649	2c. Ayia Napa Monastery	20	60
650	3c. Phini Village–panoramic view	20	60
651	4c. Kykko Monastery	20	30
652	5c. Beach at Makronissos, Ayia Napa	20	20
653	6c. Village street, Omodhos (vert)	30	20
654	10c. Panoramic sea view	45	30
655	13c. Windsurfing	55	25
656	15c. Beach at Protaras	75	25
657	20c. Forestry for development (vert)	1·00	50
658	25c. Sunrise at Protaras (vert)	1·25	1·00
659	30c. Village house, Pera	1·50	1·25
660	50c. Apollo Hylates Sanctuary, Curium	2·50	1·75
661	£1 Snow on Troodos Mountains (vert)	4·00	3·00
662	£5 Personification of Autumn, House of Dionyssos, Paphos (vert)	14·00	15·00
648/662 Set of 15		24·00	23·00

See also Nos. 684/685 and 730.

236 Clay Idols of Musicians
(7/6th-century BC)

237 Cyprus Coat
of Arms (25th
Anniversary of
Republic)

(Des and litho Harrison)

1985 (6 May). Europa. European Music Year. T **236** and similar horiz design. Multicoloured. W **58** (sideways). P 12½.

663	6c. Type **236**	50	35
664	15c. Violin, lute, flute and score from the Cyprus Suite	90	2·25

(Des G. Simonis (4c., 13c.), Harrison (others). Litho Harrison)

1985 (23 Sept). Anniversaries and Events. T **237** and similar designs. P 14½ (4, 20c.) or 14×13½ (others).

665	4c. multicoloured	15	15
666	6c. multicoloured	15	15
667	13c. multicoloured	25	1·00
668	15c. black, olive-black and yellow-orange	1·00	1·25
669	20c. multicoloured	30	1·75
665/669 Set of 5		1·60	3·75

Designs and Events: Horiz (43×30 mm)—6c. Barn of Liopetri (detail) (Pol. Georghiou) (30th Anniversary of EOKA Campaign); 13c. Three profiles (International Youth Year); 15c. Solon Michaelides (composer and conductor) (European Music Year). Vert 4c. as T **237**—20c. UN Building, New York, and flags (40th Anniversary of United Nations Organisation).

238 The Visit of the
Madonna to Elizabeth
(Lambadistis Monastery,
Kalopanayiotis)

239 Figure from Hellenistic
Spoon Handle

(Des and litho Harrison)

1985 (18 Nov). Christmas. Frescoes from Cypriot Churches. T **238** and similar vert designs. Multicoloured. P 12½.

670	4c. Type **238**	20	10
671	13c. The Nativity (Lambadistis Monastery, Kalopanayiotis)	50	50
672	20c. Candlemas-day (Asinou Church)	70	1·50
670/672 Set of 3		1·25	1·75

(Des A. Ioannides. Litho Harrison)

1986 (17 Feb). New Archaeological Museum Fund. T **239** and similar horiz designs. Multicoloured. P 15×14.

673	15c. Type **239**	30	35
674	20c. Pattern from early Ionian helmet and foot from statue	40	60
675	25c. Roman statue of Eros and Psyche	45	80
676	30c. Head of statue	50	95
673/676 Set of 4		1·50	2·40
MS677 111×90 mm. Nos. 673/676 (sold at £1)		11·00	15·00

Two-thirds of the amount received from sales of Nos. 673/677 was devoted to the construction of a new Archaeological Museum, Nicosia.

No. 676 also commemorates the 50th anniversary of the Department of Antiquities.

240 Cyprus Mouflon and Cedars

(Des G. Simonis)

1986 (28 Apr). Europa. Protection of Nature and the Environment. T **240** and similar horiz design. Multicoloured. W **58** (sideways). P 14×13.

678	7c. Type **240**	35	30
679	17c. Greater Flamingos at Larnaca Salt Lake	1·40	2·75

241 Cat's-paw Scallop
(Manupecten pesfelis)

(242)

(Des T. Katsoulides)

1986 (1 July). Sea Shells. T **241** and similar horiz designs. Multicoloured. W **58** (sideways). P 14×13½.

680	5c. Type **241**	30	15
681	7c. Atlantic Trumpet Triton (Charonia variegata)	35	15
682	18c. Purple Dye Murex (Murex brandaris)	60	70
683	25c. Yellow Cowrie (Cypraea spurca)	1·00	2·00
680/683 Set of 4		2·00	2·75

1986 (13 Oct). Nos. 653 and 655 surch as T **242**.

684	7c. on 6c. Village street, Omodhos (vert)	40	30
685	18c. on 13c. Windsurfing	1·10	70

For 15c. on 4c. see No. 730.

243 Globe, Outline Map of Cyprus
and Barn Swallows (Overseas
Cypriots' Year)

(Des T. Katsoulides)

1986 (13 Oct). Anniversaries and Events. T **243** and similar horiz designs.
Multicoloured. W **58** (sideways). P 13½×13.

686	15c. Type **243**	1·00	45
687	18c. Halley's Comet over Cyprus beach		
	(40×23 mm)	1·25	2·00
	a. Horiz pair. Nos. 687/688	2·50	4·00
688	18c. Comet's tail over sea and Edmond		
	Halley (40×23 mm)	1·25	2·00
686/688 Set of 3		3·25	4·00

Nos. 687/688 were printed together, *se-tenant*, in horizontal pairs
throughout the sheet, each pair forming a composite design.

244 Pedestrian Crossing

245 The Nativity
(Church of Panagia
tou Araka)

(Des A. Ioannides)

1986 (10 Nov). Road Safety Campaign. T **244** and similar horiz designs
Multicoloured. W **58** (sideways). P 14×13.

689	5c. Type **244**	65	30
690	7c. Motorcycle crash helmet	70	30
691	18c. Hands fastening car seat belt	1·50	3·00
689/691 Set of 3		2·50	3·25

(Des G. Simonis)

1986 (24 Nov). Christmas. International Peace Year. T **245** and similar vert
designs showing details of Nativity frescoes from Cypriot churches.
Multicoloured. W **58** (inverted). P 13½×14.

692	5c. Type **245**	35	15
693	15c. Church of Panagia tou Moutoulla	85	30
694	17c. Church of St Nicholas tis Stegis	1·00	2·00
692/694 Set of 3		2·00	2·25

246 Church of Virgin Mary,
Asinou

(Des and photo Harrison)

1987 (22 Apr). Troodos Churches on the World Heritage List. T **246** and
similar horiz designs. Multicoloured. P 12½.

695	15c. Type **246**	70	1·10
	a. Sheetlet of 9. Nos. 695/703	5·50	9·00
696	15c. Fresco of Virgin Mary, Moutoulla's Church	70	1·10
697	15c. Church of Virgin Mary, Podithou	70	1·10
698	15c. Fresco of Three Apostles, St Ioannis		
	Lampadistis Monastery	70	1·10
699	15c. Annunciation fresco, Church of the Holy		
	Cross, Pelentriou	70	1·10
700	15c. Fresco of Saints, Church of the Cross,		
	Ayiasmati	70	1·10
701	15c. Fresco of Archangel Michael and Donor,		
	Pedoula's Church of St Michael	70	1·10
702	15c. Church of St Nikolaos, Stegis	70	1·10
703	15c. Fresco of Prophets, Church of Virgin		
	Mary, Araka	70	1·10
695/703 Set of 9		5·50	9·00

Nos. 695/703 were printed together, *se-tenant*, in sheetlets of nine.

247 Proposed Central Bank of
Cyprus Building

(Des G. Simonis)

1987 (11 May). Europa. Modern Architecture. T **247** and similar horiz
design. W **58** (sideways). P 14×13½.

704	7c. multicoloured	40	30
705	18c. black, brownish grey and sage-green	85	2·00

Design: 7c. T **247**; 18c. Headquarters complex, Cyprus Telecommunications Authority.

248 Remains of Ancient Ship
and Kyrenia Castle

(Des Y. Pantsopoulos)

1987 (3 Oct). Voyage of *Kyrenia II* (replica of ancient ship). T **248** and
similar horiz designs. Multicoloured. W **58** (sideways). P 14×13½.

706	2c. Type **248**	35	20
707	3c. *Kyrenia II* under construction, 1982–1985	45	90
708	5c. *Kyrenia II* at Paphos, 1986	75	20
709	17c. *Kyrenia II* at New York, 1986	1·75	90
706/709 Set of 4		3·00	2·00

249 Hands (from Michelangelo's
Creation) and Emblem (Tenth
Anniversary of Blood Donation
Co ordinating Committee)

250 Nativity Crib

(Des A. Ioannides)

1987 (2 Nov). Anniversaries and Events. T **249** and similar horiz designs.
Multicoloured. W **58** (sideways). P 14×13½.

710	7c. Type **249**	50	25
711	15c. Snail with flowered shell and countryside		
	(European Countryside Campaign)	1·10	40
712	20c. Symbols of ocean bed and Earth's crust		
	(Troodos '87 Ophiolites and Oceanic		
	Lithosphere Symposium)	1·40	3·00
710/712 Set of 3		2·75	3·25

(Des A. Ioannides)

1987 (30 Nov). Christmas. Traditional Customs. T **250** and similar square
designs. Multicoloured. W **58** (sideways). P 14.

713	5c. Type **250**	35	15
714	15c. Door knocker decorated with foliage	1·10	35
715	17c. Bowl of fruit and nuts	1·25	2·00
713/715 Set of 3		2·40	2·25

251 Flags of Cyprus and EEC

(Des G. Simonis. Litho Alexandros Matsoukis, Athens)

1988 (11 Jan). Cypriot–EEC. Customs Union. T **251** and similar horiz
design. Multicoloured. W **58**. P 13×13½.

716	15c. Type **251**	90	1·75
717	18c. Outline maps of Cyprus and EEC countries	90	80

252 Intelpost Telefax Terminal

(Des A. Ioannides. Litho Alexandros Matsoukis, Athens)

1988 (9 May). Europa. Transport and Communications. T **252** and similar horiz designs. Multicoloured. W **58**. P 14×14½.

718	7c. Type **252**	75	1·25
	a. Horiz pair. Nos. 718/719	1·50	2·50
719	7c. Car driver using mobile telephone	75	1·25
720	18c. Nose of Cyprus Airways airliner and Greater Flamingos	3·00	3·00
	a. Horiz pair. Nos. 720/721	6·00	6·00
721	18c. Boeing airliner in flight and Greater Flamingos	3·00	3·00
718/721 Set of 4		6·75	7·50

The two designs of each value were printed together, *se-tenant*, in horizontal pairs throughout the sheet of ten.

253 Sailing **254** Conference Emblem

(Des A. Ioannides. Photo Courvoisier)

1988 (27 June). Olympic Games, Seoul. T **253** and similar vert designs. Multicoloured. Granite paper. P 12.

722	5c. Type **253**	30	20
723	7c. Athletes at start	35	40
724	10c. Shooting	40	70
725	20c. Judo	90	1·50
722/725 Set of 4		1·75	2·50

(Des A. Ioannides. Litho M. A. Moatsos, Athens)

1988 (5 Sept). Non-Aligned Foreign Ministers' Conference, Nicosia. T **254** and similar horiz designs. W **58** (sideways). P 14×13½.

726	1c. black, pale blue and emerald	10	10
727	10c. multicoloured	45	70
728	50c. multicoloured	3·50	2·50
726/728 Set of 3		3·50	3·00

Designs: 1c. T **254**; 10c. Emblem of Republic of Cyprus; 50c. Nehru, Tito, Nasser and Makarios.

255 *Cyprus 74* (wood-engraving by A. Tassos)

256 *Presentation of Christ at the Temple* (Church of Holy Cross tou Agiasmati)

(Des A. Tassos. Litho M. A. Moatsos, Athens)

1988 (12 Sept). Obligatory Tax. Refugee Fund. Design as Nos. 634/634b, but with upper and lower inscriptions redrawn and '1974' added as in T **255**. W **58**. Ordinary paper. P 13×12½.

729	**255**	1c. brownish black and brownish grey	35	10

For this design printed in photogravure and perforated 11½ see No. 747, in lithography perforated 13 see No. 807 and in lithography perforated 14½×13½ see No. 892.

1988 (3 Oct). No. 651 surch as T **242**.

730	15c. on 4c. Kykko Monastery	1·75	1·25

(Des G. Simonis. Litho M. A. Moatsos, Athens)

1988 (28 Nov). Christmas. T **256** and similar vert designs showing frescoes from Cypriot churches. Multicoloured. W **58**. P 13½×14.

731	5c. Type **256**	25	20
732	15c. *Virgin and Child* (St John Lampadistis Monastery)	70	25
733	17c. *Adoration of the Magi* (St John Lampadistis Monastery)	80	1·75
731/733 Set of 3		1·60	2·00

257 Human Rights Logo **258** Basketball

(Des G. Simonis. Litho M. A. Moatsos, Athens)

1988 (10 Dec). 40th Anniversary of Universal Declaration of Human Rights. W **58** (inverted). P 13½×14.

734	**257**	25c. azure, dull violet-blue and cobalt	1·00	1·25

(Des A. Ioannides. Litho Alexandros Matsoukis, Athens)

1989 (10 Apr). Third Small European States' Games, Nicosia. T **258** and similar horiz designs. Multicoloured. P 13½.

735	1c. Type **258**	50	15
736	5c. Javelin	30	15
737	15c. Wrestling	65	20
738	18c. Athletics	85	1·00
735/738 Set of 4		2·10	1·40
MS739 109×80 mm. £1 Angel and Laurel wreath (99×73 mm). Imperf		6·00	6·50

259 Lingri Stick Game

(Des S. Michael. Litho Alexandros Matsoukis, Athens)

1989 (8 May). Europa. Children's Games. T **259** and similar horiz designs. Multicoloured. P 13×13½.

740	7c. Type **259**	1·10	1·50
	a. Horiz pair. Nos. 740/741	2·10	3·00
741	7c. Ziziros	1·10	1·50
742	18c. Sitsia	1·25	1·60
	a. Horiz pair. Nos. 742/743	2·50	3·00
743	18c. Leapfrog	1·25	1·60
740/743 Set of 4		4·25	5·50

Nos. 740/741 and 742/743 were each printed together, *se-tenant*, in horizontal pairs throughout the sheets.

260 Universal Man

(Des A. Ioannides. Photo Courvoisier)

1989 (7 July). Bicentenary of the French Revolution. Granite paper. P 11½.

744	**260**	18c. multicoloured	1·00	60

261 Stylised Human Figures

262 Worker Bees tending Larvae

(Des A. Ioannides. Litho Alexandros Matsoukis, Athens)

1989 (4 Sept). Centenary of Interparliamentary Union (15c.) and Ninth Non-Aligned Summit Conference, Belgrade (30c.). T **261** and similar vert design. Multicoloured. P 13½.

| 745 | 15c. Type **261** | 65 | 40 |
| 746 | 30c. Conference logo | 1·10 | 1·10 |

(Photo Courvoisier)

1989 (4 Sept). Obligatory Tax. Refugee Fund. As T **255**, but reduced in size and inscr '1989' or '1990'. Chalk-surfaced. P 11½.

| 747 | **255** | 1c. brownish black and brownish grey | 60 | 50 |

(Litho Alexandros Matsoukis, Athens)

1989 (16 Oct). Bee-keeping. T **262** and similar vert designs. Multicoloured. P 13½.

748	3c. Type **262**	30	25
749	10c. Bee on Rock-rose flower	70	50
750	15c. Bee on Lemon flower	95	50
751	18c. Queen and worker bees	1·10	1·75
748/751	Set of 4	2·75	2·75

263 Outstretched Hand and Profile (aid for Armenian earthquake victims)

(Des A. Ioannides. Litho Alexandros Matsoukis, Athens)

1989 (13 Nov). Anniversaries and Events. T **263** and similar vert designs. Multicoloured. P 13½.

752	3c. Type **263**	30	1·25
753	5c. Airmail envelope (Cyprus Philatelic Society FIP membership)	45	10
754	7c. Crab symbol and Daisy (European Cancer Year)	75	1·40
755	17c. Vegetables and fish (World Food Day)	1·10	1·40
752/755	Set of 4	2·40	3·75

264 Winter (detail from *Four Seasons*)

265 Hands and Open Book (International Literacy Year)

(Litho Alexandros Matsoukis, Athens)

1989 (29 Dec). Roman Mosaics from Paphos. T **264** and similar multicoloured designs showing details. P 13 (1, 5, 7, 15c.), 13×13½ (2, 4, 18, 40c.), 13½×13 (3, 10, 20, 25c.) or 14 (50c., £1, £3).

756	1c. Type **264**	35	1·50
757	2c. Personification of Crete (32×24 mm)	45	1·50
758	3c. Centaur and Maenad (24×32 mm)	55	1·50
759	4c. Poseidon and Amymone (32×24 mm)	80	1·60
760	5c. Leda	80	20
761	7c. Apollon	1·00	25
762	10c. Hermes and Dionysos (24×32 mm)	1·50	30
763	15c. Cassiopeia	2·25	45
764	18c. Orpheus (32×24 mm)	2·25	50
765	20c. Nymphs (24×32 mm)	2·50	75
766	25c. Amazon (24×32 mm)	2·50	80

767	40c. Doris (32×24 mm)	4·00	1·75
768	50c. Heracles and the Lion (39×27 mm)	4·00	1·75
769	£1 Apollon and Daphne (39×27 mm)	7·00	3·25
770	£3 Cupid (39×27 mm)	13·00	14·00
756/770	Set of 15	38·00	27·00

(Des A. Ioannides. Litho Alexandros Matsoukis, Athens)

1990 (3 Apr). Anniversaries and Events. T **265** and similar horiz designs. Multicoloured. P 13½.

771	15c. Type **265**	65	50
772	17c. Dove and profiles (83rd Inter-Parliamentary Conference, Nicosia)	80	90
773	18c. Lions International emblem (Lions Europa Forum, Limassol)	90	90
771/773	Set of 3	2·10	2·10

266 District Post Office, Paphos

(Des A. Ioannides. Litho Alexandros Matsoukis, Athens)

1990 (10 May). Europa. Post Office Buildings. T **266** and similar horiz design. Multicoloured. P 13×13½.

| 774 | 7c. Type **266** | 1·10 | 25 |
| 775 | 18c. City Centre Post Office, Limassol | 1·40 | 3·00 |

267 Symbolic Lips (25th Anniversary of Hotel and Catering Institute)

(Des A. Ioannides. Litho Alexandros Matsoukis, Athens)

1990 (9 July). European Tourism Year. T **267** and similar horiz designs. Multicoloured. P 14.

776	5c. Type **267**	25	25
777	7c. Bell tower, St Lazarus Church (1100th anniversary)	30	25
778	15c. Butterflies and woman	2·25	45
779	18c. Birds and man	2·50	4·25
776/779	Set of 4	4·75	4·75

268 Sun (wood carving)

269 *Chionodoxa lochiae*

(Des A. Ioannides. Photo Courvoisier)

1990 (29 Sept). 30th Anniversary of Republic. T **268** and similar square designs. Multicoloured. Granite paper. P 11½.

780	15c. Type **268**	65	45
781	17c. Bulls (pottery design)	75	60
782	18c. Fish (pottery design)	85	70
783	40c. Tree and birds (woodcarving)	2·75	5·50
780/783	Set of 4	4·50	6·50
MS784	89×89 mm. £1 30th Anniversary emblem. Imperf	3·25	6·50

(Litho Alexandros Matsoukis, Athens)

1990 (5 Nov). Endangered Wild Flowers. T **269** and similar vert designs taken from book illustrations by Elektra Megaw. Multicoloured. P 13½×13.

785	2c. Type **269**	60	1·60
786	3c. *Pancratium maritimum*	60	1·60
787	5c. *Paeonia mascula*	85	20
788	7c. *Cyclamen cyprium*	90	25
789	15c. *Tulipa cypria*	1·75	30
790	18c. *Crocus cyprius*	1·90	3·75
785/790	Set of 6	6·00	7·00

270 Nativity   **271** Archangel

(Litho Alexandros Matsoukis, Athens)

1990 (3 Dec). Christmas. 16th-century Icons. T **270** and similar vert designs. Multicoloured. P 13½.

791	5c. Type **270**	60	20
792	15c. Virgin Hodegetria	1·50	30
793	17c. Nativity (different)	1·75	3·50
791/793 Set of 3		3·50	3·50

(Des A. Ioannides. Photo Courvoisier)

1991 (28 Mar). 6th-century Mosaics from Kanakaria Church. T **271** and similar vert designs. Multicoloured. Granite paper. P 12.

794	5c. Type **271**	20	15
795	15c. Christ Child	75	20
796	17c. St James	1·50	1·75
797	18c. St Matthew	1·75	2·25
794/797 Set of 4		3·75	4·00

272 Ulysses Spacecraft   **273** Young Cyprus Wheatear

(Des G. Simonis. Litho Alexandros Matsoukis, Athens)

1991 (6 May). Europa. Europe in Space. T **272** and similar horiz design. Multicoloured. P 13×13½.

798	7c. Type **272**	90	20
799	18c. Giotto and Halley's Comet	1·60	2·50

(Des A. Ioannides. Litho Alexandros Matsoukis, Athens)

1991 (4 July). Cyprus Wheatear. T **273** and similar horiz designs. Multicoloured. P 13½.

800	5c. Type **273**	1·10	40
801	7c. Adult bird in autumn plumage	1·25	40
802	15c. Adult male in breeding plumage	1·75	50
803	30c. Adult female in breeding plumage	2·00	4·00
800/803 Set of 4		5·50	4·75

274 Mother and Child with Tents   **275** The Nativity

(Des A. Ioannides. Litho Alexandros Matsoukis, Athens)

1991 (7 Oct). 40th Anniversary of UN Commission for Refugees. T **274** and similar horiz designs, each brown, orange-brown and silver. P 13½.

804	5c. Type **274**	25	15
805	15c. Three pairs of legs	90	65
806	18c. Three children	1·10	2·50
804/806 Set of 3		2·00	3·00

(Litho Gieseche & Devrient Matsoukis (No. 807a) or Alexandros Matsoukis, Athens (others))

1991 (7 Oct)–**2007**. Obligatory Tax. Refugee Fund. As T **255**, but inscr '1991', '1992', '1993', '1994', '2002', '2003', '2004', '2005', '2006' or '2007' (No. 807a only). Chalk-surfaced paper. P 13.

807	**255**	1c. brownish black and olive-grey		
		(shades)	20	20
		a. perf 13½×14 (15.3.07)	20	20

(Des Revd. D. Demosthenous. Litho Alexandros Matsoukis, Athens)

1991 (25 Nov). Christmas. T **275** and similar vert designs. Multicoloured. P 13½.

808	5c. Type **275**	40	15
	a. Sheetlet of 9. Nos. 808/810×3	5·50	
809	15c. Saint Basil	80	40
810	17c. Baptism of Jesus	1·10	2·00
808/810 Set of 3		2·10	2·25

Nos. 808/810 were issued in separate sheets of 20 and in se-tenant sheetlets of nine.

276 Swimming   **277** World Map and Emblem (EXPO '92 Worlds Fair, Seville)

(Des A. Ioannides. Photo Courvoisier)

1992 (3 Apr). Olympic Games, Barcelona. T **276** and similar vert designs. Multicoloured. Granite paper. P 12.

811	10c. Type **276**	60	35
812	20c. Long jump	1·00	70
813	30c. Running	1·40	1·40
814	35c. Discus	1·60	2·50
811/814 Set of 4		4·25	4·50

(Des S. Karamallakis. Litho Alexandros Matsoukis, Athens)

1992 (20 Apr). Anniversaries and Events. T **277** and similar horiz designs. Multicoloured. P 14.

815	20c. Type **277**	1·60	80
816	25c. European map and football (Tenth Under-16 European Football Championship)	1·75	1·10
817	30c. Symbols of Learning (inauguration of University of Cyprus)	1·75	3·00
815/817 Set of 3		4·50	4·50

278 Compass Rose and Map of Voyage

(Des G. Simonis. Litho Alexandros Matsoukis, Athens)

1992 (29 May). Europa. 500th Anniversary of Discovery of America by Columbus. T **278** and similar horiz designs. Multicoloured. P 13×13½.

818	10c. Type **278**	1·10	1·40
	a. Horiz pair. Nos. 818/819	2·10	2·75
819	10c. Departure from Palos (R. Balaga)	1·10	1·40
820	30c. Fleet of Columbus	1·50	2·00
	a. Horiz pair. Nos. 820/821	3·00	4·00
821	30c. Christopher Columbus	1·50	2·00
818/821 Set of 4		4·75	6·00

Nos. 818/819 and 820/821 were printed together, se-tenant, in separate sheets, each horizontal pair forming a composite design.

279 Chamaeleo chamaeleon

(Litho Alexandros Matsoukis, Athens)

1992 (14 Sept). Reptiles. T **279** and similar horiz designs. Multicoloured. P 13½.

822	7c. Type **279**	85	30
823	10c. Lacerta laevis troodica (Lizard)	1·25	45
824	15c. Mauremys caspica (Turtle)	1·40	80
825	20c. Coluber cypriensis (Snake)	1·60	2·75
822/825 Set of 4		4·50	3·75

280 Minoan Wine Ship of 7th-century BC

281 *Visitation of the Virgin Mary to Elizabeth,* Church of the Holy Cross, Pelendri

(Des S. Vasiliou. Litho Alexandros Matsoukis, Athens)

1992 (9 Nov). Seventh International Maritime and Shipping Conference, Nicosia. P 14.

826	**280**	50c. multicoloured	3·00	3·00

(Litho Alexandros Mataoukis, Athens)

1992 (9 Nov). Christmas. Church Fresco Paintings. T **281** and similar vert designs. Muitlcoloured. P 13½.

827	7c. Type **281**	50	15
828	15c. *Virgin and Child Enthroned,* Church of Panagia tou Araka	85	45
829	20c. *Virgin and Child,* Ayios Nikolaos tis Stegis Church	1·25	2·50
827/829 *Set of 3*		2·40	2·75

282 School Building and Laurel Wreath

283 *Motherhood* (bronze sculpture, Nicos Dymiotis)

(Des A. Ladommates. Litho Alexandros Matsoukis, Athens)

1993 (15 Feb). Centenary of Pancyprian Gymnasium (secondary school). P 14.

830	**282**	10c. multicoloured	75	60

(Litho Alexandros Matsoukis, Athens)

1993 (5 Apr). Europa. Contemporary Art. T **283** and similar multicoloured design. P 13½.

831	10c. Type **283**	75	50
832	30c. *Motherhood* (painting, Christoforos Savva) (horiz)	1·50	2·25

284 Women Athletes (13th European Cup for Women)

285 Red Squirrelfish

Two types of 20c.:
I. Incorrectly inscribed 'MUFFLON ENCOURAGEMENT CUP'
II. Inscription corrected to 'MOUFFLON ENCOURAGEMENT CUP'

(Des Maria Trillidou (10c.), G. Simonis (25c.), M. Christou (others). Litho Alexandras Matsoukis, Athens)

1993 (24 May–24 June). Anniversaries and Events. T **284** and similar multicoloured designs. P 14.

833	7c. Type **284**	40	30
834	10c. Scout symbols (80th Anniversary of Scouting in Cyprus) (vert)	55	40
835	20c. Water-skier, Dolphin and Gull (Moufflon Encouragement Cup) (I)	12·00	12·00
	a. Type II (24.6)	95	95
836	25c. Archbishop Makarios III and monastery (80th birth anniversary)	1·40	2·00
833/836 *Set of 4*		3·00	3·25

No. 835 was withdrawn on 2 June 1993, after the spelling error had been spotted. No. 835a, with the spelling corrected, was placed on sale from 24 June.

(Des A. Ioannides. Litho Alexandros Matsoukis, Athens)

1993 (6 Sept). Fish. T **285** and similar horiz designs. Multicoloured. P 13½.

837	7c. Type **285**	50	25
838	15c. Red Scorpionfish	75	55
839	20c. Painted Comber	85	85
840	30c. Grey Triggerfish	1·60	2·50
837/840 *Set of 4*		3·25	3·75

286 Conference Emblem

(Des A. Ioannides. Litho Alexandros Matsoukis, Athens)

1993 (4 Oct). 12th Commonwealth Summit Conference. P 13½.

841	**286**	35c. orange-brown and pale ochre	1·60	1·90
842		40c. bistre-brown and ochre	1·90	2·40

287 Ancient Sailing Ship and Modern Coaster

288 Cross from Stavrovouni Monastery

(Des G. Simonis. Litho Alexandros Matsoukis, Athens)

1993 (4 Oct). Maritime Cyprus '93 International Shipping Conference, Nicosia. P 13½×14.

843	**287**	25c. multicoloured	1·40	1·40

(Litho Alexandros Matsoukis, Athens)

1993 (22 Nov). Christmas. Church Crosses. T **288** and similar multicoloured designs. P 13½.

844	7c. Type **288**	40	15
845	20c. Cross from Lefkara	1·00	60
846	25c. Cross from Pedoulas (horiz)	1·25	2·50
844/846 *Set of 3*		2·40	3·00

289 Copper Smelting

290 Symbols of Disability (Persons with Special Needs Campaign)

(Des G. Simonis. Litho Alexandros Matsoukis, Athens)

1994 (1 Mar). Europa. Discoveries. Ancient Copper Industry. T **289** and similar horiz design. Multicoloured. P 13×13½.

847	10c. Type **289**	50	35
848	30c. Ingot, ancient ship and map of Cyprus	1·50	2·00

(Des E. Hadjimichael (7c., 25c.), S. Karamallakis (others). Litho Alexandros Matsoukis, Athens)

1994 (9 May). Anniversaries and Events. T **290** and similar vert designs. Multicoloured. P 13½.

849	7c. Type **290**	60	25
850	15c. Olympic rings in flame (Centenary of International Olympic Committee)	85	55
851	20c. Peace Doves (World Gymnasiade, Nicosia)	1·00	80
852	25c. Adults and unborn baby in Tulip (International Year of the Family)	1·25	2·25
849/852 *Set of 4*		3·25	3·50

291 Houses, Soldier and Family

292 Black Pine

(Des A. Ioannides. Litho Alexandros Matsoukis, Athens)

1994 (27 June). 20th Anniversary of Turkish Landings in Cyprus. T **291** and similar horiz design. Multicoloured. P 14.

853	10c. Type **291**		60	40
854	50c. Soldier and ancient columns		2·40	3·25

(Des A. Ioannides. Litho Alexandros Matsoukis, Athens)

1994 (10 Oct). Trees. T **292** and similar vert designs. Multicoloured. P 13½×14.

855	7c. Type **292**		50	25
856	15c. Cyprus Cedar		75	55
857	20c. Golden Oak		90	80
858	30c. Strawberry Tree		1·40	2·50
855/858	Set of 4		3·25	3·75

293 Airliner, Route Map and Emblem

294 Virgin Mary (detail) (Philip Goul)

(Des G. Simonis. Litho Alexandros Matsoukis, Athens)

1994 (21 Nov). 50th Anniversary of International Civil Aviation Organisation. P 14.

859	**293**	30c. multicoloured	2·00	2·00

(Litho Alexandros Matsoukis, Athens)

1994 (21 Nov). Christmas. Church Paintings. T **294** and similar horiz designs. Multicoloured. P 13½.

860	7c. Type **294**		60	15
861	20c. The Nativity (detail) (Byzantine)		1·40	60
862	25c. Archangel Michael (detail) (Goul)		1·60	2·75
860/862	Set of 3		3·25	3·25

295 Woman from Paphos wearing Foustani

296 Hearth Room Excavation, Alassa and Frieze

(Des A. Ioannides. Litho Alexandros Matsoukis, Athens)

1994 (27 Dec). Traditional Costumes. T **295** and similar vert designs. Multicoloured. Cream paper. With 1994 imprint date. P 13½×13.

863	1c. Type **295**		65	1·50
864	2c. Bride from Karpass		80	1·50
865	3c. Woman from Paphos wearing sayia		85	1·50
866	5c. Woman from Messaoria wearing foustani		1·00	1·50
867	7c. Bridegroom		1·10	20
868	10c. Shepherd from Messaoria		1·50	40
869	15c. Woman from Nicosia in festive costume		2·50	40
870	20c. Woman from Karpass wearing festive sayia		2·50	50
871	25c. Woman from Pitsillia		2·75	60
872	30c. Woman from Karpass wearing festive doupletti		2·75	70
873	35c. Countryman		2·75	1·50

874	40c. Man from Messaoria in festive costume		3·00	2·00
875	50c. Townsman		3·00	2·50
876	£1 Townswoman wearing festive sarka		4·75	4·50
863/876	Set of 14		26·00	17·00

For £1 on white paper and perforated 14 see No. 958.

(Des Andreas Ladommatos. Litho Alexandros Matsoukis, Athens)

1995 (27 Feb). Third International Congress of Cypriot Studies, Nicosia. T **296** and similar multicoloured designs. P 14.

877	20c. Type **296**		75	75
878	30c. Hypostyle hall, Kalavasos, and Mycenaean amphora		1·00	1·75
MS879	110×80 mm. £1 Old Archbishop's Palace, Nicosia (107×71 mm). Imperf		3·50	5·00

297 Statue of Liberty, Nicosia (left detail)

298 Nazi Heads on Peace Dove over Map of Europe

(Des George Simonis. Litho Alexandros Matsoukis, Athens)

1995 (31 Mar). 40th Anniversary of Start of EOKA Campaign. T **297** and similar vert designs showing different details of the statue. Multicoloured. P 13×13½.

880	20c. Type **297**		1·10	1·40
	a. Horiz strip of 3. Nos. 880/882		3·00	3·75
881	20c. Centre detail (face value at top right)		1·10	1·40
882	20c. Right detail (face value at bottom right)		1·10	1·40
880/882	Set of 3		3·00	3·75

Nos. 880/882 were printed together, se-tenant, in horizontal strips of three forming a composite design.

(Des Toulla Paphitis. Litho Alexandros Matsoukis, Athens)

1995 (8 May). Europa. Peace and Freedom. T **298** and similar vert design. Multicoloured. P 13½.

883	10c. Type **298**		1·00	50
884	30c. Concentration camp prisoner and Peace Dove		2·25	3·25

299 Symbolic Figure holding Healthy Food

300 European Union Flag and European Culture Month Logo

(Des Liza Petridou-Mala. Litho Alexandros Matsoukis, Athens)

1995 (26 June). Healthy Living. T **299** and similar multicoloured designs. P 13½.

885	7c. Type **299**		30	25
886	10c. 'AIDS' and patients (horiz)		70	60
887	15c. Drug addict (horiz)		75	60
888	30c. Smoker and barbed wire		95	1·50
885/888	Set of 4		2·40	2·75

(Des George Simonis (Nos. 889/890), Nicos Rangos (No. **MS**891). Litho Oriental Press, Bahrain (Nos. 889/890) or Alexandros Matsoukis, Athens (No. **MS**891))

1995 (18 Sept). European Culture Month and Europhilex '95 International Stamp Exhibition, Nicosia. T **300** and similar horiz designs. Royal blue, orange-yellow and pale stone (No. **MS**891) or multicoloured (others). P 13×13½.

889	20c. Type **300**		55	60
890	25c. Map of Europe and Cypriot church		70	1·25
MS891	95×86 mm. 50c. Peace Dove (42×30 mm); 50c. European Cultural Month symbol (42×30 mm). P 13½		5·00	7·00

A limited quantity of No. **MS**891 was surcharged '£5' on each stamp and sold at Europhilex '95 on 27 and 28 October 1995.

(Litho Oriental Press, Bahrain)

1995 (24 Oct). Obligatory Tax. Refugee Fund. As T **255**, but reduced in size and inscr '1995', '1996', '1997', '1998', '1999', '2000' or '2001'. Chalk-surfaced paper. P 14½×13½.

| 892 | **255** | 1c. brownish black and olive-grey (shades) | 10 | 10 |

301 Peace Dove with Flags of Cyprus and United Nations

302 Reliquary from Kykko Monastery

(Des Soteris Hadjimichael (10, 25c.), Stelios Karamallakis (15c.), Ermis Georgiades (20c.). Litho Oriental Press, Bahrain)

1995 (24 Oct). Anniversaries and Events. T **301** and similar multicoloured designs. P 13×13½ (horiz) or 13½×13 (vert).

893	10c. Type **301** (50th Anniversary of United Nations)	50	35
894	15c. Hand pushing ball over net (Centenary of volleyball) (vert)	95	50
895	20c. Safety pin on leaf (European Nature Conservation Year) (vert)	1·10	80
896	25c. Clay pigeon contestant (World Clay Target Shooting Championship)	1·25	2·25
893/896 Set of 4		3·50	3·50

(Des Stelios Karamallakis. Litho Oriental Press, Bahrain)

1995 (27 Nov). Christmas. T **302** and similar vert designs showing different reliquaries of Virgin and Child from Kykko Monastery. P 13½×13.

897	7c. multicoloured	45	15
898	20c. multicoloured	1·10	45
899	25c. multicoloured	1·40	2·25
897/899 Set of 3		2·75	2·50

303 Family (25th Anniversary of Pancyprian Organisation of Large Families)

304 Maria Synglitiki

(Des Liza Petridou-Mala. Litho Oriental Press, Bahrain)

1996 (4 Jan). Anniversaries and Events. T **303** and similar vert designs. Multicoloured. P 13½×13.

900	10c. Type **303**	50	35
901	20c. Film camera (Centenary of cinema)	1·25	70
902	35c. Silhouette of parent and child in globe (50th Anniversary of UNICEF)	1·75	1·75
903	40c. '13' and Commonwealth emblem (13th Conference of Commonwealth Speakers and Presiding Officers)	1·75	2·75
900/903 Set of 4		4·75	5·00

(Des George Simonis. Litho Oriental Press, Bahrain)

1996 (8 Apr). Europa. Famous Women. T **304** and similar vert design. Multicoloured. P 14.

| 904 | 10c. Type **304** | 1·00 | 30 |
| 905 | 30c. Queen Caterina Cornaro | 2·00 | 2·75 |

305 High Jump

(Des Maximos Christou. Litho Oriental Press, Bahrain)

1996 (10 June). Centennial Olympic Games, Atlanta. T **305** and similar horiz designs. Multicoloured. P 13×13½.

906	10c. Type **305**	75	30
907	20c. Javelin	1·25	65
908	25c. Wrestling	1·40	1·10
909	30c. Swimming	1·60	2·50
906/909 Set of 4		4·50	4·00

306 Watermill

307 Icon of Our Lady of Iberia, Moscow

(Des Ermis Georgiades. Litho Oriental Press, Bahrain)

1996 (23 Sept). Mills. T **306** and similar vert designs. Multicoloured. P 13½×13.

910	10c. Type **306**	70	40
911	15c. Olivemill	85	50
912	20c. Windmill	1·00	90
913	25c. Handmill	1·10	2·00
910/913 Set of 4		3·25	3·50

(Des Demetry Komissarov (Nos. 914, 917), George Simonis (Nos. 915/916). Litho State Ptg Wks, Moscow)

1996 (13 Nov). Cyprus–Russia Joint Issue. Orthodox Religion. T **307** and similar square designs. Multicoloured. P 11½.

914	30c. Type **307**	1·75	2·00
	a. Block of 4. Nos. 914/917	6·00	7·00
915	30c. Stravrovouni Monastery, Cyprus	1·75	2·00
916	30c. Icon of St Nicholas, Cyprus	1·75	2·00
917	30c. Voskresenskle Gate, Moscow	1·75	2·00
914/917 Set of 4		6·00	7·00

Nos. 914/917 were printed together, se-tenant, in blocks of four throughout the sheet.

Stamps in similar designs were also issued by Russia.

308 The Nativity (detail)

(Des George Koumouros. Litho Oriental Press, Bahrain)

1996 (2 Dec). Christmas. Religious Murals from Church of the Virgin of Asinou. T **308** and similar multicoloured designs. P 13½×13 (25c.) or 13×13½ (others).

918	7c. Type **308**	60	15
919	20c. Virgin Mary between the Archangels Gabriel and Michael	1·50	45
920	25c. Christ bestowing Blessing (vert)	1·90	2·75
918/920 Set of 3		3·50	3·00

309 Basketball

310 The Last Supper

(Des Stelios Karamallakis. Litho Oriental Press, Bahrain)

1997 (24 Mar). Final of European Basketball Cup. P 13½×13.

| 921 | **309** | 30c. multicoloured | 2·25 | 2·00 |

(Des George Koumouros. Litho Oriental Press, Bahrain)

1997 (24 Mar). Easter. Religious Frescoes from Monastery of St John Lambadestis. T **310** and similar horiz design. Multicoloured. P 13×13½.

922	15c. Type **310**	1·00	50
923	25c. *The Crucifixion*	1·25	1·50

311 Kori Kourelleni and Prince

312 *Oedipoda miniata* (Grasshopper)

(Des Liza Petridou-Mala. Litho Oriental Press, Bahrain)

1997 (5 May). Europa. Tales and Legends. T **311** and similar vert design. Multicoloured. P 13½×13.

924	15c. Type **311**	1·00	40
925	30c. Digenis and Charon	1·75	2·50

(Des Andreas Ladommatos. Litho Oriental Press, Bahrain)

1997 (30 June). Insects. T **312** and similar horiz designs. Multicoloured. P 13×13½.

926	10c. Type **312**	65	30
927	15c. *Acherontia atropos* (Death's Head Hawk Moth)	95	40
928	25c. *Daphnis nerii* (Oleander Hawk Moth)	1·60	1·25
929	35c. *Ascalaphus macaronius* (Owlfly)	1·75	2·50
926/929 *Set of 4*		4·50	4·00

313 Archbishop Makarios III and Chapel

314 The Nativity

(Des Charis Sophocleous Litho Oriental Press, Bahrain)

1997 (1 Aug). 20th Death Anniversary of Archbishop Makarios III. P 13×13½.

930	**313** 15c. multicoloured	1·25	50

(Des George Koumouros. Litho Oriental Press, Bahrain)

1997 (17 Nov). Christmas. Byzantine Frescos from the Monastery of St John Lambadestis. T **314** and similar vert designs. Multicoloured. P 13½×13.

931	10c. Type **314**	60	15
932	25c. Three Kings following the star	1·75	60
933	30c. Flight into Egypt	1·90	2·75
931/933 *Set of 3*		3·75	3·25

315 Green Jasper

316 Players competing for Ball

(Des Andreas Ladommatos. Litho Oriental Press, Bahrain)

1998 (9 Mar). Minerals. T **315** and similar horiz designs. Multicoloured. P 13.

934	10c. Type **315**	1·00	30
935	15c. Iron Pyrite	1·25	55
936	25c. Gypsum	1·75	1·25
937	30c. Chalcedony	1·75	3·25
934/937 *Set of 4*		5·25	4·75

(Des Charis Sophocleous. Litho Oriental Press, Bahrain)

1998 (4 May). World Cup Football Championship, France. P 14.

938	**316** 35c. multicoloured	1·75	1·40

317 Cataclysmos Festival, Larnaca

(Des Sakis Vassiliou (15c.), Andreas Ladommatos (30c.). Litho Oriental Press, Bahrain)

1998 (4 May). Europa. Festivals. T **317** and similar horiz design. Multicoloured. P 14.

939	15c. Type **317**	1·25	40
940	30c. House of Representatives, Nicosia (Declaration of Independence)	1·75	2·50

318 Mouflon Family Group

(Des Sotiris Hadjimichael. Litho Oriental Press, Bahrain)

1998 (22 June). Endangered Species. Cyprus Mouflon. T **318** and similar horiz designs. Multicoloured. P 13×13½.

941	25c. Type **318**	1·50	1·90
	a. Block of 4. Nos. 941/944	5·50	7·00
942	25c. Mouflon herd	1·50	1·90
943	25c. Head of Ram	1·50	1·90
944	25c. Ram on guard	1·50	1·90
941/944 *Set of 4*		5·50	7·00

Nos. 941/944 were printed together, *se-tenant*, in blocks of four throughout the sheet.

(Litho Oriental Press, Bahrain)

1998 (22 June). As No. 876, but different printer. White paper. With imprint date ('1998'). P 14.

958	£1 Townswoman wearing festive sarka	5·50	4·50

319 Flames and Globe Emblem

320 World 'Stamp' and Magnifying Glass

(Des Sakis Vassiliou. Litho Oriental Press, Bahrain)

1998 (9 Oct). 50th Anniversary of Universal Declaration of Human Rights. P 14.

959	**319** 50c. multicoloured	1·25	1·60

(Des Theodoros Kakoullis. Litho Oriental Press, Bahrain)

1998 (9 Oct). World Stamp Day. P 14.

960	**320** 30c. multicoloured	1·60	1·60
	a. Booklet pane of 8	13·00	

No. 960a has the horizontal edges of the pane imperforate and margins at left and right.

321 The Annunciation

322 *Pleurotus eryngii*

(Des Theodoros Kakoullis. Litho Oriental Press, Bahrain)

1998 (16 Nov). Christmas. T **321** and similar vert designs showing religious murals. Multicoloured. P 14.

961	10c. Type **321**	75	20

962	25c. The Nativity	1·75	75
963	30c. The Baptism of Christ	1·75	3·25
961/3 *Set of 3*		3·75	3·75
MS964 102×75 mm. Nos. 961/963		3·75	4·50

(Des Sakis Vassiliou. Litho Oriental Press, Bahrain)

1999 (4 Mar). Mushrooms of Cyprus. T **322** and similar vert designs. Multicoloured. P 13½×13.

965	10c. Type **322**	55	30
966	15c. *Lactarius deliciosus*	85	50
967	25c. *Sparassis crispa*	1·25	1·00
968	30c. *Morchella elata*	1·75	3·00
965/968 *Set of 4*		4·00	4·25

323 Pair of Mouflons at Tripylos Reserve

324 Council of Europe Building, Emblem and Flags

(Des Eleni Lambrou. Litho Oriental Press, Bahrain)

1999 (6 May). Europa. Parks and Gardens. T **323** and similar horiz design. Multicoloured. P 14.

969	15c. Type **323**	1·00	75
	a. Booklet pane. Nos. 969/970, each×4, with margins all round	11·00	
970	30c. Turtles on beach at Lara Reserve	2·00	2·50

(Des Stella Symeonidou. Litho Oriental Press, Bahrain)

1999 (6 May). 50th Anniversary of Council of Europe. P 14.

971	**324**	30c. multicoloured	1·50	2·00

325 Temple of Hylates Apollo, Kourion

326 Paper Aeroplane Letters and UPU Emblem

(Des Andreas Ladommatos. Des Alexandros Matsoukis, Athens)

1999 (28 June). Cyprus–Greece Joint Issue. 4000 Years of Greek Culture. T **325** and similar vert designs. Multicoloured. P 13½×13.

972	25c. Type **325**	1·50	1·90
	a. Block of 4. Nos. 972/975	5·50	7·00
973	25c. Mycenaean pot depicting warriors	1·50	1·90
974	25c. Mycenaean crater depicting horse	1·50	1·90
975	25c. Temple of Apollo, Delphi	1·50	1·90
972/975 *Set of 4*		5·50	7·00

Nos. 972/975 were printed together, *se-tenant*, in blocks of four throughout the sheet.

(Des Sakis Vassiliou. Litho Oriental Press, Bahrain)

1999 (4 Oct). 125th Anniversary of Universal Postal Union. T **326** and similar horiz design. Multicoloured. P 14.

976	15c. Type **326**	1·00	50
977	35c. '125' and UPU emblem	1·75	2·25

327 Container Ship and Cypriot Flag

(Des Thompson Communications. Litho Oriental Press, Bahrain)

1999 (4 Oct). Maritime Cyprus '99 Conference. Sheet 103×80 mm, containing T **327** and similar horiz designs. Multicoloured. P 14*.

MS978 25c. Type **327**; 25c. Binoculars and chart; 25c. Stern of container ship; 25c. Tanker .... 3·75 4·25

* On No. **MS**978 the row of perforations across the foot of the lower pair gauges 13.

328 Cypriot Refugee Fund Stamps and Barbed Wire (*Illustration further reduced. Actual size* 110×75 *mm*)

(Des Glafkos Theofylactou. Litho Oriental Press, Bahrain)

1999 (11 Nov). 25th Anniversary of Turkish Landings in Cyprus. Sheet 110×75 mm. Imperf.

MS979 **328** 30c. multicoloured .... 2·00 2·75

329 Angel

330 Woman's Silhouette with Stars and Globe

(Des Glafkos Theofylactou. Litho Oriental Press, Bahrain)

1999 (11 Nov). Christmas. T **329** and similar vert designs. Multicoloured. P 14.

980	10c. Type **329**	70	10
981	25c. The Three Kings	1·50	70
982	30c. Madonna and Child	1·60	3·00
980/982 *Set of 3*		2·50	2·50

(Des Glafkos Theofylaktou. Litho Oriental Press, Bahrain)

2000 (2 Mar). Miss Universe Beauty Contest Cyprus. Sheet 80×65 mm containing T **330** and similar vert design. Multicoloured. P 13½×13.

MS983 15c. Type **330**; 35c. Statue of Aphrodite and apple .... 2·75 3·00

331 Necklace, 4500–4000 BC

332 Building Europa

(Des A. Koutas. Litho Oriental Press, Bahrain)

2000 (30 Mar). Jewellery. T **331** and similar multicoloured designs. P 14.

984	10c. Type **331**	55	30
985	15c. Gold earrings, 3rd-century BC	75	40
986	20c. Gold earring from Lampousa, 6th/7th-century	85	60
987	25c. Brooch, 19th-century	85	60
988	30c. Gold cross, 6th/7th-century	1·10	75
989	35c. Necklace, 18th/19th-century	1·25	1·00
990	40c. Gold earring, 19th-century	1·75	1·00
991	50c. Spiral hair ring, 5th/4th-century BC	2·00	1·25
992	75c. Gold-plated silver plaques from Gialia, 700–600 BC (*horiz*)	2·75	2·75
993	£1 Gold frontlet from Egkomi, 14th/13th-century BC (*horiz*)	4·50	3·25
994	£2 Gold necklace from Egkomi, 13th-century BC (*horiz*)	8·00	8·00
995	£3 Buckles, 19th-century (*horiz*)	12·00	13·00
984/995 *Set of 12*		32·00	30·00

(Des Jean Paul Cousin. Litho Oriental Press, Bahrain)

2000 (9 May). Europa. P 14.

996	**332**	30c. multicoloured	2·50	2·50

333 '50', Cross and Map of Cyprus

334 Flame, Map of Cyprus and Broken Chain

(Des Liza Petridou. Litho Oriental Press, Bahrain)

2000 (9 May). 50th Anniversary of Red Cross in Cyprus. P 13×13½

| 997 | **333** | 15c. multicoloured | 2·25 | 1·50 |

(Des Andreas Ladommatos. Litho Oriental Press, Bahrain)

2000 (9 May). 45th Anniversary of Struggle for Independence. P 13½×13.

| 998 | **334** | 15c. multicoloured | 2·25 | 1·50 |

335 Weather Balloon, Map and Satellite

336 Monastery of Antifontis, Kalograia

(Des Liza Petridou. Litho Oriental Press, Bahrain)

2000 (9 May). 50th Anniversary of World Meteorological Organisation. P 14.

| 999 | **335** | 30c. multicoloured | 2·50 | 2·50 |

(Des Andreas Koutas. Litho Oriental Press, Bahrain)

2000 (29 June). Greek Orthodox Churches in Northern Cyprus. T **336** and similar designs. P 13½×13 (10c. and 15c.) or 13×13½ (25c. and 30c.).

1000	10c. red-brown and carmine	70	25
1001	15c. deep bluish green and bottle green	1·00	45
1002	25c. deep slate-violet and reddish violet	1·40	1·10
1003	30c. carmine-red and grey	1·50	2·50
1000/1003 *Set of 4*		4·25	3·75

Designs: Vert—10c. T **336**; 15c. Church of St Themonianos, Lysi. Horiz—25c. Church of Panagia Kanakaria, Lytrhagkomi; 30c. Church of Avgasida Monastery, Milia.

337 Council of Europe Emblem

(Des Stella Symeonidou. Litho Oriental Press, Bahrain)

2000 (29 June). 50th Anniversary of European Convention of Human Rights. P 13½×13½.

| 1004 | **337** | 30c. multicoloured | 2·00 | 2·00 |

338 Archery

(Des Maximos Christou. Litho Oriental Press, Bahrain)

2000 (14 Sept). Olympic Games, Sydney. T **338** and similar horiz designs. Multicoloured. P 13×13½.

1005	10c. Type **338**	70	25
1006	15c. Gymnastics	90	40
1007	25c. Diving	1·40	1·00
1008	35c. Trampolining	1·60	3·00
1005/1008 *Set of 4*		4·25	4·25

339 The Annunciation

340 '25' and Commonwealth Symbol

(Des Nicolas Ladommatos. Litho Oriental Press, Bahrain)

2000 (2 Nov). Christmas. Gold Gospel Covers. T **339** and similar vert designs. Multicoloured. P 13½×13.

1009	10c. Type **339**	75	25
1010	25c. *The Nativity*	1·75	80
1011	30c. *The Baptism of Christ*	1·75	3·25
1009/1011 *Set of 3*		3·75	3·75

(Des George Simonis. Litho Oriental Press, Bahrain)

2001 (12 Mar). 25th Anniversary of Commonwealth Day. P 13.

| 1012 | **340** | 30c. multicoloured | 1·75 | 2·00 |

341 Silhouette, Dove and Barbed Wire

342 Pavlos Liasides

(Des Stella Symeonidou. Litho Oriental Press, Bahrain)

2001 (12 Mar). 50th Anniversary of United Nations High Commissioner for Refugees. P 13.

| 1013 | **341** | 30c. multicoloured | 1·75 | 2·00 |

(Des Andreas Ladommatos. Litho Oriental Press, Bahrain)

2001 (12 Mar). Birth Centenary of Pavlos Liasides (poet). P 13.

| 1014 | **342** | 13c. chocolate, ochre and yellow-brown | 1·25 | 60 |

343 Bridge over River Diarizos

(Des Georgia Koulendrou. Litho Oriental Press, Bahrain)

2001 (3 May). Europa. Cypriot Rivers. T **343** and similar horiz design. Multicoloured. P 13×13½.

1015	20c. Type **343**	1·00	75
	a. Booklet pane. Nos. 1015/1016, each×4, with margins all round	11·00	
1016	30c. Mountain torrent, River Akaki	2·00	2·50

344 Parthenope massena

(Des Sakis Vassiliou. Litho Oriental Press, Bahrain)

2001 (7 June). Crabs. T **344** and similar horiz designs. Multicoloured. P 13×13½.

1017	13c. Type **344**	75	20
1018	20c. *Calappa granulate*	1·25	1·00
1019	25c. *Ocypode cursor*	1·50	1·25
1020	30c. *Pagurus bernhardus*	2·00	3·25
1017/1020 *Set of 4*		5·00	5·00

345 Icon of Virgin Mary

346 Loukis Akritas

(Des Glafkos Theofylactou. Litho Alexandros Matsoukis, Athens)

2001 (25 Oct). Christmas. 800th Anniversary of Macheras Monastery. T **345** and similar vert designs. Multicoloured. P 13½×13.

1021	13c. Type **345**	70	20
1022	25c. Macheras Monastery	1·50	75
1023	30c. Ornate gold crucifix	2·00	3·25
1021/1023	Set of 3	3·75	3·75

(Des Andreas Ladommatos. Litho Alexandros Matsoukis, Athens)

2001 (25 Oct). Loukis Akritas (writer). Commemoration. P 13½ ×13.

1024	**346**	20c. brown-olive and olive-bistre	1·75	1·50

347 Tortoiseshell and White Cat

348 Acrobat on Horseback

(Des Andreas Koutas. Litho Alexandros Matsoukis, Athens)

2002 (21 Mar). Cats. T **347** and similar horiz designs. Multicoloured. P 13×13½.

1025	20c. Type **347**	1·50	2·00
	a. Pair. Nos. 1025/1026	3·00	4·00
1026	20c. British Blue	1·50	2·00
1027	25c. Tortoiseshell and White	1·50	2·00
	a. Pair. Nos. 1027/1028	3·00	4·00
1028	25c. Red and Silver tabby	1·50	2·00
1025/1028	Set of 4	5·50	7·25

Nos. 1025/1026 and 1027/1028 were each printed together, *se-tenant*, as horizontal and vertical pairs throughout the sheets of 16.

(Des Glafkos Theofylactou. Litho Alexandros Matsoukis, Athens)

2002 (9 May). Europa. Circus. T **348** and similar vert design. Multicoloured. P 13½ ×13.

1029	20c. Type **348**	1·00	75
	a. Booklet pane. Nos. 1029/1030, each×4 with margins all round	11·00	
1030	30c. Clown on high wire	2·00	2·50

349 *Myrtus communis*

350 Mother Teresa

(Des Maria Trillidou. Litho Alexandros Matsoukis, Athens)

2002 (13 June). Medicinal Plants. T **349** and similar horiz designs. Multicoloured. P 13×13½.

1031	13c. Type **349**	1·00	30
1032	20c. *Lavandula stoechas*	1·50	1·25
1033	25c. *Capparis spinosa*	1·75	1·50
1034	30c. *Ocimum basilicum*	2·25	3·25
1031/1034	Set of 4	6·00	5·75

(Des Toula Paphitou. Litho A. Matsoukis, Athens)

2002 (12 Sept). Mother Teresa (founder of Missionaries of Charity) Commemoration. P 13½×13.

1035	**350**	40c. multicoloured	2·75	2·75

351 Blackboard on Easel

(Des Katia Georgiadou. Litho A. Matsoukis, Athens)

2002 (12 Sept). International Teachers' Day. T **351** and similar horiz design. Multicoloured. P 13×13½.

1036	13c. Type **351**	1·50	1·75
	a. Horiz pair. Nos. 1036/1037	3·75	4·50
1037	30c. Computer	2·25	2·75

Nos. 1036/1037 were printed together, *se-tenant*, as horizontal pairs throughout sheets of 20.

352 Agate Seal-stone (5th-century BC)

(Des Glafkos Theofylaktou and Nicos Rangos (No. **MS**1044) or Glafkos Theofylaktou (others). Litho A. Matsoukis, Athens)

2002 (22 Oct). Cyprus–Europhilex '02, Stamp Exhibition, Nicosia. Cypriot Antiquities showing Europa. T **352** and similar horiz designs. Multicoloured. P 13×13½.

1038	20c. Type **352**	1·25	1·50
	a. Horiz strip of 3. Nos. 1038/1040	3·25	4·00
1039	20c. Silver coin of Timochares (5th/4th-century BC)	1·25	1·50
1040	20c. Silver coin of Stasioikos (5th-century BC)	1·25	1·50
1041	30c. Clay lamp (green backgound) (2nd-century AD)	1·50	1·75
	a. Horiz strip of 3. Nos. 1041/1043	4·00	4·75
1042	30c. Statuette of Europa on the Bull (7th/6th-century BC)	1·50	1·75
1043	30c. Clay lamp (purple backgound) (1st-century BC)	1·50	1·75
1038/1043	Set of 6	7·50	8·75
MS1044	105×71 mm. 50c. Statue of Aphrodite with maps of Crete and Cyprus; 50c. *Europa on the Bull* (painting by Francesco di Giogio)	7·00	8·00

Nos. 1038/1040 and 1041/1043 were each printed together, *se-tenant*, as horizontal strips of three throughout sheets of 12.

353 Nativity

(Des Andreas Koutas. Litho A. Matsoukis, Athens)

2002 (21 Nov). Christmas. Details from *Birth of Christ* (wall painting), Church of Metamorphosis Sotiros, Palechori. T **353** and similar multicoloured designs. P 13½ (30c.) or 13×13½ (others).

1045	13c. Type **353**	1·00	20
1046	25c. Three Wise Men	2·00	1·00
1047	30c. *Birth of Christ* (complete painting) (38×38 mm)	2·50	3·75
1045/1047	Set of 3	5·00	4·50

354 Triumph Roadster 1800, 1946

355 'POSTER IS ART'

(Des Glafkos Theofylaktou. Litho A. Matsoukis, Athens)

2003 (20 Mar). International Historic Car Rally. T **354** and similar horiz designs. Multicoloured. P 13.

1048	20c. Type **354**	1·75	3·00
	a. Vert strip of 3. Nos. 1048/1050	4·75	5·50
1049	25c. Ford model T, 1917	1·75	2·00
1050	30c. Baby Ford Y 8hp, 1932	1·75	2·00
1048/1050 Set of 3		4·75	5·50

Nos. 1048/1050 were printed together, *se-tenant*, in vertical strips of three throughout the sheet.

(Des Sakis Vassiliou. Litho A. Matsoukis, Athens)

2003 (5 May). Europa. Poster Art. P 13½×13.

1051	**355**	20c. multicoloured	1·00	50
		a. Perf 13½	1·00	1·50
		b. Booklet pane. Nos. 1051/1052, each×4	9·00	
1052	–	30c. multicoloured	1·50	2·00
		a. Perf 13½	1·50	2·25

Nos. 1051a and 1052a were only issued in £2 booklets, No. SB5.
Booklet pane No. 1051b has the horizontal edges of the pane imperforate and margins at left and right.

356 Bat in Flight

357 Stylised Owl

(Des Owen Bell. Litho A. Matsoukis, Athens)

2003 (12 June). Endangered Species. Mediterranean Horseshoe Bat. T **356** and similar horiz designs. Multicoloured. P 13×13½.

1053	25c. Type **356**	1·25	2·00
	a. Block of 4. Nos. 1053/1056	5·50	7·25
1054	25c. Head of Bat (facing forwards)	1·50	2·00
1055	25c. Bats roosting	1·50	2·00
1056	25c. Head of Bat (facing sideways, mouth open)	1·50	2·00
1053/1056 Set of 4		5·50	7·25

Nos. 1053/1056 were printed together, *se-tenant*, in blocks of four throughout sheets of 16.

(Des Sakis Vassiliou. Litho A. Matsoukis, Athens)

2003 (12 June). Seventh Conference of European Ministers of Education, Nicosia. P 13½×13.

1057	**357**	30c. multicoloured	2·00	2·25

358 Eleonora's Falcon

359 Constantinos Spyridakis (historian, author and Minister of Education 1965–1970)

(Des Glafkos Theofylaktou. Litho A. Matsoukis, Athens)

2003 (25 Sept). Birds of Prey. T **358** and similar triangular designs. Multicoloured. P 14.

1058	20c. Type **358**	1·75	2·00
	a. Horiz pair. Nos. 1058/1059	3·50	4·00
1059	20c. Eleonora's Falcon in flight	1·75	2·00
1060	25c. Imperial Eagle	1·75	2·00
	a. Horiz pair. Nos. 1060/1061	3·50	4·00
1061	25c. Imperial Eagle in flight	1·75	2·00
1062	30c. Little Owl	1·75	2·00
	a. Horiz pair. Nos. 1062/1063	3·50	4·00
1063	30c. Little Owl in flight and eggs in nest	1·75	2·00
1058/1063 Set of 6		9·50	11·00

Nos. 1058/1059, 1060/1061 and 1062/1063 were each printed together, *se-tenant*, in horizontal pairs in sheets of 12.

(Des Stella Symeonidou. Litho A. Matsoukis, Athens)

2003 (13 Nov). Birth Centenaries of T **359** and similar design. P 13×13½ (No. 1064) or 13½×13 (No. 1065).

1064	5c. black and drab	65	1·00
1065	5c. blackish olive and grey-olive	65	1·00

Design: 23×31 mm.—No. 1065, Tefkros Anthias (poet). Horiz—No. 1064, T **359**.

360 Three Angels

361 Stylised Footballer

(Des Pana Kazazi El-Alwani and Melanie Efsthathiadou. Litho A. Matsoukis, Athens)

2003 (13 Nov). Christmas. T **360** and similar multicoloured designs. P 13 (13, 30c) or 14 (40c).

1066	13c. Type **360**	1·00	20
1067	30c. Three Wise Men	2·00	1·00
1068	40c. Nativity (37×59 mm)	2·50	3·75
1066/1068 Set of 3		5·00	4·50

Nos. 1066/1067 show details from icon of Nativity in Church of Virgin Mary, Kourdali. No. 1068 shows the complete painting.

(Des Elena Eliadou. Litho A. Matsoukis, Athens)

2004 (11 Mar). Centenary of FIFA (Fédération Internationale de Football Association). P 13½.

1069	**361**	30c. multicoloured	1·75	2·00

362 Stylised Footballer

363 Flags of New Member Countries

(Des Kakia Katselli. Litho A. Matsoukis, Athens)

2004 (11 Mar). 50th Anniversary of UEFA (Union of European Football Associations). P 13½×13.

1070	**362**	30c. multicoloured	1·75	2·00

(Des Jean Pierre Mizzi. Litho A. Matsoukis, Athens)

2004 (1 May). Enlargement of the European Union. P 14.

1071	**363**	30c. multicoloured	1·75	2·00

364 Yiannos Kranidiotis and EU Emblem

365 Sailing Boat and Ancient Amphitheatre

(Des Nicolas Ladommatos. Litho A. Matsoukis, Athens)

2004 (1 May). Fifth Death Anniversary of Yiannos Kranidiotis (politician). P 13×13½.

1072	**364**	20c. multicoloured	1·50	1·00

(Des Melanie Efstathiadou. Litho A. Matsoukis, Athens)

2004 (1 May). Europa. Holidays. T **365** and similar horiz design. Multicoloured. P 13½.

1073	20c. Type **365**	1·00	1·00
	a. Booklet pane. Nos. 1073/1074, each×4	10·00	
1074	30c. Family at seaside and statue	1·75	2·50

The exact gauge of the perforations on the sheet stamps is 13.7×13.3, but stamps from the booklet pane measure 13.7 all round.
Booklet pane No. 1073a has the horizontal edges of the pane imperforate and margins at left and right.

366 Horse Racing

(Des Glafkos Theofylaktou. Litho Alexandros Matsoukis)

2004 (10 June). Olympic Games, Athens. T **366** and similar horiz designs showing ancient Olympic sports. Multicoloured. P 13×13½.

1075	13c. Type **366**	80	35
1076	20c. Running	1·25	60
1077	30c. Diving	1·50	1·10
1078	40c. Discus	1·75	3·50
1075/1078 Set of 4		4·75	5·00

367 Dolphin   **368** Choir of Angels

(Des Antonia Hadjigeorgiou. Litho Alexandros Matsoukis)

2004 (9 Sept). Mammals. T **367** and similar horiz designs. Multicoloured. P 13½.

1079	20c. Type **367**	1·50	1·50
1080	20c. Dolphin (blue background)	1·50	1·50
1081	30c. Fox (white background)	1·75	1·75
1082	30c. Fox (green background)	1·75	1·75
1083	40c. Hare (white background)	2·00	2·00
1084	40c. Hare (yellow background)	2·00	2·00
1079/1084 Set of 6		9·50	9·50

(Des Liza Petridou-Mala. Litho Alexandros Matsoukis)

2004 (11 Nov). Christmas. T **368** and similar multicoloured designs. P 14×13½ (13c., 30c.) or 14 (40c., £1).

1085	13c. Type **368**	1·00	20
1086	30c. Three Wise Men	2·00	1·00
1087	40c. Annunciation to the Shepherds (37×60 mm)	2·50	3·75
1085/1087 Set of 3		5·00	4·50
MS1088 63×84 mm. £1 Virgin and Child (38×38 mm)		7·00	8·00

The stamp in No. **MS**1088 was printed along the bottom edge of the sheet and was imperforate at foot.

369 Georgios Philippou Pierides   **370** Carolina Pelendritou and Medal

(Des Liza Petridou-Mala. Litho Alexandros Matsoukis)

2004 (11 Nov). Intellectual Personalities. T **369** and similar vert design. Multicoloured. P 13½×13.

1089	5c. Type **369**	65	1·00
1090	5c. Emilios Chourmouzios (wearing tie)	65	1·00

Nos. 1091/1092 were relisted. See No. 807.

(Des Antonia Hadjigeorgiou. Litho A. Matsoukis, Athens)

2005 (3 Mar). Carolina Pelendritou's Gold Medal for 100 Metres Swimming at Paralympic Games, Athens (2004). P 13½×14.

1093	**370**	20c. multicoloured	1·50	1·00

371 Emblem   **372** The Entrance (Kyriacos Koulli)

(Des Antonia Hadjigeorgiou. Litho A. Matsoukis, Athens)

2005 (3 Mar). Centenary of Rotary International. P 13½×14.

1094	**371**	40c. multicoloured	1·40	1·90

(Des Antonia Hadjigeorgiou. Litho A. Matsoukis, Athens)

2005 (3 Mar). 50th Anniversary of EOKA Struggle. P 13½×14.

1095	**372**	50c. multicoloured	2·00	2·50

373 Table with Fish, Casserole, Wine, Garlic, Tomato and Bread   **374** German Shepherd Dog and Police Dog with Handler

(Des Glafkos Theofylactou. Litho Alexandros Matsoukis)

2005 (5 May). Europa. Gastronomy. T **373** and similar vert design. Multicoloured. P 13½×13.

1096	20c. Type **373**	1·00	50
	a. Perf 13½×14	1·00	1·50
	ab. Booklet pane. Nos. 1096a/1097a, each×4	9·00	
1097	30c. Table with coffee, cheese, cocktail and desserts	1·50	2·00
	a. Perf 13½×14	1·50	2·25

No. 1096a has no white margins at left and No. 1097a has no white margins at right.

Nos. 1096a and 1097a were only issued in horizontal pairs, each pair forming a composite design, from booklet pane No. 1096ab from £2 booklets, No. SB7.

Booklet pane No. 1096ab has the horizontal edges imperforate and margins at left and right.

(Des Nicolas Ladommatos. Litho Alexandros Matsoukis)

2005 (16 June). Dogs in Man's Life. T **374** and similar square designs. Multicoloured. P 13½.

1098	13c. Type **374**	85	30
	a. Booklet pane. Nos. 1098/1101 with margins all round	5·25	
1099	20c. Hungarian Vizsla and hunter with Dog	1·25	85
1100	30c. Labrador and man with Guide Dog	1·75	1·40
1101	40c. Dalmatian and boy with pet Dog	2·00	3·00
1098/1101 Set of 4		5·25	5·00

375 Angel appearing to Shepherds

(Des Melanie Efstathiadou. Litho Alexandros Matsoukis)

2005 (10 Nov). Christmas. T **375** and similar multicoloured designs. P 13½ (13, 30c.) or 14 (40c.).

1102	13c. Type **375**	1·00	20
1103	30c. Holy Family and shepherds	2·00	1·00
1104	40c. Virgin Mary and Jesus Christ (37×59 mm)	2·50	3·75
1102/1104 Set of 3		5·00	4·50

Nos. 1102/1103 show details from icon Birth of Christ and No. 1104 shows icon of the Virgin Mary Karmiotissa.

376 1964 150c. Flower Stamp

(Des Melanie Efstathiadou. Litho Alexandros Matsoukis)

2006 (23 Feb). 50th Anniversary of First Europa Stamp. T **376** and similar square designs showing Cyprus Europa stamps. Multicoloured. P 14.

MS1105 94×84 mm. 30c. Type **376**; 30c. 1962 40m. Doves stamp; 30c. 1963 40m. tree stamp; 30c. 1963 150m. CEPT stamp .... 4·00 5·50

The stamps within No. **MS**1105 have composite background designs.

377 '25' and Hand Stamp

378 Self-portrait and *The Anatomy Lesson of Dr. Nicolaes Tulp*

(Des Melanie Efstathiadou. Litho Alexandros Matsoukis)

2006 (30 Mar). 25th Anniversary of the Postal Museum, Nicosia. P 14×13½.
1106   **377**   25c. multicoloured .... 1·50   1·25

(Des Melanie Efstathiadou. Litho Alexandros Matsoukis)

2006 (30 Mar). 400th Birth Anniversary of Rembrandt (artist). P 14×13½.
1107   **378**   40c. multicoloured .... 2·75   2·75

379 Footballer kicking Ball

380 Stamna or Kouza (Pitcher) Dance, Cyprus

(Des Liza Petridou. Litho Alexandros Matsoukis)

2006 (30 Mar). World Cup Football Championship, Germany. P 13½×14.
1108   **379**   50c. multicoloured .... 2·25   2·75

(Des Glafkos Theofylactou. Litho Alexandros Matsoukis, Athens)

2006 (12 Apr). Folk Dances. Sheet 100×70 mm containing T **380** and similar horiz design. Multicoloured. P 13×13½.
MS1109 40c. Type **380**; 40c. Nati dance, Himachal
  Pradesh, India... 3·50   4·50
Stamps in similar designs were issued by India.

381 Stylised Hand and Swallow

382 *Elaeagnus angustifolia* (Olive)

(Des Sakis Vasiliou. Litho Alexandros Matsoukis, Athens)

2006 (4 May). Europa. Integration. Multicoloured, background colour given. P 13½×13.
1110   **381**   30c. bright green .... 1·75   50
      a. Perf 13½×14 .... 1·75   2·25
      ab. Booklet pane. Nos. 1110a/1111a,
        each×4.. 14·00
1111   40c. bright cerise-pink .... 2·00   2·75
      a. Perf 13½×14 .... 2·25   3·00
Nos. 1110a and 1111a were only issued in £2·80 booklets, No. SB9.
Booklet pane No. 1110ab has the horizontal edges of the pane imperforate and margins at left and right.

(Des Costas Panayi. Litho Alexandros Matsoukis)

2006 (15 June). Cyprus Fruits. T **382** and similar multicoloured designs. P 13½×14 (vert) or 14×13½ (horiz).
1112   20c. Type **382**...................................... 1·75   70
1113   25c. *Mespilus germanica* (Medlar) (horiz).......... 1·75   75
1114   60c. *Opuntia ficus barbarica* (Prickly Pear) .... 3·50   5·50
1112/1114 *Set of 3*... 6·25   6·25

383 Flowers and Silhouettes

(Des Melanie Efstathiadou. Litho Alexandros Matsoukis)

2006 (15 June). Transplants. P 13.
1115   **383**   13c. multicoloured .... 1·00   60

384 Bedford Water Carrier, 1997

385 Nicos Nicolaides

(Des Antonia Hadjigeorgiou. Litho Alexandros Matsoukis)

2006 (14 Sept). Fire Engines. T **384** and similar horiz designs. Multicoloured. P 14×13½.
1116   13c. Type **384**...................................... 1·75   40
1117   20c. Hino fire engine, 1994................... 2·25   1·00
1118   50c. Bedford fire engine with turntable
      ladder, 1959....................................... 3·75   5·00
1116/1118 *Set of 3*... 7·00   5·75

(Des Liza Petridou. Litho Alexandros Matsoukis)

2006 (16 Nov). 50th Death Anniversary of Nicos Nicolaides (writer). P 13½×13.
1119   **385**   5c. multicoloured 65   70

386 Wood-carved Iconostasis (Arsenios), 1868

387 *Antedon mediterranea* (Feather Star)

(Des Sophia Malekou. Litho Alexandros Matsoukis)

2006 (16 Nov). Christmas. T **386** and similar vert designs showing carvings from Agiou Eleftheriou Church, Nicosia. Multicoloured. P 13½×14.
1120   13c. Type **386**...................................... 1·00   25
1121   30c. Christ on the Cross from top of
      iconostasis.. 2·00   1·25
1122   40c. Stone bas-relief showing cross, spear
      and sponge.. 2·25   3·50
1120/1122 *Set of 3*... 4·75   4·50

(Des Ioanna Kalli. Litho Alexandros Matsoukis)

2007 (8 Feb). Echinodermata of Cyprus. T **387** and similar horiz designs. Multicoloured. P 14×13½.
1123   25c. Type **387**...................................... 1·75   2·00
      a. Horiz strip of 4. Nos. 1123/1126 .... 6·25   7·25
1124   25c. *Centrostephanus longispinus*
      (Sea Urchin)....................................... 1·75   2·00
1125   25c. *Astropecten jonstoni* (Starfish)......... 1·75   2·00
1126   25c. *Ophioderma longicaudum* (Brittle Star) ... 1·75   2·00
1123/1126 *Set of 4*... 6·25   7·25
Nos. 1123/1126 were printed together, *se-tenant*, in sheetlets of eight stamps containing two horizontal strips of four.

388 St Zenon the Postman

(Des Sophia Malekou. Litho Alexandros Matsoukis)

2007 (8 Feb). St Zenon the Postman. Sheet 75 ×65 mm. Imperf.
MS1127 **388** £1 multicoloured.................................... 7·50 9·00

389 Triumph Daytona T100R, 1972

(Des Xenia Christodoulou. Litho Alexandros Matsoukis)

2007 (15 Mar). Old Motorcycles. T **389** and similar horiz designs. Multicoloured. P 14×13½.
1128	13c.	Type **389**	90	30
1129	20c.	Matchless G3L, 1941	1·60	70
1130	40c.	BSA M20, 1940	2·25	2·00
1131	60c.	Ariel Red Hunter NH 359, 1939	2·50	3·75
1128/1131 *Set of 4*			6·50	6·00

390 Emblem   **391** Ear of Wheat and Scout Badge

(Des Melanie Efstathiadou. Litho Alexandros Matsoukis)

2007 (3 May). 50th Anniversary of the Treaty of Rome. P 13½×14.
1132	**390**	30c. multicoloured	1·40	1·75

(Des Melanie Efstathiadou. Litho and embossed Alexandros Matsoukis)

2007 (3 May). Europa. Centenary of Scouting. P 13½×14.
1133	**391**	30c. multicoloured	1·75	2·00
		a. Booklet pane. Nos. 1133/1134, each×4	14·00	
1134		40c. multicoloured	2·25	2·75

Booklet pane 1133a has the horizontal edges imperforate and margins at left and right.

392 '50' and Stylised Figures

(Des Sakis Vassiliou. Litho Alexandros Matsoukis)

2007 (14 June). 50th Anniversary of Social Insurance. T **392** and similar horiz design. Multicoloured. P 13×13½.
1135	40c.	Type **392** (inscr in Greek)	1·50	2·00
		a. Horiz pair. Nos. 1135/1136	3·00	4·00
1136	40c.	Stylised figures (at left) and '50' (inscr '50 YEARS OF SOCIAL INSURANCE' in English)	1·50	2·00

Nos. 1135/1136 were printed together, *se-tenant*, as horizontal pairs in sheets of 16 stamps, each pair forming a composite design.

393 Pygmy Hippopotamus, 10000 BC

(Des Melanie Efstathiadou, Glafkos Theofylactou and Liza Petridou. Litho Giesecke and Devrient Matsoukis, Greece)

2007 (2 Oct). Cyprus through the Ages (1st series). T **393** and similar square designs. Multicoloured. P 14.
1137	25c.	Type **393**	1·40	1·50
		a. Sheetlet of 8. Nos. 1137/1144	10·00	11·00
1138	25c.	Stone vessel, 7000 BC	1·40	1·50
1139	25c.	Ruins of Choirokoitia settlement of 7000 BC	1·40	1·50
1140	25c.	Figurine of a woman, 3000 BC	1·40	1·50
1141	25c.	Terracotta vessel, 2000 BC	1·40	1·50
1142	25c.	Greek inscription on a bronze skewer, 1000 BC	1·40	1·50
1143	25c.	Bird-shaped vessel, 800 BC	1·40	1·50
1144	25c.	Map of 1718 showing the ancient Kingdoms of Cyprus in the first millennium BC	1·40	1·50
1137/1144 *Set of 8*			10·00	11·00

Nos. 1137/1144 were printed together, *se-tenant*, in sheetlets of eight stamps.

See also Nos. 1170/1177, 1198/1205 and 1225/1232.

394 Limassol District Administration Building

(Des Antonis Farmakas and Melanie Efstathiadou. Litho Alexandros Matsoukis)

2007 (2 Oct). Neoclassical Buildings of Cyprus. T **394** and similar horiz designs. Multicoloured. P 14×13½.
1145	13c.	Type **394**	80	75
1146	15c.	National Bank of Greece Building, Nicosia	90	80
1147	20c.	Archaeological Research Unit's Building, Nicosia	1·10	95
1148	30c.	National Art Gallery Building, Nicosia	1·25	1·00
1149	40c.	Paphos Municipal Library Building	1·40	1·40
1150	50c.	Office Building of A. G. Leventis Foundation, Nicosia	1·75	2·00
1151	£1	Limassol Municipal Library Building	3·75	4·00
1152	£3	Phaneromeni Gymnasium Building, Nicosia	8·50	12·00
1145/1152 *Set of 8*			18·00	21·00

395 Virgin Mary and Christ Child

(Des Costas Panayi. Litho Giesecke and Devrient Matsoukis, Greece)

2007 (15 Nov). Christmas. T **395** and similar vert designs showing murals taken from Chapel of St Themonianus, Lysi. Multicoloured. P 14.
1153	13c.	Type **395**	80	20
1154	30c.	Archangel Gabriel	1·75	1·25
1155	40c.	Christ Pantocrater (34×44 *mm*)	2·25	2·75
1153/1155 *Set of 3*			4·25	3·75

(New Currency: 100 cents = 1 euro)

396 *Aphrodite* (statue) **397** *Cyprus 74* (wood-engraving by A. Tassos)

(Litho Giesecke and Devrient Matsoukis, Greece)

2008 (1 Jan). Adoption of the Euro Currency. Sheet 100×62 mm containing T **396** and similar square design. Multicoloured. P 14.
MS1156 €1 Type **396**; €1 *Sleeping Lady* Statuette of
Malta .... 7·50   9·00
No. **MS**1156 was denominated in both euros and Cyprus pounds.
A similar miniature sheet was issued by Malta.

(Litho Giesecke and Devrient Matsoukis, Greece)

2008 (1 Jan). Obigatory Tax. Refugee Fund. Design as T **255** but denominated in cents and euros as T **397**. Inscr '2008'. Chalk-surfaced paper. P 13½×14.
1157   **397**   2c. brownish black and brownish grey....................   15   15
See also Nos. 1181, 1218a, 1245, 1265, 1290, 1319, 1363, 1387, 1409 and 1431.

Nos. 1158/1169 were denominated in both euros and Cyprus pounds.

398 Pink Anemone **399** 'CYPRUS' on Letters

(Des Stelios Karamallakis. Litho Giesecke and Devrient Matsoukis, Greece)

2008 (6 Mar). *Anemone coronaria.* T **398** and similar vert designs. Multicoloured. P 13½×14.
1158   26c. Type **398**...................................   1·00   70
1159   34c. White Anemone.........................   1·25   90
1160   51c. Red Anemone.............................   1·90   1·90
1161   68c. Mauve Anemone........................   2·40   3·75
1158/1161 *Set of 4*.....................................   6·00   6·50

(Des Glafkos Theofylaktou. Litho Giesecke and Devrient Matsoukis)

2008 (2 May). Europa. The Letter. T **399** and similar vert design. Multicoloured. P 13½×14.
1162   51c. Type **399**...................................   1·75   2·00
       a. Booklet pane. Nos. 1162/1163, each×4...   14·00
1163   68c. 'CYPRUS' on ballot boxes..............   2·25   2·75
Booklet pane No. 1162a has the horizontal edges imperforate and margins at left and right.

400 Ancient Pottery Vase and Silver Vase

(Des Sophia Malekou. Litho Giesecke and Devrient Matsoukis)

2008 (2 May). Fourth International Congress of Cypriot Studies, Nicosia. Sheet 75×65 mm. P 14×imperf (at foot).
MS1164   **400**   85c. multicoloured ....   4·50   5·50

401 Windsurfing **402** Emblem

(Des Theodoros Kakoulis. Litho Giesecke and Devrient Matsoukis)

2008 (5 June). Olympic Games, Beijing. T **401** and similar horiz designs. Multicoloured. P 13×13½.
1165   22c. Type **401**...................................   90   55
1166   34c. High jump..................................   1·40   1·00
1167   43c. Volleyball....................................   1·90   2·00
1168   51c. Shooting.....................................   2·50   3·00
1165/1168 *Set of 4*.....................................   6·00   6·00

(Des Sakis Vassiliou. Litho Giesecke & Devrient Matsoukis)

2008 (5 June). 12th Francophone Summit, Québec. P 14.
1169   **402**   85c. multicoloured ....   2·50   3·00

403 Coin, Archaic Period (750–480 BC) **404** Archangel Gabriel

(Des Liza Petridou and Melanie Efstathiadou. Litho Giesecke and Devrient Matsoukis)

2008 (2 Oct). Cyprus through the Ages (2nd series). T **403** and similar square designs. Multicoloured. P 14.
1170   43c. Type **403**...................................   1·25   1·50
       a. Sheetlet of 8. Nos. 1170/1177..............   9·00   11·00
1171   43c. Ancient ship, Archaic period (750–780 BC).................   1·25   1·50
1172   43c. Statue of Athenian General Kimon and sailing galley, Classical period (480–310 BC)................   1·25   1·50
1173   43c. Tombs of the Kings, Hellenistic period (310–30 BC)......   1·25   1·50
1174   43c. Coin, Hellenistic period (310–30 BC)...   1·25   1·50
1175   43c. St Paul (missionary to Cyprus, 45 AD)......   1·25   1·50
1176   43c. Bronze statue of Roman Emperor Septimus Severus, Roman period (30 BC–324 AD)....................   1·25   1·50
1177   43c. Granting of privileges to Church of Cyprus, Byzantine period (324–481 AD) .   1·25   1·50
1170/1177 *Set of 8*.....................................   9·00   11·00
Nos. 1170/1177 were printed together, *se-tenant*, in sheetlets of eight stamps.

(Des Antonia Hadjigeorgiou. Litho Geisecke and Devrient Matsoukis)

2008 (13 Nov). Christmas. T **404** and similar vert designs showing icons from Panagia Catholic Church, Pelendri. Multicoloured. P 13½×13.
1178   22c. Type **404**...................................   80   65
1179   51c. Archangel Michael ....   2·00   1·40
1180   68c. Virgin Mary and Christ Child.............   2·50   4·00
1178/1180 *Set of 3*.....................................   4·75   5·50

┌───┐
PERSONALISED STAMPS. In 2009 Cyprus Post made five stamp designs available for personal or corporate use. The stamps thus produced had labels attached and were sold at a premium over face value. They are therefore not listed in this catalogue.
The 2009 stamp designs were: 34c. Father Christmas, 34c. Bicycle, 43c. galley, 51c. Football and 68c. 'running horse'. Five further designs were released in 2010: 34c. Wedding rings, 34c. Dove over font, 34c. Cyclamen, 34c. plant and 43c. statue of Aphrodite.
└───┘

(Litho Giesecke & Devrient Matsoukis)

2009 (12 Mar). Obligatory Tax. Refugee Fund. Inscr '2009'. Chalk-surfaced paper. P 13½×14.
1181   **397**   2c. black and grey-lilac..............................   20   20

405 Stylised Euro Coin

406 Centenary Emblem

(Des Nicolas Ladommatos. Litho Giesecke and Devrient Matsoukis)

2009 (12 Mar). Tenth Anniversary of the Euro. T **405** and similar square design. Multicoloured. P 13½.

1182	51c. Type **405**	1·25	1·50
1183	68c. Euro coin showing map of Europe	1·75	2·75

(Des Elena Eliadou. Litho Giesecke and Devrient Matsoukis)

2009 (12 Mar). Anniversaries. T **406** and similar square design. Multicoloured. P 13½.

1184	26c. Type **406** (Centenary of the Cyprus Co-operative Movement)	75	55
1185	68c. Louis Braille (birth bicentenary)	2·25	3·00

No. 1185 has the face value in Braille.

407 Satellite Image of the Americas

408 Cassiopeia

(Des Constantinos Panayi. Litho Giesecke and Devrient Matsoukis)

2009 (4 May). International Year of Planet Earth (2008). T **407** and similar horiz design. Multicoloured. P 13.

1186	51c. Type **407**	2·00	2·25
	a. Horiz pair. Nos. 1186/1187	4·00	4·50
1187	51c. Satellite image of Europe, Asia and North Africa	2·00	2·25

Nos. 1186/1187 were printed together, *se-tenant*, as horizontal pairs in sheetlets of eight stamps (4×2), each pair forming a composite design showing the Earth's continents enclosed in a heart.

(Des Christina Vasiliadou. Litho Giesecke and Devrient Matsoukis)

2009 (4 May). Europa. Astronomy. T **408** and similar vert design showing constellations. Multicoloured. P 13×13½.

1188	51c. Type **408**	1·75	2·00
	a. Booklet pane. Nos. 1188/1189, each×4	14·00	
1189	68c. Andromeda	2·25	2·75

Booklet pane No. 1188a has the horizontal edges imperforate and margins at left and right.

409 Letters forming Player with Racket

410 Map of Cyprus on Stamp on Globe

(Des Andria Talli. Litho Giesecke and Devrient Matsoukis)

2009 (1 June). 13th Games of the Small States of Europe, Nicosia and Limassol. T **409** and similar vert designs. Multicoloured. P 13×13½.

1190	22c. Type **409**	60	60
1191	34c. Letters forming sailor and yacht	1·00	1·25
1192	43c. Letters forming cyclist	2·00	2·25
1190/1192 *Set of 3*		3·25	3·50

(Des Yiota Tsiaklidou. Litho and embossed Giesecke & Devrient Matsoukis)

2009 (1 June). 50th Anniversary of Cyprus Philatelic Society. Sheet 67×67 mm. P 13½.

MS1193 **410**	85c. multicoloured	4·25	5·00

411 Pigeon

412 St Paraskevi Church (9th-century)

(Des Theodoros Kakoulis. Litho Giesecke and Devrient Matsoukis)

2009 (10 Sept). Domestic Fowl. T **411** and similar horiz designs. Multicoloured. P 13½.

1194	22c. Type **411**	75	65
1195	34c. Turkey	1·40	1·25
1196	43c. Cockerel	1·50	1·50
1197	51c. Duck	1·75	2·50
1194/1197 *Set of 4*		4·75	5·50

(Des Melanie Efstathiadou, Liza Petridou-Mala and Glafkos Theofylaktou. Litho Giesecke and Devrient Matsoukis)

2009 (10 Sept). Cyprus through the Ages (3rd series). T **412** and similar square designs. Multicoloured. P 13½.

1198	43c. Type **412**	1·40	1·75
	a. Sheetlet of 8. Nos. 1198/1205	10·00	12·50
1199	43c. Monastery of St Chrysostomos (1090–1100)	1·40	1·75
1200	43c. Lusignan Coat of Arms (1192–1489)	1·40	1·75
1201	43c. Chronicle of Machairas (early 15th-century)	1·40	1·75
1202	43c. Queen Cornaro passes crown to Venice	1·40	1·75
1203	43c. Nicosia's Venetian walls (1567–1570)	1·40	1·75
1204	43c. Ottoman siege of Nicosia (1570)	1·40	1·75
1205	43c. Larnaca aqueduct (18th-century)	1·40	1·75
1198/1205 *Set of 8*		10·00	12·50

Nos. 1198/1205 were printed together, *se-tenant*, in sheetlets of eight stamps.

413 European Court of Human Rights, Strasbourg

(Des R. Rogers and C. Bucher. Litho Giesecke & Devrient Matsoukis)

2009 (12 Nov). 50th Anniversary of European Court of Human Rights, Strasbourg. P 13.

1206	**413**	51c. multicoloured	1·50	2·00

414 Birth of Christ (16th-century fresco), Church of Archangel Michael, Vyzakia

415 Mauve Star within Silver Star

(Des Xenia Christadoulou. Litho (Nos. 1208/1209 also recess) Giesecke and Devrient Matsoukis)

2009 (12 Nov). Christmas. Multicoloured.

(a) P 13×13½

1207	22c. Type **414**	70	30

*(b) As T **415**. P 13½*

1208	51c. Type **415**	1·75	1·50
1209	68c. Silver star	2·50	3·75
1207/1209 *Set of 3*		4·50	5·50

416 Arms of Cyprus

417 Pig

(Des Marianna Iacovu. Litho Giesecke and Devrient Matsoukis)

2010 (27 Jan). 50th Anniversary of the Republic of Cyprus. P 13½.

1210	**416**	68c. multicoloured	2·25	2·50
1211		85c. multicoloured	2·75	3·50

(Des Theodoros Kakoullis. Litho Giesecke and Devrient Matsoukis)

2010 (17 Mar). Farm Animals. T **417** and similar horiz designs. Multicoloured. P 13½.

1212	22c. Type **417**		70	60
1213	26c. Sheep		85	75
1214	34c. Goat		1·25	1·10
1215	43c. Cow		1·75	1·25
1216	€1.71 Rabbit		8·00	10·00
1212/1216 Set of 5			11·00	12·00

418 Emblem and 'Better City Better Life'

(Des Ioanna Kalli. Litho Giesecke and Devrient Matsoukis)

2010 (17 Mar). Expo 2010, Shanghai, China. P 13.

1217	**418**	51c. multicoloured	1·50	1·75

419 Football

420 Stack of Books and Flowering Tree

(Des Antonia Hadjigeorgiou. Litho Giesecke and Devrient Matsoukis)

2010 (17 Mar). World Cup Football Championship, South Africa. P 13½.

1218	**419**	€1.71 multicoloured	7·25	8·00

(Litho Giesecke and Devrient Matsoukis)

2010 (5 May). Obligatory Tax. Refugee Fund. Inscr '2010'. Chalk-surfaced paper. P 13½×14.

1218a	**397**	2c. black and cinnamon	20	20

(Des Christina Vasiliadou. Litho Giesecke and Devrient Matsoukis)

2010 (5 May). Europa. Children's Books. T **420** and similar vert designs. Multicoloured. P 13×13½.

1219	51c. Type **420**		1·75	2·00
	a. Horiz pair. Nos. 1219/1220		3·50	4·00
	b. Booklet pane. Nos. 1219/1220, each×4...	12·00	
1220	51c. Stack of books (at left)		1·75	2·00

Nos. 1219/1220 were printed, *se-tenant*, as horizontal pairs in sheetlets of 16, each pair forming a composite design of a stack of books.

Booklet pane 1219a has the horizontal edges imperforate and margins at left and right.

421 Pope Benedict XVI, Ayia Kyriaki Church and Ancient Temple Pillars, Paphos

(Des Melanie Efstathiadou. Litho Giesecke and Devrient Matsoukis)

2010 (4 June). Visit of Pope Benedict XVI to Cyprus. P 13½×14.

1221	**421**	51c. multicoloured	2·25	2·00

422 Steam Locomotive

423 Treaties of Sevres, 1920, and Lausanne, 1923

(Des Andreas Mavrogenis. Litho Giesecke and Devrient Matsoukis)

2010 (4 June). The Cyprus Railway 1905–1951. T **422** and similar horiz design. Multicoloured. P 13½×13.

1222	43c. Type **422**		1·75	1·50
	a. Pair. Nos. 1222/1223		3·50	3·00
1223	43c. Steam locomotive (seen from front)		1·75	1·50
MS1224 70×70 mm. 85c. Steam train and map of railway			3·25	3·75

Nos. 1222/1223 were printed together, *se-tenant*, in horizontal and vertical pairs in sheetlets of eight stamps (4×2).

(Des Melanie Efstathiadou, Liza Petridou-Mala and Glafkos Theofylaktou. Litho Giesecke and Devrient Matsoukis)

2010 (1 Oct). Cyprus through the Ages (4th series). T **423** and similar square designs. Multicoloured. P 13½.

1225	43c. Type **423**		1·75	2·00
	a. Sheetlet of 8. Nos. 1225/1232		12·50	14·50
1226	43c. Burnt Government House, 1931		1·75	2·00
1227	43c. 'Imprisoned Graves' of EOKA fighters, Central Prisons, 1955–1959		1·75	2·00
1228	43c. Statue of Gregoris Afxentiou (EOKA second in command), 1957		1·75	2·00
1229	43c. Presidential Palace, 1960		1·75	2·00
1230	43c. *The Black Summer of 1974* (Telemachos Kanthos)		1·75	2·00
1231	43c. President Tassos Papadopoulos signing EU Treaty of Accession, 16 April 2003		1·75	2·00
1232	43c. National Flag of Republic of Cyprus		1·75	2·00
1225/1232 Set of 8			12·50	14·50

Nos. 1225/1232 were printed together, *se-tenant*, in sheetlets of eight stamps.

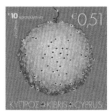

424 Birth of Christ (16th-century icon), Church of Agios Nicolas, Klonari

425 White Bauble

(Des Xenia Christodoulou. Litho (Nos. 1234/1235 also recess) Giesecke and Devrient Matsoukis)

2010 (10 Nov). Christmas. Multicoloured designs as Types **424/425**. P 13½.

1233	22c. Type **424**		65	30
1234	51c. Type **425**		1·40	1·10
1235	68c. Filigree bauble		2·00	3·00
1233/1235 Set of 3			3·75	4·00

426 Wine Barrels

427 Emblem

(Des Melanie Efstathiadou. Litho Giesecke and Devrient Matsoukis)

2010 (10 Nov). Viticulture. Sheet 80×60 mm containing T **426** and similar horiz design. Multicoloured. P 13½×14.

MS1236	**426**	51c. Type **426**; 51c. Grapes and decorated ceramic wine jug		5·50	6·00

Stamps from No. **MS**1236 were imperforate at either left (T **426**) or right (other stamp) sides.

Stamps in similar designs were issued by Romania.

(Des Rodoula Nicolaou. Litho Giesecke and Devrient Matsoukis)

2011 (28 Jan). Centenary of Anorthosis Ammochostos (football and volleyball club). P 13½.

1237	**427**	34c. multicoloured	1·10	1·25

428 Johann Sebastian Bach

(Des Theodoros Kakoullis. Litho Giesecke and Devrient Matsoukis)

2011 (28 Jan). Famous 18th-century Composers. T **428** and similar horiz designs. Multicoloured. P 14.

1238	51c. Type **428**	1·75	2·00
	a. Horiz strip of 3. Nos. 1238/1240	4·75	5·50
1239	51c. Wolfgang Amadeus Mozart	1·75	2·00
1240	51c. Ludwig van Beethoven	1·75	2·00
1238/1240	Set of 3	4·75	5·50

Nos. 1238/1240 were printed together, se-tenant, as horizontal strips of three stamps in sheetlets of six.

429 Embroidery

(Des Konstantinos Panagi. Litho Giesecke and Devrient Matsoukis)

2011 (23 Mar). Cyprus Embroidery. T **429** and similar horiz design. Multicoloured. P 13½×14.

1241	26c. Type **429**	75	65
1242	43c. Embroidery (pattern of diamonds)	1·25	1·40

Nos. 1241/1242 were printed in separate sheetlets of eight stamps.

430 Roses

431 Forest at Dusk with Fox and Owl

(Des Elena Eliadou. Litho Giesecke and Devrient Matsoukis)

2011 (23 Mar). Aromatic Flowers and Herbs (1st issue). Roses. T **430** and similar square design. Multicoloured. P 14.

1243	34c. Type **430**	1·00	1·25
MS1244	75×75 mm. 85c. Roses and rosebuds	3·50	4·00

Nos. 1243/**MS**1244 have a rose scent.

See also Nos. 1277/**MS**1278 and 1299/**MS**1300.

(Litho Giesecke and Devrient Matsoukis)

2011 (4 May). Obligatory Tax. Refugee Fund. Inscr '2011'. Chalk-surfaced paper. P 13½×14.

1245	**397**	2c. black and pale green	15	15

(Des Stelios Karamallakis. Litho Giesecke and Devrient Matsoukis)

2011 (4 May). Europa. Forests. T **431** and similar horiz design. Multicoloured. P 14.

1246	51c. Type **431**	2·50	2·00
	a. Booklet pane. Nos. 1246/1247, each×4	20·00	
1247	68c. Forest in daytime with mouflon and bird	3·25	4·00

432 Paphos Lighthouse

433 Galleon

(Des Melanie Efstathiadou. Litho Giesecke and Devrient Matsoukis)

2011 (4 May). Lighthouses. T **432** and similar vert designs. Multicoloured. P 13½×13 (No. **MS**1250) or 14 (others).

1248	34c. Type **432**	2·25	1·50
1249	43c. Cape Greco Lighthouse	2·75	2·25
MS1250	70×65 mm. €1·71 Cape Kiti Lighthouse	11·00	10·00

(Des Antonia Hadjigeorgiou. Litho Giesecke and Devrient)

2011 (8 June). Sailing Ships. T **433** and similar square designs. Multicoloured. P 13½.

1251	22c. Type **433**	1·00	60
1252	43c. Caravel	2·00	1·25
1253	85c. Brig	3·75	5·50
1251/1253	Set of 3	6·00	6·50

Nos. 1251/1253 were each printed in sheetlets of eight stamps.

434 Christopher Pissarides and Nobel Medal

(Des Melanie Efstathiadou. Litho Giesecke and Devrient)

2011 (8 June). Award of Nobel Prize for Economics to Christopher Pissarides (2010). P 14.

1254	**434**	€1·71 multicoloured	7·25	7·75

No. 1254 was printed in sheetlets of six stamps.

(Litho)

2011 (26 July). Booklet Stamps for Postcards. Designs as T **397** (Refugee Fund) and No. 1249 (Cape Greco Lighthouse). Self-adhesive. Die-cut perf 13½×14 (2c.) or 13½×13 (43c.).

1255	2c. black and pale green	50	1·25
	a. Booklet pane. Nos. 1255/1256, each×6	14·00	
1256	43c. multicoloured	2·25	2·50

Nos. 1255/1256 were issued in €2·70 booklets, No. SB15.

435 Hare

(Des Ioanna Kalli. Litho Giesecke and Devrient Matsoukis)

2011 (5 Oct). Aesop's Fables (1st series). The Hare and the Tortoise. T **435** and similar multicoloured designs. Self-adhesive. Die-cut perf 11½×12 (vert) or 12×11½ (horiz).

1257	34c. Type **435**	1·25	1·50
	a. Booklet pane. Nos. 1257/1261	5·75	6·75
1258	34c. Tortoise	1·25	1·50
1259	34c. Tortoise passing sleeping Hare (horiz)	1·25	1·50
1260	34c. Hare running fast in vain attempt to catch up	1·25	1·50
1261	34c. Tortoise winning race	1·25	1·50
1257/1261	Set of 5	5·75	6·75

Nos. 1257/1261 were only issued in €1·70 booklets, No. SB16. The stamps and background of booklet pane No. 1257a form a composite background design showing a meadow and road.

See also Nos. 1281/1285.

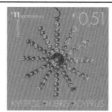

436 Birth of Christ (detail from mural, Cathedral Church of Agios Ioannis)

437 Star

(Des Xenia Christodoulou. Litho (51, 68c. also recess) Giesecke and Devrient Matsoukis)

2011 (11 Nov). Christmas. Multicoloured designs as Types **436**/**437**. P 13×13½ (22c.) or 13½ (51, 68c.).

1262	22c.	Type **436**	75	30
1263	51c.	Type **437**	1·75	1·25
1264	68c.	Star (different)	2·50	4·00
1262/1264	Set of 3		4·50	5·00

438 Cyprus 74 (wood-engraving by A. Tassos)

439 Palomino and Bay Horses

(Litho Giesecke and Devrient Matsoukis)

2012 (31 Jan). Obligatory Tax. Refugee Stamp. Design as T **397** but changed inscription at top left as T **438**. Inscr '2012'. Chalk-surfaced paper. P 13½.

1265	**438**	2c. black and turquoise-blue	20	20

(Des Melanie Efstathiadou. Litho Giesecke and Devrient Matsoukis)

2012 (31 Jan). Horses. T **439** and similar horiz designs. Multicoloured. P 13½×13.

1266	26c.	Type **439**	1·00	60
1267	34c.	Grey and black Horses	1·50	85
1268	51c.	Chestnut Horse jumping	2·50	2·25
1269	85c.	Mare and foal	3·75	4·50
1266/1269	Set of 4		8·00	7·50

440 Gymnast

(Des Ioanna Kalli. Litho and die-stamped Giesecke and Devrient Matsoukis)

2012 (21 Mar). Olympic Games, London. T **440** and similar horiz designs. Multicoloured. P 14.

1270	22c.	Type **440**	80	40
1271	26c.	Tennis	90	60
1272	34c.	High jump	1·40	1·40
1273	43c.	Shooting	1·75	2·50
1270/1273	Set of 4		4·25	4·50

441 Football

442 Family and Sunset

(Des Glafkos Theofylactou. Litho Giesecke and Devrient Matsoukis)

2012 (21 Mar). Football Excitement. Sheet 110×65 mm. P 14.

MS1274	**441**	€1.71 multicoloured	6·00	7·00

(Des Stelios Karamallakis. Litho Giesecke and Devrient Matsoukis)

2012 (2 May). Europa. Visit Cyprus. T **442** and similar horiz design. Multicoloured. P 13½×13.

1275	51c.	Type **442**	1·75	1·00
		a. Perf 13½	1·75	1·75
		ab. Booklet pane. Nos. 1275a/1276a, each×4	17·00	
1276	68c.	Cyclists and coast path	3·00	3·50
		a. Perf 13½	3·00	4·00

Nos. 1275a and 1276a were only issued in €4.76 booklets, No. SB16.

Booklet pane No. 1275ab has the horizontal edges of the pane imperforate, giving stamps imperforate at either top or foot, and margins at left and right.

443 Jasmine Flowers

444 Emblem

(Des Elena Eliadou. Litho Giesecke and Devrient Matsoukis)

2012 (2 May). Aromatic Flowers and Herbs (2nd issue). Jasmine (*Jasminum grandiflorum*). T **443** and similar square design. Multicoloured. P 13½.

1277	34c.	Type **443**	1·25	1·40
MS1278	75×75 mm. 85c. Jasmine flowers (different)		3·00	3·50

Nos. 1277/**MS**1278 have a Jasmine scent.

(Des Partners Consortium. Recess and litho Giesecke and Devrient Matsoukis)

2012 (1 July). Cyprus Presidency of the Council of the European Union, 1 July to 31 December 2012. Multicoloured. P 13½.

1279	51c.	Type **444**	1·40	1·75
MS1280	85×55 mm. €10 Type **444**		21·00	24·00

(Des Ioanna Kalli. Litho Giesecke and Devrient Matsoukis)

2012 (3 Oct). Aesop's Fables (2nd series). *The Cricket and the Ant*. Vert designs as T **435**. Multicoloured. Self-adhesive. Die-cut perf 11½×12.

1281	34c.	Cricket playing fiddle	1·25	1·50
		a. Booklet pane. Nos. 1281/1285	5·75	6·75
1282	34c.	Ant gathering seeds for winter store	1·25	1·50
1283	34c.	Ant carrying seeds back to nest	1·25	1·50
1284	34c.	Ant playing fiddle and autumn tree	1·25	1·50
1285	34c.	Cold and hungry Cricket in winter snow and Ant retreating into his house	1·25	1·50
1281/1285	Set of 5		5·75	6·75

Nos. 1281/1285 were only issued in €1.70 stamp booklets, No. SB17.

The stamps and background of booklet pane No. 1281a form a composite background design showing meadows and trees with summer turning to winter.

445 Pavlos Kontides

446 Virgin holding the Child in a Wooden Throne

(Des Melanie Efstathiadou. Litho Giesecke and Devrient Matsoukis)

2012 (14 Nov). Pavlos Kontides' Silver Medal for Laser Sailing, Olympic Games, London. P 14.

1286	**445**	34c. multicoloured	1·25	1·40

(Des Constantinos Tsaggerides and Antonia Hadjigeorgiou. Litho Giesecke and Devrient Matsoukis)

2012 (14 Nov). Christmas. Icons from the Byzantine Museum of the Archbishop Makarios III Foundation. T **446** and similar multicoloured designs. P 13×13½.

1287	22c.	Type **446**	80	30
1288	51c.	*Panagia Odigitria* (The Guiding Virgin)	1·60	1·40
MS1289	66×66 mm. 68c. Virgin Mary enthroned between St George and St Nicholas and icon benefactors. Imperf		2·50	3·00

(Litho Giesecke and Devrient Matsoukis)

2013 (30 Jan). Obligatory Tax. Refugee Fund. Inscr '2013'. Chalk-surfaced paper. P 13½.
1290 **438** 2c. black and cinnamon.................... 20 20

447 Nurse at Refugee Camp   **448** Boy and Girl Scouts

(Des Manolis Emmanouel. Litho Giesecke and Devrient Matsoukis)

2013 (30 Jan). Cyprus Red Cross. P 14.
1291 **447** 22c. multicoloured.................... 1·25 1·00

(Des Melanie Efstathiadou. Litho Giesecke and Devrient Matsoukis)

2013 (30 Jan). Centenary of Cyprus Scouts Association. P 13½.
1292 **448** 43c. multicoloured.................... 1·75 1·75

449 Ethnarch Makarios III   **450** Christ's Entry into Jerusalem (icon of 1546 from Archbishop Makarios III Foundation Museum)

(Des Melanie Efstathiadou. Litho Giesecke and Devrient Matsoukis)

2013 (30 Jan). Birth Centenary of Ethnarch Makarios III (first President of Cyprus). P 14.
1293 **449** 85c. multicoloured.................... 2·75 3·00

(Des Costas Panayi. Litho Giesecke and Devrient Matsoukis)

2013 (3 Apr). Easter. T **450** and similar vert designs. Multicoloured. P 13½×14.
1294 26c. Type **450**.................... 75 20
1295 34c. The Crucifixion (fresco), Cathedral of St John, Nicosia.................... 1·00 30
1296 €1.71 The Resurrection (fresco), Cathedral of St John, Nicosia.................... 5·50 6·50
1294/1296 Set of 3.................... 6·50 6·50

451 Modern Cyprus Post Mail Van

(Des Theodoros Kakoullis. Litho Giesecke and Devrient Matsoukis)

2013 (2 May). Europa. Postal Vehicles. T **451** and similar horiz design. Multicoloured. P 14.
1297 34c. Type **451**.................... 1·50 1·25
        a. Booklet pane. Nos. 1297/1298, each×4.... 13·00
1298 51c. Cyprus Post Minivan.................... 2·25 2·75
Booklet pane No. 1297a has the horizontal edges imperforate and margins at left and right.

452 Oregano (*Origanum dubium*)   **453** Sea Horse

(Des Prodromos Apostolou. Litho Giesecke and Devrient Matsoukis)

2013 (2 May). Aromatic Flowers and Herbs (3rd issue). Oregano (*Origanum dubium*). T **452** and similar square design. Multicoloured. P 13½.
1299 22c. Type **452**.................... 1·25 1·00
MS1300 76×75 mm. 85c. As Type **452** but showing top three flower clusters.................... 3·00 3·50

(Des Sofia Malekou. Litho Giesecke and Devrient Matsoukis)

2013 (5 June). Organisms of the Mediterranean Marine Environment. T **453** and similar square designs. Multicoloured. P 13½.
1301 34c. Type **453**.................... 1·00 30
1302 43c. Sea Anemone.................... 1·25 40
1303 €1.71 Sea Fan Coral.................... 5·50 7·00
1301/1303 Set of 3.................... 7·00 7·00
See also No. 1362.

454 Santa and Christmas Tree (Maria Eleftheriou)   **455** Spanos tricking Dragon with Fake Smoke Cloud of Ash

(Litho Giesecke and Devrient Matsoukis)

2013 (13 Nov). Christmas. Children's Drawings. T **454** and similar multicoloured designs. P 13½×14 (85c.) or 14×13½ (others).
1304 22c. Type **454**.................... 1·00 20
1305 34c. Houses, trees and snowman (Andreas Kefalas).................... 1·25 35
1306 85c. Christmas tree (Hara Drousiotou) (*vert*) .. 3·00 4·75
1304/1306 Set of 3.................... 4·75 4·75

(Des Hambis Tsangaris (linocut) and Christina Vasiliadou Mezavorian (artwork). Litho Giesecke and Devrient)

2013 (13 Nov). *Spanos and the Forty Dragons* (folk tale). T **455** and similar multicoloured designs. Self-adhesive. Die-cut perf 13.
1307 34c. Type **455**.................... 1·25 1·50
        a. Booklet pane. Nos. 1307/1311.................... 5·75 6·75
1308 34c. Spanos in tree and Wild Boar spearing itself on pointed branch (*vert*).................... 1·25 1·50
1309 34c. Spanos leaping over flowing river and thankful villagers.................... 1·25 1·50
1310 34c. Spanos and Dragon.................... 1·25 1·50
1311 34c. Spanos pouring hot resin onto Dragon .. 1·25 1·50
1307/1311 Set of 5.................... 5·75 6·75
Nos. 1307/1311 were issued in €1.70 booklets, No. SB19. The stamps and background of booklet pane No. 1307a form a composite background design.

456 Olive Tree   **457** Girl holding Umbrella (Winter)

(Des Marianna Iacovou. Litho Giesecke and Devrient Matsoukis)

2014 (30 Jan). The Olive Tree and its Products. T **456** and similar horiz designs. Multicoloured. P 14.
1312 34c. Type **456**.................... 1·50 40
1313 51c. Ripening Olives.................... 2·00 2·75
        a. Horiz pair. Nos. 1313/1314.................... 4·00 5·50
1314 51c. Ripening Olives and pitchers of Olive Oil.................... 2·00 2·75
1312/1314 Set of 3.................... 5·00 5·50
Nos. 1313/1314 were printed together, *se-tenant*, as horizontal pairs in sheetlets of eight (4×2), each pair forming a composite design of ripening Olives.

(Des Melanie Efstathiadou. Litho Giesecke and Devrient Matsoukis)

2014 (12 Mar). Four Seasons. T **457** and similar square designs. Multicoloured. P 13½.
1315 22c. Type **457**.................... 75 20
1316 43c. Butterfly and girl in flowering meadow (Spring).................... 1·75 25
1317 85c. Girl on beach (Summer).................... 2·50 2·00
1318 €1.71 Child holding autumn leaf (Autumn).................... 5·00 7·50
1315/1318 Set of 4.................... 9·00 9·00
See also Nos. 1327/1329.

(Litho Giesecke and Devrient Matsoukis)

2014 (12 Mar). Obligatory Tax. Refugee Fund. Inscr '2014'. Chalk-surfaced paper. P 13½.
1319 **438** 2c. blackish-brown and pale grey-brown 20 20

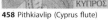

458 Pithkiavlip (Cyprus flute)

459 El Greco (Dominikos Theotokópoulos) (1541–1614, painter)

(Des Ioanna Kalli. Litho Giesecke and Devrient Matsoukis)

2014 (2 May). Europa. National Musical Instruments. T **458** and similar horiz design. Multicoloured. P 14.
1320 34c. Type **458** .... 1·25 1·00
  a. Booklet pane. Nos. 1320/1321, each×4.... 11·00
1321 51c. Laouton (lute) .... 1·75 2·00
Booklet pane No. 1320a has the horizontal edges imperforate and margins at left and right.

(Des Prodromos Apostolou, Larnaca. Litho Giesecke and Devrient Matsoukis)

2014 (30 June). Intellectual Pioneers. T **459** and similar horiz designs. Multicoloured. P 14.
1322 41c. Type **459** .... 1·25 60
1323 50c. Michaelangelo di Lodovico Buonarroti (1475–1564, sculptor and painter) .... 1·60 1·25
1324 64c. Galileo Galilei (1564–1642, astronomer). 2·00 2·25
1325 75c. Henri de Toulouse Lautrec (1864–1901, painter) .... 2·50 3·25
1322/1325 Set of 4 .... 6·50 6·50

460 Globe showing Mediterranean Sea

(461)

€0,04

(Des Amany Ahmed Ali, Egypt Post and Prodromos Apostolou, Larnaca. Litho Giesecke and Devrient Matsoukis)

2014 (9 July). Euromed Postal (Postal Union for the Mediterranean). The Mediterranean Sea. P 14.
1326 **460** 60c. multicoloured .... 1·75 1·75
Similar designs were issued by Egypt, France, Greece, Jordan, Lebanon, Libya, Malta, Morocco, Palestine, Slovenia and Syria.

2014 (1 Aug). Nos. 1315/1316 and 1318 surch as T **461**.
1327 4c. on 22c. Type **457** 40 70
1328 €1 on 43c. Butterfly and girl in flowering meadow (Spring) .... 2·75 2·75
1329 €1.88 on €1.71 Child holding autumn leaf (Autumn) .... 5·50 6·50
1327/1329 Set of 3 .... 7·75 9·00

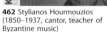

462 Stylianos Hourmouzios (1850–1937, cantor, teacher of Byzantine music)

463 Prince of Venice and Princess of Cyprus flying

(Des Costas Panayi, Marianna Iacovou, Sofia Malecos and Xenia Christodoulou. Litho Giesecke and Devrient Matsoukis)

2014 (10 Oct)–**15**. Intellectual Personalities of Cyprus. T **462** and similar horiz designs. Multicoloured. P 14.
1330 4c. Type **462** 20 30
  a. Pair. Nos. 1330/1331 .... 40 60
1331 4c. Theodoulos Kallinikos (1904–2004 cantor, scholar of Byzantine and Cypriot folk music) 20 30

1332 4c. Adamantios Diamantis (1900–1994, artist) 20 30
  a. Pair. Nos. 1332/1333 .... 40 60
1333 4c. Theodosis Pierides (1908–1968, poet)..... 20 30
1334 34c. Achilleas Lymbourides (1917–2008, composer of Cypriot folk songs, playwright and author) 70 70
  a. Pair. Nos. 1334/1335 .... 1·40 1·40
1335 34c. Sozos Tombolis (1914–2002 cantor, choirmaster and scholar of Cypriot folk music) 70 70
1336 41c. Loukia Nicolaidou (1909–1994, painter) 90 90
  a. Pair. Nos. 1336/1337 .... 1·75 1·75
1337 41c. Telemachus Kanthos (1910–1993, painter, etcher and stage designer)........ 90 90
1338 50c. Michael Kashalos (1885–1974, painter) .... 1·10 1·10
  a. Pair. Nos. 1338/1339 .... 2·10 2·10
1339 50c. George Pol Georgiou (1901–1972, painter) .... 1·10 1·10
1340 50c. Maria Rousia (1894–1957, writer) .... 1·10 1·10
  a. Pair. Nos. 1340/1341 .... 2·10 2·10
1341 50c. Melis Nicolaides (1892–1979, writer) ...... 1·10 1·10
1342 60c. Kyriakos Hadjioannou (1909–1997, writer, teacher, researcher and folklorist) .... 1·25 1·25
  a. Pair. Nos. 1342/1343 .... 2·50 2·50
1343 60c. Polyxeni Loizia (1855–1942, writer, educationist and feminist) .... 1·25 1·25
1344 64c. Antis Pernaris (1903–1980, poet, novelist, journalist and educationalist) ... 1·25 1·25
  a. Pair. Nos. 1344/1345 .... 2·50 2·50
1345 64c. Kypros Chrysanthis (1915–1998, novelist and poet) .... 1·25 1·25
1346 75c. Loizos Philippou (1895–1950, scholar, historian, researcher, educator and publisher) .... 1·40 1·40
  a. Pair. Nos. 1346/1347 .... 2·75 2·75
1347 75c. Persefoni Papadopoulou (1888–1948, writer, educationist and feminist)............. 1·40 1·40
1348 85c. Costas Montis (1914–2004, poet and playwright) .... 1·50 1·50
  a. Pair. Nos. 1348/1349 .... 3·00 3·00
1349 85c. Glafkos Alithersis (1897–1965, poet and writer) .... 1·50 1·50
1350 €1 Georgios S. Frangoudes (1869–1939, lawyer and politician) .... 2·00 2·00
  a. Pair. Nos. 1350/1351 .... 4·00 4·00
1351 €1 Porfyrios Dikaios (1904–1971, archaeologist) .... 2·00 2·00
1352 €1.50 Nicos Pantelides (1906–1984, actor and director) .... 2·75 2·75
  a. Pair. Nos. 1352/1353 .... 5·50 5·50
1353 €1.50 Pavlos Xioutas (1908–1991, scholar, writer and folklorist) .... 2·75 2·75
1330/1353 Set of 24 .... 24·00 24·00
Nos. 1330/1331, 1332/1333, 1334/1335, 1336/1337, 1338/1339, 1340/1341, 1342/1343, 1344/1345, 1346/1347, 1348/1349, 1350/1351 and 1352/1353 were each printed together, se-tenant, as horizontal and vertical pairs in sheets of eight stamps (4×2).

(Des Hambis Tsangaris. Litho Giesecke and Devrient Matsoukis)

2014 (24 Nov). *The Prince of Venice* (folk tale). T **463** and similar multicoloured designs. Self-adhesive. Die-cut perf 13½.
1354 41c. Type **463** .... 1·50 1·60
  a. Booklet pane. Nos. 1354/1358.................. 6·75 7·00
1355 41c. King's ship .... 1·50 1·60
1356 41c. King of Cyprus (vert) .... 1·50 1·60
1357 41c. Princess of Cyprus holding lock of Prince's hair (vert) .... 1·50 1·60
1358 41c. Prince of Venice and Princess of Cyprus (vert) .... 1·50 1·60
1354/1358 Set of 5 .... 6·75 7·00
Nos. 1354/1358 were issued in €2.05 booklets, No. SB21. The stamps and background of booklet pane No. 1354a form a composite background design.

464 Birth of Christ

(465)

€0,34

(Des Yiota Tsiaklidou. Litho Giesecke and Devrient Matsoukis)

2014 (24 Nov). Christmas. Icons. I **464** and similar vert designs. Multicoloured. P 14.

1359	41c. Type **464**	1·25	25
1360	64c. Virgin Mary and baby Jesus	1·75	1·25
1361	75c. Birth of Christ with Virgin Mary and baby Jesus, Temptation of Joseph, Bathing of the Infant and Annunciation to the Shepherds	2·25	3·25
1359/1361 *Set of 3*		4·75	4·25

2015 (4 Feb). No. 1302 surch as T **465**.

1362	34c. Sea Anemone	1·00	70

(Litho Giesecke and Devrient Matsoukis)

2015 (2 Apr). Obligatory Tax. Refugee Fund. Inscr '2015'. Chalk-surfaced paper. P 13½.

1363	**438**	2c. black and azure	20	20

466 Candied Green Bitter Orange

(Des Elena Eliadou. Litho Giesecke and Devrient Matsoukis)

2015 (2 Apr). Cypriot Dishes. Sweets. T **466** and similar square designs. Multicoloured. P 13½.

1364	34c. Type **466**	75	30
1365	41c. Candied bitter Orange	1·00	40
1366	€1.88 Candied Cherries	4·25	5·50
1364/1366 *Set of 3*		5·50	5·50

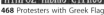

467 Melkonian Orphanage, Lefkosia, 1940s

(Des Haigez Mangoian. Litho Giesecke and Devrient Matsoukis)

2015 (2 Apr). Centenary of the Armenian Genocide. P 13½×14.

1367	**467**	64c. multicoloured	2·00	2·00

A similar design was issued by Armenia.

468 Protesters with Greek Flag

469 Boy with Spinning Top

(Des Nicos Ierodiaconou. Litho Giesecke and Devrient Matsoukis)

2015 (2 Apr). 60th Anniversary of EOKA Campaign. Sheet 69×70 mm. P 13½.

MS1368	**468** multicoloured	4·75	5·00

(Des Costas Panayi, Mitsero. Litho Giesecke and Devrient Matsoukis)

2015 (5 May). Europa. Old Toys. T **469** and similar vert design. Multicoloured. P 14.

1369	34c. Type **469**	75	75
	a. Booklet pane. Nos. 1369/1370, each×4	9·00	
1370	64c. Two boys playing with marbles	1·75	2·00

Booklet pane No. 1369a has the horizontal edges imperforate and margins at left and right.

470 Akamas Peninsula

(Des George Papaioannou. Litho Giesecke and Devrient)

2015 (9 July). The Beauty of Akamas. P 14.

1371	34c. Type **470**	1·25	50
1372	64c. Avakas Gorge (*vert*)	2·50	2·75

471 Four Types of Boats and Map of Mediterranean

472 Buffavento Castle

(Des Prodromos Apostolou. Litho Giesecke and Devrient Matsoukis)

2015 (9 July). Euromed Postal (Postal Union for the Mediterranean). Boats of the Mediterranean. P 14.

1373	**471**	75c. multicoloured	2·75	2·75

(Des Prodromos Apostolou. Litho Giesecke and Devrient Matsoukis)

2015 (14 Sept). Castles. T **472** and similar horiz designs. Multicoloured. P 13½×13.

1374	4c. Type **472**	30	40
1375	34c. Kantara Castle	1·25	50
1376	41c. St Hilarion Castle	1·75	65
1377	75c. Kyrenia Castle	2·75	3·50
1374/1377 *Set of 4*		5·50	4·50

473 Traditional Symmetrical Engravings using Pyrography on Dried Pumpkins

(Des Theodoros Kakoullis. Litho Giesecke and Devrient Matsoukis)

2015 (14 Sept). Cypriot Folk Art. I **473** and similar horiz designs. Multicoloured. P 14.

1378	34c. Type **473**	1·25	1·25
	a. Pair. Nos. 1378/1379	2·50	2·50
1379	34c. Hand-carved chair	1·25	1·25
1380	64c. Pottery including anthropomorphic clay vessel	2·25	2·25
	a. Pair. Nos. 1380/1381	4·50	4·50
1381	64c. Silver merrecha (small ceremonial vessel used to sprinkle people with fragrance)	2·25	2·25
1378/1381 *Set of 4*		6·25	6·25

Nos. 1378/1379 and 1380/1381 were each printed together, *se-tenant*, as horizontal and vertical pairs in sheetlets of eight (4×2).

474 Early Telecommunications

475 Throwing Olive Leaves into Fire at New Year

(Des Nicos Ierodiaconou. Litho Giesecke and Devrient Matsoukis)

2015 (14 Sept). 150th Anniversary of ITU (International Telecommunications Union). P 14.

1382	**474**	64c. multicoloured	2·50	2·25

(Des Yiota Tsaklidou and Melanie Efstathiasou. Litho Giesecke and Devrient Matsoukis)

2015 (19 Nov). Christmas. T **475** and similar vert designs. Multicoloured. P 14.

1383	34c. Type **475**	1·00	25
1384	41c. Virgin Mary holding Christ Child (icon)	1·50	35
1385	64c. Girl posting Christmas card	2·75	4·00
1383/1385 *Set of 3*		4·75	4·25
MS1386	66×75 mm. €2 Birth of Christ (Solon (Solomos Frangoulides), icon from Panaya Agrou Elousa Church	7·00	7·50

(Litho Giesecke and Devrient Matsoukis)

2016 (10 Mar). Obligatory Tax. Refugee Fund. Inscr '2016'. P 13½.

1387	**438**	2c. blackish-brown and pale grey-brown	20	20

476 Basket Weaving

(Des Nicos Ierodiaconou. Litho Veridos Matsoukis S.A., Greece)

2016 (10 Mar). Traditional Cypriot Popular Crafts. T **476** and similar horiz design. Multicoloured. P 14.

1388	41c. Type **476**	1·50	75
1389	64c. Wood carving	2·50	3·25

477 Taekwondo

(Des Antonia Hadjigeorgiou. Litho Veridos Matsoukis)

2016 (11 Apr). Olympic Games, Rio de Janeiro. T **477** and similar square designs. Multicoloured. P 13½.

1390	34c. Type **477**	1·00	40
1391	41c. Tennis	1·50	50
1392	64c. High jump	2·50	2·75
1393	75c. Athlete sprinting	2·75	4·00
1390/1393 *Set of 4*		7·00	7·00

478 Family in Green Landscape under Green Rainbow

479 Couple holding Flower (Andri Kouti)

(Des Doxia Sergidou. Litho Veridos Matsoukis)

2016 (9 May). Europa. Think Green. T **478** and similar horiz design. Multicoloured. P 14.

1394	34c. Type **478**	75	75
	a. Booklet pane. Nos. 1394/1395, each×4	8·00	
1395	64c. Polluted and clean environments	1·25	1·50

Booklet pane No. 1394a has the horizontal edges imperforate and margins at left and right.

(Des Adapted Ioanna Kalli. Litho Veridos Matsoukis)

2016 (9 May). Principles and Values of the European Union. Winning Entries from Stamp Design Competition 'Stamp Art: The EU and Cyprus All Around the World'. T **479** and similar multicoloured designs. P 14.

1396	34c. Type **479**	75	40
1397	41c. Man fleeing burning building (Elizaveta Tolskaia) (*vert*)	1·00	55
1398	64c. People on trunk and in canopy of Euro tree (Marianthia Filippou) (*vert*)	1·50	2·25
1396/1398 *Set of 3*		3·00	3·00

480 Panayia Fount, Pafos   **481** Fish

(Des Nicos Ierodiaconou. Litho Veridos Matsoukis)

2016 (8 July). Old Founts in Cyprus. T **480** and similar horiz design. Multicoloured. P 14.

1399	34c. Type **480**	70	70
1400	41c. Fount of the Pegia Women	90	90

(Des Maximos Christou. Litho Veridos Matsoukis)

2016 (8 July). Euromed Postal (Postal Union for the Mediterranean). Fish of the Mediterranean. P 14.

1401	**481** €1.88 multicoloured	4·00	4·50

The fish depicted in T **481** is a montage of five species: Painted Comber, Parrotfish, Peacock Wrasse, Annular Sea Bream and Snapper.

482 Georgios Paraskevaides (1916–2007)   **483** Christmas Lights

(Des Theodoros Kakoullis. Litho Veridos Matsoukis)

2016 (17 Oct). Great Cypriot Benefactors. T **482** and similar vert designs. Multicoloured. P 14.

1402	34c. Type **482**	80	80
1403	34c. Anastasios Leventis (1902–1978)	80	80
1404	34c. Stelios Joannou (1915–1999)	80	80
1402/1404 *Set of 3*		2·25	2·25

(Des Marianna Iacovu and Nicolas Ladommatos. Litho Veridos Matsoukis)

2016 (17 Nov). Christmas. P 14.

1405	34c. Type **483**	75	25
1406	41c. Green baubles forming Christmas tree with star on top	1·00	35
1407	64c. Adoration of the Magi icon from Byzantine Museum of the Archbishop Makarios III Foundation, Nicosia (*horiz*)	1·50	2·25
1405/1407 *Set of 3*		3·00	2·50

484 Emblem   **485** Crocus hartmannianus

(Des Manolis Emmanouil (artwork) and Alexandros Neofytou. Litho Veridos Matsoukis)

2016 (17 Nov). Cyprus Chairmanship of the Council of Europe. P 13½.

1408	**484** €1 multicoloured	2·25	2·50

(Litho Veridos Matsoukis)

2017 (16 Feb). Obligatory Tax. Refugee Fund. Inscr '2017'. P 13½×14.

1409	**438** 2c. brownish black and pale violet-blue	20	20

(Des Melani Efstathiadou. Litho Veridos Matsoukis)

2017 (16 Feb). Wild Flowers of Cyprus (1st series). T **485** and similar vert designs. Multicoloured. P 14.

1410	34c. Type **485**	85	30
1411	41c. *Carlina pygmaea*	1·25	40

1412   64c. *Centaurea akamantis* .... 1·75   1·75
1413   €1 *Tulipa cypria* .... 3·00   4·25
1410/1413 *Set of 4* .... 6·25   6·00
  See also Nos. 1432/1435.

486 Emblem

(Des Panayiota Epiphaniou (34c.), Xenia Christodoulou (41c.) and
George Papioannou (64c.). Litho Veridos Matsoukis)

2017 (24 Mar). Anniversaries. T **486** and similar horiz designs.
Multicoloured. P 14.
1414   34c. Type **486** (60th anniversary of Cyprus
        Television) 75   40
1415   41c. '50' emblem with '0' formed from
        stethoscope (50th anniversary of
        Cyprus Medical Association) .... 1·00   60
1416   64c. Emblem with Lion profiles (centenary of
        Lions International) .... 1·50   2·00
1414/1416 *Set of 3* .... 3·00   2·75

487 Cliffs and Beach

(Des Nicos Ierodiaconu. Litho Veridos Matsoukis)

2017 (24 Mar). Pafos 2017 European Capital of Culture. T **487** and similar
horiz designs. Multicoloured. P 14.
1417   64c. Type **487** .... 1·75   2·00
       a. Horiz strip of 3. Nos. 1417/1419 .... 4·75   5·50
1418   64c. Emblem over sea and 'PAFOS 2017' .... 1·75   2·00
1419   64c. Stone columns .... 1·75   2·00
1417/1419 *Set of 3* .... 4·75   5·50
  Nos. 1417/1419 were printed together, *se-tenant*, as horizontal strips
of three stamps in sheetlets of 12 (3×4), each horizontal strip forming a
composite design of coastal cliffs and stacks, sea and archaeological site.

488 Larnaka Castle

(Des Ioanna Kalli. Litho Veridos Matsoukis)

2017 (4 May). Europa. Castles. T **488** and similar horiz design.
Multicoloured. P 14.
1420   41c. Type **488** .... 1·00   1·00
       a. Booklet pane. Nos. 1420/1421, each×4 ... 8·50
1421   64c. Pafos Castle .... 1·40   1·75
  Booklet pane No. 1420a has the horizontal edges imperforate and
margins at left and right.

489 Beach and 2012 Europa
Visit Cyprus 68c. Stamp with
Nicosia Cancellation

490 Tree

(Des Manolis Emmanouil. Litho Veridos Matsoukis)

2017 (4 May). International Year of Sustainable Tourism for Development.
Philately and Tourism. P 14.
1422   **489** 64c. multicoloured .... 1·40   1·40

(Des Christina Vasiliadou. Litho Veridos Matsoukis)

2017 (10 July). Euromed Postal (Postal Union for the Mediterranean). Trees
of the Mediterranean. P 14.
1423   **490** 64c. multicoloured .... 1·75   2·00

491 St Minas the
Egyptian

492 Girl unwrapping
Present

(Des Nicos Ierodiaconu and Doxia Sergidou. Litho Veridos Matsoukis)

2017 (24 Nov). Christmas. Multicoloured. P 14.

(a) Vert designs as T **491**
1424   34c. Type **491** 90   90
       a. Horiz strip of 3. Nos. 1424/1426 .... 2·50   2·50
1425   34c. Virgin Mary holding Christ Child, St
        Luke and sailing ship 90   90
1426   34c. St Spyridon, Bishop of Trymythous 90   90

(b) Vert designs as T **492**
1427   41c. Type **492** .... 1·10   1·10
       a. Horiz pair. Nos. 1427/1428 .... 2·10   2·10
1428   41c. Boy unwrapping present .... 1·10   1·10
1429   64c. Boy wearing Santa hat writing letter to
        Santa .... 1·60   1·60
1424/1429 *Set of 6* .... 6·00   6·00
  Nos. 1424/1426 were printed together, *se-tenant*, as horizontal strips of
three stamps in sheetlets of 12 (6×2).
  Nos. 1427/1428 were printed together, *se-tenant*, as horizontal pairs in
sheetlets of eight (4×2), each pair forming a composite design.

(Des Manolis Emmanouel. Litho Veridos Matsoukis)

2017 (30 Nov). 150th Anniversary of Monastery of Apostolos Andreas.
P 14.
MS1430 75×75 mm. **493** €10 multicoloured .... 22·00   24·00
  No. **MS**1430 was issued in a folder.
  T **493** is unavailable.

(Litho Veridos Matsoukis)

2018 (12 Feb). Obligatory Tax. Refugee Fund. Inscr '2018'. P 13½.
1431   **438** 2c. brownish black and greenish grey.. 20   20

494 *Allium
sphaerocephalon*

495 Halloumi

(Des Manolis Emmanouel. Litho Veridos Matsoukis)

2018 (12 Feb). Wild Flowers of Cyprus (2nd series). T **494** and similar vert
designs. Multicoloured. P 13×13½.
1432   34c. Type **494** 75   30
1433   41c. *Anthemis tricolor* .... 1·00   40
1434   64c. *Onobrychis venosa* .... 1·50   60
1435   €1.88 *Tragopogon porrifolius* .... 4·25   4·75
1432/1435 *Set of 4* .... 6·75   6·25

(Des Nicos Ierodiaconu. Litho Veridos Matsoukis)

2018 (28 Mar). Halloumi (Cypriot cheese). P 14.
1436   **495** 41c. multicoloured .... 1·00   80

496 Football Match

(Des Melanie Efstathiadou. Litho Veridos Matsoukis)

2018 (28 Mar). Football World Cup Championships, Russia. P 14.
1437   **496**   64c. multicoloured .... 1·40   1·50

497 Marios Tokas

(Des Marianna Iacovou. Litho Veridos Matsoukis)

2018 (27 Apr). Tenth Death Anniversary of Marios Tokas (1954–2008, composer of traditional music). P 13×14.
1438   **497**   64c. multicoloured .... 1·40   1·50

498 Kelefos Bridge

(Des Ioanna Kalli. Litho Veridos Matsoukis)

2018 (2 May). Europa. Bridges. T **498** and similar horiz design. Multicoloured. P 14.
1439   34c. Type **498** 70   70
        a. Booklet pane. Nos. 1439/1440, each×4.... 6·50
1440   64c. Akapnou Bridge .... 1·10   1·40
   Booklet pane No. 1439a has the horizontal edges imperforate and margins at left and right.

499 Traditional Buildings in Old Town of Lefkosia

(Des Panayiota Epifaniou. Litho Veridos Matsoukis)

2018 (9 July). Euromed. Houses of the Mediterranean. P 14.
1441   **499**   64c. multicoloured .... 1·50   1·75

500 Emblem

(Des Manolis Emmanouel. Litho Veridos Matsoukis)

2018 (9 July). 25th Anniversary of Interparliamentary Assembly on Orthodoxy (IAO). P 13½×14.
1442   **500**   64c. multicoloured .... 1·50   1·75

501 *Carduelis carduelis* (European Goldfinch)

(Des Melani Efstathiadou. Litho Veridos Matsoukis)

2018 (27 Sept). Birds of Cyprus. T **501** and similar horiz designs. Multicoloured. P 14.
1443   34c. Type **501** 80   70
1444   64c. *Chloris chloris* (European Greenfinch) ...... 1·50   1·75
1445   €1 *Fringilla coelebs* (Common Chaffinch)   2·40   2·75
1443/1445 *Set of 3* .... 4·25   4·75

502 Children with Snowman   **503** Birth of Christ Icon, Church of Panagia Odigitria, Galata

(Des Antonia Hadjigeorgiou and Yiota Tsiaklidou. Litho Veridos Matsoukis)

2018 (8 Nov). Christmas. Horiz designs as Types **502** and **503**. Multicoloured. P 14.
1446   34c. Type **502** 80   70
1447   41c. Type **503** .... 1·00   1·25
1448   64c. Girl and boy carol singers with girl also playing triangle .... 1·50   1·75
        a. Horiz pair. Nos. 1448/1449 .... 3·00   3·50
1449   64c. Boy and girl carol singers with boy also playing drum and girl holding small Christmas tree .... 1·50   1·75
1446/1449 *Set of 4* .... 4·25   5·00
   Nos. 1448/1449 were printed together, *se-tenant*, as horizontal pairs in sheetlets of 8 (4×2), each pair forming a composite design.

MACHINE LABELS

From 29 May 1989 gummed labels in the above design, ranging in value from 1c. to £99.99, were available from machines at Eleftheria Square PO, Nicosia ('001') (until 1991), District Post Office, Nicosia ('001') (1991 to January 1992) and District PO, Limassol ('002') (until January 1999).

Machines issuing labels in a revised design (above) were gradually introduced from 12 May 1999 onwards. The multicoloured labels exist with or without machine number indicator and were initially available with face values of 11, 16, 21, 26, 31, 41 and 75 cents. Subsequent rate changes in further values.

From 2 January 2002 labels in five different designs depicting wild flowers of Cyprus with face values of 14c., 21c., 26c., 31c., 41c. and £1 were available from machines at Nicosia and Limassol District Post Offices and Agia Napa and Kato Paphos Post Offices. From May 2002 they were also available from Larnaca and Famagusta.

From 3 March 2005 labels in two different designs showing Apricot blossom and Poppies with face values of 14c., 21c., 26c., 31c., 41c. and £1 were available from machines at Nicosia, Famagusta, Limassol, Paphos and Larnaca.

STAMP BOOKLETS

Stamp-vending machines were introduced by the Cyprus Post Office in 1962. These were originally fitted to provide stamps to the value of 50m., but in 1979 some were converted to accept 100m. coins and, a year later, others were altered to supply 150, 200 or 300m. worth of stamps.

The stamps contained in these booklets were a haphazard selection of low values to the required amount, attached by their sheet margins to the cardboard covers. From 1968 these covers carried commercial advertising and details of postage rates.

Following the change of currency in 1983 the machines were converted to supply 5, 10, 20 or 30c. booklets.

B **1** World 'Stamp' and Magnifying Glass

1998 (9 Oct). World Stamp Day. Multicoloured cover, 98×60 mm, as T B **1**. Pane attached by selvedge.
SB1   £2·40 booklet containing pane of 8×30c. (No. 960a) .... 13·00

B **2** Turtles on Beach at Lara Reserve

1999 (6 May). Europa. Parks and Gardens. Multicoloured cover, 100×95 mm, as T B **2**. Pane attached by selvedge.
SB2   £1·80 booklet containing se-tenant pane of eight
      (No. 969a) (4×2).. 11·00

B **3** River Diarizos

2001 (3 May). Europa. Cypriot Rivers. Multicoloured cover, 100×95 mm, as T B **3**. Pane attached by selvedge.
SB3   £2 booklet containing se-tenant pane of eight
      (No. 1015a).. 11·00

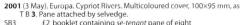

B **4** Clown on High Wire

2002 (9 May). Europa. Circus. Multicoloured cover, 101×96 mm, as T B **4**. Pane attached by selvedge.
SB4   £2 booklet containing se-tenant pane of eight
      (No. 1029a).. 11·00

B **5**

2003 (8 May). Europa. Poster Art. Multicoloured cover, 101×94 mm, as T B **5**. Pane attached by selvedge.
SB5   £2 booklet containing se-tenant pane of eight
      (No. 1051b) .... 9·00

B **6** Family at Seaside and Statue

2004 (1 May). Europa. Holidays. Multicoloured cover, 100×75 mm, as T B **6**. Pane attached by selvedge.
SB6   £2 booklet containing se-tenant pane of eight
      (No. 1073a).. 10·00

B **7** Table with Coffee, Cheese, Cocktail and Desserts

2005 (5 May). Europa. Gastronomy. Multicoloured cover, 95×90 mm, as T B **7**. Pane attached by selvedge.
SB7   £2 booklet containing *se-tenant* pane of eight
            (No. 1096ab) .... 9·00

B **10** Scout Badge and Stylised Figure

2007 (3 May). Europa. Centenary of Scouting. Multicoloured cover, 86×92 mm, as T B **10**. Pane attached by selvedge.
SB10   £2·80 booklet containing *se-tenant* pane of eight
            (No. 1133a).. 14·00

B **8** Hunter with Hungarian Vizsla and Man with Labrador Guide Dog

2005 (16 June). Dogs in Man's Life. Black and grey cover, 95×75 mm, as T B **8**. Pane attached by selvedge.
SB8   £1·03 booklet containing *se-tenant* pane of four
            (No. 1098a).. 5·25

B **11** Letters

2008 (2 May). Europa. The Letter. Multicoloured cover, 85×90 mm, as T B **11**. Pane attached by selvedge.
SB11   €4.76 booklet containing *se-tenant* pane of eight
            (No. 1162a).. 14·00

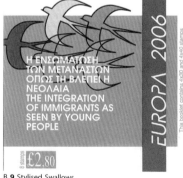

B **9** Stylised Swallows

2006 (4 May). Europa. Integration. Multicoloured cover, 99×95 mm, as T B **9**. Pane attached by selvedge.
SB9   £2·80 booklet containing *se-tenant* pane of eight
            (No. 1110ab).. 14·00

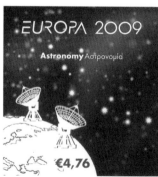

B **12** Telescopes on Earth and Starry Sky

2009 (4 May). Europa. Astronomy. Multicoloured cover, 85×90 mm, as T B **12**. Pane attached by selvedge.
SB12   €4.76 booklet containing *se-tenant* pane of eight
            (No. 1188a).. 14·00

B **13** Flowering Tree, Tulip and Sun

2010 (5 May). Europa. Children's Books. Multicoloured cover, 85×91 mm, as T B **13**. Pane attached by selvedge.
SB13   €4.08 booklet containing *se-tenant* pane of eight
(No. 1219b) .... 12·00

B **14** Forest

2011 (4 May). Europa. Forests. Multicoloured cover, 105×70 mm, as T B **14**. Stamps attached by selvedge.
SB14   €4.76 booklet containing *se-tenant* pane of eight
(No. 1246b) .... 20·00

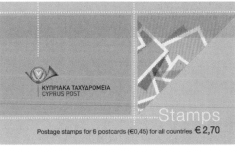

B **15** *(illustration further reduced)*

2011 (26 July). Booklet Stamps for Postcards. Multicoloured cover, 150×90 mm, as T B **15**. Self-adhesive.
SB15   €2.70 booklet containing pane of 6×2c. and 6×43c.
(No. 1255a) .... 14·00

B **16** Hare and Tortoise

2011 (5 Oct). Aesop's Fables (1st series). *The Hare and the Tortoise.* Multicoloured cover, 90×90 mm, as T B **16**. Self-adhesive.
SB16   €1.70 booklet containing *se-tenant* pane of 5×34c.
(No. 1257a) .... 5·75

B **17** Family and Sunset

2012 (2 May). Europa. Visit Cyprus. Multicoloured cover, 105×80 mm, as T B **17**. Pane attached by selvedge.
SB17   €4.76 booklet containing *se-tenant* pane of eight
(No. 1275ab) .... 17·00

2012 (3 Oct). Aesop's Fables (2nd series). *The Cricket and the Ant.* Multicoloured cover, 90×90 mm, as T B **16**. Self-adhesive.
SB18   €1.70 booklet containing *se-tenant* pane of 5×34c.
(No. 1281a) .... 5·75

B **18**

2013 (2 May). Europa. Postal Vehicles. Multicoloured cover, 105×70 mm, as T B **18**. Stamps attached by selvedge.
SB19   €3.40 booklet containing *se-tenant* pane of eight
(No. 1297a) .... 13·00

B **19** Spanos and Dragons

2013 (13 Nov). *Spanos and the Forty Dragons* (folk tale). Multicoloured cover, 91×90 mm, as T B **19**. Self-adhesive.
SB20   €1.70 booklet containing *se-tenant* pane of 5×34c.
(No. 1307a) .... 5·75

B **20** Laouton (lute)

2014 (2 May). Europa. National Musical Instruments. Multicoloured cover, 105×70 mm, as T B **20**. Pane attached by selvedge.
SB21   €3.40 booklet containing *se-tenant* pane of eight
(No. 1320a).. 11·00

B **21**

2014 (24 Nov). *The Prince of Venice* (folk tale). Multicoloured cover, 91×90 mm, as T B **21**. Self-adhesive.
SB22   €2.05 booklet containing *se-tenant* pane of 5×41c.
(No. 1354a).. 6·75

B **22** Boys playing Marbles

2015 (5 May). Europa. Old Toys. Multicoloured cover, 79×94 mm, as T B **22**. Stamps attached by selvedge.
SB23   €3.92 booklet containing *se-tenant* pane of eight
(No. 1369a).. 9·00

B **23** Family in Green Landscape with Wind Turbines

2016 (9 May). Europa. Think Green. Multicoloured cover, 104×69 mm, as T B **23**. Stamps attached by selvedge.
SB24   €3.92 booklet containing *se-tenant* pane of eight
(No. 1394a).. 8·00

B **24** Pafos Castle

2017 (4 May). Europa. Castles. Multicoloured cover, 105×70 mm, as T B **24**. Stamps attached by selvedge.
SB25   €4.20 booklet containing *se-tenant* pane of eight
(No. 1420a).. 8·50

B **25** Akapnou Bridge

2018 (2 May). Europa. Bridges. Multicoloured cover, 105×70 mm, as T B **25**. Stamps attached by selvedge.
SB26   €3.92 booklet containing *se-tenant* pane of eight
(No. 1439a).. 6·50

Turkish Cypriot Posts

After the inter-communal clashes during December 1963, a separate postal service was established on 6 January 1964 between some of the Turkish Cypriot areas, using handstamps inscribed 'KIBRIS TURK POSTALARI' around a moon and star device. The Handstamps of some offices included the date '6.1.64' between two stars, the remainder showed a single star at foot. During 1964, however, an agreement was reached between representatives of the two communities for the restoration of postal services. This agreement, to which the United Nations representatives were a party, was ratified in November 1966 by the Republic's Council of Ministers. Under the scheme postal services were provided for the Turkish Cypriot communities in Famagusta, Larnaca, Limassol, Lefka, Nicosia and Paphos staffed by Turkish Cypriot employees of the Cypriot Department of Posts.

On 8 April 1970 5m. and 15m. locally-produced labels, originally designated 'Social Aid Stamps', were issued by the Turkish Cypriot community and these can be found on commercial covers. These local stamps are outside the scope of this catalogue.

On 29 October 1973 Nos. 1/7 were placed on sale, but were used only on mail between the Turkish Cypriot areas.

Following the intervention by the Republic of Turkey on 20 July 1974, these stamps replaced issues of the Republic of Cyprus in that part of the island, north and east of the Attila Line, controlled by the Autonomous Turkish Cypriot Administration.

(Currency. 1000 mils = £1)

1 50th Anniversary Emblem   (2)

(Des F. Direkoglu Miss E. Ata and G. Pir. Litho Darbhane, Istanbul)

1974 (27 July*). 50th Anniversary of Republic of Turkey. T **1** and similar designs in vermilion and black (15m.) or multicoloured (others). P 12×11½ (vert) or 11½×12 (horiz).

1	3m. Woman sentry (vert)	32·00	32·00
2	5m. Military Parade, Nicosia	60	40
3	10m. Man and woman with Turkish flags (vert)	50	20
4	15m. Type **1**	2·50	1·50
5	20m. Atatürk statue, Kyrenia Gate, Nicosia (vert)	70	20
6	50m. The Fallen (vert)	2·00	1·50
7	70m. Turkish flag and map of Cyprus	17·00	17·00
1/7 Set of 7		50·00	50·00

* This is the date on which Nos. 1/7 became valid for international mail.

On 13 February 1975 a Turkish Cypriot Federated State was proclaimed in that part of Cyprus under Turkish occupation and later 9,000 Turkish Cypriots were transferred from the South to the North of the island.

1975 (3 Mar). Proclamation of the Turkish Federated State of Cyprus. Nos. 3 and 5 surch as T **2** by Halkin Sesi, Nicosia.

8	30m. on 20m. Atatürk statue, Kyrenia Gate, Nicosia	50	75
9	100m. on 10m. Man and woman with Turkish flags	1·00	1·50

On No. 9 the surcharge appears at the top of the stamp and the inscription at the bottom.

3 Namik Kemal's Bust, Famagusta

4 Map of Cyprus

(Des I. Özisik. Litho Güzel Sanatlar Matbaasi, Ankara)

1975 (21 Apr). Multicoloured designs as T **3**. Imprint at foot with date '1975'. P 13.

10	3m. Type **3**	15	40
11	10m. Atatürk Statue, Nicosia	25	10
12	15m. St Hilarion Castle	35	20
13	20m. Atatürk Square, Nicosia	45	20

14	25m. Famagusta Beach	45	30
15	30m. Kyrenia Harbour	55	10
16	50m. Lala Mustafa Pasha Mosque, Famagusta (vert)	60	10
17	100m. Interior, Kyrenia Castle	80	90
18	250m. Castle walls, Kyrenia	1·00	2·25
19	500m. Othello Tower, Famagusta (vert)	1·50	4·50
10/19 Set of 10		5·50	8·00

See also Nos. 25/26 and 37/38.

(Des B. Erkmen (30m.), S. Tuga (50m.), N. Cünes (160m.). Litho Ajans-Türk Matbaasi, Ankara)

1975 (20 July). Peace in Cyprus. T **4** and similar multicoloured designs. P 13.

20	30m. Type **4**	20	15
21	50m. Map, Laurel and broken chain	25	20
22	150m. Map and Laurel-sprig on globe (vert)	65	1·40
20/22 Set of 3		1·00	1·60

5 Pomegranates (I. V. Guney)

(Litho Güzel Sanatlar Matbaasi, Ankara)

1975 (29 Dec). Europa. Paintings. T **5** and similar horiz design. Multicoloured. P 13.

23	90m. Type **5**	1·40	1·75
24	100m. Harvest Time (F. Direkoglu)	1·40	1·75

10 M ———
(6)

7 Expectation

1976 (28 Apr). Nos. 16/17 surch as T **6** at Government Printing House, Nicosia in horizontal clichés of ten.

25	10m. on 50m. Lala Mustafa Pasha Mosque, Famagusta	35	70
26	30m. on 100m. Interior, Kyrenia Castle	35	80

(Litho Ajans-Türk Matbaasi, Ankara)

1976 (3 May). Europa. T **7** and similar vert design showing ceramic statuette. Multicoloured. P 13.

27	60m. Type **7**	60	80
28	120m. Man in Meditation	80	1·75

8 Carob

9 Olympic Symbol 'Flower'

(Des S. Atlihan. Litho Güzel Sanatlar Matbaasi, Ankara)

1976 (28 June). Export Products. Fruits. T **8** and similar horiz designs. Multicoloured. P 13.

29	10m. Type **8**	15	10
30	25m. Mandarin	20	10
31	40m. Strawberry	25	25
32	60m. Orange	35	50
33	80m. Lemon	40	1·50
29/33 Set of 5		1·25	2·25

See also Nos. 74/77.

(Des C. Mutver (60m.), A. B. Kocamanoglu (100m.). Litho Güzel Sanatlar Matbaasi, Ankara)

1976 (17 July). Olympic Games, Montréal. T **9** and similar horiz design. Multicoloured. P 13.

34	60m. Type **9**	25	20
35	100m. Olympic symbol and Doves	35	25

10 Kyrenia Harbour

11 Liberation Monument, Karaeglanoolu (Ay. Georghios)

(Des I. Özisik. Litho Ajans-Türk Matbaasi, Ankara)

1976 (2 Aug). New design (5m.) or as Nos. 12/13 but redrawn with lettering altered and new imprint at foot with date '1976'. P 13.

36	5m. Type **10**	40	15
37	15m. St Hilarion Castle	40	15
38	20m. Atatürk Square, Nicosia	40	15
36/38 Set of 3		1·10	40

Nos. 39/46 are vacant.

(Des D. Erimez and C. Gizer. Litho Ajans-Türk Matbaasi, Ankara)

1976 (1 Nov). Liberation Monument. T **11** and similar vert design. P 13.

47	**11**	30m. light turquoise-blue, light flesh and black	15	20
48	–	150m. light vermilion, light flesh and black	35	80

No. 48 shows a different view of the Monument.

12 Hotel, Salamis Bay

(Litho Türk Tarih Kurumu Basimevi, Ankara)

1977 (2 May). Europa. T **12** and similar horiz design. Multicoloured. P 13.

49	80m. Type **12**	65	1·10
50	100m. Kyrenia Port	75	1·10

13 Pottery

14 Arap Ahmet Pasha Mosque, Nicosia

(Litho Güzel Sanatlar Matbaasi, Ankara)

1977 (27 June). Handicrafts. T **13** and similar designs. Multicoloured. P 13.

51	15m. Type **13**	10	10
52	30m. Decorated gourds (vert)	10	10
53	125m. Basketware	30	50
51/53 Set of 3		40	65

(Litho APA Ofset Baeimevi, Istanbul)

1977 (2 Dec). Turkish Buildings in Cyprus. T **14** and similar horiz designs. Multicoloured. P 13.

54	20m. Type **14**	10	10
55	40m. Paphos Castle	10	10
56	70m. Bekir Pasha aqueduct	15	20
57	80m. Sultan Mahmut library	15	25
54/57 Set of 4		45	60

15 Namik Kemal (bust) and House, Famagusta

16 Old Man and Woman

(Des B. Ozak. Litho Ticaret Matbaacilik TAS, Izmir)

1977 (21 Dec). Namik Kemal (patriotic poet). T **15** and similar multicoloured design. P 12½×13 (30m.) or 13×12½ (140m.).

58	30m. Type **15**	15	15
59	140m. Namik Kemal (portrait) (vert)	35	60

(New Currency. 100 kurus = 1 lira)

(Des G. Pir. Litho Ajans-Türk Matbaasi, Ankara)

1978 (17 Apr). Social Security. T **16** and similar vert designs. P 13×13½.

60	150k. black, yellow and blue	10	10
61	275k. black, red-orange and green	15	15
62	375k. black, blue and red-orange	25	20
60/62 Set of 3		45	40

Designs: 150k. T **16**; 275k. Injured man with crutch; 375k. Woman with family.

17 Oratory in Büyük Han, Nicosia

18 Motorway Junction

(Des I. Özisik. Litho APA Ofset Basimevi, Istanbul)

1978 (2 May). Europa. T **17** and similar horiz design. Multicoloured. P 13.

63	225k. Type **17**	75	50
64	450k. Cistern in Selimiye Mosque, Nicosia	1·00	1·50

(Litho APA Ofset Basimevi, Istanbul)

1978 (10 July). Communications. T **18** and similar horiz designs. Multicoloured. P 13.

65	75k. Type **18**	15	10
66	100k. Hydrofoil	15	10
67	650k. Boeing 720 at Ercan Airport	50	60
65/67 Set of 3		70	70

19 Dove with Laurel Branch

20 Kemal Atatürk

(Des E. Kaya (725k.), C. Kirkbesoglu (others). Litho APA Ofset Basimevi, Istanbul)

1978 (13 Sept). National Oath. T **19** and similar designs. P 13.

68	150k. orange-yellow, violet and black	10	10
69	225k. black, Indian red and orange-yellow	10	10
70	725k. black, cobalt and orange-yellow	20	20
68/70 Set of 3		35	35

Designs: Vert—225k. Taking the Oath. Horiz—150k. T **19**; 725k. Symbolic Dove.

(Des C. Mutver. Litho Türk Tarih Kurumu Basimevi, Ankara)

1978 (10 Nov). Kemal Atatürk Commemoration. P 13.

71	**20**	75k. pale turquoise-green and turquoise-green	10	10
72		450k. pale flesh and light brown	15	15
73		650k. pale blue and light blue	20	25
71/73 Set of 3			40	40

50 Krs.
XXXXX
(21)

22 Gun Barrel with Olive
Branch and Map of Cyprus

1979 (4 June). Nos. 30/33 surch as T **21**, by Government Printing Office, Lefkosa.

74	50k. on 25m. Mandarin	10	10
75	1l. on 40m. Strawberry	15	10
76	3l. on 60m. Orange	15	10
77	5l. on 80m. Lemon	35	15
74/77 *Set of 4*		65	30

(Des N. Dündar. Litho Ajans-Türk Matbaasi, Ankara)

1979 (20 July). Fifth Anniversary of Turkish Peace Operation in Cyprus. Sheet 72×52 mm. Imperf.

MS78 **22** 15l. black, deep turquoise-blue and pale
green 80   1·00

23 Postage Stamp and Map of
Cyprus

24 Symbolised
Microwave Antenna

(Des S. Mumcu. Litho Ajans-Türk Matbaasi, Ankara)

1979 (20 Aug). Europa. Communications. T **23** and similar horiz designs. Multicoloured. P 13.

79	2l. Type **23**	20	10
80	3l. Postage stamps, building and map	20	10
81	8l. Telephones, Earth and satellite	70	30
79/81 *Set of 3*		1·00	45

(Litho Ticaret Matbaacilik TAS, Izmir)

1979 (24 Sept). 50th Anniversary of International Consultative Radio Committee. P 13×12½.

82	**24**	2l. multicoloured	20	10
83		5l. multicoloured	20	10
84		6l. multicoloured	25	15
82/84 *Set of 3*			60	30

25 School Children

26 Lala Mustafa
Pasha Mosque,
Magusa

(Des H. Hastürk (1½l.) G. Akansel (4½l.), P. Yalyali (6l.). Litho APA Ofset Basimevi, Istanbul)

1979 (29 Oct). International Year of the Child. Children's Drawings. T **25** and similar multicoloured designs. P 13.

85	1½l. Type **25**	25	20
86	4½l. Children and globe (*horiz*)	40	45
87	6l. College children	60	45
85/87 *Set of 3*		1·10	1·00

(Des S. Mumcu (20l.), I. Özisik (others). Litho Ajans-Türk Matbaasi, Ankara)

1980 (23 Mar). Islamic Commemorations. T **26** and similar vert designs. Multicoloured. P 13.

88	2½l. Type **26**	10	10
89	10l. Arap Ahmet Pasha Mosque, Lefkosa	30	15
90	20l. Mecca and Medina	50	20
88/90 *Set of 3*		80	40

Commemorations: 2½l. First Islamic Conference in Turkish Cyprus; 10l. General Assembly of World Islam Congress; 20l. Moslem Year 1400AH.

27 Ebu-Su'ud Efendi
(philosopher)

28 Omer's Shrine, Kyrenia

(Litho Ajans-Türk Matbaasi, Ankara)

1980 (23 May). Europa. Personalities. T **27** and similar vert design. Multicoloured.

91	5l. Type **27**	20	10
92	30l. Sultan Selim II	80	40

(Litho Güzel Sanatlar Matbaasi, Ankara)

1980 (25 June). Ancient Monuments, T **28** and similar horiz designs. P 13.

93	2½l. new blue and stone	10	10
94	3½l. grey-green and pale rose-pink	10	10
95	5l. lake and pale blue-green	15	10
96	10l. deep mauve and pale green	20	10
97	20l. dull ultramarine and pale greenish yellow	35	25
93/97 *Set of 5*		70	45

Designs: 2½l. T **28**; 3½l. Entrance gate, Famagusta; 5l. Funerary monuments (16th-century), Famagusta; 10l. Bella Poise Abbey, Kyrenia; 20l. Selimiye Mosque, Nicosia.
See also No. 204/206.

29 Cyprus 1880 6d.

30 Dome of the
Rock

(Des S. Mumcu. Litho Ajans-Türk Matbaasi, Ankara)

1980 (16 Aug). Cyprus Stamp Centenary. T **29** and similar designs showing stamps. P 14.

98	7½l. black, drab and grey-olive	20	10
99	15l. brown, grey-blue and blue	25	10
100	50l. black, rose and grey	65	60
98/100 *Set of 3*		1·00	70

Designs: Horiz—15l. Cyprus 1960 Constitution of the Republic 30m. commemorative. Vert—7½l. T **29**; 50l. Social Aid local, 1970.

(Litho Güzel Sanatlar Matbaasi, Ankara)

1980 (16 Oct). Palestinian Solidarity. T **30** and similar multicoloured design. P 13.

101	15l. Type **30**	30	15
102	35l. Dome of the Rock (*horiz*)	70	30

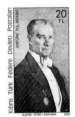

31 Extract from World
Muslim Congress
Statement in Turkish

32 Atatürk
(F. Duran)

(Des S. Mumcu. Litho Türk Tarih Kurumu Basimevi, Ankara)

1981 (24 Mar). Solidarity with Islamic Countries Day. T **31** and similar vert design showing extract from World Muslim Congress statement. P 13.

103	1l. rosine, stone and olive-sepia	15	75
104	35l. black, pale blue-green and myrtle-green	55	1·00

Designs: 1l. T **31**; 35l. Extract in English.

(Litho Ajans-Türk Matbaasi, Ankara)

1981 (19 May). Atatürk Stamp Exhibition, Lefkosa. P 13.
105 **32** 20l. multicoloured........................ 25 35
No. 105 was printed in sheets of 100, including 50 *se-tenant* stamp-size labels.

33 Folk-dancing

(Litho Tiçaret Matbaacilik TAS, Izmir)

1981 (29 June). Europa, Folklore. T **33** and similar horiz design showing folk-dancing. P 12½×13.
106 10l. Type **33** multicoloured........................ 40 25
107 30l. multicoloured........................ 60 1·25

34 *Kemal Atatürk* (I. Calli) **35** Wild Convolvulus

(Litho Basim Ofset, Ankara)

1981 (23 July). Birth Centenary of Kemal Atatürk. Sheet 70×96 mm. Imperf.
MS108 **34** 150l. multicoloured........................ 1·10 1·25

(Litho Türk Tarih Kurumu Basimevi, Ankara)

1981 (28 Sept)–**82**. Flowers, Multicoloured designs as T **35**. P 13.
109 1l. Type **35**........................ 10 10
110 5l. Persian Cyclamen (*horiz*) (22.1.82)........................ 10 10
111 10l. Spring Mandrake (*horiz*)........................ 10 15
112 25l. Corn Poppy........................ 15 20
113 30l. Wild Arum (22.1.82)........................ 15 10
114 50l. Sage-leaved Rock Rose (*horiz*) (22.1.82)........................ 20 20
115 100l. *Cistus salviaefolius L.* (22.1.82)........................ 30 30
116 150l. Giant Fennel (*horiz*)........................ 50 1·00
109/116 *Set of 8*........................ 1·40 1·75
See also Nos. 144/147 and 207.

36 Stylised Disabled Person in Wheelchair

37 Turkish and Palestinian Flags

(Des H. Uluçam (7½l.), N. Kozal (others). Litho Türk Tarih Kurumu Basimevi, Ankara)

1981 (16 Oct). Commemorations. T **36** and similar multicoloured designs. P 13.
117 7½l. Type **36**........................ 25 35
118 10l. Heads of people of different races, Peace Dove and barbed wire (*vert*)........................ 35 55
119 20l. People of different races reaching out from globe, with dishes (*vert*)........................ 50 85
117/119 *Set of 3*........................ 1·00 1·60
Commemorations: 7½l. International Year for Disabled Persons; 10l. Anti-apartheid Publicity; 20l. World Food Day.

(Des H. Uluçam. Litho Türk Tarih Kurumu Basimevi, Ankara)

1981 (29 Nov). Palestinian Solidarity. P 13.
120 **37** 10l. multicoloured........................ 45 60

38 Prince Charles and Lady Diana Spencer

39 Charter issued by Sultan Abdul Aziz to Archbishop Sophronios

(Des H. Uluçam. Litho Türk Tarih Kurumu Basimevi, Ankara)

1981 (30 Nov). Royal Wedding. P 13.
121 **38** 50l. multicoloured........................ 1·00 85

(Des H. Uluçam, Litho Tezel Ofset, Lefkosa)

1982 (30 July). Europa (CEPT). Sheet 83×124 mm containing T **39** and similar vert design. Multicoloured. P 12½×13.
MS122 30l.×2. Type **39**×2; 70l.×2, Turkish forces landing at Tuzla, 1571×2........................ 3·50 4·50

40 Buffavento Castle **41** *Wedding* (A. Örek)

(Des H. Uluçam. (Nos. 123/125). Litho Tezel Ofset, Lefkosa)

1982 (20 Aug). Tourism. T **40** and similar multicoloured designs. P 12.
123 5l. Type **40**........................ 10 10
124 10l. Windsurfing (*horiz*)........................ 15 10
125 15l. Kantara Castle (*horiz*)........................ 25 15
126 30l. Shipwreck (300 BC) (*horiz*)........................ 60 40
123/126 *Set of 4*........................ 1·00 65

(Litho Ajans-Türk Matbaasi, Ankara)

1982 (3 Dec). Art (1st series). T **41** and similar multicoloured design. P 13.
127 30l. Type **41**........................ 15 30
128 50l. *Carob Pickers* (Naxim Selenge) (*vert*)........................ 30 70
See also Nos. 132/133, 157/158, 176/177, 185/186, 208/209, 225/227, 248/250, 284/285, 315/316, 328/329, 369/370, 436/437, 567/568, 629/630 and 654/655.

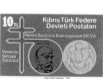

42 Cross of Lorraine, Koch and Bacillus (Centenery of Koch's Discovery of Tubercle Bacillus)

43 Calloused Hands (Salih Oral)

(Des H. Uluçam. Litho Tezel Ofset, Lefkosa)

1982 (15 Dec). Anniversaries and Events. T **42** and similar multicoloured designs. P 12.
129 10l. Type **42**........................ 1·00 25
130 30l. Spectrum on football pitch (World Cup Football Championships, Spain)........................ 1·00 50
131 70l. '75' and Lord Baden-Powell (75th Anniversary of Boy Scout movement and 125th birth anniversary) (*vert*)........................ 1·10 2·50
129/131 *Set of 3*........................ 2·75 3·00

(Litho Ajans-Türk Matbaasi, Ankara)

1983 (16 May). Art (2nd series). T **43** and similar vert design. Multicoloured. P 13.

132	30l.	Type **43**	55	1·00
133	35l.	*Malya—Limassol Bus* (Emin Cizenel)	55	1·00

44 Old Map of Cyprus by Piri Reis

45 First Turkish Cypriot 10m. Stamp

(Litho Türk Tarih Kurumu Basimevi, Ankara)

1983 (30 June). Europa. Sheet 82×78 mm, containing T **44** and similar horiz design. Multicoloured. P 13.

MS134 100l. Type **44**; 100l. Cyprus as seen from *Skylab* .   30·00   15·00

(Des E. Ata (15l.), A. Hasan (20l.), G. Pir (25l.), H. Uluçam (others). Litho Ajans-Türk Matbaasi, Ankara)

1983 (1 Aug). Anniversaries and Events. T **45** and similar multicoloured designs commemorating World Communications Year (30, 50l.) or 25th Anniversary of TMT (Turkish Cypriot Resistance Organisation). P 13.

135	15l.	Type **45**	90	50
136	20l.	Turkish Achievements in Cyprus (*horiz*) ..	90	60
137	25l.	Liberation Fighters	1·00	80
138	30l.	Dish aerial and telegraph pole (*horiz*)......	1·25	1·50
139	50l.	Dove and envelopes (*horiz*)	2·75	3·75
135/139 Set of 5			6·25	6·50

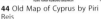

46 European Bee-eater

(47)

(Des E. Çizenel. Litho Ajans-Türk Matbaasi, Ankara)

1983 (10 Oct). Birds of Cyprus. T **46** and similar horiz designs. Multicoloured. P 13.

140	10l.	Type **46**	65	1·25
		a. Block of 4. Nos. 140/143	3·00	4·50
141	15l.	Eurasian Goldfinch	80	1·25
142	50l.	European Robin	90	1·25
143	65l.	Golden Oriole	1·00	1·25
140/143 Set of 4			3·00	4·50

Nos. 140/143 were printed together, *se-tenant*, in blocks of four throughout the sheet.

1983 (7 Dec). Establishment of the Republic. Nos. 109, 111/112 and 116 surch as T **47** (No. 145) or optd only.

144	10l.	Spring Mandrake	20	15
145	15l.	on 1l. Type **35**	20	15
		a. Surch inverted	80·00	
146	25l.	Corn Poppy	25	25
147	150l.	Giant Fennel	1·25	2·75
144/147 Set of 4			1·75	3·00

48 CEPT 25th Anniversary Logo.

49 Olympic Flame

(Des J. Larrivière. Litho Tezel Ofset, Lefkosa)

1984 (30 May). Europa. P 12×12½.

148	**48**	50l. lemon, chestnut and black	1·75	3·00
		a. Pair. Nos. 148/149	3·50	6·00

149		100l. pale blue, bright blue and black......	1·75	3·00

Nos. 148/149 were printed together, *se-tenant*, in horizontal and vertical pairs throughout the sheet.

(Des H. Uluçam. Litho Tezel Ofset, Lefkosa)

1984 (19 June). Olympic Games, Los Angeles. T **49** and similar multicoloured designs. P 12½×12 (10l.) or 12×12½ (others).

150	10l.	Type **49**	15	10
151	20l.	Olympic events within rings (*horiz*)	35	25
152	70l.	Martial arts event (*horiz*)	60	1·75
150/152 Set of 3			1·00	1·90

50 Atatürk Cultural Centre

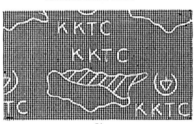

51

(Des H. Uluçam. Litho Tezel Ofset, Lefkosa)

1984 (20 July). Opening of Atatürk Cultural Centre, Lefkosa. W **51**. P 12×12½.

153	**50**	120l. stone, black and chestnut	1·25	1·75

52 Turkish Cypriot Flag and Map

(Des C. Güzeloglu (20l.), M. Gozbebek (70l.). Litho Tezel Ofset, Lefkosa)

1984 (20 July). Tenth Anniversary of Turkish Landings in Cyprus. T **52** and similar horiz design. Multicoloured. W **51**. P 12×12½.

154	20l.	Type **52**	50	25
155	70l.	Turkish Cypriot flag within book	1·00	2·00

53 Burnt and Replanted Forests

(Des H. Uluçam. Litho Tezel Ofset, Lefkosa)

1984 (20 Aug). World Forestry Resources. W **51**. P 12×12½.

156	**53**	90l. multicoloured	1·25	1·75

54 *Old Turkish Houses, Nicosia* (Cevdet Cagdas)

55 Kemal Atatürk, Flag and Crown

(Litho Tezel Ofset, Lefkosa)

1984 (21 Sept). Art (3rd series). T **54** and similar horiz design. Multicoloured. W **51**. P 13×12½.

157	20l. Type **54**..	50	40
158	70l. *Scenery* (Olga Rauf).................................	1·10	2·00

See also Nos. 176/177, 185/186, 208/209, 225/227, 248/250, 284/285, 315/316 and 328/329.

(Des H. Uluçam (20l.), F. Isiman 70l.). Litho Tezel Ofset, Lefkosa)

1984 (15 Nov). First Anniversary of Turkish Republic of Northern Cyprus. T **55** and similar multicoloured design. W **51** (sideways on 20 l., inverted on 70 l.). P 12½.

159	20l. Type **55**..	50	40
160	70l. Legislative Assembly voting for Republic (*horiz*)...................................	1·10	2·00

56 Taekwondo Bout

57 *Le Regard*
(Saulo Mercader)

(Des H. Uluçam. Litho Tezel Ofset, Lefkosa)

1984 (10 Dec). International Taekwondo Championship, Girne. T **56** and similar horiz design. W **51** (sideways on 10l.). P 12½.

161	10l. black, pale cinnamon and grey-black......	40	25
162	70l. multicoloured..	1·60	2·50

Designs: 10l. T **56**; 70l. Emblem and flags of competing nations.

(Litho Tezel Ofset, Lefkosa)

1984 (10 Dec). Exhibition by Saulo Mercader (artist). T **57** and similar multicoloured design. W **51** (sideways on 20l.). P 12½×13 (20l.) or 13 ×12½ (70l.).

163	20l. Type **57**..	30	25
164	70l. *L'equilibre de L'esprit* (*horiz*)...............	1·10	2·25

58 Musical Instruments and Music

59 Dr. Fazil Küçük
(politician)

(Des H. Uluçam. Litho Tezel Ofset, Lefkosa)

1984 (10 Dec). Visit of Nurnberg Chamber Orchestra. W **51** (sideways). P 12½.

165	**58**	70l. multicoloured.....................	1·50	2·25

(Des Y. Calli (20l.), E. Çizenel (70l.). Litho Tezel Ofset, Lefkosa)

1985 (15 Jan). First Death Anniversary of Dr. Fazil Küçük (politician). T **59** and similar vert design. Multicoloured. W **51** (inverted on 70l.). P 12½×12.

166	20l. Type **59**..	25	30
167	70l. Dr. Fazil Küçük reading newspaper..........	75	2·00

60 Goat

61 George Frederick Handel

(Des E. Çizenel. Litho Tezel Ofset, Lefkosa)

1985 (29 May). Domestic Animals. T **60** and similar horiz designs. Multicoloured. W **51**. P 12×12½.

168	100l. Type **60**..	40	30
169	200l. Cow and calf..	70	80
170	300l. Ram...	80	1·75
171	500l. Donkey..	1·40	2·75
168/171	*Set of 4*...	3·00	5·00

(Litho Tezel Ofset, Lefkosa)

1985 (26 June). Europa. Composers. T **61** and similar vert designs. W **51** (sideways). P 12½×12.

172	20l. brown-purple, myrtle-green and pale green..	2·00	2·50
	a. Block of 4. Nos. 172/175....................	7·00	10·00
173	20l. brown-purple, lake-brown and pale pink	2·00	2·50
174	100l. brown-purple, steel blue and pale grey-blue..	2·00	3·00
175	100l. brown-purple, bistre-brown and pale cinnamon...	2·00	3·00
172/175	*Set of 4*...	7·00	10·00

Designs: No. 172, T **61**; No. 173, Guiseppe Domenico Scarlatti; No. 174, Johann Sebastian Bach; No. 175, Buhurizade Mustafa Itri Efendi.

Nos. 172/175 were printed together, *se-tenant*, in blocks of four throughout the sheet.

(Litho Tezel Ofset, Lefkosa)

1985 (15 Aug). Art (4th series). Vert designs as T **54**. Multicoloured. W **51**. P 12½×13.

176	20l. *Village Life* (Ali Atakan).......................	50	50
177	50l. *Woman carrying Water* (Ismet V. Güney)..	1·10	2·25

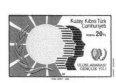

62 Heads of Three Youths

63 Parachutist
(Aviation League)

(Des H. Uluçam. Litho Tezel Ofset, Letkosa)

1985 (29 Oct). International Youth Year. T **62** and similar horiz design. Multicoloured. W **51** (sideways). P 12×12½.

178	20l. Type **62**..	75	40
179	100l. Dove and globe...................................	2·50	4·50

(Des H. Uluçam. Litho Tezel Ofset, Lefkosa)

1985 (29 Nov). Anniversaries and Events. T **63** and similar designs. W **51** (inverted on Nos, 181/182, sideways on No. 1834. P 12×12½ (No. 1834) or 12½×12 (others).

180	20l. multicoloured..	1·75	45
181	50l. grey-black. light brown and dull ultramarine...	2·00	1·25
182	100l. light brown...	1·75	2·75
183	100l. multicoloured......................................	1·75	2·75
184	100l. multicoloured......................................	2·25	2·75
180/184	*Set of 5*...	8·50	9·00

Designs: Vert—No. 180, T **63**; No. 181, Louis Pasteur (Centenary of Discovery of Rabies vaccine); No. 182 İsmet İnönü (Turkish statesman) (birth centenary (1984). Horiz—No. 183, '40' in figures and symbolic flower (40th Anniversary of United Nations Organisations; No. 184, Patient receiving blood transfusion (Prevention of Thalassaemia).

(Litho Tezel Ofset, Lefkosa)

1986 (20 June). Art (5th series). Horiz designs as T **54**. Multicoloured. W **51** (sideways). P 13×12½.

185	20l. *House with Arches* (Gönen Atakol)...........	40	30
186	100l. *Atatürk Square* (Yalkin Muhtaroglu).........	1·60	1·75

64 Griffon Vulture

(Des E. Çizenel (100l.), H. Uluçam (200l.). Litho Tezel Ofset, Lefkosa)

1986 (20 June). Europa. Protection of Nature and the Environment. Sheet 82×76 mm. containing T **64** and similar horiz design. Multicoloured. W **51** (sideways). P 12½×12.

MS187	100l. Type **64**; 200l. Litter on Cyprus landscape..		10·00	7·50

65 Karagöz Show Puppets

66 Old Bronze Age Composite Pottery

(Des Y. Yazgin. Litho Tezel Ofset, Lefkosa)

1986 (25 July). Karagöz Folk Puppets. W **51** (inverted). P 12½×13.

188	**65**	100l. multicoloured	1·75	2·50

(Litho Tezel Ofset, Lefkosa)

1886 (15 Sept). Archaeological Artifacts. Cultural Links with Anatolia. T **66** and similar multicoloured designs. W **51** (sideways on 10, 50l., inverted on 20, 100l.). P 12×12½ (10, 50l.) or 12½×12 (20, 100l.).

189	10l. Type **66**		40	20
190	20l. Late Bronze Age bird jug (*vert*)		70	30
191	50l. Neolithic earthenware pot		1·40	2·00
192	100l. Roman statue of Artemis (*vert*)		2·00	3·50
189/192 *Set of 4*			4·00	5·50

See also No. 301.

67 Soldiers, Defence Force Badge and Atatürk (Tenth Anniversary of Defence Forces)

(Des. H. Uluçam (No. 196). Litho Tezel Ofset, Lefkosa)

1986 (13 Oct). Anniversaries and Events. T **67** and similar multicoloured designs. W **51** (inverted on 20, 50l., sideways on others). P 12½×12 (vert) or 12×12½ (horiz).

193	20l. Type **67**	1·25	30
194	50l. Woman and two children (40th Anniversary of Food and Agriculture Organisation)	1·40	1·40
195	100l. Football and world map (World Cup Football Championship, Mexico) (*horiz*)	3·00	4·25
196	100l. Orbit of Halley's Comet and *Giotto* spacecraft (*horiz*)	3·00	4·25
193/196 *Set of 4*		7·75	9·25

68 Güzelyurt Dam and Power Station

(Litho Tezel Ofset, Letkoea)

1986 (17 Nov). Modern Development (1st series). T **68** and similar horiz designs. Multicoloured. W **51** (sideways). P 12×12½.

197	20l. Type **68**	1·25	30
198	50l. Low cost housing project, Lefkosa	1·40	1·40
199	100l. Kyrenia Airport	3·25	4·25
197/199 *Set of 3*		5·50	5·50

See also Nos. 223/224 and 258/263.

69 Prince Andrew and Miss Sarah Ferguson

70 Locomotive No. 11 and Trakhoni Station

(Litho Tezel Ofset, Lefkosa)

1986 (20 Nov). 60th Birthday of Queen Elizabeth II and Royal Wedding. T **69** and similar vert design. Multicoloured. P 12½×13. W **51** (inverted).

200	100l. Type **69**	2·40	3·00
	a. Pair. Nos. 200/201	4·75	6·00
201	100l. Queen Elizabeth II	2·40	3·00

Nos. 200/201 were printed together, *se-tenant*, in horizontal and vertical pairs throughout the sheet.

(Des H. Uluçam (50l.). Litho Tezel Ofset, Lefkosa)

1986 (31 Dec). Cyprus Railway. T **70** and similar horiz design. Multicoloured. W **51** (sideways). P 12×12½.

202	50l. Type **70**	3·75	2·75
203	100l. Locomotive No. 1	4·25	4·75

Kuzey Kıbrıs Türk Cumhuriyeti

(**71**)

1987 (18 May). Nos. 94, 96/97 and 113 optd as T **71** or surch also.

204	10l. deep mauve and pale green	50	80
205	15l. on 3½l. grey-green and pale rose-pink	50	80
206	20l. dull ultramarine and pale greenish yellow	55	85
207	30l. multicoloured	70	1·25
204/207 *Set of 4*		2·00	3·25

(Litho Tezel Ofset, Letkosa)

1987 (27 May). Art (6th series). Vert designs as T **54**. Multicoloured. W **51** (inverted). P 12½×13.

208	50l. *Shepherd* (Feridun Isiman)	1·00	1·25
209	125l. *Pear Woman* (Mehmet Uluhan)	1·40	3·00

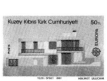

72 Modern House (architect A. Vural Behaeddin)

73 Kneeling Folk Dancer

(Des H. Uluçam (60l.). Litho Tezel Ofset, Lefkosa)

1987 (30 June). Europa. Modern Architecture. T **72** and similar horiz design. Multicoloured. W **51** (sideways). P 12×12½.

210	50l. Type **72**	1·00	30
	a. Perf 12×imperf	2·00	3·25
	ab. Booklet pane. Nos. 210a/211a, each×2	7·50	
211	200l. Modern house (architect Necdet Turgay)	1·75	3·25
	a. Perf 12×imperf	2·00	3·25

Nos. 210a and 211a come from 500l. stamp booklets containing *se-tenant* pane No. 210ab.

(Des B. Ruhi. Litho Tezel Ofset, Lefkosa)

1987 (20 Aug). Folk Dancers. T **73** and similar vert designs. Multicoloured. W **51** (inverted). P 12½×12.

212	20l. Type **73**	70	20
213	50l. Standing male dancer	80	40
214	200l. Standing female dancer	1·75	1·75
215	1000l. Woman's headdress	4·00	6·50
212/215 Set of 4		6·50	8·00

See also No. 302.

74 Regimental Colour (First Anniversary of Infantry Regiment)

75 Ahmet Belig Pasha (Egyptian judge)

(Des H. Uluçam. Litho Tezel Ofset, Lefkosa)

1987 (30 Sept–2 Nov). Anniversaries and Events. T **74** and similar multicoloured designs. W **51** (inverted on vert designs, sideways on horiz). P 12½×12 (vert) or 12×12½ (horiz).

216	50l. Type **74**	1·40	1·00
217	50l. President Denktash and Turgut Özal (First Anniversary of Turkish Prime Minister's visit) (horiz) (2.11)	1·40	1·00
218	200l. Emblem and Crescent (Fifth Islamic Summit Conference, Kuwait)	2·50	4·25
219	200l. Emblem and Laurel leaves (Membership of Pharmaceutical Federation) (horiz)	2·50	4·25
216/219 Set of 4		7·00	9·50

(Des H. Uluçam. Litho Tezel Ofset, Lefkosa)

1987 (22 Oct). Turkish Cypriot Personalities. T **75** and similar vert designs. W **51** (inverted). P 12½×12.

220	**75** 50l. brown and greenish yellow	65	40
221	– 50l. multicoloured	65	40
222	– 125l. multicoloured	1·50	3·00
220/222 Set of 3		2·50	3·50

Designs: 50l. (No. 221) Mehmet Emin Pasha (Ottoman Grand Vizier); 125l. Mehmet Kâmil Pasha (Ottoman Grand Vizier).

76 Tourist Hotel, Girne

77 Piyale Pasha (tug)

(Des A. Erduran. Litho Tezel Ofset, Lefkosa)

1987 (20 Nov). Modern Development (2nd series). T **76** and similar horiz design. Multicoloured. W **51** (sideways). P 12×12½.

223	150l. Type **76**	1·50	1·50
224	200l. Dogu Akdeniz University	1·75	2·25

(Litho Tezel Ofset, Lefkosa)

1988 (2 May). Art (7th series). Multicoloured designs as T **54**. W **51** (inverted on 20, 150l. sideways on 50l.) P 12½×13 (20, 150l.) or 13×12½ (50l.).

225	20l. Woman making Pastry (Ayhan Mentes) (vert)	50	30
226	50l. Chair Weaver (Osman Güvenir)	75	75
227	150l. Woman weaving a Rug (Zekâi Yesiladali) (vert)	1·75	4·00
225/227 Set of 3		2·75	4·50

(Des H. Uluçam. Litho Tezel Ofset, Lefkosa)

1988 (31 May). Europa. Transport and Communications. T **77** and similar multicoloured design. W **51** (sideways on 200l., inverted on 500l.) P 12×12½ (200l.) or 12½×12 (500l.).

228	200l. Type **77**	2·00	75
229	500l. Dish aerial and antenna tower, Selvilitepe (vert)	2·75	5·00

No. 229 also commemorates the 25th anniversary of Bayrak Radio and Television Corporation.

78 Lefkosa

79 Bülent Ecevit

(Litho Tezel Ofset, Lefkosa)

1988 (17 June). Tourism. T **78** and similar horiz designs. Multicoloured. W **51** (sideways). P 12×12½.

230	150l. Type **78**	80	80
231	200l. Gazi-Magusa	90	1·00
232	300l. Girne	1·50	2·00
230/232 Set of 3		2·75	3·50

(Litho Tezel Ofset, Lefkosa)

1988 (20 July). Turkish Prime Ministers. T **79** and similar vert designs. Multicoloured. W **51**. P 12½×12.

233	50l. Type **79**	60	85
234	50l. Bülent Ulusu	60	85
235	50l. Turgut Özal	60	85
233/235 Set of 3		1·60	2·25

80 Red Crescent Members on Exercise

81 Hodori the Tiger (Games mascot) and Fireworks

(Des N. Kozel. Litho Tezel Ofset, Lefkosa)

1988 (8 Aug). Civil Defence. W **51** (sideways). P 12×12½.

236	**80** 150l. multicoloured	1·75	2·25

(Des E. Çizenel (200l.), N. Kozal (250l.), H. Uluçam (400l.). Litho Tezel Ofset, Lefkosa)

1988 (17 Sept). Olympic Games, Seoul. T **81** and similar horiz designs. Multicoloured. W **51** (sideways). P 12×12½.

237	200l. Type **81**	1·40	1·00
	a. Imperf (pair)	90·00	
238	250l. Athletics	1·60	1·25
239	400l. Shot and running track with letters spelling 'SEOUL'	2·25	2·00
237/239 Set of 3		4·75	3·75

82 Sedat Simavi (journalist)

83 Kemal Atatürk (I. Calli)

(Des H. Uluçam (Nos. 241/243). Litho Tezel Ofset, Lefkosa)

1988 (17 Oct). Anniversaries and Events. T **82** and similar designs. W **51** (inverted on Nos. 240, 243 and 245, sideways on Nos. 241 and 244). P 12½×12 (vert) or 12×12½ (horiz).

240	50l. olive-green	25	25
241	100l. multicoloured	75	35
242	300l. multicoloured	60	75
243	400l. multicoloured	1·75	2·00
244	400l. multicoloured	1·00	2·00
245	600l. multicoloured	2·25	2·75
240/245 Set of 6		6·00	7·25

Designs: Horiz—No. 241, Stylised figures around table and flags of participating countries (International Girne Conferences); No. 244, Presidents Gorbachev and Reagan signing treaty (Summit Meeting). Vert—No. 240, No. 242, Cogwheels as flowers (North Cyprus Industrial Fair); No. 243, Globe (125th Anniversary of International Red Cross); No. 245, 'Medical Services' (40th Anniversary of WHO).

(Litho Tezel Ofset, Lefkosa)

1988 (10 Nov). 50th Death Anniversary of Kemal Atatürk. Sheet 72×102 mm containing T **83** and similar vert designs. Multicoloured. W **51** (inverted). P 12½×12.

MS246	250l.	Type **83**; 250l. *Kemal Atatürk* (N. Ismail); 250l. in army uniform; 250l. In profile	2·50	3·00

84 Abstract Design

(Des E. Çizenel. Litho Tezel Ofset, Lefkosa)

1988 (15 Nov). Fifth Anniversary of Turkish Republic of Northern Cyprus. Sheet 98×76 mm. W **51** (sideways). Imperf.

MS247	**84**	500l. multicoloured	2·25	2·25

(Litho Tezel Ofset, Lefkosa)

1989 (28 Apr). Art (8th series). Multicoloured designs as T **54**. W **51** (sideways on 150, 400l., inverted on 600l.). P 12½×13 (600l.) or 13×12½ (others).

248	150l.	*Dervis Pass Mansion, Lefkosa* (Inci Kansu)	90	60
249	400l.	*Gamblers' Inn, Lefkosa* (Osman Güvenir)..	1·75	2·25
250	600l.	*Mosque, Paphos* (Hikmet Uluçam) (*vert*)..	2·50	3·00
248/250	*Set of 3*		4·75	5·25

85 Girl with Doll   **86** Meeting of Presidents Vassiliou and Denktas

(Des N. Kozal. Litho Tezel Ofset, Lefkosa)

1989 (31 May). Europa. Children's Games. T **85** and similar vert design. Multicoloured. W **51**. P 12½×12.

251	600l.	Type **85**.	2·25	1·25
	a.	Imperf×p 12	2·50	4·00
	ab.	Booklet pane. Nos. 251a/252a, each×2	9·00	
252	1000l.	Boy with kite	2·50	4·00
	a.	Imperf×p 12	2·50	4·00

Nos. 251a and 252a come from 3200l. stamp booklets containing *se-tenant* pane No. 251ab.

(Litho Tezel Ofset, Lefkosa)

1989 (30 June). Cyprus Peace Summit, Geneva, 1988. W **51** (sideways). P 12½×12½.

253	**86**	500l deep rose-red and black	1·25	1·25

87 Chukar Partridge   **88** Road Construction

(Des E. Çizenel. Litho Tezel Ofset, Lefkosa)

1989 (31 July). Wildlife. T **87** and similar horiz designs. Multicoloured. W **51** (sideways). P 12×12½.

254	100l.	Type **87**	65	25
255	200l.	Cyprus Hare	70	30
256	700l.	Black Partridge	2·50	1·50
257	2000l.	Red Fox	2·50	2·75
254/257	*Set of 4*		5·50	4·25

(Litho Tezel Ofset, Lefkosa)

1989 (29 Sept). Modern Development (3rd series). T **88** and similar multicoloured designs. W **51** (sideways on 100, 700l.). P 12×12½ (100, 700l.) or 12½×12 (others).

258	100l.	Type **88**.	25	15
259	150l.	Laying water pipeline (*vert*)	30	20
260	200l.	Seedling trees (*vert*)	40	30
261	450l.	Modern telephone exchange (*vert*)	1·00	1·00
262	650l.	Steam turbine power station (*vert*)	1·25	1·75
263	700l.	Irrigation reservoir	1·50	1·75
258/263	*Set of 6*		4·25	4·50

89 Unloading *Polly Pioneer* (freighter) at Quayside (15th Anniversary of Gazi Magusa Free Port)   **90** Erdal Inonu

(Des E. Çizenel (450, 600l.), Ö. Özünalp (500l.), S. Oral (1000l.). Litho Tezel Ofset, Lefkosa)

1989 (17 Nov). Anniversaries. T **89** and similar designs. W **51** (inverted on 450l., sideways on others). P 12½×13 (450l.) or 12×12½ (others).

264	100l.	multicoloured	70	20
265	450l.	black, dull ultramarine and scarlet-vermilion	60	50
266	500l.	black, yellow-ochre and olive-grey	60	50
267	600l.	black, vermilion and new blue	1·75	2·00
268	1000l.	multicoloured	2·50	3·75
264/268	*Set of 5*		5·50	6·25

Designs: Vert (26×47 *mm*)—450l. Airmail letter and stylised bird (25th same of Turkish Cypriot postal service). Horiz—100l. T **89**; 500l. Newspaper and printing press (centenary of *Saded* newspaper); 600l. Statue of Aphrodite, lifebelt and seabird (30th Anniversary of International Maritime Organisation); 1000l. Soldiers (25th Anniversary of Turkish Cypriot resistance).

(Litho Tezel Ofset, Lefkosa)

1989 (15 Dec). Visit of Professor Erdal Inonu (Turkish politician). W **51** (inverted). P 12½×12.

269	**90**	700l. multicoloured	80	1·00

91 Mule-drawn Plough   **92** Smoking Ashtray and Drinks

(Des N. Kozal. Litho Tezel Ofset, Lefkosa)

1989 (25 Dec). Traditional Agricultural Implements. T **91** and similar multicoloured designs. W **51** (sideways on 150, 450l.). P 12½×12 (550l.) or 12×12½ (others).

270	150l.	Type **91**	30	25
271	450l.	Ox-drawn threshing sledge	75	85
272	650l.	Olive press (*vert*)	90	1·25
270/272	*Set of 3*		1·75	2·10

(Des Ö. Özünalp (200l.), H. Uluçam (700l.). Litho Tezel Ofset, Lefkosa)

1990 (19 Apr). World Health Day. T **92** and similar horiz design. Multicoloured. W **51** (sideways) P 12×12½.

273	200l.	Type **92**.	1·25	40
274	700l.	Smoking cigarette and heart	2·50	3·25

93 Yenierenköy Post Office   **94** Song Thrush

(Des H. Billur. Litho Tezel Ofset, Lefkosa)

1990 (31 May). Europa. Post Office Buildings. T **93** and similar horiz design. Multicoloured. W **51** (sideways). P 12×12½.

275	1000l. Type **93**	1·75	75
276	1500l. Atatürk Meydani Post Office	2·25	3·75
MS277	105×72 mm. Nos. 275/276, each×2	6·00	8·50

(Des H. Billur. Litho Tezel Ofset, Lefkosa)

1990 (5 June). World Environment Day. T **94** and similar vert designs showing birds. Multicoloured. W **51** (inverted). P 12½×12.

278	150l. Type **94**	2·75	65
279	300l. Blackcap	3·50	1·00
280	900l. Black Redstart	6·00	4·75
281	1000l. Chiff-chaff	6·00	4·75
278/281	*Set of 4*	16·00	10·00

See also No. 389.

95 Two Football Teams | **96** Amphitheatre, Soli

(Des H. Billur (1000l.). Litho Tezel Ofset, Lefkosa)

1990 (8 June). World Cup Football Championship, Italy. T **95** and similar horiz design. Multicoloured. W **51** (sideways). P 12×12½.

282	300l. Type **95**	75	50
283	1000l. Championship symbol, globe and ball	2·50	3·50

(Litho Tezel Ofset, Lefkosa)

1990 (31 July). Art (9th series). Multicoloured designs as T **54**. W **51** (sideways on 300l.). P 13×12½ (300l.) or 12½×13 (1000l.).

284	300l. *Abstract* (Filiz Ankaçç)	40	25
285	1000l. Wooden sculpture (S. Tekman) (*vert*)	1·25	1·75

(Litho Tezel Ofset, Lefkosa)

1990 (24 Aug). Tourism. T **96** and similar vert design. Multicoloured. W **51**. P 12½.

286	150l. Type **96**	40	20
287	1000l. Swan mosaic, Soli	1·75	2·50

97 Kenan Evren and Rauf Denktas | **98** Road Signs and Heart wearing Seat Belt

(Litho Tezel Ofset, Lefkosa)

1990 (19 Sept). Visit of President Kenan Evren of Turkey. W **51** (sideways). P 12½.

288	**97** 500l. multicoloured	1·00	1·00

(Des H. Billur. Litho Tezel Ofset, Lefkosa)

1990 (21 Sept). Traffic Safety Campaign. T **98** and similar horiz designs. Multicoloured. W **51** (sideways). P 12½.

289	150l. Type **98**	1·25	30
290	300l. Road signs, speeding car and spots of blood	1·50	50
291	1000l. Traffic lights and road signs	3·75	4·50
289/291	*Set of 3*	6·00	4·25

99 Yildirim Akbulut | **100** *Rosularia cypria*

(Litho Tezel Ofset, Lefkosa)

1990 (1 Oct). Visit of Turkish Prime Minister Yildrim Akbulat. W **51** (inverted). P 12½.

292	**99** 1000l. multicoloured	1·10	1·10

(Des D. Viney and P. Jacobs 1200, 1500l.), D. Viney and C. Hessenberg (others). Litho Tezel Ofset, Lefkosa)

1990 (31 Oct). Plants. T **100** and similar vert designs. Multicoloured. W **51**. P 12½.

293	150l. Type **100**	70	20
294	200l. *Silene fraudratrix*	80	30
295	300l. *Scutellaria sibthorpii*	90	35
296	600l. *Sedum lampusae*	1·40	85
297	1000l. *Onosma caespitosum*	1·50	2·25
298	1500l. *Arabis cypria*	2·25	4·00
293/298	*Set of 6*	6·75	7·25

See also No. 303 and 391.

250 TL

101 *Kemal Atatürk at Easel* (wood carving) | (**102**)

(Des M. Uzel (300l.), H. Billur (750l.). Litho Tezel Ofset, Letkosa)

1990 (24 Nov). International Literacy Year. T **101** and similar horiz design. Multicoloured. W **51** (sideways). P 12½.

299	300l. Type **101**	1·25	35
300	750l. Globe, letters and books	2·50	3·50

1991 (3 June). Nos. 189, 212 and 293 surch as T **102**.

301	250l. on 10l. Type **66**	1·50	1·50
302	250l. on 20l. Type **73**	1·50	1·50
303	500l. on 150l. Type **100**	2·00	2·50
	a. Surch inverted	55·00	
301/303	*Set of 3*	4·50	5·00

> **PRINTER.** Issues from Nos. 304/305 onwards were printed in lithography by the State Printing Works, Lefkosa, *unless otherwise stated.*

103 *Ophrys lapethica* | **104** *Hermes* (projected shuttle)

1991 (8 July). Orchids (1st series). T **103** and similar vert design. Multicoloured. W **51** (inverted). P 14.

304	250l. Type **103**	1·25	60
305	500l. *Ophrys kotschyi*	2·25	2·75

See also Nos. 311/314.

1991 (29 July). Europa. Europe in Space. Sheet 78×82 mm containing T **104** and similar vert design. Multicoloured. W **51**. P 12½.

MS306 2000l. Type **104**; 2000l. *Ulysses* (satellite) ... 9·00 10·00

105 Kucuk Medrese Fountain, Lefkosa | **106** Symbolic Roots (Year of Love to Yunus Emre)

(Des H. Billur)

1991 (9 Sept). Fountains T **105** and similar horiz designs. Multicoloured. W **51** (sideways). P 12½.

307	250l. Type **105**	55	15
308	500l. Cafer Pasa Fountains, Magusa	75	30
309	1500l. Sarayönü Mosque Fountains, Lefkosa	1·50	1·60
310	3500l. Arabahmet Mosque Fountains, Lefkosa	3·75	6·50
307/310 Set of 4		6·00	7·75

1991 (10 Oct). Orchids (2nd series). Vert design as T **103** Mutlicoloured. W **51** (sideways). P 14.

311	100l. *Serapias Levantina*	85	20
312	500l. *Dactylorhiza romana*	2·50	50
313	2000l. *Orchis simia*	4·25	4·50
314	3000l. *Orchis sancta*	4·75	5·00
311/314 Set of 4		11·00	9·00

1991 (5 Nov). Art (10th series). Multicoloured designs as T **54**. W **51**. P 12½×13.

315	250l. *Hindiler* (S. Çizel) (*vert*)	1·50	1·50
316	500l. *Düsme* (A. Mene) (*vert*)	2·00	3·50

See also No. 390.

(Des K. Sarikavak (250l.) H Billur (500, 1500l.)

1991 (20 Nov). Anniversaries and Events T **106** and similar designs. W **51** (sideways on 1500l. inverted on others). P 12×12½ (1500l.) or 12½×12 (others).

317	250l. greenish yellow, black and bright magenta	25	25
318	500l. multicoloured	45	60
319	500l. multicoloured	45	60
320	1500l. multicoloured	5·50	5·50
317/320 Set of 4		6·00	6·25

Designs: Vert—No. 318, Mustafa Cagatay commemoration; No. 319, University building (Fifth Anniversary of Eastern Mediterranean University). Horiz—No. 317, T **106**; No. 320, Mozart (death bicentenary). See also No. 388.

107 Four Sources of Infection

108 Lighthouse, Gazimagusa

1991 (13 Dec). AIDS Day. W **51** (sideways). P 12×12½.

321	**107** 1000l. multicoloured	30	15

(Des H. Billur)

1991 (16 Dec). Lighthouses. T **108** and similar horiz designs. Multicoloured. W **51** (sideways). P 12×12½.

322	250l. Type **108**	3·00	65
323	500l. Ancient lighthouses, Girne harbour	3·75	1·25
324	1500l. Modern lighthouse, Girne harbour	6·50	7·00
322/324 Set of 3		12·00	8·00

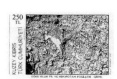

109 Elephant and Hippopotamus Fossils, Karaoglanoglu

110 Fleet of Columbus and Early Map

1991 (27 Dec). Tourism (1st series). T **109** and similar horiz designs. Multicoloured. W **51** (sideways). P 12.

325	250l. Type **109**	1·50	55
326	500l. Roman fish ponds, Lambusa	1·75	80
327	1500l. Roman remains, Lambusa	2·75	5·00
325/327 Set of 3		5·50	5·75

See also Nos. 330/333 and 351/352.

1992 (31 Mar). Art (11th series). Multicoloured designs as T **54**, but 31×49 mm. W **51** (sideways). P 14.

328	500l. *Ebru* (A. Kandulu)	1·00	40
329	3500l. *Street in Lefkosa* (I. Tatar)	3·50	6·00

1992 (21 Apr). Tourism (2nd series). Multicoloured designs as T **109**. W **51** (sideways). P 14×13½ (1500l.) or 13½×14 (others).

330	500l. Bugday Camii, Gazimagusa	60	65
331	500l. Clay pigeon shooting	60	60
332	1000l. Salamis Bay Hotel, Gazimagusa	1·25	1·25
333	1500l. Casino, Girne (*vert*)	2·00	3·50
330/333 Set of 4		4·00	5·50

(Des H. Billur)

1992 (29 May). Europa. 500th Anniversary of Discovery of America by Columbus. Sheet, 80×76 mm, containing T **110** and similar horiz design. Multicoloured. W **51** (sideways). P 13½×14.

MS334 1500l. Type **110**; 3500l. Christopher Columbus and signature .... 3·25   4·25

111 Green Turtle   **112** Gymnastics

(Des H. Billur)

1992 (30 June). World Environment Day. Sea Turtles. Sheet 105×75 mm containing T **111** and similar horiz design. W **51** (sideways). P 13½×14.

MS335 1000l.×2, Type **111**×2; 1500l.×2, Loggerhead Turtle×2 .... 6·50   7·50

(Des H. Billur)

1992 (25 July). Olympic Games, Barcelona. T **112** and similar multicoloured designs. W **51** (inverted on 500l., sideways on 1000, 1500l.). P 14×13½ (500l.) or 13½×14 (others).

336	500l. Type **112**	80	1·00
	a. Horiz pair. Nos. 336/337	1·60	2·00
337	500l. Tennis	80	1·00
338	1000l. High jumping (*horiz*)	1·00	1·25
339	1500l. Cycling (*horiz*)	4·50	4·50
336/339 Set of 4		6·25	7·00

Nos. 336/337 were printed together, *se-tenant*, in horizontal pairs throughout the sheet.

113 New Generating Station, Girne

(Des H. Billur (Nos. 341/342), Therese Coustry (No. 343))

1992 (30 Sept). Anniversaries and Events (1st series). T **113** and similar horiz designs. Multicoloured. W **51** (sideways). P 14.

340	500l. Type **113**	50	50
341	500l. Symbol of Housing Association (15th Anniversary)	50	50
342	1500l. Domestic animals and birds (30th Anniversary of Veterinary Service)	3·75	4·00
343	1500l. Cat (International Federation of Cat Societies Conference)	3·75	4·00
340/343 Set of 4		7·75	8·00

114 Airliner over Runway

(Des H. Billur)

1992 (20 Nov). Anniversaries and Events (2nd series). T **114** and similar horiz designs. Multicoloured. W **51** (sideways). P 13×14.

344	1000l. Type **114** (17th Anniversary of civil aviation)	3·00	2·75
345	1000l. Meteorological instruments and weather (18th Anniversary of Meteorological Service)	3·00	2·75
346	1200l. Surveying equipment and map (14th Anniversary of Survey Department)	4·00	4·00
344/346 Set of 3		9·00	8·50

115 Zübiye

(Des A. Erduran)

1992 (14 Dec). International Conference on Nutrition, Rome. Turkish Cypriot Cuisine. T **115** and similar horiz designs. W **51** (sideways). P 13½×14.

347	2000l. Type **115**	1·50	1·50
348	2500l. Çiçek Dolması	1·75	1·75
349	3000l. Tatar Böregi	2·00	2·50
350	4000l. Seftali Kebabi	2·25	2·75
347/350	Set of 4	6·75	7·75

1993 (1 Apr). Tourism (3rd series). Horiz designs as T **109**. Multicoloured. W **51** (sideways). P 13½×14.

351	500l. Saint Barnabas Church and Monastery, Salamis	50	20
352	10000l. Ancient pot	6·00	7·50

116 Painting by Turksal Ince

117 Olive Tree, Girne

(Des T. Ince and I. Onsoy)

1993 (5 May). Europa. Contemporary Art. Sheet 79×69 mm containing T **116** and similar vert design. Multicoloured. W **51**. P 14.
MS353 2000l. Type **116**; 3000l. Painting by Ilkay Onsoy.   1·75   2·50

1993 (11 June). Ancient Trees. T **117** and similar vert designs. Multicoloured. W **51** (inverted). P 14.

354	500l. Type **117**	45	15
355	1000l. River Red Gum, Kyrenia Gate, Lefkosa	80	40
356	3000l. Oriental Plane, Lapta	1·75	2·25
357	4000l. Calabrian Pine, Cinarli	2·00	2·50
354/357	Set of 4	4·50	4·75

118 Traditional Houses

119 National Flags turning into Doves

(Des H. Billur)

1993 (20 Sept). Arabahmet District Conservation Project, Lefkosa. T **118** and similar horiz design. Multicoloured. W **51** (sideways). P 13½×14.

358	1000l. Type **118**	1·00	40
359	3000l. Arabahmet street	2·50	3·25

(Des H. Uluçam (5000l.), H. Billur (others))

1993 (15 Nov). Tenth Anniversary of Proclamation of Turkish Republic of Northern Cyprus. T **119** and similar designs. W **51** (sideways on Nos. 361/363). P 14×13½ (No. 360) or 13½×14 (others).

360	500l. carmine-red, black and new blue	30	30
361	500l. rosine and new blue	30	30
362	1000l. carmine-red, black and new blue	40	30
363	5000l. multicoloured	1·75	3·00
360/363	Set of 4	2·50	3·50

Designs: Vert—No. 360, T **49**. Horiz—No. 361, National Flag forming figure '10'; No. 362, Dove carrying National Flag; No. 363, Map of Cyprus and figure '10' wreath.

120 Kemal Atatürk

121 'Söyle Falci' (Göral Ozkan)

(Des H. Billur (Nos. 366/368))

1993 (27 Dec). Anniversaries. T **120** and similar multicoloured designs. W **51** (inverted on No. 364 or sideways on others). P 14×13½ (No. 384) or 13½×14 (others).

364	500l. Type **120** (55th Anniversary)	30	30
365	500l. Stage and emblem (30th Anniversary of Turkish Cypriot theatre) (horiz)	30	30
366	1500l. Branch badges (35th Anniversary of TMT organisation) (horiz)	70	70
367	2000l. World map and computer (20th Anniversary of Turkish Cypriot news agency) (horiz)	2·00	1·75
368	5000l. Ballet dancers and Caykovski'nin (Death centenary) (horiz)	6·00	5·50
364/368	Set of 5	8·50	7·75

1994 (31 Mar). Art (12th series). T **121** and similar vert design. Multicoloured. W **51**. P 14.

369	1000l. Type **121**	30	20
370	6500l. IV. Hareket (sculpture) (Senol Ozdevrim).	1·50	2·25

See also Nos. 436/437.

122 Dr. Küçük and Memorial

1994 (1 Apr). Tenth Death Anniversary of Dr. Fazil Küçük (politician). W **51** (sideways). P 14.

371	**122** 1500l. multicoloured	70	85

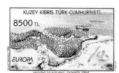

123 Neolithic Village, Girne

(Des H. Billur)

1994 (16 May). Europa. Archaeological Discoveries. Sheet 73×79 mm containing T **123** and similar horiz design. Multicoloured. W **51** (sideways). P 13½×14.
MS372 8500l. Type **123**; 8500l. Neolithic man and implements.   4·50   5·50

124 Peace Doves and Letters over Pillar Box

(Des H. Billur)

1994 (30 June). 30th Anniversary of Turkish Cypriot Postal Service. W **51** (sideways). P 13½×14.

373	**124** 50000l. multicoloured	2·25	3·75

125 World Cup Trophy

126 Peace Emblem

(Des H. Billur)

1994 (30 June). World Cup Football Championship, USA T **125** and similar multicoloured design. W **51** (sideways on 10000l.). P 14×13½ (2500l.) or 13½×14 (10000l.).

374	2500l. Type **125**		50	25
375	10000l. Footballs on map of USA (horiz)		2·00	2·75

(Des H. Billur (2500, 8500l.))

1994 (20 July). 20th Anniversary of Turkish Landings in Cyprus. T **126** and similar designs. W **51** (sideways on horiz designs). P 14×13½ (2500l.) or 13½×14 (others).

376	2500l. greenish yellow, emerald and black		30	30
377	5000l. multicoloured		50	60
378	7000l. multicoloured		70	1·00
379	8500l. multicoloured		80	1·50
376/379	Set of 4		2·10	3·00

Designs: Vert—2500l. T **126**. Horiz—5000l. Memorial; 7000l. Sculpture; 8500l. Peace Doves forming map of Cyprus and flame.

127 Cyprus 1934 4½pi. Stamp and Karpas Postmark

1994 (15 Aug). Postal Centenary. T **127** and similar horiz designs. Multicoloured. W **61** (sideways). P 13½×14.

380	1500l. Type **127**		20	20
381	2500l. Turkish Cypriot Posts 1979 Europa 2l. and Gazimagusa postmark		40	30
382	5000l. Cyprus 1938 6pi. and Bey Keuy postmark		70	90
383	7000l. Cyprus 1955 100m. and Aloa postmark		1·00	1·50
384	8500l. Cyprus 1938 18pi. and Pyla postmark		1·25	2·00
380/384	Set of 5		3·25	4·50

128 Trumpet Triton (*Charonia tritonis*)

***

(**129**)

1994 (15 Nov). Sea Shells. T **128** and similar horiz designs. Multicoloured. W **51** (sideways). P 13½×14.

385	2500l. Type **128**		45	30
386	12500l. Mole Cowrie (*Cypraea talpa*)		1·00	1·50
387	12500l. Giant Tun (*Tonna galea*)		1·00	1·50
385/387	Set of 3		2·25	3·00

1994 (12 Dec)–**95**. Nos. 280, 295, 315 and 317 surch as T **129**.

388	1500l. on 250l. Type **106**		50	20
389	2000l. on 900l. Black Redstart (21.4.95)		6·50	2·75
390	2500l. on 250l. *Hindiler* (S. Cizel)		50	35
391	3500l. on 300l. *Scutellaria sibthorpii* (21.4.95)		4·00	3·25
388/391	Set of 4		10·00	6·00

Nos. 389/390 show the surcharge value horizontally.

130 Donkeys on Mountain **131** Peace Dove and Globe

1995 (10 Feb). European Conservation Year. T **130** and similar horiz designs. W **51** (sideways). P 13½×14.

392	2000l. Type **130**		40	20
393	3500l. Coastline		40	30
394	15000l. Donkeys in field		1·75	2·50
392/394	Set of 3		2·25	2·75

(Des Hüseyin Billur)

1995 (20 Apr). Europa. Peace and Freedom. Sheet 72×78 mm containing T **131** and similar horiz design. W **51** (sideways). P 13½×14.

MS395 Type **131** 15000l. Peace Doves over map of Europe   2·75   3·50

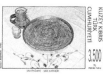

132 Sini Katmeri **133** Papilio machaon

1995 (29 May). Turkish Cypriot Cuisine. T **132** and similar horiz designs. Multicoloured. W **51** (sideways). P 13¼×14.

396	3500l. Type **132**		20	20
397	10000l. Kolokas musakka and bullez kizartma		55	65
398	14000l. Enginar dolmasi		90	1·60
396/398	Set of 3		1·50	2·25

(Des Hüseyin Billur)

1995 (30 June). Butterflies. T **133** and similar horiz designs. Multicoloured. W **51** (sideways). P 13½×14.

399	3500l. Type **133**		30	15
400	4500l. *Charaxes jasius*		35	20
401	15000l. *Cynthia cardui*		1·00	1·40
402	30000l. *Vanessa atalanta*		1·75	2·50
399/402	Set of 4		3·00	3·75

134 Forest **135** Beach, Girne

1995 (7 Aug). Obligatory Tax. Forest Regeneration Fund. P 14×13½.

403	**134** 1000l. emerald and black		3·75	40

No. 403 was for compulsory use on all mail, in addition to the normal postage, between 7 August and 6 February 1996. It was intended to provide funds for the replanting of those forests destroyed by fire in June 1995. A similar 50000l. stamp was issued for fiscal use only.

1995 (21 Aug). Tourism. T **135** and similar multicoloured designs. W **51** (sideways on horiz designs). P 13½×14 (horiz) or 14×13½ (vert).

404	3500l. Type **135**		30	20
405	7500l. Sail boards		50	45
406	15000l. Ruins of Salamis (vert)		1·00	1·25
407	20000l. St George's Cathedral, Gazimagusa (vert)		1·00	1·25
401/407	Set of 4		2·50	2·75

136 Süleyman Demirel and Rauf Denktaş **137** Stamp Printing Press

1995 (21 Aug). Visit of President Süleyman Demirel of Turkey. W **51** (sideways). P 14.

408	**136** 5000l. multicoloured		60	60

(Des H. Billur (Nos. 410/414))

1995 (7 Nov). Anniversaries. T **137** and similar designs. W **51** (sideways on horiz designs). P 14×13½ (No. 414) or 13½×14 (others).

409	3000l. multicoloured		40	40
410	3000l. multicoloured		40	40
411	5000l. multicoloured		70	70
412	22000l. dull ultramarine, new blue and black		80	1·50
413	30000l. multicoloured		1·00	2·25
414	30000l. multicoloured		1·00	2·25
409/414	Set of 6		3·75	6·50

Designs: Horiz—No. 409, T **137** (20th Anniversary of State Printing Works); No. 410, Map of Turkey (75th Anniversary of Turkish National Assembly); No. 411, Louis Pasteur (chemist) and microscope (Death centenary); No. 412, United Nations anniversary emblem (50th Anniversary); No. 413, Guglielmo Marconi (radio pioneer) and dial (Centenary of first radio transmissions). Vert—No. 414, Stars and reel of film (Centenary of cinema).

138 Kültegin Epitaph and Sculpture

139 *Bosnia* (sculpture)

(Des Hüseyin Billur)

1995 (28 Dec). Centenary of Deciphering of Orhon Epitaphs. T **138** and similar vert design. W **51**. P 14.

415	5000l. Type **138**	1·00	50
416	10000l. Epitaph and tombstone	1·75	2·25

(Des S. Özdevrim)

1996 (31 Jan). Support for Moslems in Bosnia and Herzegovina. W **51** (inverted). P 14×13½.

417	**139** 10000l. multicoloured	1·75	2·00

140 Striped Red Mullet

141 Palm Trees

(Des Hüseyin Billur)

1996 (29 Mar). Fish. T **140** and similar horiz designs. Multicoloured. W **51** (sideways). P 13½×14.

418	6000l. Type **140**	1·00	30
419	10000l. Peacock Wrasse	1·25	45
420	28000l. Common Two-banded Seabream	2·25	2·50
421	40000l. Dusky Grouper	2·75	3·50
418/421	*Set of 4*	6·50	6·00

See also No. 515.

1996 (26 Apr). Tourism. T **141** and similar multicoloured designs. W **51** (sideways on horiz designs). P 14×13½ (vert) or 13½×14 (horiz).

422	100000l. Type **141**	1·25	45
423	150000l. Pomegranate	1·75	1·00
424	250000l. Ruins of Bella Paise Abbey (*horiz*)	2·25	3·00
425	500000l. Traditional dancers (*horiz*)	4·75	6·50
422/425	*Set of 4*	9·00	10·00

142 Beria Remzi Ozoran

143 Established Forest

(Des Hüseyin Billur)

1996 (31 May). Europa. Famous Women. T **142** and similar horiz design. Multicoloured. W **51** (sideways). P 13½×14.

426	15000l. Type **142**	1·00	25
427	50000l. Kadriye Hulusi Hacibulgur	2·25	3·50

1996 (28 June). World Environment Day. Sheet 72×78 mm containing T **143** and similar horiz design. Multicoloured. W **51** (sideways). P 13½×14.

MS428	50000l. Type **143**; 50000l. Conifer plantation	8·00	8·00

144 Basketball

145 Symbolic Footballs

(Des Hüseyin Billur)

1996 (31 July). Olympic Games, Atlanta. Sheet 105×74 mm containing T **144** and similar horiz designs. Multicoloured. W **51** (sideways). P 13½×14.

MS429 15000l. Type **144**; 15000l. Discus throwing; 5000l. Javelin throwing; 50000l. Volleyball...... 3·50 4·25

(Des Hüseyin Billur)

1996 (31 Oct). European Football Championship, England. T **145** and similar horiz design. Multicoloured. W **51** (sideways). P 13½×14.

430	15000l. Type **145**	1·25	65
	a. Pair. Nos. 430/431	3·50	3·75
431	35000l. Football and flags of participating nations	2·25	3·25

In addition to separate sheets Nos. 430/431 were also available in pairs, *se-tenant* horizontally and vertically.

146 Houses on Fire (Auxiliary Fire Service)

147 *Amanita phalloides*

(Des Özer Oker (10000l.), Hüseyin Billur (50000, 75000l.))

1996 (23 Dec). Anniversaries and Events. T **146** and similar multicoloured designs. W **51** (inverted on 20000l., sideways on others). P 14×13½ (20000l.) or 13½×14 (others).

432	10000l. Type **146**	1·00	40
433	20000l. Colour party (20th Anniversary of Defence Forces) (*vert*)	1·10	55
434	50000l. Children by lake (Nasreddin-Hoca Year)..	1·40	1·60
435	75000l. Flowers (Children's Rights)	1·75	3·00
432/435	*Set of 4*	4·75	5·00

1997 (31 Jan). Art (13th series). Multicoloured designs as T **121**. W **51** (sideways). P 14.

436	25000l. 'City' (Lebibe Sonuç) (*horiz*)	1·25	50
437	70000l. *Woman opening Letter* (Ruzen Atakan) (*horiz*)	2·50	3·25

(Des Hüseyin Billur)

1997 (31 Mar). Fungi. T **147** and similar vert designs. Multicoloured. W **51** (inverted). P 14×13½.

438	15000l. Type **147**	1·00	30
439	25000l. *Morchella esculenta*	1·25	1·50
440	25000l. *Pleurotus eryngii*	1·25	1·50
441	70000l. *Amanita muscaria*	2·50	3·50
438/441	*Set of 4*	5·50	6·00

148 Flag on Hillside

149 Mother and Children playing Leapfrog

(Des Hüseyin Billur)

1997 (23 Apr). Besparmak Mountains Flag Sculpture. W **51** (inverted). P 14×13½.

442	**148** 60000l. multicoloured	2·00	2·25

(Des Hüseyin Billur)

1997 (30 May). Europa. Tales and Legends. T **149** and similar horiz design. Multicoloured. W **51** (sideways). P 13½×14.

443	25000l. Type **149**	1·50	30
444	70000l. Apple tree and well	3·00	3·50

150 Prime Minister
Necmettin Erbakan
of Turkey

151 Golden Eagle

1997 (20 June). Visit of the President and the Prime Minister of Turkey. T **150** and similar multicoloured design. W **51** (sideways on 80000l.). P 14×13½ (vert) or 13½×14 (horiz).

445	15000l. Type **150**	50	30
446	80000l. President Süleyman Demirel of Turkey (horiz)	2·25	3·25

(Des Hüseyi. Billur)

1997 (31 July). Birds of Prey. T **151** and similar vert designs. Multicoloured. W **51**. P 14×13½.

447	40000l. Type **151**	2·25	1·75
448	40000l. Eleonora's Falcon	2·25	1·75
449	75000l. Common Kestrel	3·50	2·75
450	100000l. Western Honey Buzzard	3·75	3·25
447/450	Set of 4	10·50	8·50

152 Coin of
Sultan Abdulaziz,
1861–1876

153 Open Book and Emblem

1997 (28 Oct). Rare Coins. T **152** and similar vert designs. Multicoloured. W **51**. P 14×13½.

451	25000l. Type **152**	60	20
452	40000l. Coin of Sultan Mahmud II, 1808–1839	80	45
453	75000l. Coin of Sultan Selim II, 1566–1574	1·50	1·75
454	100000l. Coin of Sultan Mehmed V, 1909–1918	1·75	2·50
451/454	Set of 4	4·25	4·50

(Des Hüseyin Billur)

1997 (22 Dec). Anniversaries. T **153** and similar designs. W **51** (sideways on horiz designs). P 13½×14 (horiz) or 14×13½ (vert).

455	25000l. multicoloured	75	20
456	40000l. multicoloured	1·10	30
457	100000l. black, bright scarlet and yellow ochre (vert)	3·00	2·50
458	150000l. multicoloured	3·75	4·00
455/458	Set of 4	7·75	6·25

Designs: Horiz—25000l. T **153** (Centenary of Turkish Cypriot Scouts); 40000l. Guides working in field (90th Anniversary of Turkish Cypriot Guides); 150000l. Rudolf Diesel and diesel motor (Centenary of the diesel engine). Vert—100000l. Couple and symbols (AIDS prevention campaign).

154 Ahmet and Ismet Sevki

155 *Agrion spleondens* (Dragonfly)

1998 (28 Jan). Ahmet and Ismet Sevki (photographers) Commemoration. T **154** and similar multicoloured design. W **51** (sideways on 40000l.). P 13½×14 (horiz) or 14×13½ (vert).

459	40000l. Type **154**	75	25
460	106000l. Ahmet Sevki (vert)	2·00	3·00

(Des Hüseyin Billur)

1998 (30 Mar). Useful Insects. T **155** and similar horiz designs. Multicoloured. W **51** (sideways). P 13½×14.

461	40000l. Type **155**	80	25

462	65000l. *Ascalaphus macaronius* (Owl-fly)	1·40	40
463	125000l. *Podalonia hirsuta*	2·25	2·75
464	150000l. *Rhyssa persuasoria*	2·50	3·25
461/464	Set of 4	6·25	6·00

See also No. 783.

156 Wooden Double Door

157 Legislative Assembly Building (Republic Establishment Festival)

(Des Hüseyin Billur)

1998 (30 Apr). Old Doors. T **156** and similar vert design showing different door. W **51**. P 14×13½.

465	**156** 115000l. multicoloured	2·25	2·50
466	– 140000l. multicoloured	2·25	2·50

(Des Hüseyin Billur)

1998 (30 May). Europa. Festivals. T **157** and similar multicoloured design. W **51** (sideways on 40000l., inverted on 160000l.) P 13½×14 (horiz) or 14×13½ (vert).

467	40000l. Type **157**	1·25	25
468	150000l. Globe, flags and map (International Children's Folk Dance Festival) (vert)	4·25	4·75

158 Marine Life

159 Prime Minister Mesut Yilmaz of Turkey

(Des Hüseyin Billur)

1998 (30 June). International Year of the Ocean. T **158** and similar horiz design showing different underwater scene. W **51** (sideways). P 13½×14.

469	**158** 40000l. multicoloured	1·00	40
470	– 90000l. multicoloured	2·00	2·50

See also No. 784.

1998 (20 July). Prime Minister Yilmaz's Visit to Northern Cyprus. W **51** (sideways). P 13½×14.

471	**159** 75000l. multicoloured	1·75	2·00

160 President Süleyman Demirel of Turkey

161 Victorious French Team

1998 (25 July). President Demirel's Water for Peace Project. T **160** and similar multicoloured design. W **51** (inverted on 75000l., sideways on 175000l.). P 14×13½ (vert) or 13½×14 (horiz).

472	75000l. Type **160**	1·25	50
473	175000l. Turkish and Turkish Cypriot leaders with inflatable water tank (horiz)	2·50	3·50

1998 (31 July). World Cup Football Championship, France. T **161** and similar multicoloured design. W **51** (sideways on 75000l., inverted on 175000l.). P 13½×14 (horiz) or 14×13½ (vert).

474	75000l. Type **161**	1·50	50
475	175000l. World Cup trophy (vert)	2·50	3·50

162 Deputy Prime Minister Bulent Ecevit

163 Itinerant Tinsmiths

1998 (5 Sept). Visit of the Deputy Prime Minister of Turkey. W **51** (inverted). P 14×13½.

476	**162**	200000l. multicoloured	2·00	2·25

(Des Hüseyin Billur)

1998 (26 Oct). Local Crafts. T **163** and similar multicoloured designs. W **51** (sideways on horiz designs, inverted on vert). P 13½×14 (horiz designs) or 14×13½ (others).

477	50000l. Type **163**	45	25
478	75000l. Basket weaver (*vert*)	65	35
479	130000l. Grinder sharpening knife (*vert*)	1·25	1·40
480	400000l. Wood carver	3·50	5·00
477/480 *Set of 4*		5·25	6·25

164 Stylised Satellite Dish

165 Dr. Fazil Küçük

(Des Hüseyin Billur and Hikmet Uluçam)

1998 (15 Nov). Anniversaries. T **164** and similar multicoloured designs (except No. 483). W **51** (inverted on 175000l. sideways on others). P 14×13½ (175000l.) or 13½×14 (others).

481	50000l. Type **164**	80	30
482	75000l. Stylised birds and '15'	1·25	1·40
483	75000l. '75' and Turkish flag (rosine, black and dull orange)	1·25	1·40
484	175000l. Scroll, '50' and quill pen (*vert*)	2·00	3·50
481/484 *Set of 4*		4·75	6·00
MS485 72×78 mm. 75000l. As No. 452; 75000l. Map of Northern Cyprus		2·50	3·00

Anniversaries—No. 481, 35th Anniversary of Bayrak Radio and Television; Nos. 482, **MS**485, 15th Anniversary of Turkish Republic of Northern Cyprus; No. 483, 75th Anniversary of Turkish Republic; No. 484, 50th Anniversary of Universal Declaration of Human Rights.

1999 (15 Jan). 15th Death Anniversary of Dr. Fazil Küçük (politician). W **51** (inverted). P 14×13½.

486	**165**	75000l. multicoloured	1·50	1·50

166 *Otello*

167 *Malpolon monspessulanus insignitus* (Montepellier)

1999 (30 Jan). Performance of Verdi's Opera *Otello* in Cyprus. Sheet, 78×74 mm, containing T **166** and similar vert design. Multicoloured. W **51** (inverted). P 14×13½.

MS487 200000l. Type **166**; 200000l. Desdemona dead in front of fireplace......... 6·00 6·00

1999 (26 Mar). Snakes. T **167** and similar horiz designs. Multicoloured. W **51** (sideways). P 13½×14.

488	50000l. Type **167**	85	30
489	75000l. *Hierophis jugularis*	1·10	45

490	195000l. *Vipera lebetina lebetina* (Levantine Viper)	2·00	2·75
491	220000l. *Natrix natrix* (Grass Snake)	2·00	2·75
488/491 *Set of 4*		5·50	5·50

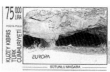

168 Entrance to Cave

1999 (17 May). Europa. Parks and Gardens. Incirli Cave. T **168** and similar multicoloured design. W **51** (sideways on 75000l., inverted on 200000l.). P 13½×14 (horiz) or 14×13½ (vert).

492	75000l. Type **168**	1·75	60
493	200000l. Limestone rocks inside cave (*vert*)	2·75	3·75

169 Peace Dove and Map

170 Air Mail Envelope and of Cyprus Labels (35th Anniversary of Turkish Cypriot Posts)

(Des Hüseyin Billur)

1999 (20 July). 25th Anniversary of Turkish Landings in Cyprus. T **169** and similar horiz designs. Multicoloured. W **51** (sideways). P 13½×14.

494	150000l. Type **169**	2·00	1·50
495	250000l. Peace Dove, map of Cyprus and Sun	2·50	3·25

(Des Hüseyin Billur)

1999 (12 Nov). Anniversaries and Events. T **170** and similar horiz designs. Multicoloured. W **51** (sideways). P 13½×14.

496	75000l. Type **170**	1·00	40
497	225000l. '125' and UPU emblem (125th Anniversary of UPU)	1·50	2·00
498	250000l. Total eclipse of the Sun, August 1999	2·00	2·50
496/498 *Set of 3*		4·00	4·50

171 Turkish Gateway, Limassol

172 Mobile Phone

1999 (3 Dec). Destruction of Turkish Buildings in Southern Cyprus. T **171** and similar grey-brown and orange-brown designs. W **51** (sideways on horiz designs). P 14×13½ (No. 502) or 13½×14 (others).

499	75000l. Type **171**	60	40
500	150000l. Mosque, Evdim	85	55
501	210000l. Bayraktar Mosque, Lefkosa	1·25	1·00
502	1000000l. Kebir Mosque, Baf (*vert*)	5·50	8·00
499/502 *Set of 4*		7·50	9·00

(Des H. Billur)

2000 (2 Mar). New Millennium. Technology. T **172** and similar horiz designs. W **51** (sideways). P 14.

503	75000l. black, emerald and new blue	70	40
504	150000l. black and new blue	90	60
505	275000l. multicoloured	1·60	2·50
506	300000l. multicoloured	2·00	3·00
503/506 *Set of 4*		4·75	6·00

Designs: 75000l. T **172**; 150000l. 'Hosgeldin 2000'; 275000l. Computer and internet in squares; 300000l. Satellite over Earth.

173 Beach Scene

174 Building Europe

(Des H. Billur and A. Tosun)

2000 (29 Apr). Holidays. T **173** and similar horiz design. Multicoloured.
W **51** (sideways). P 13½×14.

507	300000l. Type **173**	1·75	2·00
508	340000l. Deck-chair on sea-shore	1·75	2·00

(Des J.-P. Cousin and H. Billur)

2000 (31 May). Europa. Sheet 77×68 mm containing T **174** and similar vert
design. Multicoloured. W **51** (inverted). P 14.

MS509 300000l. Type **174**; 300000l. Map of Europe
with flower creating Council of Europe emblem and
map of Cyprus .... 3·50　4·25

175 Bellapais Abbey

176 President
Ahmet Sezer
of Turkey

(Des A. Tosun and H. Billur)

2000 (21 June). Fourth International Bellapais Music Festival. T **175** and
similar multicoloured design. W **51** (sideways on No. 510). P 13½×14
(No. 510) or 14×13½ (No. 511).

510	150000l. Type **175**	1·00	60
511	350000l. Emblem (*vert*)	2·25	3·00

2000 (22 June). Visit of President Ahmet Sezer of Turkey. W **51** (inverted).
P 14×13½.

512	**176** 150000l. multicoloured	1·50	1·50

177 Olympic Torch　　(178)
and Rings

(Des Alev B. Tosun (125000l.), Hüseyin Billur (200000l.))

2000 (25 July). Olympic Games, Sydney. T **177** and similar multicoloured
design. W **51** (inverted on 125000l., sideways on 200000l.) P 14×13½
(125000l.) or 13½×14 (200000l.).

513	125000l. Type **177**	1·25	1·25
514	200000l. Runner (*horiz*)	1·75	2·00

2000 (28 Sept). No. 418 surch with T **178**.

515	50000l. on 6000l. Type **140**	2·75	2·75

179 Mantid on　　180 Traditional Kerchief
Cactus

(Des Gazi Yüksel)

2000 (16 Oct). Nature. Insects and Flowers. T **179** and similar vert designs.
Multicoloured. W **51**. P 13½×14.

516	125000l. Type **179**	1·00	25
517	200000l. Butterfly on flower	2·00	55
518	275000l. Bee on flower	1·75	1·50
519	600000l. Snail on flower	3·00	5·50
516/519 *Set of 4*		7·00	7·00

(Des Gazi Yüksel)

2000 (28 Nov). Traditional Handicrafts. Kerchiefs. T **180** and similar horiz
designs showing different kerchiefs. W **51** (sideways). P 14.

520	**180** 125000l. multicoloured	70	30
521	– 200000l. multicoloured	1·10	60
522	– 265000l. multicoloured	1·40	1·75
523	– 350000l. multicoloured	2·00	3·25
520/523 *Set of 4*		4·75	5·50

181 Lusignan House, Lefkosa　　182 *Cuprum Kuprum Bakir
Madeni* (Inci Kansu)

(Des Hüseyin Billur)

2001 (28 Mar). Restoration of Historic Buildings. T **181** and similar horiz
design. Multicoloured. W **51** (sideways). P 13½×14.

524	125000l. Type **181**	1·25	50
525	200000l. The Eaved House, Lefkosa	2·00	2·50

2001 (30 Mar). Modern Art. T **182** and similar multicoloured designs.
W **51** (sideways on horiz designs). P 14×13½ (350000l.) or 13½×14
(others).

526	125000l. Type **182**	1·00	30
527	200000l. *Varolus* (Emel Samioglu)	1·60	55
528	350000l. *Ask Kuslara Ucar* (Ozden Selenge) (*vert*)	2·25	3·25
529	400000l. *Suyun Yolculugu* (Ayhatun Atesin)	2·25	3·25
526/529 *Set of 4*		6·25	6·50

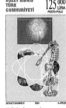

183 Degirmenlik　　184 Atomic　　185 Ottoman
Reservoir　　Symbol and X-ray　　Policeman, 1885

2001 (31 May). Europa. Water Resources. T **183** and similar vert design.
Multicoloured. W **51**. P 14×13½.

530	200000l. Type **183**	1·50	30
531	500000l. The Waters of Sinar	2·25	3·00

(Des Ayhatun Atesin)

2001 (22 June). World Environment Day. Radiation. T **184** and similar vert
design. Multicoloured. W **51**. P 14.

532	125000l. Type **184**	1·00	20
533	450000l. Radiation symbol and x-ray of hand	2·25	3·00

(Des Hüseyin Billur)

2001 (24 Aug). Turkish Cypriot Police Uniforms. T **185** and similar vert
designs. Multicoloured. W **51**. P 14.

534	125000l. Type **185**	1·75	50
535	200000l. Colonial policeman, 1933	2·50	80
536	500000l. Mounted policeman, 1934	3·50	3·00
537	750000l. Policewoman, 1983	4·50	6·00
534/537 *Set of 4*		11·00	9·25

186 MG TF Sports Car, 1954　　187 Graduate at Top of Steps
and College Names

(Des Hüseyin Billur)

2001 (21 Nov). Classic Cars. T **186** and similar horiz designs. Multicoloured.
W **51** (sideways). P 14.

538	175000l. Type **186**	1·00	30
539	300000l. Vauxhall 14, 1948	1·75	75
540	475000l. Bentley, 1922	2·25	3·00
541	600000l. Jaguar XK 120, 1955	2·50	3·50
538/541 *Set of 4*		6·75	6·75

2001 (24 Dec). Anniversaries. T **187** and similar design. W **51** (sideways on No. 542). P 13½×14 (horiz) or 14×13½ (vert).

542	200000l. multicoloured		1·60	1·75
543	200000l. black, magenta and yellow-brown		1·60	1·75

Designs: Horiz—No. 542, T **187** (Centenary of Higher Education). Vert—No. 543, Book cover of *The Genocide Files* by Harry Scott Gibbons (Anniversary of publication).

188 Chef mincing Logs into Letters (Utku Karsu)

189 Turtle

2002 (28 Feb). Caricatures. T **188** and similar multicoloured designs. W **51** (sideways on horiz design). P 13½×14 (No. 545) or 14×13½ (others).

544	250000l. Type **188**		1·25	40
545	300000l. Overfed people drinking from inflated cow, and starving children (Musa Kayra) (*horiz*)		1·40	55
546	475000l. Can of cola parachuting down to pregnant African woman (Serhan Gazi)		1·75	2·00
547	850000l. Artist painting trees in city (Mustafa Tozaki)		2·75	4·50
544/547 *Set of 4*			6·25	6·75

2002 (27 Mar). Tourism. Underwater Scenes. T **189** and similar horiz designs. Multicoloured. W **51** (sideways). P 13½×14.

548	250000l. Type **189**		1·25	45
549	300000l. Starfish on rock		1·40	60
550	500000l. Fish in rocks		1·90	1·90
551	750000l. Part of wreck		2·75	4·25
548/551 *Set of 4*			6·50	6·50

190 Stilt-walker

191 Turkish Football Team

(Des Hüseyin Billur)

2002 (27 May). Europa. Circus. Sheet, 79×72 mm, containing T **190** and similar vert design. Multicoloured. W **51** (inverted). P 13½.

MS552 600000l. Type **190**; 600000l. Child on high wire . 4·25 5·50

2002 (24 June). World Cup Football Championship, Japan and South Korea (2002). T **191** and similar horiz design. Multicoloured. W **51** (sideways). P 13½×14.

553	300000l. Type **191**		1·25	30
554	1000000l. Football Stadium, World Cup Trophy and footballer		3·25	3·75

192 Woman in White Tunic and Trousers

193 *Accident by Bridge* (Mehmet Ali Alpdogan)

(Des Hüseyin Billur)

2002 (8 Aug). Traditional Costumes. T **192** and similar vert designs. Multicoloured. W **51**. P 14×13½.

555	250000l. Type **192**		1·25	35

556	300000l. Man wearing grey jacket		1·40	55
557	425000l. Man in blue jacket and trousers		2·00	2·00
558	700000l. Woman in yellow tunic		3·50	4·50
555/558 *Set of 4*			7·25	6·75

2002 (30 Sept). Children's Paintings. T **193** and similar multicoloured designs. W w **51** (sideways on 300000l.). P 13½.

559	300000l. Type **193**		1·25	60
560	600000l. *Burning House* (Sercan avci) (*vert*)		2·50	3·50

194 Sureyya Ayhan (athlete)

195 Oguz Karayel (footballer) (70th birth anniversary)

2002 (28 Oct). Sporting Celebrities. T **194** and similar vert design. Multicoloured. W **51** (inverted). P 14×13½.

561	300000l. Type **194**		1·00	40
562	1000000l. Grand Master Park Jung-tae (taekwondo)		2·50	3·75

(Des Hüseyin Billur)

2002 (3 Dec). Celebrities' Anniversaries. T **195** and similar multicoloured designs. W **51** (sideways on No. 566, inverted on others). P 13½×14 (No. 566) or 13½×14 (others).

563	100000l. Type **195**		55	15
564	175000l. Mete Adanir (footballer) (40th birth anniversary)		85	40
565	300000l. M. Necati Ozkan (30th death anniversary)		1·50	90
566	575000l. Osman Turkay (astronomer) (First death anniversary) (*horiz*)		2·75	5·00
563/566 *Set of 4*			5·00	6·00

196 Untitled Painting by Salih Bayraktar

197 Tree containing Meadow and Forest in Polluted Industrial Landscape

2003 (21 Feb). Art (14th series). T **196** and similar vert design. Multicoloured. W **51**. P 14×13½.

567	250000l. Type **196**		1·25	50
568	1000000l. Untitled painting of woman's head (Feryal Sükan)		3·00	4·25

(Des Hüseyin Billur)

2003 (8 May). Europa. Poster Art. Sheet 78×72 mm containing T **197** and similar vert design. Multicoloured. W **51**. P 14×13½.

MS569 600000l. Type **197**; 600000l. Question mark containing wildlife in polluted Landscape .... 2·25 3·00

198 Cyprus Wheatear

199 Carved Wooden Chest

(Des Hüseyin Billur)

2003 (30 June). World Environment Day. Birds. T **198** and similar multicoloured designs. W **51** (sideways on horiz designs). P 13½×14 (horiz) or 14×13½ (vert).

570	100000l. Type **198**		1·25	65
571	300000l. Cyprus Warbler		2·00	1·00

572	500000l. Pygmy Cormorant (*vert*)........................	2·75	3·25
573	600000l. Greater Flamingo (*vert*)	2·75	3·25
570/573	*Set of 4*...	8·00	7·25

2003 (25 July). Wooden Chests. T **199** and similar horiz designs. Multicoloured. W **51** (sideways). P 13½×14.

574	250000l. Type **199**...	50	25
575	300000l. Chest carved with circular designs	60	30
576	525000l. Chest carved with turquoise-blue figures..	1·00	1·25
577	1000000l. Chest carved with flower heads and white birds.......................................	1·75	3·00
574/577	*Set of 4*..	3·50	4·25

200 Gladiolus triphyllus

201 Kemal Atatürk and Flag of Turkish Republic of Northern Cyprus

(Des Hüseyin Billur)

2003 (21 Oct). Flowers. T **200** and similar vert designs. Multicoloured. W **51**. P 14×13½.

578	150000l. Type **200**.........................	40	20
579	175000l. *Tulipa cypria*	60	45
580	500000l. *Ranunculus asiaticus*	1·25	1·75
581	525000l. *Narcissus tazetta*	1·25	1·75
578/581	*Set of 4*...................................	3·25	3·75

(Des Hüseyin Billur)

2003 (14 Nov). Political Anniversaries. T **201** and similar horiz design. Multicoloured. W **51** (sideways). P 13½×14.

502	300000l. Type **201** (20th anniversary of proclamation of Turkish Republic of Northern Cyprus)...........................	3·25	4·00
	a. Pair. Nos. 582/583	6·50	8·00
583	300000l. Kemal Atatürk and Turkish flag (80th Anniversary of Republic of Turkey)	3·25	4·00

Nos. 582/583 were printed together, *se-tenant*, in horizontal and vertical pairs in sheets of 40.

202 Horse-drawn Plough and Modern Farm Machinery

2003 (12 Dec). Anniversaries. T **202** and similar horiz design. Multicoloured. W **51** (sideways). P 13½×14.

584	300000l. Type **202** (60th Anniversary of International Federation of Agricultural Producers)....................	75	40
585	500000l. Emblem (40th Anniversary of Lions Clubs in Cyprus)	1·25	1·75

203 Post Office and Pillar Box

204 Beach and Harbour Scenes

(Des Hüseyin Billur)

2004 (30 Apr). 40th Anniversary of Turkish Cyprus Postal Services. T **203** and similar horiz design. Multicoloured. W **51** (sideways). P 13½×14.

586	250000l. Type **203**.........................	50	25
587	1500000l. Globe and winged envelopes................	2·25	3·00

2004 (25 May). Europa. Holidays. Sheet 72×75 mm containing T **204** and similar horiz design. Multicoloured. W **51** (sideways). P 13½×14.

MS588	600000l. Type **204**; 600000l. Seated woman with drink and beachside café........................	2·50	3·25
	a. Imperf....................................	3·25	3·75

205 Pack Animals and Caravanserai

206 Salvia veneris

2004 (7 June). Silk Road. W **51** (sideways). P 13½×14.

589	**205** 300000l. multicoloured	1·50	80

(Des Hüseyin Billur)

2004 (9 July). Plants. T **206** and similar vert designs. Multicoloured. W **51** (inverted on 250000l.). P 14×13½.

590	250000l. Type **206**.........................	50	25
591	300000l. *Phlomis cypria*	60	30
592	500000l. *Pimpinella cypria*	1·00	1·00
593	600000l. *Rosularia cypria*	1·25	1·75
590/593	*Set of 4*...................................	3·00	3·00

207 Inside Stadium

208 Footballer

2004 (28 Aug). 50th Anniversary of UEFA (Union of European Football Associations). T **207** and similar horiz design. Multicoloured. W **51** (sideways). P 14.

594	300000l. Type **207**.........................	60	30
595	1000000l. View from top of stadium....................	1·90	2·50

(Des Gamze Anil)

2004 (24 Sept). Olympic Games, Athens. T **208** and similar vert designs. Multicoloured. W **51** (inverted). P 14.

596	300000l. Type **208**.........................	65	75
	a. Horiz pair. Nos. 596/597	1·25	1·50
597	300000l. Boxing and horse riding....................	65	75
598	500000l. Weight lifting and gymnastics..............	1·00	1·40
	a. Horiz pair. No. 598/599	2·00	2·75
599	500000l. Pole vaulting and tennis	1·00	1·40
596/599	*Set of 4*...................................	3·00	4·00

Nos. 596/597 and 598/599, respectively, were each printed together, *se-tenant*, in horizontal pairs with the backgrounds forming composite designs.

(New Currency. 100 yeni kurus = 1 yeni lira)

209 Students Celebrating

(Des Gamze Anil (15, 30ykr.). Serkan Saçildi (50ykr.))

2005 (15 Feb). Anniversaries. T **209** and similar horiz designs. Multicoloured. W **51** (sideways). P 14.

600	15ykr. Type **209** (25th Anniversary of Eastern Mediterranean University, Gazimagusa)............................	35	30
601	30ykr. Eye and outlines of stamps (25th Anniversary of Cyprus Turkish Philatelic Association)...................................	65	65
602	50ykr. Turtle emblem and outline map (www.studyinnorthcyprus.org).................	95	1·25
600/602	*Set of 3*...................................	1·75	2·00

210 Stylised Dinghy

211 Boy and Girl in Orchard (Elmaziye Demirci)

(Des Görel Korol Sönmezer)

2005 (9 Mar). Tourism. T **210** and similar horiz design. Multicoloured. W **51** (sideways). P 14.
603	10ykr. Type **210**	20	20
604	1ytl. Temple ruins, setting sun and windsurfer	1·50	2·00

2005 (22 Apr). Children's Paintings. T **211** and similar vert design. Multicoloured. W **51** (inverted). P 14.
605	25ykr. Type **211**	55	45
606	50ykr. Couple (Elçim Öztemiz)	1·10	1·40

212 Brick Oven and Table laden with Food

213 *Dianthus cyprius*

(Des Hüseyin Billur)

2005 (30 May). Europa. Gastronomy. T **212** and similar horiz designs. Multicoloured. W **51** (sideways). P 14.
607	60ykr. Type **212**	65	1·00
	a. Pair. Nos. 607/608	1·25	2·00
608	60ykr. Table laden with food and wine	65	1·00
MS609 113×77 mm. Nos. 607/608, each×2		2·25	3·00

Nos. 607/608 were printed together, *se-tenant*, in horizontal and vertical pairs in sheets of 40.

(Des Hüseyin Billur)

2005 (8 July). Endemic and Medicinal Plants. T **213** and similar vert designs. Multicoloured. W **51** (inverted on 15, 25ykr.). P 14.
610	15ykr. Type **213**	35	25
611	25ykr. *Delphinium caseyi*	50	35
612	30ykr. *Brassica hilarionis*	55	50
613	50ykr. *Limonium albidum* ssp. *cyprium*	95	1·40
610/613 *Set of 4*		2·10	2·25

214 Olive Branches and Sun Umbrellas

215 Ercan Airport

(Des Görel Korol Sönmezer)

2005 (9 Sept). Cultural and Art Activities. T **214** and similar horiz designs. Multicoloured. W **51** (sideways). P 14.
614	10ykr. Type **214** (International Olive Festival, Girne)	20	20
615	25ykr. Lala Mustafa Pasa Mosque and musical notes (International Culture and Art Festival, Gazimagusa)	50	35
616	50ykr. Folk dancers and Kyrenia Gate (International Folk Dances Festival, Lefkosa)	85	1·10
617	1ytl. Masks and stage (International Cyprus Theatre Festival)	1·50	2·00
614/617 *Set of 4*		2·75	3·25

(Des Özge Luricinali)

2005 (23 Nov). Developments. T **215** and similar multicoloured designs. W **51** (inverted on 50ykr., sideways on 1ytl.). P 14.
618	50ykr. Type **215**	1·25	1·10
619	1ytl. Emblem and Middle East Technical University Northern Cyprus Campus, Güzelyurt (*horiz*)	1·50	2·00

216 Outline Map of Cyprus

217 *Helianthemum obtusifolium*

2006 (6 Jan). 50th Anniversary of First Europa Stamp. T **216** and similar horiz design. Multicoloured. W **51** (sideways). P 13½×14.
620	1ytl.40 Type **216**	1·75	2·50
621	1ytl.40 View of Cyprus from satellite orbiting Earth	1·75	2·50
MS622 83×78 mm. Nos. 620/621		3·50	5·00
MS622 also exists imperforate.			

(Des Hüseyin Billur)

2006 (28 Feb). Wild Flowers. T **217** and similar multicoloured designs. W **51** (sideways on horiz designs). P 14.
623	15ykr. Type **217**	30	25
624	25ykr. *Iris sisyrhinchium* (*horiz*)	40	35
625	40ykr. *Ranunculus asiaticus* (*horiz*)	65	95
626	50ykr. *Crocus veneris* (*horiz*)	75	1·00
627	60ykr. *Anemone coronaria* (*horiz*)	85	1·25
628	70ykr. *Cyclamen persicum*	95	1·60
623/628 *Set of 6*		3·50	4·75

218 *Adaption of a Woman's Figure to an Amphora* (ceramic by Semral Oztan)

219 Birds (Selma Gürani)

2006 (7 Apr). Art (15th series). T **218** and similar vert design. Multicoloured. W **51** (inverted). P 14.
629	55ykr. Type **218**	1·00	1·40
630	60ykr. *Female Figures* (Mustafa Hastürk)	1·00	1·40

2006 (18 May). Europa. Integration. T **219** and similar vert design showing winning entries in thematic drawing competition for high school students. Multicoloured. W **51**. P 14.
631	70ykr. Type **219**	1·25	1·50
632	70ykr. Pregnant woman and flags of many nations (Suzan Özcan)	1·25	1·50
MS633 78×72 mm. Nos. 631/632		2·50	3·00
No. **MS**633 was also available imperforate.			

220 Dr. Fazil Küçük

221 Mustafa Kemal Atatürk

2006 (18 May). Birth Centenary of Dr. Fazil Küçük (Deputy President (1959–1973) of Republic of Cyprus). W **51**. P 14.
634	**220** 40ykr. multicoloured	1·25	1·00

2006 (18 May). 125th Birth Anniversary of Mustafa Kemal Atatürk (first President (1923–1938) of Turkey). W **51**. P 14.

635	**221**	1ytl. multicoloured	2·00	2·25

222 World Cup Trophy and Map of Germany

223 Lapwing

(Des Görel Korol Sönmezer)

2006 (7 July). World Cup Football Championship, Germany. T **222** and similar vert design. Multicoloured. W **51** (inverted). P 14.

636	50ykr. Type **222**		75	1·25
	a. Pair. Nos. 636/637		2·25	3·00
637	1ytl. Football, player and Brandenburg Gate, Berlin		1·50	1·75

Nos. 636/637 were printed together, se-tenant, in horizontal and vertical pairs in sheets of 16 stamps.

(Des Hüseyin Billur)

2006 (22 Sept). Birds. T **223** and similar vert designs. Multicoloured. W **51** (inverted on 40ykr., 1ytl.). P 14.

638	40ykr. Type **223**	2·00	1·00
639	50ykr. Mallard	2·25	1·25
640	60ykr. Kingfisher	2·50	1·75
641	1ytl. Black-winged Stilt	3·25	3·75
638/641 Set of 4		9·00	7·00

224 Trees ('Protect our Forests against Fire')

225 Naci Talat

(Des Görel Korol Sönmezer)

2006 (10 Nov). Anniversaries and Events. T **224** and similar diamond-shaped design. Multicoloured. W **51** (inverted on 1ytl.50). P 14.

642	50ykr. Type **224**	1·00	75
643	1ytl.50 Yachts (Eastern Mediterranean Yacht Rally)	2·25	3·00

2006 (10 Nov). 15th Death Anniversary of Naci Talat (former General Secretary of Turkish Cypriot Republican Turkish Party). W **51**. P 14.

644	**225**	70ykr. multicoloured	1·00	1·00

226 Skeletal Leaf   **227** Ewer

(Des Görel Korol Sönmezer)

2007 (19 Feb). International Conference on Environment: Survival and Sustainability, Lefkosa. T **226** and similar vert design. Multicoloured. W **51**. P 14.

645	50ykr. Type **226**	1·00	75
646	80ykr. Red globe and parched ground	1·40	1·75

(Des Görel Korol Sönmezer)

2007 (6 Apr). Antique Household Utensils. T **227** and similar multicoloured designs. W **51** (sideways on horiz designs; inverted on vert). P 13½×14 (horiz) or 14×13½ (vert).

647	70ykr. Type **227**	1·00	1·00
648	80ykr. Coal iron	1·40	1·50
649	1ytl.50 Oil lamp (vert)	2·25	2·75
650	2ytl. Coffee pot on stove (vert)	3·50	4·00
647/650 Set of 4		7·25	8·25

228 Scout and Camp in Countryside   **229** Painting by Osman Keten

(Des Hüseyin Billur)

2007 (4 May). Europa. Centenary of Scouting. T **228** and similar vert design. Multicoloured. W **51**. P 14×13½.

651	80ykr. Type **228**	2·25	2·25
652	80ykr. Three scouts playing music	2·25	2·25
MS653	79×73 mm. Nos. 651/652. Wmk inverted. Imperf	4·50	4·50

2007 (12 July). Art (16th series). T **229** and similar multicoloured design. W **51** (sideways on horiz design). P 14.

654	50ykl. Type **229**	1·00	80
655	70ykl. FRAGMENT CITY INTEGRI CITY (Senih Çavusoglu) (horiz)	1·25	1·25

230 Chair-caner   **231** Post Pigeon and Pigeon carrying Letter

(Des Hüseyin Billur)

2007 (14 Sept). Crafts. T **230** and similar horiz designs. Multicoloured. W **51** (sideways). P 13½×14.

656	40ykr. Type **230**	70	70
657	65ykr. Barrow man	90	1·25
658	70ykr. Cobbler	1·00	1·25
659	1ytl. Shoeshine man	1·75	2·00
656/659 Set of 4		4·00	4·75

(Des Görel Korol Sönmezer. Litho State Ptg Wks, Lefkosa)

2007 (16 Nov). Post Office Past and Present. T **231** and similar multicoloured designs. W **51** (inverted on 50ykr., sideways on horiz designs). P 14.

660	50ykr. Type **231**	1·25	80
661	60ykr. Mounted postman and early motor vehicles	1·50	1·25
662	1ytl. Postman on bicycle and wall letter box (horiz)	2·25	2·75
663	1ytl.25 Modern postman on moped and post box (horiz)	2·75	3·25
660/663 Set of 4		7·00	7·25

232 Asphodelus aestivus   **233** Woman writing Letter

(Des Görel Korol Sönmezer (25, 60, 80ykr., 2ytl.20, 5ytl.)
or Hüseyin Billur (others))

2008 (20 Mar). Wild Flowers. T **232** and similar vert designs. Multicoloured. W **51**. P 14.

664	25ykr. Type **232**	50	40
665	50ykr. *Ophrys fusca* ssp. *iricolor*	1·00	80
666	60ykr. *Bellis perennis*	1·50	90
667	70ykr. *Ophrys sphegodes*	1·50	1·25
668	80ykr. *Dianthus strictus*	1·75	1·75
669	1ytl.60 *Ophrys argolica* ssp. *elegans*	2·50	2·25
670	2ytl.20 *Crocus cyprius*	4·00	3·50
671	3ytl. *Limodorum abortivum*	6·00	6·00
672	5ytl. *Carlina pygmaea*	9·00	9·50
673	10ytl. *Ophrys kotschyi*	18·00	20·00
664/673 *Set of 10*		42·00	42·00

(Des Görel Korol Sönmezer)

2008 (8 May). Europa. The Letter. T **233** and similar vert design. Multicoloured. W **51** (inverted). P 14×13½.

674	80ykr. Type **233**	1·75	2·00
675	80ykr. World map and fragments of printed paper	1·75	2·00

234 Diver

235 Anniversary Emblem

(Des Görel Korol Sönmezer. Litho State Ptg Works, Lefkosa)

2008 (24 July). Olympic Games, Beijing. Sheet 78×73 mm containing T **234** and similar vert design. Multicoloured. W **51** (inverted). P 14.

MS676	65ykr. Type **234**; 65ykr. Gymnast	4·25	4·50

No. **MS676** also exists imperforate.

(Des Görel Korol Sönmezer. Litho State Ptg Works, Lefkosa)

2008 (1 Aug). 50th Anniversary of Türk Mukavemet Teskilati'nin (Turkish resistance organisation). Sheet 73×78 mm containing T **235** and similar horiz design. Multicoloured. W **51** (sideways). Imperf.

MS677	1ytl. Type **235**; 1ytl. Monument	6·25	6·25

236 Council Buildings

237 Coin

(Des Görel Korol Sönmezer (55, 80ykr., 1ytl.50).
Litho State Ptg Works, Lefkosa)

2008 (18 Sept). Anniversaries and Events. T **236** and similar multicoloured designs. W **51** (sideways on 1ytl.). P 14×13½ (vert) or 13½×14 (horiz).

678	55ykr. Type **236** (50th Anniversary of Lefkosa Turkish Municipality)	1·40	1·10
679	80ykr. Gateway and emblems (Inner Wheel)	2·50	2·00
680	1ytl. Airliner (35th Anniversary of Cyprus Turkish Airlines) (*horiz*)	2·75	2·75
681	1ytl.50 Landing of Turkish forces, 1974 (32nd Anniversary of Turkish Federated State of Northern Cyprus)	3·50	3·50
678/681 *Set of 4*		9·00	8·50

(Des Görel Korol Sönmezer. Litho State Ptg Wks, Lefkosa)

2008 (15 Nov). 25th Anniversary of the Establishment of the Turkish Republic of Northern Cyprus. W **51**. P 14.

682	**237**	1ytl. multicoloured	4·00	3·00

238 Halit Karabina (upholsterer)

(Des Hüseyin Billur. Litho State Ptg Wks, Lefkosa)

2008 (20 Nov). The Masters and the Craftsmen. T **238** and similar horiz designs. Multicoloured. W **51** (sideways). P 13½×14.

683	60ykr. Type **238**	1·50	1·25
684	70ykr. Burhan Bardak (oil miller)	1·75	1·75
685	80ykr. Kemal Köse (bicycle repairer)	2·00	2·00
686	2ytl. Kemal Sah (circumciser)	5·00	6·00
683/686 *Set of 4*		9·25	10·00

239 Gold Brooch

(Des Görel Korol Sönmezer. Litho State Ptg Wks, Lefkosa)

2009 (23 Mar). The Golden Leaves of Soli Exhibition, Museum of Archaeology and Nature, Güzelyurt. T **239** and similar horiz design. Multicoloured. W **51** (sideways). P 13½.

687	60ykr. Type **239**	1·50	1·10
688	2ytl. Golden leaves	5·50	6·00

240 Galaxy and Comet

241 *Cistus creticus*

(Des Hüseyin Billur. Litho State Ptg Wks, Lefkosa)

2009 (5 May). Europa. Astronomy. T **240** and similar horiz design. Multicoloured. W **51** (sideways). P 13½.

689	80ykr. Type **240**	2·25	2·25
	a. Horiz pair. Nos. 689/690	4·50	4·50
690	80ykr. Solar system	2·25	2·25

Nos. 689/690 were printed together, *se-tenant*, as horizontal and vertical pairs in sheets of 40.

(Des Hüseyin Billur. Litho State Ptg Wks, Lefkosa)

2009 (9 July). Medicinal Plants. T **241** and similar vert designs. Multicoloured. W **51**. P 13½.

691	50ykr. Type **241**	1·50	1·00
692	60ykr. *Capparis spinosa*	1·60	1·25
693	70ykr. *Pancratium maritimum*	1·90	2·00
694	1ytl. *Passiflora caerulea*	3·00	3·75
691/694 *Set of 4*		7·25	7·25

242 *Agama stellio*

(Des Görel Korol Sönmezer. Litho State Ptg Wks, Lefkosa)

2009 (14 Sept). Fauna. T **242** and similar triangular design. Multicoloured. W **51** (sideways). P 13.

695	80ykr. Type **242**	3·00	3·00
696	1ytl.50 *Bufo viridis* (Toad)	5·50	6·00

243 Control Tower and Aircraft

(Des Görel Korol Sönmezer. Litho State Ptg Wks, Lefkosa)

2009 (12 Nov). Our Institutions and Foundations. T **243** and similar multicoloured designs. W **51** (sideways on 65ykr.). P 13½×14 (horiz) or 14×13½ (vert).

697	65ykr. Type **243** (CTATCA Cyprus Turkish Air Traffic Controllers)	2·00	1·50
698	1ytl. Open door leading to globe and ktto emblems (Turkish Cypriot Chamber of Commerce) (*vert*)	3·00	3·00
699	1ytl.50 Ziya Rizki (Ziya Rizki Vakfı) (*vert*)	4·50	5·00
697/699 *Set of 3*		8·50	8·50

244 Islamic Architecture, Emblem, Flag and Outline Map

245 Girls reading (Nadide Keles)

(Des Görel Korol Sönmezer. Litho State Ptg Wks, Lefkosa)

2010 (17 Mar). 34th Anniversary of Representation of Turkish Cyprus at Organisation of Islamic Conference. T **244** and similar vert design. Multicoloured. W **51**. P 14×13½.

700	70ykr. Type **244**	2·25	2·25
701	1ytl. Arch, emblem and minaret	3·00	3·00

(Litho State Ptg Wks, Lefkosa)

2010 (28 May). Europa. Children's Books. T **245** and similar horiz design showing children's paintings. Multicoloured. W **51** (sideways). P 13½×14.

702	80ykr. Type **245**	2·25	2·25
	a. Pair. Nos. 702/703	4·50	4·50
703	80ykr. Girl reading with book characters at her shoulders (Afet Deniz)	2·25	2·25

Nos. 702/703 were printed together, *se-tenant*, as horizontal and vertical pairs in sheetlets of 16.

Nos. 702/703 were also issued in vertical panes of four containing two vertical pairs of Nos. 702/703, attached by the selvedge to an illustrated card and sold for 4ytl., a premium of 80ykr. over the face value. Stamps from these panes have imperforate vertical edges.

246 *Larus audouinii*

247 World Cup Trophy and Crowd

(Des Hüseyin Billur. Litho State Ptg Wks, Lefkosa)

2010 (4 June). Endangered Species. Seagulls. T **246** and similar horiz designs. Multicoloured. W **51** (sideways). P 14.

704	25ykr. Type **246**	1·60	1·25
705	25ykr. *Larus melanocephalus*	1·60	1·25
706	30ykr. *Larus ridibundus*	1·75	1·60
707	30ykr. *Larus genei*	1·75	1·60
704/707 *Set of 4*		6·00	5·25

(Des Görel Korol Sönmezer. Litho State Ptg Wks, Lefkosa)

2010 (8 July). World Cup Football Championship, South Africa. T **247** and similar vert design. Multicoloured. W **51** (inverted). P 14×13½.

708	50ykr. Type **247**	1·50	1·00
709	2ytl. Footballer, South African flag, Elephants and mascot	6·00	6·00

247a Kemal Asik

248 *Bozcaada* (ferry) and Temple Ruins

2010 (1 Sept). Journalists. T **247a** and similar vert designs. Multicoloured. Litho. W **51** (inverted on 70, 80ykr., 1ytl.). P 14.

709a	60ykr. Type **247a**	1·50	1·25
709b	70ykr. Abdi Ipekçi	1·75	1·75
709c	80ykr. Adem Yavuz	2·50	2·50
709d	1ytl. Sedat Simavi	2·75	3·00
709a/709d *Set of 4*		7·75	7·75

(Des Görel Korol Sönmezer. Litho State Ptg Wks, Lefkosa)

2010 (20 Oct). Passenger Ships which Sail to Cyprus. T **248** and similar horiz design. Multicoloured. W **51** (sideways). P 13½×14.

710	1ytl.50 Type **248**	4·50	4·50
711	2ytl. *Yesilada* (ferry)	6·00	6·00

249 Özdemir Kenngöglu

250 University Building and Arms

(Des Görel Korol Sönmezer. Litho State Ptg Wks, Lefkosa)

2010 (24 Dec). Personalities. T **249** and similar vert designs. Multicoloured. W **51** (sideways). P 14×13½.

712	50ykr. Type **249**	1·75	1·25
713	60ykr. Osman Örek	2·25	2·25
714	70ykr. Salih Miroglu	2·50	2·75
715	80ykr. Özker Özgür	2·75	3·25
712/715 *Set of 4*		8·25	8·50

(Des Görel Korol Sönmezer. Litho State Ptg Wks, Lefkosa)

2010 (24 Dec). 25th Anniversary of Girne American University. W **51** (sideways). P 13½×14.

716	**250** 1ytl. multicoloured	3·00	3·00

251 Dr. Niyazi Manyera

252 Ayios Philon Church

(Des Hüseyin Billur. Litho State Ptg Wks, Lefkosa)

2011 (9 Mar). Turkish Cypriot Vice President and Government Ministers. T **251** and similar vert designs. Multicoloured. W **51**. P 14×13½.

717	80ykr. Type **251** (Minister of Health 1963–1974)	2·25	2·25
718	1ytl.10 Mustafa Fazil Plümer (Agriculture Minister, Republic of Cyprus, 1960–1963)	3·25	3·50
719	2ytl. Osman Örek (Prime Minister of Northern Cyprus 1978)	5·50	6·50
720	2ytl.20 Dr. Fazil Küçük (Vice President, Republic of Cyprus, 1960–1963)	6·50	7·50
717/720 *Set of 4*		16·00	18·00

(Des Görel Korol Sönmezer. Litho State Ptg Wks, Lefkosa)

2011 (18 Apr). Tourism. T **252** and similar multicoloured designs. W **51**
(sideways on horiz designs). P 13½×14 (horiz) or 14×13½ (vert).

721	50ykr. Type **252**	1·75	1·25
722	80ykr. Ruins of Salamis (*vert*)	2·75	2·75
723	1ytl.10 Ruins	3·25	3·25
724	2ytl. Apostolos Andreas Monastery and Karpaz Peninsula (*vert*)	6·75	7·50
721/724 *Set of 4*		13·00	13·00

253 Log and Forest

254 Prince William and Miss Catherine Middleton

255 400 Year Old Cyprus Oak, Minareliköy Village

(Des Görel Korol Sönmezer. Litho State Press Office, Lefkosa)

2011 (16 May). Europa. Forests. T **253** and similar vert design.
Multicoloured. W **51** (inverted). P 14×13½.

725	1ytl.50 Type **253**	5·25	5·25
726	1ytl.50 Pine cone and forest	5·25	5·25
MS727 77×72 mm. Nos. 725/726		10·00	10·00

(Litho State Ptg Wks, Lefkosa)

2011 (27 May). Royal Wedding. W **51** (inverted). P 14×13½.

728	**254**	1ytl. multicoloured	3·00	3·00

(Des Görel Korol Sönmezer. Litho State Ptg Wks, Lefkosa)

2011 (18 July). Ancient Trees. T **255** and similar vert design. Multicoloured.
W **51**. P 14.

729	1ytl. Type **255**	3·00	2·50
730	2ytl.50 700 year old Afrodit Olive tree, Kalkanli region	7·00	7·50

256 Painting by Birol Ruhi

257 Ziziphus lotus

(Litho State Ptg Wks, Lefkosa)

2011 (14 Sept). Works of Art. T **256** and similar multicoloured designs.
W **51** (inverted on 70, 80ykr., sideways on 1ytl.). P 14.

731	60ykr. Type **256**	2·00	1·50
732	70ykr. Painting by Kemal Ankaç	2·25	2·00
733	80ykr. Sculpture by Baki Bogaç	2·50	2·75
734	1ytl. Painting by Salih Bayraktar	2·75	3·00
731/734 *Set of 4*		8·50	8·25

(Des Hüseyin Billur (25, 50ykr., 1ytl.50) or Görel Korol Sönmezer (60, 70, 80ykr.). Litho State Ptg Wks, Lefkosa)

2011 (25 Nov). Plants. T **257** and similar square designs. Multicoloured.
W **51** (inverted on 60ykr. to 1ytl.50). P 13½.

735	25ykr. Type **257**	1·25	65
736	50ykr. Cynara cardunculatus	2·00	1·40
737	60ykr. Oxalis pes-caprae	2·25	1·75
738	70ykr. Malva sylvestris	2·50	2·50
739	80ykr. Rubus sanctus	2·75	3·00
740	1ytl.50 Crataegus monogyna	4·00	4·50
735/741 *Set of 6*		13·00	13·00

258 Rauf Denktaş

259 Tower, Gateway and Harbourside Walk

(Litho State Ptg Wks, Lefkosa)

2012 (16 Mar). Rauf Denktaş (founding President of Turkish Republic
of Northern Cyprus) Commemoration. Sheet 78×100 mm
containing T **258** and similar vert designs. Multicoloured. W **51**. P 14.

MS741 60ykr. Type **258**; 60ykr. Rauf Denktaş (colour
photo); 1ytl. Rauf Denktaş speaking (black/white
photo); 1ytl. Rauf Denktaş (sepia photo) ...... 4·50 5·00

(Des Hüseyin Billur. Litho State Ptg Wks, Lefkosa)

2012 (8 May). Europa. Visit North Cyprus. T **259** and similar horiz design.
Multicoloured. W **51** (sideways). P 13½×14.

742	80 ykr. Type **259**	3·00	3·00
	a. Horiz pair. Nos. 742/743	6·00	6·00
743	80ykr. Kyrenia castle and harbour	3·00	3·00

Nos. 742/743 were printed together, *se-tenant*, as horizontal pairs in
sheets of 16, each pair forming a composite design showing Kyrenia castle
and harbour.

260 Queen Elizabeth II

(Litho State Ptg Wks, Lefkosa)

2012 (1 June). Diamond Jubilee. W **51** (sideways). P 14.

744	**260**	80ykr. multicoloured	3·00	3·00

261 Players and Football

262 Athlete sprinting

(Des Görel Korol Sönmezer. Litho State Ptg Wks, Lefkosa)

2012 (29 June). European Football Championship, Poland and
Ukraine. T **261** and similar vert design. Multicoloured. W **51**. P 14.

745	70ykr. Type **261**	2·00	1·75
746	1ytl. Footballers, stadium and Ukrainian landscape	3·25	3·50

(Des Görel Korol Sönmezer. Litho State Ptg Wks, Lefkosa)

2012 (27 July). Olympic Games, London. T **262** and similar square design.
Multicoloured. W **51** (sideways). P 13½.

747	2ytl. Type **262**	5·00	5·50
748	2ytl.20 Dinghy race and Big Ben	5·00	5·50

263 Triumph Tiger Twin, 1952

(Des Görel Korol Sönmezer. Litho State Ptg Wks, Lefkosa)

2012 (22 Nov). Old Buses and Motorbikes. T **263** and similar horiz designs.
Multicoloured. W **51** (sideways). P 13½×14.

749	60ykr. Type **263**	2·50	2·00

750	70ykr. Ariel army W110, 1948		2·75	2·25
751	80ykr. Bedford bus, 1963		3·00	3·00
752	1ytl. Fagor bus, 1960		3·75	3·75
749/752 Set of 4			11·00	11·00

264 Ahmet Mithat Berberoglu (1921–2002) **265** Damaged Pedestrian Road Sign

(Litho State Ptg Wks, Lefkosa)

2013 (12 Mar). Personalities. T **264** and similar vert designs. P 14.

753	**264**	60ykr. dull ultramarine	1·75	1·25
754	–	70ykr. pale maroon	2·00	1·75
755	–	80ykr. violet	2·25	2·50
756	–	1ytl. deep dull green	2·75	3·00
753/756 Set of 4			8·00	7·75

Designs: 70ykr. Faiz Kaymak (1904–1982); 80ykr. Professor Dr. Mehmet Derviş Manizade (1903–2003); 1ytl. Mehmet Zeka (1903–1984).

(Des Can Kelic (1ytl.) or Ali Cüneyt Genç (2ytl.20).
Litho State Ptg Wks, Lefkosa)

2013 (18 Apr). Prevention of Traffic Accidents. T **265** and similar vert design. Multicoloured. P 14×13½.

757	1ytl. Type **265**	3·00	2·25
758	2ytl.20 Traffic lights with red light enclosed within eye	6·00	6·50

266 Postman's Bicycle

(Des Görel Korol Sönmezer. Litho State Ptg Wks, Lefkosa)

2013 (6 May). Europa. Postal Vehicles. T **266** and similar horiz design. Multicoloured. P 13½.

759	80ykr. Type **266**	3·50	3·00
760	80ykr. Post van	3·50	3·00

267 Upupa epops (Eurasian Hoopoe) **268** Leather Shield (late 18th-century)

(Des Görel Korol Sönmezer (50k.) or Hüseyin Billur (60k.).
Litho State Ptg Wks, Lefkosa)

2013 (8 July). Flora and Fauna. T **267** and similar multicoloured designs. W **51** (sideways). P 14 (25ykr.) or 13 (others).

761	25ykr. Iris oratoria (Mediterranean Mantis) and Polyommatus icarus (Common Blue Butterfly) (rectangular 52×36 mm)	1·50	1·00
762	50ykr. Type **267**	3·00	2·50
763	60ykr. Teucrium divaricatum ssp. canescens (Branched Germander)	2·50	2·75
761/763 Set of 3		6·25	5·50

(Des Görel Korol Sönmezer. Litho State Ptg Wks, Lefkosa)

2013 (10 Sept). Islamic Art and Culture. T **268** and similar vert designs. Multicoloured. W **51** (inverted). P 14.

764	60ykr. Type **268**	1·25	1·00
765	70ykr. Prayer rug (19th-century)	1·50	1·25
766	2ytl. Tombak candlestick (16th-century)	3·25	4·00
764/766 Set of 3		5·50	5·50

269 Anniversary Emblem **270** Cyprus Turkish Post 1964 Postmark on 10m. Red Cross Stamp

(Des Görel Korol Sönmezer (60, 70ykr.) or Hüseyin Billur (80ykr.).
Litho State Ptg Wks, Lefkosa)

2013 (20 Nov). Anniversaries and Events. T **269** and similar designs. W **51** (sideways on 80ykr.). P 14×13½ (60, 70ykr.) or 13½×14 (80ykr.).

767	**269**	60ykr. brownish grey-black and black	1·75	1·75
768	–	70ykr. carmine-vermilion, emerald and black	1·90	1·90
769	–	80ykr. rosine and black	2·25	2·25
767/769 Set of 3			5·50	5·50

Designs: 60 ykr. T **269** (50th Anniversary of Inter-Communal Violence); 70ykr. Laurel wreath, Dove and Northern Cyprus flag emblem (30th Anniversary of Turkish Republic of Northern Cyprus); 80ykr. Turkish and EU flag emblem and 'TÜRKIYE CUMHURIYETI 1923–2013' (90th Anniversary of Republic of Turkey).

(Litho State Ptg Wks, Lefkosa)

2014 (6 Jan). 50th Anniversary of Establishment of Cyprus Turkish Post Covers with Cyprus Turkish Post Postmarks. T **270** and similar horiz designs. Multicoloured. W **51** (sideways). P 13½×14.

770	50ykr. Type **270**	1·50	1·00
771	60ykr. Cyprus Turkish Post postmark on cover with 1963 30m. Europa stamp sent to Diss, Norfolk	1·75	1·25
772	1ytl. Cyprus Turkish Post postmark on cover with 1963 75m, Freedom from Hunger and US stamps sent to Seattle, USA then forwarded to London	3·00	3·75
770/772 Set of 3		5·50	5·50

271 Entrance to Turkish Education College

(Des Görel Korol Sönmezer. Litho State Ptg Wks, Lefkosa)

2014 (27 Jan). 50th Anniversary of Turkish Education College. W **51** (sideways). P 14.

773	**271** 2ytl.20 multicoloured	3·25	3·50

272 Footballer and Cathedral Spires **273** Desdemona (Dilara Karace) and Othello (Ahmed Kasim)

(Des Görel Korol Sönmezer. Litho State Ptg Wks, Lefkosa)

2014 (17 Feb). World Cup Football Championship, Brazil. T **272** and similar square design. Multicoloured. W **51**. P 13½.

774	70ykr. Type **272**	1·75	1·25
775	2ytl. Footballer and stadium	4·00	4·50

(Des Görel Korol Sönmezer. Litho State Ptg Wks, Lefkosa)

2014 (10 Mar). *The Only Witness was the Cumbez!* (Fig tree) (live performance dramatising history of Famagusta by Abdullah Öztoprak). T **273** and similar vert designs. Multicoloured. W **51**. P 14×13½.

776	25ykr. Type **273**	60	35
777	60ykr. People of Ottoman Empire period and		
	whirling dervish (Hakan Sevinç)	1·25	1·00
778	70ykr. Caterine Cornaro	1·40	1·25
779	1ytl. Canbulat Pasha and Bragadino	2·00	2·75
776/779 *Set of 4*		4·75	4·75

274 Tambourine

(Des Hüseyin Billur. Litho State Ptg Wks, Lefkosa)

2014 (23 May). Europa. National Musical Instruments. T **274** and similar horiz design. Multicoloured. W **51** (sideways on Nos. 780/781). P 13½.

780	80ykr. Type **274**	1·50	1·25
781	1ytl.80 Drum and zurna (wind instrument)	3·00	3·25
MS782 68×79 mm. Nos. 780/781		5·50	5·50

(**275**)　　　　　(**276**)

2014 (4 July). Nos. 461 and 470 surcharged with Types **275/276**.

783	30ykr. on 40000l. Type **155**	70	90
784	40ykr. on 90000l. multicoloured	80	1·00

277 Emblem and Map

(Des Görel Korol Sönmezer. Litho State Ptg Wks, Lefkosa)

2014 (8 Aug). 50th Anniversary of Erenköy's Resistance Struggle. P 14.

785	**277**	1ytl. multicoloured	2·25	2·50

278 Apple Blossom

(Des Hüseyin Billur (60ykr., 1ytl.) or Görel Korol Sönmezer (70, 80ykr.). Litho State Ptg Wks, Lefkosa)

2014 (19 Sept). Fruit Tree Flowers. T **278** and similar square designs. Multicoloured. P 13½.

786	60ykr. Type **278**	1·75	1·25
787	70ykr. Orange blossom	2·00	1·50
788	80ykr. Pomegranate blossom	2·25	1·75
789	1ytl. Peach blossom	3·00	3·50
786/789 *Set of 4*		8·00	7·00

279 Couple

(Des Görel Korol Sönmezer. Litho State Ptg Wks, Lefkosa)

2015 (9 Feb). St Valentine's Day. W **51** (inverted). P 14.

790	**279** 2ytl.20 multicoloured	1·50	1·50

280 Çanakkale Martyrs Monuments in Çanakkale and Famagusta, Gallipoli Star Medal and Minelayer *Nusrat*

(Des Görel Korol Sönmezer. Litho State Ptg Wks, Lefkosa)

2015 (18 Mar). Centenary of the Naval Victory in Çanakkale. W **51** (sideways). P 14.

791	**280**	2ytl. multicoloured	1·40	1·40

281 Boy (Negin Malekpaur)

(Litho State Ptg Wks, Lefkosa)

2015 (1 Apr). Struggle with Cancer. Winning Designs from Competition between High Schools. T **281** and similar vert design. Multicoloured. W **51**. P 13½.

792	80ykr. +10ykr. Type **281**	60	60
793	1ytl. +10ykr. Ribcage with pink Roses and		
	smoking lungs (Birsu Çağhan)	80	80

See also Nos. 836/837.

282 Pedestrian

283 Toy Cars

(Des Görel Korol Sönmezer. Litho State Ptg Wks, Lefkosa)

2015 (14 May). Traffic. T **282** and similar triangular design. Multicoloured. W **51** (sideways). P 13.

794	1ytl. Type **282** (inscr 'BİLİNCLİ SÜRÜCÜ GÜVENLİ TOPLUM' (Conscious driver is safe society)	1·00	1·00
795	2ytl.20 Motorcycle (inscr 'YOL YARIŞ PİSTİ DEĞİLDİR!' (The Road is not a Racetrack)	2·00	2·00

(Des Görel Korol Sönmezer. Litho State Ptg Wks, Lefkosa)

2015 (16 June). Europa. Old Toys. T **283** and similar vert design. Multicoloured. W **51**. P 13½.

796	70ykr. Type **283**	50	50
797	80ykr. Dolls	60	60
MS798	78×67 mm. Nos. 796/797. Imperf.	1·10	1·10

284 Cat

285 Colossal Statue of God Bes holding a Lion, Istanbul Archaeological Museum

(Des Görel Korol Sönmezer and Hüseyin Billur. Litho State Ptg Wks, Lefkosa)

2015 (5 Aug). Cats and Dogs. T **284** and similar vert designs. Multicoloured. W **51**. P 14.

799	60ykr. Type **284**	45	45
800	60ykr. Papillon (Dog)	45	45
801	70ykr. Beagle (Dog)	50	50
802	70ykr. Tabby Cat	50	50
799/802 Set of 4		1·75	1·75

(Litho State Ptg Wks, Lefkosa)

2015 (12 Oct). Cypriot Archaeological Artefacts in World Museums. T **285** and similar multicoloured designs. W **51** (sideways on horiz design). P 13½.

803	60ykr. Type **285**	45	45
804	70ykr. Silver plate from Lambousa Treasure depicting introduction of David to King Saul, Metropolitan Museum of Art, New York	50	50
805	80ykr. Statue of Athena driving chariot, Medelhavsmuseet (Museum of Mediterranean and Near Eastern Antiquities), Stockholm (horiz)	55	55
806	1ykl. Limestone head of statue, Medelhavsmuseet, Stockholm	70	70
803/806 Set of 4		2·00	2·00

286 Women harvesting Almonds

(Litho State Ptg Wks, Lefkosa)

2015 (23 Nov). Traditional Production of Almond Paste (macun). T **286** and similar horiz designs. Multicoloured. W **51** (sideways). P 13½.

807	50ykr. Type **286**	35	35
808	70ykr. Women making almond paste	50	50
809	1ytl. Women with small macun bowl	70	70
810	2ytl. Almond paste on tray	1·25	1·25
807/810 Set of 4		2·50	2·50

287 Eiffel Tower and Stadium

(Des Görel Korol Sönmezer. Litho State Ptg Wks, Lefkosa)

2016 (25 Feb). UEFA European Football Championship, France. T **287** and similar square design. Multicoloured. P 13½.

811	40ykr. Type **287**	35	20
812	6ytl. Footballer and stadium	3·75	4·00

288 Athlete

(Des Görel Korol Sönmezer. Litho State Ptg Wks, Lefkosa)

2016 (28 Apr). Olympic Games, Rio de Janeiro. T **288** and similar horiz designs. Multicoloured. W **51** (sideways). P 13½.

813	1ytl.30 Type **288**	80	80
814	2ytl.20 Male gymnast on rings	1·40	1·40
815	3ytl.05 Swimmer	2·00	2·00
813/815 Set of 3		3·75	3·75

289 Polluted and Clean Environments

(Des Doxia Sergidou (No. 816) and Hüseyin Billur (No. 817). Litho State Ptg Wks, Lefkosa)

2016 (12 May). Europa. Think Green. T **289** and similar horiz design. Multicoloured. W **51** (sideways). P 13½.

816	2ytl.80 Type **289**	1·75	1·75
817	2ytl.80 Grey polluted environment and Butterflies, Daisies and Tulip in green environment	1·75	1·75

290 Traditional Kitchen

(Des Görel Korol Sönmezer. Litho State Ptg Wks, Lefkosa)

2016 (22 Sept). Ethnographic Objects. T **290** and similar vert design. Multicoloured. W **51**. P 14.

818	1ytl.60 Type **290**	1·00	1·00
819	2 ytl. Traditional bedroom	1·25	1·25

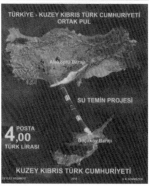

291 Map showing Undersea Water Supply
Pipe from Turkey to Turkish Cyprus

(Des Görel Korol Sönmezer. Litho State Ptg Wks, Lefkosa)

2016 (17 Oct). Water Supply Project. W **51** (sideways). Imperf.
MS820 54×64 mm. **291** 4ytl. multicoloured........................ 2·50   2·50

292 Apis mellifera

(Des Hüseyin Billur. Litho State Ptg Wks, Lefkosa)

2016 (24 Nov). Bees. T **292** and similar square designs. Multicoloured.
W **51** (sideways). P 13½.
821	1ytl. Type **292**	70	70
822	1ytl.50 Apis mellifera (on pink flower)	1·00	1·00
823	20ytl. Apis mellifera cypria	10·00	11·00
821/823 Set of 3		10·50	11·50

293 Dolphin (Delphinus delphis)

(Des Görel Korol Sönmezer. Litho State Ptg Wks, Lefkosa)

2017 (23 Feb). Dolphin (Delphinus delphis). W **51** (sideways). P 14.
824   **293**   1ytl. multicoloured   75   75

294 Mehmetçik

(Des Görel Korol Sönmezer. Litho State Ptg Wks, Lefkosa)

2017 (23 Mar). Cittaslow Member Towns in Northern Cyprus. T **294** and
similar horiz designs. Multicoloured. W **51** (sideways). P 13½×14.
825	60ykr. Type **294**	45	45
826	1ytl. Yenibogaziçi	70	70
827	2ytl. Lefke	1·25	1·25
825/827 Set of 3		2·25	2·25

295 Saint Hilarion Castle

(Des Görel Korol Sönmezer. Litho State Ptg Wks, Lefkosa)

2017 (11 May). Europa. Castles. T **295** and similar horiz design.
Multicoloured. W **51** (sideways). P 13½.
828	1ytl.50 Type **295**	1·00	70
829	3ytl.30 Girne (Kyrenia) Castle	2·00	2·40

296 Teucrium divaricatum subsp.
canescens

(Des Hüseyin Billur. Litho State Ptg Wks, Lefkosa)

2017 (31 July). Endemic Plants. T **296** and similar multicoloured designs.
W **51** (sideways on horiz designs). P 13½.
830	1ytl. Type **296**	60	60
831	1ytl.50 Dianthus strictus subsp. troodi	90	90
832	1ytl.65 Teucrium salaminium (vert)	1·00	1·00
833	1ytl.80 Sideritis cypria (vert)	1·10	1·10
830/833 Set of 4		3·25	3·25

297 Hakan Asik selling Sulu
Muhallebi (traditional dessert
of cornflour and rose syrup)
from Pushcart

(Des Görel Korol Sönmezer. Litho State Ptg Wks, Lefkosa)

2017 (5 Oct). The Masters of Tradition. T **297** and similar multicoloured
design. W **51** (sideways on 1ytl.). P 14.
834	1ytl. Type **297**	50	50
835	1ytl.50 Hasan Eminaga working in his pottery workshop Dizayn 74 in Girne (vert)	75	75

1.50 TÜRK LIRASI

(298)

2 TÜRK LIRASI

(299)

2018 (6 Apr). Nos. 792/793 surch with T **298/299**.
836	1ytl.50 on 80ykr.+10ykr. Type **281**	95	95
837	2ytl. on 1ytl.+10ykr. Ribcage with pink Roses and smoking lungs (Birsu Çağhan)	1·25	1·25

300 Değirmenlik

(Des Hüseyin Billur. Digitally printed Bolan
Digital Printing Ltd, Lefkosa)

2018 (18 May). Europa. Bridges. T **300** and similar horiz design.
Multicoloured. W **51** (sideways). P 13½.
838	1ytl.50 Type **300**	95	95
	a. Sheetlet of 4. Nos. 838/839, each×2	4·25	4·25
839	2ytl. Ortaköy	1·25	1·25

Nos. 838/839 were printed in separate sheets of nine and also in
se-tenant sheetlets of four, No. 838a, containing two of each design.

301 Stadium, Football
and Mascot

(Des Görel K. Sönmezer. Digitally printed
Bolan Digital Printing Ltd., Lefkosa)

2018 (14 June). World Cup Football Championship, Russia. T **301** and
similar square designs. Multicoloured. W **51** (inverted). P 13½.
840   1ytl.50 Type **301**..   90   90
       a. Horiz pair. Nos. 840/841 ....   1·75   1·75
841   1ytl.50 Stadium (*different*), mascot and football   90   90
    Nos. 840/841 were printed together, *se-tenant*, as horizontal pairs in
sheets of 40 and sheetlets of six (2×3).

302 *Mauremys rivulata*

(Des Görel Korol Sönmezer. Digitally printed Bolan
Digital Printing Ltd., Lefkosa)

2018 (31 July). Protected Animals. Reptiles. T **302** and similar horiz design.
Multicoloured. P 14×13½.
842   1ytl.50 Type **302**   90   90
       a. Sheetlet of 4. Nos. 842/843, each×2 ....   4·25   4·25
843   1ytl.65 *Phoeniçolacerta troodica* ....   1·00   1·00
    Nos. 842/843 were printed in separate sheets of nine and also in
se-tenant sheetlets of four, No. 842a, containing two of each design.

303 Hand holding Safety
Helmet

(Des Görel Korol Sönmezer. Digitally printed Bolan Digital Printing
Ltd, Lefkosa)

2018 (25 Sep). Occupational Health and Safety. W **51**. P 14.
844   **303**   2ytl. multicoloured ....   1·25   1·25

304 Kayakers and
Divers

(Des Görel Korol Sönmezer. Digitally printed Bolan Digital Printing
Ltd, Lefkosa)

2018 (13 Dec). Outdoor Sports. T **304** and similar vert design.
Multicoloured. W **51** (inverted on 4ytl.). P 14×13½.
845   2ytl.50 Type **304**..   1·50   1·50
846   4ytl. Cyclists and rock-climbers...........................   2·50   2·50

STAMP BOOKLETS

Following the inauguration of the Turkish Cypriot postal service in 1974
several postmasters continued to use the covers previously supplied by
the Cyprus Post Office in conjunction with Turkish Cypriot Posts issues.

B **1**

1987 (30 June). Europa. Modern. Architecture. Black on bluish grey cover,
    61×50 mm, showing Europa symbols. Pane attached by selvedge.
SB1   500l. booklet containing *se-tenant* pane of 4
       (No. 210ab)..   7·50

B **2**

1989 (31 May). Europa. Children's Games. Black on pale blue-green cover,
    62×48 mm, showing Europa symbols. Pane attached by selvedge.
SB2   3200l. booklet containing *se-tenant* pane of 4
       (No. 251ab)..   9·00

Faröe Islands
UNDER BRITISH OCCUPATION

The Faröe islands were under British administration from 12 April 1940 to 1945 to prevent their seizure by the Germans, who had occupied Denmark.

Types of Denmark overprinted

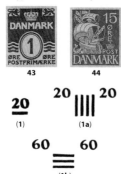

43 44

20
(1)

20 ‖‖‖ 20
(1a)

60 ═ 60
(1b)

1940 (2 Nov)–**41**. T **44** of Denmark, surch with T **1** by H. N. Jacobsen, Tórshavn.
1	20ö. on 15ö. scarlet (II)	60·00	10·00
	a. Surcharge bar omitted (4.41)	—	£650
	aa. Do. Surch double	—	£750

No. 1a is from proof sheets (200 stamps), later sold over PO counter. Nearly all copies were used.

1940–41. T **43** of Denmark, surch by H. N. Jacobsen, Tórshavn, with T **1a** (No. 3) or as T **1b** (others).
2	20ö. on 1ö. blackish green (B.) (2.5.41)	30·00	35·00
3	20ö. on 5ö. maroon (B.) (17.3.41)	20·00	12·00
4	50ö. on 5ö. maroon (6.12.40)	£200	35·00
5	60ö. on 6ö. orange (21.12.40)	90·00	£100

During a shortage of stamps in May and June 1941 circular post paid cancellations were used inscribed 'FAERØERNE FRANCO-BETALT' and the value in the centre: 5, 10 or 20 ØRE and also with the centre blank and a higher value inserted by hand. These are mainly seen on clippings from money order forms but are very rare on complete covers.

Gibraltar

CROWN COLONY

Early details of postal arrangements in Gibraltar are hard to establish, although it is known that postal facilities were provided by the Civil Secretary's Office from 1749. Gibraltar became a packet port in July 1806, although the Civil Secretary's office continued to be responsible for other mail. The two services were amalgamated on 1 January 1857 as a Branch Office of the British GPO, the control of the postal services not reverting to Gibraltar until 1 January 1886.

Spanish stamps could be used at Gibraltar from their introduction in 1850 and, indeed, such franking was required on letters weighing over ½ oz. sent to Spain after 1 July 1854. From 1 July 1856 until 31 December 1875 all mail to Spain required postage to be prepaid by Spanish stamps and these issues were supplied by the Gibraltar postal authorities, acting as a Spanish Postal Agent. The mail forwarded under this system was cancelled at San Roque with a horizontal barred oval, later replaced by a cartwheel type mark showing numeral 63. From 1857 combination covers showing the 2d. ship mail fee paid in British stamps and the inland postage by Spanish issues exist.

Stamps of Great Britain were issued for use in Gibraltar from 3 September 1857 (earliest recorded cover is dated 7 September 1857) to the end of 1885.

The initial supply contained 1d., 4d. and 6d. values. No supplies of the 2d. or 1s. were sent until the consignment of October 1857. No other values were supplied until early 1862.

Z 1 Z 2

Z 3

Z 4

Z 5

Z 6

Stamps of GREAT BRITAIN cancelled 'G' as T Z **1** or Z **2** (3 Sept 1857 to 19 Feb 1859).
Z1	1d. red-brown (1841), imperf	£3250
Z1a	1d. red-brown (1854) Die I, wmk Small Crown, perf 16	£425

Z2	1d. red-brown (1855), Die II, wmk Small Crown, perf 16		£800
Z3	1d. red-brown (1855), Die II, wmk Small Crown, perf 14		£375
Z4	1d. red-brown (1855), Die II, wmk Large Crown, perf 14		£100
Z5	1d. rose-red (1857), Die II, wmk Large Crown, perf 14		25·00
Z6	2d. blue (1855), wmk Small Crown, perf 14		£500
Z7	2d. blue (1855–1858), wmk Large Crown, perf 14		£400
Z8	2d. blue (1855), wmk Large Crown, perf 14 .... From Plate Nos. 5, 6.		75·00
Z9	2d. blue (1858) (Plate No. 7)		£350
Z10	4d. rose (1857)		60·00
	a. Thick glazed paper		
Z11	6d. lilac (1856)		42·00
Z12	6d. lilac (1856) (*blued paper*)		£850
Z13	1s. green (1856)		£130
	a. Thick paper		
Z14	1s. green (1856) (*blued paper*)		£1500

Stamps of GREAT BRITAIN cancelled 'A26' as in Types Z **3**, Z **4**, Z **5**, Z **6** or similar or circular or oval datestamps (20 Feb 1859 to 31 Dec 1885).

Z15	½d. rose-red (1870–1879) .... From Plate Nos. 4, 5, 6, 8, 10, 11, 12, 13, 14, 15, 19, 20		42·00
Z16	1d. red-brown (1841), imperf		£2500
Z17	1d. red-brown (1855), wmk Large Crown, perf 14		£250
Z18	1d. red-brown (1857), wmk Large Crown, perf 14		14·00
Z19	1d. rose-red (1864–1879) .... From Plate Nos. 71, 72, 73, 74 ,76, 78, 79, 80, 81, 82, 83, 84, 85, 86, 87, 88, 89, 90, 91, 92, 93, 94, 95, 96, 97, 98, 99, 100, 101, 102, 103, 104, 105, 106, 107, 108, 109, 110, 111, 112, 113, 114, 115, 116, 117, 118, 119, 120, 121, 122, 123, 124, 125, 127, 129, 130, 131, 132, 133, 134, 135, 136, 137, 138, 139, 140, 141, 142, 143, 144, 145, 146, 147, 148, 149, 150, 151, 152, 153, 154, 155, 156, 157, 158, 159, 160, 161, 162, 163, 164, 165, 166, 167, 168, 169, 170, 171, 172, 173, 174, 175, 176, 177, 178, 179, 180, 181, 182, 183, 184, 185, 186, 187, 188, 189, 190, 191, 192, 193, 194, 195, 196, 197, 198, 199, 200, 201, 202, 203, 204, 205, 206, 207, 208, 209, 210, 211, 212, 213, 214, 215, 216, 217, 218, 219, 220, 221, 222, 223, 224, 225.		24·00
Z20	1½d. lake-red (1870) (Plate No. 3)		£750
Z21	2d. blue (1855), wmk Large Crown, perf 14. Plate No. 6.		£160
Z22	2d. blue (1858–1869) .... From Plate Nos. 7, 8, 9, 12, 13, 14, 15.		24·00
Z23	2½d. rosy mauve (1875) (*blued paper*) .... From Plate Nos. 1, 2, 3.		£100
Z24	2½d. rosy mauve (1875–1876) .... From Plate Nos. 1, 2, 3.		32·00
Z25	2½d. rosy mauve (*Error of Lettering*)		£3750
Z26	2½d. rosy mauve (1876–1879) .... From Plate Nos. 3, 4, 5, 6, 7, 8, 9, 10, 11, 12, 13, 14, 15, 16, 17.		21·00
Z27	2½d. blue (1880–1881) .... From Plate Nos. 17, 18, 19, 20.		13·00
Z28	2½d. blue (1881) (Plate Nos. 21, 22, 23) .... From		10·00
Z29	3d. carmine-rose (1862)		£350
Z30	3d. rose (1865) (Plate No. 4)		90·00
Z31	3d. rose (1867–1873) .... From Plate Nos. 4, 5, 6, 7, 8, 9, 10.		65·00
Z32	3d. rose (1873–1876) .... From Plate Nos. 11, 12, 14, 15, 16, 17, 18, 19, 20.		85·00
Z33	3d. rose (1881) (Plate Nos. 20, 21)		
Z34	3d. lilac (1883) (3d. *on* 3d.)		£225
Z35	4d. rose (1857)		£110
Z36	4d. red (1862) (Plate No. 3, 4) .... From		48·00
Z37	4d. vermilion (1865–1873) .... From Plate Nos. 7, 8, 9, 10, 11, 12, 13, 14.		30·00
Z38	4d. vermilion (1876) (Plate No. 15)		£325
Z39	4d. sage-green (1877) (Plate Nos. 15, 16)		£140
Z40	4d. grey-brown (1880) wmk Large Garter .... Plate No. 17.		£425
Z41	4d. grey-brown (1880) wmk Crown .... From Plate Nos. 17, 18.		75·00
Z42	6d. lilac (1856)		42·00
Z43	6d. lilac (1862) (Plate Nos. 3, 4) .... From		40·00
Z44	6d. lilac (1865–1867) (Plate Nos. 5, 6) .... From		35·00
Z45	6d. lilac (1867) (Plate No. 6)		48·00
Z46	6d. violet (1867–1870) (Plate Nos. 6, 8, 9) .... From		32·00
Z47	6d. buff (1872–1873) (Plate Nos. 11, 12) .... From		£150
Z48	6d. chestnut (1872) (Plate No. 11)		38·00
Z49	6d. grey (1873) (Plate No. 12)		95·00
Z50	6d. grey (1874–1880) .... From Plate Nos. 13, 14, 15, 16, 17.		40·00
Z51	6d. grey (1881) (Plate Nos. 17, 18)		£375
Z52	6d. lilac (1883) (6d. *on* 6d.)		£130
Z53	8d. orange (1876)		£750
Z54	9d. bistre (1862)		£450

Z55	9d. straw (1862)		£900
Z56	9d. straw (1865)		£850
Z57	9d. straw (1867)		£325
Z57a	10d. brown (1848), embossed		£5000
Z58	10d. red-brown (1867)		£150
Z59	1s. green (1856)		£110
Z60	1s. green (1862)		70·00
Z61	1s. green (1862) ('K' *variety*)		£2500
Z62	1s. green (1865) (Plate No. 4)		60·00
Z63	1s. green (1867–1873) (Plate Nos. 4, 5, 6, 7) ...... From		40·00
Z64	1s. green (1873–1877) .... From Plate Nos. 8, 9, 10, 11, 12, 13.		90·00
Z65	1s. orange-brown (1880) (Plate No. 13)		£475
Z66	1s. orange-brown (1881) .... From Plate Nos. 13, 14.		£130
Z67	2s. blue (1867)		£350
Z68	5s. rose (1867) (Plate No. 1)		£1000
1880.			
Z69	½d. deep green		30·00
Z70	½d. pale green		30·00
Z71	1d. Venetian red		30·00
Z72	1½d. Venetian red		£400
Z73	2d. pale rose		75·00
Z74	2d. deep rose		75·00
Z75	5d. indigo		£160
1881.			
Z76	1d. lilac (14 *dots*)		45·00
Z77	1d. lilac (16 *dots*)		11·00
1884.			
Z78	½d. slate-blue		35·00
Z79	2d. lilac		£140
Z80	2½d. lilac		19·00
Z81	3d. lilac		
Z82	4d. dull green		£200
Z83	6d. dull green		
Z83a	1s. dull green		£500

POSTAL FISCAL

Z83b	1d. purple (Die 4) (1878) wmk Small Anchor		£700
Z84	1d. purple (1881), wmk Orb		£1100

PRICES FOR STAMPS ON COVER TO 1945		
Nos.	1/2	*from ×* 25
No.	3	*from ×* 10
No.	4	*from ×* 25
Nos.	5/6	*from ×* 8
Nos.	7/33	*from ×* 6
Nos.	39/45	*from ×* 5
Nos.	46/109	*from ×* 3
Nos.	110/113	*from ×* 4
Nos.	114/117	*from ×* 3
Nos.	118/120	*from ×* 5
Nos.	121/131	*from ×* 3

GIBRALTAR
(1)

1886 (1 Jan). Contemporary types of Bermuda optd with T **1** by D.L.R. Wmk Crown CA. P 14.

1	**9**	½d. dull green	23·00	12·00
2	**1**	1d. rose-red	85·00	6·00
3	**2**	2d. purple-brown	£140	85·00
		w. Wmk inverted		
4	**11**	2½d. ultramarine	£200	3·25
		a. Optd in blue-black	£500	£150
		w. Wmk inverted	—	£550
5	**10**	4d. orange-brown	£190	£110
6	**4**	6d. deep lilac	£300	£225
7	**5**	1s. yellow-brown	£450	£375
1/7	Set of 7		£1200	£700
1s/3s, 4as/7s Optd 'SPECIMEN' Set of 7			£5500	

Nos. 1/7 were overprinted on special printings of the underlying Bermuda stamps. The ½d., 2d. and 1s. values were not issued in these colours in Bermuda until 1893, while the 4d. was not issued on CA paper in Bermuda until 1904. The 6d. does not exist without opt. Collectors should be aware of Bermuda stamps with forged 'GIBRALTAR' overprints.

PRINTER. All Gibraltar stamps to No. 109 were typographed by De La Rue & Co, Ltd.

2    3

4    5

1886 (Nov)–**87**. Wmk Crown CA. P 14.

8	**2**	½d. dull green (1.87)	19·00	4·25
		w. Wmk inverted	†	£1000
9	**3**	1d. rose (2.87)	50·00	4·75
10	**4**	2d. brown-purple (12.86)	30·00	35·00
		w. Wmk inverted	£850	
11	**5**	2½d. blue	85·00	3·00
		w. Wmk inverted	£400	90·00
12	**4**	4d. orange-brown (16.4.87)	85·00	85·00
13		6d. lilac (16.4.87)	£140	£140
14		1s. bistre (2.87)	£250	£200
		w. Wmk inverted		

8/14 Set of 7	£600	£400
8s/14s Optd 'SPECIMEN' Set of 7	£500	

Examples of Nos. 3, 6/7 and 14 are known showing a forged Gibraltar postmark dated 'JU·13 87'.

See also Nos. 39/45.

5 CENTIMOS
(6)

Normal	'5' with short foot (all stamps in 1st, 5th and 6th vertical columns (5c. on ½d.) or all stamps in 2nd vertical column (25c. on 2d., 25c. on 2½d., 50c. on 6d. and 75c. on 1s.)

1889 (1 Aug). Surch as T **6**.

15	**2**	5c. on ½d. green	14·00	32·00
		a. '5' with short foot	14·00	32·00
16	**3**	10c. on 1d. rose	15·00	19·00
17	**4**	25c. on 2d. brown-purple	4·75	11·00
		a. '5' with short foot	10·00	22·00
		ab. Small 'I' (R. 6/2)	£100	£170
		b. Broken 'N' (R. 10/5)	£100	£170
18	**5**	25c. on 2½d. bright blue	29·00	2·50
		a. '5' with short foot	55·00	5·00
		ab. Small 'I' (R. 6/2)	£325	£100
		b. Broken 'N' (R. 10/5)	£325	£100
19	**4**	40c. on 4d. orange-brown	55·00	75·00
20		50c. on 6d. bright lilac	55·00	80·00
		a. '5' with short foot	£140	£170
21		75c. on 1s. bistre	55·00	65·00
		a. '5' with short foot	£150	£160

15/21 Set of 7	£200	£250
15s/21s Optd 'SPECIMEN' Set of 7	£375	

10c., 40c. and 50c. values from this issue and that of 1889–1896 are known bisected and used for half their value from various post offices in Morocco (price on cover from £500). These bisects were never authorised by the Gibraltar Post Office.

5c. Broken 'M' (Pls 1 & 2 R. 4/5)

7

20c. Flat top to 'C' (Pl 2 R. 4/4)

40c. Exclamation mark for 'I' (Pl 2 R. 8/4)

1889 (8 Oct*)–**96**. Issue in Spanish currency. Wmk Crown CA. P 14.

22	**7**	5c. green	6·50	1·00
		a. Broken 'M'	£190	85·00
		w. Wmk inverted	£300	£325
23		10c. carmine	4·50	50
		b. Value omitted	£7000	
24		20c. olive-green and brown (2.1.96)	27·00	24·00
		w. Wmk inverted	—	£850
25		20c. olive-green (8.7.96)	18·00	£100
		a. Flat top to 'C'	£350	
26		25c. ultramarine	27·00	70
		a. Deep ultramarine	38·00	1·00
27		40c. orange-brown	3·75	4·75
		a. Exclamation mark for 'I'	£150	£150
28		50c. bright lilac (1890)	3·25	2·75
29		75c. olive-green (1890)	32·00	32·00
30		1p. bistre (11.89)	75·00	20·00
31		1p. bistre and ultramarine (6.95)	5·00	8·50
32		2p. black and carmine (2.1.96)	12·00	30·00
33		5p. slate-grey (12.89)	42·00	£100

22/33 Set of 12	£225	£300
22s/24s, 26s/33s Optd 'SPECIMEN' Set of 11	£450	

* Earliest recorded postmark date.

Due to a shortage of 5c. and 10c. stamps between 13 and 21 February 1891, outgoing mail was paid for in cash and handstamped with the 'OFFICIAL PAID' datestamp in red.

1898 (1 Oct). Reissue in Sterling currency. Wmk Crown CA. P 14.

39	**2**	½d. grey-green	14·00	1·75
		w. Wmk inverted		
40	**3**	1d. carmine	14·00	50
		w. Wmk inverted	†	£1400
41	**4**	2d. brown-purple and ultramarine	29·00	2·50
42	**5**	2½d. bright ultramarine	45·00	50
		w. Wmk inverted	£350	90·00
43	**4**	4d. orange-brown and green	18·00	4·00
		a. 'FOUR PENCE' trimmed at top (Pl 2 R. 6/4 and 5, R. 8/4-6)	£500	
44		6d. violet and red	45·00	22·00
45		1s. bistre and carmine	45·00	8·00
		w. Wmk inverted		

39/45 Set of 7	£190	35·00
39s/45s Optd 'SPECIMEN' Set of 7	£275	

No. 39 is greyer than No. 8, No. 40 brighter and deeper than No. 9 and No. 42 much brighter than No. 11.

The degree of 'trimming' on No. 43a varies, but is most prominent on R. 6/4 and 5.

8   9

Normal	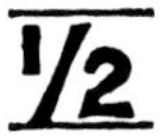 Large '2'

2½d.

This occurs on R. 10/1 in each pane of 60. The diagonal stroke is also longer.

1903 (1 May). Wmk Crown CA. P 14.

46	**8**	½d. grey-green and green	14·00	11·00
47		1d. dull purple/red	35·00	60
48		2d. grey-green and carmine	32·00	42·00
49		2½d. dull purple and black/blue	8·50	60
		a. Large '2' in '½'	£325	£130
50		6d. dull purple and violet	40·00	21·00
51		1s. black and carmine	28·00	38·00
52	**9**	2s. green and blue	£200	£275
53		4s. dull purple and green	£150	£225
54		8s. dull purple and black/blue	£170	£200
55		£1 dull purple and black/red	£650	£750

46/55 Set of 10	£1200	£1400
46s/55s Optd 'SPECIMEN' Set of 10	£550	

1904–08. Wmk Mult Crown CA. Ordinary paper (½d. to 2d. and 6d. to 2s.) or chalk-surfaced paper (others). P 14.

56	**8**	½d. dull and bright green (4.4.04*)	24·00	4·25
		a. Chalk-surfaced paper (10.05)	15·00	8·50
57		1d. dull purple/red (6.9.04*)	32·00	50
		a. Bisected (½d.) (on card or cover)	†	£1800
		bw. Wmk inverted	†	£950
		c. Chalk-surfaced paper (16.9.05)	8·50	85

58		2d. grey-green and carmine (9.1.05)........	40·00	17·00
		a. Chalk-surfaced paper (2.07)...............	10·00	18·00
59		2½d. purple and black/*blue* (4.5.07)	35·00	90·00
		a. Large '2' in '½'..............................	£600	£1000
60		6d. dull purple and violet (19.4.06)	50·00	40·00
		a. Chalk-surfaced paper (4.08)...............	32·00	22·00
61		1s. black and carmine (13.10.05)	65·00	24·00
		a. Chalk-surfaced paper (4.06)...............	55·00	24·00
62	**9**	2s. green and blue (2.2.05)	£120	£140
		a. Chalk-surfaced paper (10.07)	£120	£150
63		4s. deep purple and green (6.08)	£350	£425
64		£1 deep purple and black/*red*		
		(15.3.08)	£650	£700
56/64 *Set of 9*...			£1100	£1300

* Earliest known date of use.

1906 (Oct)–**11**. Colours changed. Wmk Mult Crown CA. Chalk-surfaced paper (6d. to 8s.). P 14.

66	**8**	½d. blue-green (1907)..........................	15·00	1·75
		x. Wmk reversed	†	£2000
67		1d. carmine.....................................	5·50	60
		a. Wmk sideways..............................	£3750	£3500
		w. Wmk inverted	†	£550
68		2d. greyish slate (5.10)	10·00	11·00
69		2½d. ultramarine (6.07)........................	9·00	1·75
		a. Large '2' in '½'..............................	£300	£120
70		6d. dull and bright purple (4.12.11)*	£150	£375
71		1s. black/*green* (1910)........................	23·00	21·00
72	**9**	2s. purple and bright blue/*blue* (4.10)..	65·00	48·00
73		4s. black and carmine (4.10)	£170	£190
		x. Wmk reversed	£1800	£2000
74		8s. purple and green (1911)	£250	£250
66/74 *Set of 9*			£600	£800
67s/74s Optd 'SPECIMEN' *Set of 8*.............			£600	

* Earliest known date of use.

Examples of Nos. 54, 55, 64 and 73/74 are known showing a forged oval registered postmark dated '6 OC 10'.

10	**11**

1912 (17 July)–**24**. Wmk Mult Crown CA. Ordinary paper (½d. to 2½d) or chalk-surfaced paper (others). P 14.

76	**10**	½d. blue-green	3·25	70
		a. Yellow-green (4.17)	7·00	2·00
		w. Wmk inverted	†	£1200
		x. Wmk reversed	†	£1800
77		1d. carmine-red...............................	4·50	75
		a. Scarlet (6.16)................................	9·00	1·25
		ay. Wmk inverted and reversed	†	£2000
78		2d. greyish slate..............................	21·00	1·50
79		2½d. deep bright blue.........................	10·00	3·00
		a. Large '2' in '½'..............................	£300	£160
		b. Pale ultramarine (1917)...................	12·00	3·00
		ba. Large '2' in '½'.............................	£300	£160
80		6d. dull purple and mauve	9·00	17·00
81		1s. black/*green*	19·00	3·25
		a. Ordinary paper (8.18)......................	£900	
		b. On blue-green, olive back (1919)	29·00	26·00
		c. On emerald surface (12.23)	30·00	70·00
		d. On emerald back (3.24)....................	32·00	£110
		ds. Optd 'SPECIMEN'...........................	75·00	
82	**11**	2s. dull purple and blue/*blue* (*shades*)..	29·00	4·25
		sa. Opt 'SPECIMEN' double....................	£650	
83		4s. black and carmine	38·00	55·00
84		8s. black and green	£100	£130
85		£1 dull purple and black/*red*	£140	£275
76/85 *Set of 10*			£325	£425
76s/85s Optd 'SPECIMEN' *Set of 10*			£500	

WAR TAX
(12)

1918 (15 Apr). Optd with T **12** by Beanland, Malin & Co, Gibraltar.

86	**10**	½d. green..	1·00	2·00
		a. Opt double..................................	£900	
		w. Wmk inverted	£850	
		y. Wmk inverted and reversed	£550	

Two printings of this overprint exist, the second being in slightly heavier type on a deeper shade of green.

3 PENCE	**THREE PENCE**	
(I)	(II)	

1921–27. Wmk Mult Script CA. Chalk-surfaced paper (6d. to 8s.). P 14.

89	**10**	½d. green (25.4.27).............................	1·50	1·50
90		1d. carmine-red (2.21)........................	1·75	1·00
91		1½d. chestnut (1.12.22)........................	2·00	55
		a. Pale chestnut (7.24)........................	2·75	30
		w. Wmk inverted	†	£1300
93		2d. grey (17.2.21)..............................	1·25	1·25
94		2½d. bright blue (2.21).........................	24·00	60·00
		a. Large '2' in '½'..............................	£600	£850
95		3d. bright blue (I) (1.1.22)...................	3·50	4·50
		a. Ultramarine	2·50	1·50
97		6d. dull purple and mauve (1.23)...........	6·00	6·00
		a. Bright purple and magenta		
		(22.7.26)	1·60	3·50
98		1s. black/*emerald* (20.6.24)................	10·00	25·00
99	**11**	2s. grey-purple and blue/*blue*		
		(20.6.24)....................................	19·00	80·00
		a. Reddish purple and blue/*blue*		
		(1925)..	7·00	45·00
100		4s. black and carmine (20.6.24).............	70·00	£130
101		8s. dull purple and green (20.6.24).........	£325	£550
89/101 *Set of 11*			£400	£750
89s/101s Optd 'SPECIMEN' *Set of 11*			£1000	

The ½d. exists in coils, constructed from normal sheets, first issued in February 1937.

1925 (15 Oct)–**32**. New values and colours changed. Wmk Mult Script CA. Chalk-surfaced paper. P 14.

102	**10**	1s. sage-green and black (8.1.29)...........	14·00	40·00
		a. Olive and black (1932)....................	14·00	20·00
103	**11**	2s. red-brown and black (8.1.29)............	10·00	40·00
104		2s.6d. green and black	10·00	29·00
105		5s. carmine and black	20·00	75·00
106		10s. deep ultramarine and black	32·00	80·00
107		£1 red-orange and black (16.11.27)........	£190	£300
108		£5 violet and black	£1600	£6000
		s. Optd 'SPECIMEN'............................	£800	
102/107 *Set of 6*			£250	£475
102s/107s Optd or Perf (1s., 2s.) 'SPECIMEN' *Set of 6*.........			£500	

Examples of Nos. 83/85, 99/101 and 102/108 are known showing forged oval registered postmarks dated '24 JA 25' or '6 MY 35'.

1930 (11 Apr). T **10** inscribed 'THREE PENCE'. Wmk Mult Script CA. P 14.

109		3d. ultramarine (II)	8·00	2·25
		s. Perf 'SPECIMEN'	80·00	

13 The Rock of Gibraltar

(Des Captain H. St. C. Garrood. Recess D.L.R.)

1931–33. Wmk Mult Script CA. P 14.

110	**13**	1d. scarlet (1.7.31)............................	2·50	2·50
		a. Perf 13½×14...............................	22·00	8·00
111		1½d. red-brown (1.7.31)........................	1·75	2·25
		a. Perf 13½×14...............................	17·00	4·00
112		2d. pale grey (1.11.32)........................	13·00	1·75
		a. Perf 13½×14...............................	24·00	4·50
113		3d. blue (1.6.33)..............................	11·00	3·00
		a. Perf 13½×14...............................	42·00	42·00
110/113 *Set of 4*			25·00	8·50
110a/113a *Set of 4*			90·00	50·00
110s, 111s/113s Perf 'SPECIMEN' *Set of 4*			£200	

Figures of value take the place of both corner ornaments at the base of the 2d. and 3d.

Extra flagstaff	Short extra flagstaff
(Plate 1 R. 9/1)	(Plate 2 R. 2/1)

Lightning conductor
(Plate 3 R. 2/5)

Flagstaff on right-hand
turret (Plate 5 R. 7/1)

Double flagstaff
(Plate 6 R. 5/2)

1935 (6 May). Silver Jubilee. As Nos. 144/147 of Cyprus but ptd by B.W.
P 11×12.

114	2d. ultramarine and grey-black		1·60	2·50
	a. Extra flagstaff		75·00	£130
	b. Short extra flagstaff		£160	£275
	c. Lightning conductor		£110	£170
	d. Flagstaff on right-hand turret		£425	£450
	e. Double flagstaff		£425	£450
115	3d. brown and deep blue		3·75	5·00
	a. Extra flagstaff		£325	£375
	b. Short extra flagstaff		£325	£375
	c. Lightning conductor		£350	£400
116	6d. green and indigo		14·00	19·00
	a. Extra flagstaff		£275	£325
	b. Short extra flagstaff		£500	£550
	c. Lightning conductor		£300	£350
117	1s. slate and purple		18·00	28·00
	a. Extra flagstaff		£225	£275
	b. Short extra flagstaff		£550	£550
	c. Lightning conductor		£275	£325
114/117 Set of 4			32·00	48·00
114s/117s Perf 'SPECIMEN' Set of 4			£200	

1937 (12 May). Coronation. As Nos. 148/150 of Cyprus. P 11×11½.

118	½d. green		25	50
119	2d. grey-black		3·00	3·25
120	3d. blue		3·00	3·25
118/120 Set of 3			5·75	6·25
118s/120s Perf 'SPECIMEN' Set of 3			£190	

14 King
George VI

15 Rock of Gibraltar

16 The Rock (North Side)

17 Europa Point

18 Moorish Castle

19 Southport Gate

20 Eliott Memorial

21 Government House

22 Catalan Bay

2d. Ape on rock (R. 1/5)

2s. Bird on memorial (R. 9/3)

Broken second 'R' in 'GIBRALTAR'
(Frame Pl 2 R. 9/4)

(Des Captain H. St. C. Garrood. Recess D.L.R.)

1938 (25 Feb)–**51**. Types **14/22**. Mult Script CA.

121	14	½d. deep green (P 13½×14)	10	40
122	15	1d. yellow-brown (P 14)	30·00	2·25
		a. Perf 13½ (1940)	30·00	2·25
		ab. Perf 13½. Wmk sideways (1940)	6·50	7·00
		b. Perf 13. Wmk sideways. *Red-brown* (1942)	2·25	60
		c. Perf 13. Wmk sideways. *Deep brown* (1944)	3·25	3·50
		d. Perf 13. *Red-brown* (1949)	6·00	1·50
123		1½d. carmine (P 14)	35·00	1·00
		a. Perf 13½	£275	18·00
123b		1½d. slate-violet (P 13) (1.1.43)	75	1·00
124	16	2d. grey (P 14)	32·00	40
		aa. Ape on rock	£700	£110
		a. Perf 13½ (1940)	9·00	35
		ab. Perf 13½. Wmk sideways (1940)	£800	45·00
		b. Perf 13. Wmk sideways (1943)	4·25	3·00
		ba. 'A' of 'CA' missing from wmk	£1700	
124c		2d. carmine (P 13) (*wmk sideways*) (15.7.44)	2·00	60
125	17	3d. light blue (P 13½)	45·00	1·00
		a. Perf 14	£130	6·00
		b. Perf 13 (1942)	4·50	30
		ba. 'A' of 'CA' missing from wmk	£2000	
		bb. *Greenish blue* (2.51)	8·50	1·00
125c		5d. red-orange (P 13) (1.10.47)	1·75	1·25
126	18	6d. carmine and grey-violet (P 13½) (16.3.38)	48·00	3·75
		a. Perf 14	£120	1·25
		b. Perf 13 (1942)	11·00	1·40
		c. Perf 13. *Scarlet and grey-violet* (1945)	13·00	3·75
127	19	1s. black and green (P 14) (16.3.38)	45·00	38·00
		a. Perf 13½	75·00	6·00
		b. Perf 13 (1942)	3·25	4·25
		ba. Broken 'R'	£950	
128	20	2s. black and brown (P 14) (16.3.38)	65·00	23·00
		a. Perf 13½	£130	50·00
		b. Perf 13 (1942)	15·00	6·50
		ba. Broken 'R'	£1300	
		bb. Bird on memorial	£700	£500
129	21	5s. black and carmine (P 14) (16.3.38)	£100	£170
		a. Perf 13½	50·00	14·00

		b. Perf 13 (1944)		42·00	17·00
		ba. Broken 'R'		£4000	
130	22	10s. black and blue (P 14) (16.3.38)		70·00	£130
		a. Perf 13 (1943)		42·00	25·00
		ab. Broken 'R'		£5000	£3250
131	14	£1 orange (P 13½×14) (16.3.38)		42·00	55·00
121/131 Set of 14				£180	£100
121s/131s Perf 'SPECIMEN' Set of 14				£850	

The ½d., 1d. and both colours of the 2d. exist in coils constructed from normal sheets. These were originally joined vertically, but, because of technical problems, the 1d. and 2d. grey were subsequently issued in horizontal coils. The 2d. carmine only exists in the horizontal version.

Examples of Nos. 129/131 are known showing forged oval registered postmarks dated '6 OC 43', '18 OC 43', '3 MR 44' and '4 AU 44'.

1946 (12 Oct). Victory. As Nos. 164/165 of Cyprus.

132		½d. green	30	1·50
133		3d. ultramarine	50	1·25
132s/133s Perf 'SPECIMEN' Set of 2			£160	

1948 (1 Dec). Royal Silver Wedding. As Nos. 166/167 of Cyprus.

134		½d. green	1·50	3·00
135		£1 brown-orange	60·00	80·00

1949 (10 Oct). 75th Anniversary of Universal Postal Union. As Nos. 168/171 of Cyprus but country name typo on Nos. 137/138.

136		2d. carmine	1·00	1·25
137		3d. deep blue	2·00	1·50
138		6d. purple	1·75	2·00
139		1s. blue-green	1·75	5·00
136/139 Set of 4			6·00	8·75

No. 139 is known with the 'A' of 'CA' almost completely missing from the watermark.

NEW CONSTITUTION 1950
(23)

Stop before '2' in '½' in right-hand value tablet (Pl. 1A–5A, R. 4/4)

1950 (1 Aug). Inauguration of Legislative Council. Nos. 124c, 125ba, 126b and 127b optd as T **23**.

140	16	2d. carmine	60	1·50
141	–	3d. greenish blue	65	1·00
142	–	6d. carmine and grey-violet	75	2·00
		a. Opt double	£1000	£1300
143	–	1s. black and green (R.)	75	2·25
		a. Broken 'R'	£130	
140/143 Set of 4			2·50	6·00

Four sheets of No. 142 received double overprints. On some examples the two impressions are almost coincident.

1953 (2 June). Coronation. As No. 172 of Cyprus.

144		½d. black and bronze-green	75	2·25
		a. Stop before '2' in '½'	16·00	

24 Cargo and Passenger Wharves

25 South View from Straits

26 Gibraltar Fish Canneries

27 Southport Gate

28 Sailing in the Bay

29 Saturnia (liner)

30 Coaling wharf

31 Airport

32 Europa Point

33 Straits from Buena Vista

34 Rosia Bay and Straits

35 Main Entrance, Government House

36 Tower of Homage, Moorish Castle

37 Arms of Gibraltar

5d. Major re-entry causing doubling of 'ALTA' in 'GIBRALTAR' (R. 4/6)

1s. Re-entry causing doubling of lines of sea wall and buildings (R. 6/3-5)

(Des D.L.R., based on photographs by N. Cummings. Recess (except £1, centre litho) De La Rue)

1953 (19 Oct)–**59**. Types **24/37**. Wmk Mult Script CA. P 13.

145	24	½d. indigo and grey-green	15	30
146	25	1d. bluish green	1·50	1·00
		a. Deep bluish green (31.12.57)	4·25	1·50
147	26	1½d. black	1·00	2·25
148	27	2d. deep olive-brown	3·00	1·25
		a. Sepia (18.6.58)	5·00	1·50
149	28	2½d. carmine	4·75	1·25
		a. Deep carmine (11.9.56)	8·50	1·50
		aw. Wmk inverted	£750	
150	29	3d. light blue	4·75	20
		a. Deep greenish blue (8.6.55)	11·00	55
		b. Greenish blue (18.6.58)	27·00	2·50

151	**30**	4d. ultramarine	7·00	3·50
		a. Blue (17.6.59)	35·00	13·00
152	**31**	5d. maroon	1·75	1·50
		a. Major re-entry	55·00	
		b. Deep maroon (31.12.57)	4·75	2·50
		ba. Major re-entry	£100	
153	**32**	6d. black and pale blue	7·50	2·00
		a. Black and blue (24.4.57)	10·00	3·00
		b. Black and grey-blue (17.6.59)	19·00	11·00
154	**33**	1s. pale blue and red-brown	1·25	2·25
		a. Re-entry	29·00	
		b. Pale blue and deep red-brown		
		(27.3.56)	1·00	2·25
		ba. Re-entry	29·00	
155	**34**	2s. orange and reddish violet	50·00	16·00
		a. Orange and violet (17.6.59)	35·00	8·50
156	**35**	5s. deep brown	40·00	17·00
157	**36**	10s. reddish brown and ultramarine	45·00	45·00
158	**37**	£1 scarlet and orange-yellow	55·00	55 00
145/158 *Set of 14*			£180	£120

Nos. 145/146, 148 and 150 exist in coils, constructed from normal sheets by Harrison.

1954 (10 May). Royal Visit. As No. 150 but inscr 'ROYAL VISIT 1954' at top.

159		3d. greenish blue	1·00	20

38 Gibraltar Candytuft

39 Moorish Castle

40 St George's Hall

41 The Keys

42 The Rock by moonlight

43 Catalan Bay

44 Map of Gibraltar

45 Air terminal

46 American War Memorial

47 Barbary Ape

48 Barbary Partridge

49 Blue Rock Thrush

50 Rock Lily
(*Narcissus niveus*)

51 Rock and Badge of
Gibraltar Regiment

1d. Retouch right
of flag appears
as an extra flag
(Pl. 1B, R. 5/5)

1d. Jagged brown flaw in wall
to right of gate appears as a
crack (Pl. 1B, R. 2/5)

6d. Large white spot on
map SW of 'CEUTA'
(Pl. 1B, R. 4/5)

(Des J. Celecia (½d., 2d., 2½d., 2s., 10s.), N. A. Langdon frames of ½d. to 10s. and 1d., 3d., 6d., 7d., 9d., 1s.), M. Bonilla (4d.), L. V. Gómez (5s.), Sergeant T. A. Griffiths (£1). Recess (£1) or photo (others) D.L.R.)

1960 (29 Oct)–**62**. Designs as Types **38/51**. W w **12** (upright). P 14 (£1) or 13 (others).

160	**38**	½d. bright purple and emerald-green	15	50
161	**39**	1d. black and yellow-green	20	10
		a. Crack in wall	13·00	
		b. 'Phantom flag'	13·00	
162	**40**	2d. indigo and orange-brown	1·00	20
163	**41**	2½d. black and blue	1·75	80
		a. Black and grey-blue (16.10.62)	1·75	30
164	**42**	3d. deep blue and red-orange	1·75	10
165	**43**	4d. deep red-brown and turquoise	2·75	70
166	**44**	6d. sepia and emerald	1·00	70
		a. White spot on map	28·00	
167	**45**	7d. indigo and carmine-red	2·50	1·75
168	**46**	9d. grey-blue and greenish blue	1·25	1·00
169	**47**	1s. sepia and bluish green	1·50	70
170	**48**	2s. chocolate and ultramarine	20·00	3·25
171	**49**	5s. turquoise-blue and olive-brown	8·00	10·00
172	**50**	10s. yellow and blue	27·00	26·00
173	**51**	£1 black and brown-orange	22·00	26·00
160/173 *Set of 14*			80·00	60·00

New plates were made for all values other than the £1, incorporating a finer screen (250 dots per inch, rather than the original 200), giving clearer, deeper, better-defined impressions. No. 163*a* comes from the later plate of the 2½d.

Nos. 160/162, 164 and 166 exist in coils, constructed from normal sheets by Harrison.

See also No.199.

The 1d. imperforate comes from stolen printer's waste.

51a Protein foods

51b Red Cross Emblem

(Des M. Goaman. Photo Harrison)

1963 (4 June). Freedom from Hunger. W w **12**. P 14×14½.

174	**51a**	9d. sepia	2·50	2·50

(Des V. Whiteley. Litho B.W.)

1963 (2 Sept). Red Cross Centenary. W w **12**. P 13½.

175	**51b**	1d. red and black	1·00	2·00
176		9d. red and blue	2·00	5·50

51c Shakespeare and Memorial Theatre, Stratford-upon-Avon

NEW CONSTITUTION 1964.
(52)

(Des R. Granger Barrett. Photo Harrison)

1964 (23 Apr). 400th Birth Anniversary of William Shakespeare. W w **12**. P 11×11½.

177	**51c**	7d. bistre-brown	60	20

1964 (16 Oct). New Constitution. Nos. 164 and 166 optd with T **52**.

178	3d. deep blue and red-orange	20	10
179	6d. sepia and emerald	20	60
	a. No stop after '1964' (R. 2/5)	19·00	50·00
	b. White spot on map	19·00	50·00

52a ITU Emblem

52b ICY Emblem

(Des M. Goaman. Litho Enschedé)

1965 (17 May). ITU Centenary. W w **12**. P 11×11½.

180	**52a**	4d. light emerald and yellow	2·00	50
		w. Wmk inverted	38·00	
181		2s. apple-green and deep blue	5·50	5·00

(Des V. Whiteley. Litho Harrison)

1965 (25 Oct). International Co-operation Year. W w **12**. P 14½.

182	**52b**	½d. deep bluish green and lavender	20	2·75
183		4d. reddish purple and turquoise-green	80	50

The value of the ½d. stamp is shown as '1/2'.

52c Sir Winston Churchill and St Paul's Cathedral in Wartime

(Des Jennifer Toombs. Photo Harrison)

1966 (24 Jan). Churchill Commemoration. Printed in black, cerise and gold and with background in colours stated. W w **12**. P 14.

184	**52c**	½d. new blue	20	2·75
		w. Wmk inverted	75·00	
185		1d. deep green	30	10
186		4d. brown	1·50	10
187		9d. bluish violet	1·25	2·50
184/187 Set of 4			3·00	4·75

52d Footballer's legs, ball and Jules Rimet cup

(Des V. Whiteley. Litho Harrison)

1966 (1 July). World Cup Football Championship. W w **12** (sideways). P 14.

188	**52d**	2½d. violet, yellow-green, lake and yellow and brown	75	2·25
189		6d. chocolate, blue-green, lake and yellow and brown	1·00	75

PRINTERS. All stamps from here to No. 239 were printed in photogravure by Harrison and Sons Ltd, London.

53 Red Seabream

4d. Break at top right corner of 'd' of value (R. 9/3).

(Des A. Ryman)

1966 (27 Aug). European Sea Angling Championships, Gibraltar. T **53** and similar designs. W w **12** (sideways on 1s.). P 13½×14 (1s.) or 14×13½ (others).

190		4d. rosine, bright blue and black	30	10
		a. Broken 'd'	6·00	
191		7d. rosine, deep olive-green and black	60	1·50
		a. Black (value and inscr) omitted	£1800	
		w. Wmk inverted	3·00	
192		1s. lake-brown, emerald and black	50	30
190/192 Set of 3			1·75	1·75

Designs: Horiz—4d. T **53**; 7d. Red Scorpionfish. Vert—1s. Stone Bass.

54 WHO Building

(Des M. Goaman. Litho Harrison)

1966 (20 Sept). Inauguration of WHO Headquarters, Geneva. W w **12** (sideways). P 14.

193	**54**	6d. black, yellow-green and light blue	3·00	1·50
194		9d. black, light purple and yellow-brown	3·50	4·75

56 'Our Lady of Europa'

(Des A. Ryman)

1966 (15 Nov). Centenary of Re-enthronement of 'Our Lady of Europa'. W w **12**. P 14×14½.

195	**56**	2s. bright blue and black	30	80

56a 'Education'

56b 'Science'

56c 'Culture'

(Des Jennifer Toombs. Litho Harrison)

1966 (1 Dec). 20th Anniversary of UNESCO. W w **12** (sideways). P 14.

196	**56a**	2d. slate-violet, red, yellow and orange	60	10
197	**56b**	7d. orange-yellow, violet and deep olive	2·25	10
198	**56c**	5s. black, bright purple and orange	4·50	3·25
196/198 *Set of 3*			6·50	3·25

1966 (23 Dec). As No. 165 but wmk w **12** sideways.

199	4d. deep red-brown and turquoise	30	2·75

57 HMS *Victory*

½d. Gash in shape of boomerang in topsail (Pl. 1A, R. 8/4).

½d. Grey mark in topsail resembling a stain (Pl. 1A, R. 8/6).

7d. Bold shading on sail appearing as patch (Pl. 1A, R. 10/5).

(Des A. Ryman)

1967 (3 Apr)–**69**. Horiz designs as T **57**. Multicoloured. W w **12**. P 14×14½.

200	½d. Type **57**	10	20
	a. Grey (sails, etc) omitted	£800	
	b. Gash in sail	1·50	
	c. Stained sail	1·50	
201	1d. *Arab* (early steamer)	10	10
	w. Wmk inverted	3·25	4·75

202	2d. HMS *Carmania* (merchant cruiser)	15	10
	a. Grey-blue (hull) omitted	£8500	
203	2½d. *Mons Calpe* (ferry)	40	30
204	3d. *Canberra* (liner)	20	10
	w. Wmk inverted	45·00	9·00
205	4d. HMS *Hood* (battle cruiser)	1·50	10
	aw. Wmk inverted		
205b	5d. *Mirror* (cable ship) (7.7.69)	2·00	55
	bw. Wmk inverted	†	£1500
206	6d. Xebec (sailing vessel)	30	50
207	7d. *Amerigo Vespucci* (Italian cadet ship)	30	1·50
	a. Patched sail	14·00	
	w. Wmk inverted	19·00	
208	9d. *Raffaello* (liner)	30	1·75
209	1s. *Royal Katherine* (galleon)	30	35
210	2s. HMS *Ark Royal* (aircraft carrier), 1937	5·00	3·50
211	5s. HMS *Dreadnought* (nuclear submarine)	3·50	7·50
212	10s. *Neuralia* (liner)	12·00	23·00
213	£1 *Mary Celeste* (sailing vessel)	12·00	23·00
200/213 *Set of 15*		32·00	55·00

No. 202a results from the misaligning of the grey-blue cylinder. The bottom horizontal row of the sheet involved has this colour completely omitted except for the example above the cylinder numbers which shows the grey-blue '1A' towards the top of the stamp.

The ½d., 1d., 2d., 3d., 6d., 2s., 5s. and £1 exist with PVA gum as well as gum arabic, but the 5d. exists with PVA gum only.

Nos. 201/202, 204/205 and 206 exist in coils constructed from normal sheets.

58 Aerial Ropeway

(Des A. Ryman)

1967 (15 June). International Tourist Year. T **58** and similar designs but horiz. Multicoloured. W w **12** (sideways on 7d.). P 14½×14 (7d.) or 14×14½ (others).

214	7d. Type **58**	15	15
215	9d. Shark fishing	15	20
216	1s. Skin-diving	20	15
214/216 *Set of 3*		45	45

59 Mary, Joseph and Child Jesus

60 Church Window

1967 (1 Nov). Christmas. W w **12** (sideways* on 6d.). P 14.

217	**59**	2d. multicoloured	15	10
		w. Wmk inverted	1·00	
218	**60**	6d. multicoloured	15	10
		w. Wmk Crown to right of CA	£475	

* The normal sideways watermark shows Crown to left of CA, *as seen from the back of the stamp.*

61 General Eliott and Route Map

62 Eliott directing Rescue Operations

(Des A. Ryman)

1967 (11 Dec). 250th Birth Anniversary of General Eliott. Multicoloured designs as T **61** (4d. to 1s.) or T **62**. W w **12** (sideways on horiz designs). P 14×15 (1s.) or 15×14 (others).

219	4d. Type **61**	15	10
220	9d. Heathfield Tower and Monument, Sussex (38×22 *mm*)	15	10
221	1s. General Eliott (22×38 *mm*)	15	10
222	2s. Type **62**	25	50
219/222 *Set of 4*		65	70

65 Lord Baden-Powell

(Des A. Ryman)

1968 (27 Mar). 60th Anniversary of Gibraltar Scout Association. T **65** and similar horiz designs. W w **12**. P 14×14½.

223	4d. buff and bluish violet	15	10
224	7d. ochre and blue-green	20	20
225	9d. bright blue, yellow-orange and black	20	30
226	1s. greenish yellow and emerald	20	30
223/226 *Set of 4*		65	75

Designs: 4d. T **65**; 7d. Scout Flag over the Rock; 9d. Tent, scouts and salute; 1s. Scout badges.

66 Nurse and WHO Emblem

68 King John signing *Magna Carta*

(Des A. Ryman)

1968 (1 July). 20th Anniversary of World Health Organisation. T **66** and similar horiz design. W w **12**. P 14×14½.

227	2d. ultramarine, black and yellow	10	15
228	4d. slate, black and pink	10	10

Design: 2d. T **66**; 4d. Doctor and WHO emblem.

(Des A. Ryman)

1968 (26 Aug). Human Rights Year. T **68** and similar vert design. W w **12** (sideways). P 13½×14.

229	1s. yellow-orange, brown and gold	15	10
230	2s. myrtle and gold	25	1·00

Designs: 1s. T **68**; 2s. 'Freedom' and Rock of Gibraltar.

70 Shepherd, Lamb and Star

72 Parliament Houses

(Des A. Ryman)

1968 (1 Nov). Christmas. T **70** and similar vert design. Multicoloured. W w **12**. P 14½×13½.

231	4d. Type **70**	10	10
	a. Gold (star) omitted	£850	£850
232	9d. Mary holding Holy Child	15	20

(Des A. Ryman)

1969 (26 May). Commonwealth Parliamentary Association Conference. T **72** and similar designs. W w **12** (sideways on 2s.). P 14×14½ (2s.) or 14½×14 (others).

233	4d. green and gold	10	10
234	9d. bluish violet and gold	10	10
235	2s. multicoloured	15	30
233/235 *Set of 3*		30	40

Designs: Horiz—4d. T **72**; 9d. Parliamentary emblem and outline of 'The Rock'. Vert—2s. Clock Tower, Westminster (Big Ben) and Arms of Gibraltar.

75 Silhouette of Rock, and Queen Elizabeth II

77 Soldier and Cap Badge, Royal Anglian Regiment, 1969

(Des A. Ryman)

1969 (30 July). New Constitution. W w **12**. P 14×13½ (in addition, the outline of the Rock is perforated).

236	**75**	½d. gold and orange	10	10
237		5d. silver and bright green	20	10
		a. Portrait and inscr in gold and silver*		
238		7d. silver and bright purple	20	10
239		5s. gold and ultramarine	65	1·10
236/239 *Set of 4*			1·00	1·25

* No. 237a was first printed with the head and inscription in gold and then in silver but displaced slightly to lower left

(Des A. Ryman. Photo D.L.R.)

1969 (6 Nov). Military Uniforms (1st series). T **77** and similar vert designs. Multicoloured. W w **12**. P 14.

240	1d. Royal Artillery officer, 1758 and modern cap badge	15	10
241	6d. Type **77**	20	15
242	9d. Royal Engineers' Artificer, 1786 and modern cap badge	30	20
243	2s. Private, Fox's Marines, 1704 and modern Royal Marines cap badge	75	1·25
240/243 *Set of 4*		1·25	1·50

Nos. 240/243 have a short history of the Regiment printed on the reverse side over the gum, therefore, once the gum is moistened the history disappears.

See also Nos. 248/251, 290/293, 300/303, 313/316, 331/334, 340/343 and 363/366.

80 *Madonna of the Chair* (detail, Raphael)

83 Europa Point

(Des A. Ryman. Photo Enschedé)

1969 (1 Dec). Christmas. T **80** and similar vert designs. Multicoloured. W w **12** (sideways). P 14×Roulette 9.

244	5d. Type **80**	10	35
	a. Strip of 3. Nos. 244/246	45	1·00
	ab. Grey omitted		
245	7d. *Virgin and Child* (detail, Morales)	20	35
246	1s. *The Virgin of the Rocks* (detail, Leonardo da Vinci)	20	40
244/246 *Set of 3*		45	1·00

Nos. 244/246 were issued together in *se-tenant* strips of three throughout the sheet.

The grey omitted error affects the background tone of all three stamps. It is best collected with printer's check marks attached.

(Des A. Ryman. Photo Enschedé)

1970 (8 June). Europa Point. W w **12**. P 13½.

247	**83**	2s. multicoloured	45	1·50
		w. Wmk inverted	2·00	3·25

(Des A. Ryman. Photo D.L.R.)

1970 (28 Aug). Military Uniforms (2nd series). Vert designs as T **77**.
Multicoloured. W w **12**. P 14.

248	2d. Royal Scots officer, 1839 and cap badge	25	10
249	5d. South Wales Borderers private, 1763 and cap badge	35	10
250	7d. Queens Royal Regiment private, 1742 and cap badge	35	10
251	2s. Royal Irish Rangers piper, 1969 and cap badge	1·00	1·25
248/251	Set of 4	1·75	1·25

Nos. 248/251 have a short history of the Regiment printed on the
reverse side under the gum.

88 No. 191a and Rock of
Gibraltar

(Des A. Ryman. Litho D.L.R.)

1970 (18 Sept). Philympia 1970 Stamp Exhibition, London. T **88** and
similar horiz design. W w **12** (sideways). P 13.

252	1s. vermilion and bronze-green	15	10
253	2s. bright blue and magenta	25	65

Designs: T **88**; 2s. Victorian stamp (No. 23b) and Moorish Castle.
The stamps shown in the designs are well-known varieties with values
omitted.

90 *The Virgin Mary* (stained-glass
window by Gabriel Loire)

(Photo Enschedé)

1970 (1 Dec). Christmas. W w **12**. P 13×14.

254	**90**	2s. multicoloured	30	1·25

(New Currency: 100 pence = £1)

91 Saluting Battery, Rosia

92 Saluting Battery, Rosia,
Modern View

(Des A. Ryman. Litho Questa)

1971 (15 Feb). Decimal Currency. Designs as Types **91/92**. W w **12**
(sideways* on horiz designs). P 14.

255	½p. multicoloured	20	30
	a. Pair. Nos. 255/256	40	60
256	½p. multicoloured	20	30
257	1p. multicoloured	80	30
	a. Pair. Nos. 257/258	1·60	60
258	1p. multicoloured	80	30
259	1½p. multicoloured	20	80
	a. Pair. Nos. 259/260	40	1·60
260	1½p. multicoloured	20	80
261	2p. multicoloured	1·25	2·25
	a. Pair. Nos. 261/262	2·50	4·50
262	2p. multicoloured	1·25	2·25
263	2½p. multicoloured	20	70
	a. Pair. Nos. 263/264	40	1·40

264	2½p. multicoloured	20	70
265	3p. multicoloured	20	20
	a. Pair. Nos. 265/266	40	40
266	3p. multicoloured	20	20
267	4p. multicoloured	1·40	2·50
	a. Pair. Nos. 267/268	2·75	5·00
268	4p. multicoloured	1·40	2·50
269	5p. multicoloured	35	80
	a. Pair. Nos. 269/270	70	1·60
270	5p. multicoloured	35	85
271	7p. multicoloured	60	65
	aw. Wmk Crown to right of CA	85·00	
	b. Pair. Nos. 271/272	1·10	1·25
	bw. Pair. Nos. 271aw/272aw	£170	
272	7p. multicoloured	60	65
	aw. Wmk Crown to right of CA	85·00	
273	8p. multicoloured	60	80
	a. Pair. Nos. 273/2/4	1·10	1·60
274	8p. multicoloured	60	80
275	9p. multicoloured	60	80
	a. Pair. Nos. 275/276	1·10	1·60
276	9p. multicoloured	60	80
277	10p. multicoloured	70	80
	aw. Wmk Crown to right of CA	£130	
	b. Pair. Nos. 277/278	1·40	1·60
	bw. Pair. Nos. 277aw/278aw	£260	
278	10p. multicoloured	70	80
	aw. Wmk Crown to right of CA	£130	
279	12½p. multicoloured	90	1·50
	a. Pair. Nos. 279/280	1·75	3·00
280	12½p. multicoloured	90	1·50
281	25p. multicoloured	95	1·50
	a. Pair. Nos. 281/282	1·90	3·00
282	25p. multicoloured	95	1·50
283	50p. multicoloured	1·25	2·50
	a. Pair. Nos. 283/284	2·50	5·00
284	50p. multicoloured	1·25	2·50
285	£1 multicoloured	2·00	3·75
	a. Pair. Nos. 285/286	4·00	7·50
286	£1 multicoloured	2·00	3·75
255/286	Set of 32	21·00	35·00

Designs (the two versions of each value show the same Gibraltar
view taken from an early 19th-century print (first design) or modern
photograph (second design): Horiz—1p. Prince George of Cambridge
Quarters and Trinity Church; 1½p. The Wellington Bust, Alameda Gardens;
2p. Gibraltar from the North Bastion; 2½p. Catalan Bay; 3p. Convent
Garden; 4p. The Exchange and Spanish Chapel; 5p; Commercial Square
and Library; 7p. South Barracks and Rosia Magazine; 8p. Moorish Mosque
and Castle; 9p. Europa Pass Road; 10p. South Barracks from Rosia Bay;
12½p. Southport Gates; 25p. Trooping the Colour, The Alameda. Vert—
50p. Europa Pass Gorge; £1 Prince Edward's Gate.

The two designs of each value were printed together, *se-tenant*, in
horizontal and vertical pairs throughout. Prices are for horizontal pairs,
vertical pairs are worth less.

* The normal sideways watermark shows Crown to left of CA, *as seen from
the back of the stamp.*

See also Nos. 317/320 and 344/345.

93   **94** Regimental Arms

(Des A. Ryman. Photo Harrison)

1971 (15 Feb). Coil Stamps. W w **12**. P 14½×14.

287	**93**	½p. red-orange	15	30
		a. Coil strip (Nos. 287×2, 288×2 and 289 se-tenant)	1·00	1·50
288		1p. blue	15	30
289		2p. bright green	60	1·10
287/289	Set of 3		80	1·50

(Des A. Ryman. Litho Questa)

1971 (6 Sept). Military Uniforms (3rd series). Multicoloured designs
as T **77**, showing uniform and cap badge. W w **12**. P 14.

290	1p. The Black Watch (1845)	25	30
291	2p. Royal Regt of Fusiliers (1971)	40	30
	w. Wmk inverted	£110	
292	4p. King's Own Royal Border Regt (1704)	60	50
293	10p. Devonshire and Dorset Regt (1801)	2·25	2·50
	w. Wmk inverted	3·75	6·50
290/293	Set of 4	3·25	3·25

Nos. 290/293 have a short history of the regiment printed on the reverse
side under the gum.

(Des A. Ryman. Litho Harrison)

1971 (25 Sept). Presentation of Colours to the Gibraltar Regiment. W w **12** (sideways). P 12½×12.

294	**94**	3p. black, gold and red	55	30

95 Nativity Scene   **96** Soldier Artificer, 1773

(Des A. Ryman. Photo Enschedé)

1971 (1 Dec). Christmas. T **95** and similar horiz design. Multicoloured. W w **12**. P 13×13½.

295	3p. Type **95**	40	60
296	5p. Mary and Joseph going to Bethlehem	40	65

(Des A. Ryman. Litho Questa)

1972 (6 Mar). Bicentenary of Royal Engineers in Gibraltar. T **96** and similar multicoloured designs. W w **12** (sideways on 1 and 3p.). P 13½×14 (5p.) or 14×13½ (others).

297	1p. Type **96**	30	50
298	3p. Modern tunneller	40	70
299	5p. Old and new uniforms and badge (horiz)	60	80
297/299 Set of 3		1·10	1·75

(Des A. Ryman. Litho Questa)

1972 (19 July). Military Uniforms (4th series). Multicoloured designs as T **77**. W w **12** (sideways). P 14.

300	1p. Duke of Cornwall's Light Infantry, 1704	50	20
301	3p. King's Royal Rifle Corps, 1830	1·00	40
302	7p. Officer, 37th North Hampshire, 1825	1·75	70
303	10p. Royal Navy, 1972	2·00	1·50
300/303 Set of 4		4·75	2·50

Nos. 300/303 have a short history of the Regiment printed on the reverse side under the gum.

97 Our Lady of Europa   **98** Keys of Gibraltar and *Narcissus niveus*

(Des A. Ryman. Litho Harrison)

1972 (4 Oct). Christmas. W w **12** (sideways*). P 14½×14.

304	**97**	3p. multicoloured	10	20
		a. Inscription on reverse omitted	15·00	
		w. Wmk Crown to right of CA	15·00	
305		5p. multicoloured	10	35
		w. Wmk Crown to right of CA	1·00	

* The normal sideways watermark shows Crown to left of CA, *as seen from the back of the stamp.*
These stamps have an inscription printed on the reverse side.

(Des (from photograph by D. Groves) and photo Harrison)

1972 (20 Nov). Royal Silver Wedding. Multicoloured; background colour given. W w **12**. P 14×14½.

306	**98**	5p. carmine-red	25	20
		w. Wmk inverted	70·00	
307		7p. deep grey-green	25	20
		w. Wmk inverted	£550	

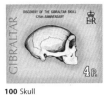

99 Flags of Member Nations and EEC Symbol   **100** Skull

(Des A. Ryman. Litho Questa)

1973 (22 Feb). Britain's Entry into EEC. W w **12** (sideways). P 14½×14.

308	**99**	5p. multicoloured	40	50
309		10p. multicoloured	60	1·00

(Des A. Ryman. Litho B.W.)

1973 (22 May). 125th Anniversary of Gibraltar Skull Discovery. T **100** and similar horiz designs. Multicoloured. W w **12**. P 13 (10p.) or 13½ (others).

310	4p. Type **100**	1·00	35
	a. Gold ('GIBRALTAR') omitted	£5000	
311	6p. Prehistoric man	1·10	80
312	10p. Prehistoric family (40×26 *mm*)	1·40	2·25
310/312 Set of 3		3·25	3·00

Several mint examples of No. 310a have been found in presentation packs.

(Des A. Ryman. Litho Questa)

1973 (22 Aug). Military Uniforms (5th series). Multicoloured designs as T **77**. W w **12** (sideways). P 14.

313	1p. King's Own Scottish Borderers, 1770	50	50
314	4p. Royal Welsh Fusiliers, 1800	1·00	80
315	6p. Royal Northumberland Fusiliers, 1736	1·50	1·75
316	10p. Grenadier Guards, 1898	2·25	4·00
313/316 Set of 4		4·75	6·25

Nos. 313/316 have a short history of the Regiment printed on the reverse side under the gum.

1973 (12 Sept). As Nos. 261/262 and 267/268 but W w **12** upright.

317	2p. multicoloured	1·25	2·50
	aw. Wmk inverted	†	—
	b. Pair. Nos. 317/318	2·50	5·00
	bw. Pair. Nos. 317aw/318aw	†	—
318	2p. multicoloured	1·25	2·50
	aw. Wmk inverted	†	—
319	4p. multicoloured	1·40	2·75
	a. Pair. Nos. 319/320	2·75	5·50
320	4p. multicoloured	1·40	2·75
317/320 Set of 4		4·75	9·50

Prices are for horizontal pairs, vertical pairs are worth less.

101 *Nativity* (Danckerts)

(Des and litho Enschedé)

1973 (17 Oct). Christmas. W w **12**. P 12½×12.

321	**101**	4p. violet and Venetian red	30	15
322		6p. magenta and turquoise-blue	40	1·10

101a Princess Anne and Captain Mark Phillips   **102** Victorian Pillar Box

1973 (14 Nov). Royal Wedding. Centre multicoloured. W w **12** (sideways). P 13½.

323	**101a**	6p. turquoise	10	10
324		14p. yellow-green	20	20

(Des A. Ryman. Litho Walsall)

1974 (2 May). Centenary of Universal Postal Union. T **102** and similar vert designs. Multicoloured.

*(a) W w***12** *(sideways). P 14½*

325	2p. Type **102**	15	30
326	6p. Pillar Box of George VI	20	35
327	14p. Pillar Box of Elizabeth II	30	80
325/327	*Set of 3*	60	1·25

(b) No wmk. Imperf×roul 5*. Self-adhesive (from booklets)

328	2p. Type **102**	20	1·00
	a. Booklet pane Nos. 328/330 *se-tenant*	4·00	
	b. Booklet pane Nos. 328×3 and 329×3	1·00	
329	6p. As No. 326	20	1·00
330	14p. As No. 327	4·00	8·50
328/330	*Set of 3*	4·00	9·50

* Nos. 328/330 were separated by various combinations of rotary knife (giving a straight edge) and roulette.

(Des A. Ryman. Litho Questa)

1974 (21 Aug). Military Uniforms (6th series). Multicoloured designs as T **77**. W w **12** (sideways). P 14.

331	4p. East Lancashire Regt, 1742	40	50
332	6p. Somerset Light Infantry, 1833	60	70
333	10p. Royal Sussex Regt, 1790	80	1·40
334	16p. RAF officer, 1974	2·00	4·00
	w. Wmk Crown to right of CA	£180	
331/334	*Set of 4*	3·50	6·00

* The normal sideways watermark shows Crown to left of CA, *as seen from the back of the stamp.*

Nos. 331/334 have a short history of the regiment printed on the reverse side under the gum.

103 *Madonna with the Green Cushion* (Solario)

104 Churchill and Houses of Parliament

(Des A. Ryman and M. Infante. Litho Questa)

1974 (5 Nov). Christmas. T **103** and similar vert design. Multicoloured. W w **14**. P 14.

335	4p. Type **103**	40	30
336	6p. *Madonna of the Meadow* (Bellini)	60	95

(Des L. Curtis. Litho Harrison)

1974 (30 Nov). Birth Centenary of Sir Winston Churchill. T **104** and similar horiz design. W w **12**. P 14×14½.

337	6p. black, reddish purple and light lavender	25	15
338	20p. brownish black, lake-brown and light orange–red	35	45
MS339	114×93 mm. Nos. 337/338. W w **12** (sideways*). P 14	2·75	5·50
	w. Wmk Crown to right of CA	£500	

Designs: 6p. T **104**; 20p. Churchill and *King George V* (battleship).

* The normal sideways watermark shows Crown to left of CA, *as seen from the back of the stamp.*

(Des A. Ryman. Litho Questa)

1975 (14 Mar). Military Uniforms (7th series). Multicoloured designs as T **77**. W w **14**. P 14.

340	4p. East Surrey Regt, 1846	30	20
341	6p. Highland Light Infantry, 1777	40	40
342	10p. Coldstream Guards, 1704	60	70
343	20p. Gibraltar Regt, 1974	1·10	2·50
340/343	*Set of 4*	2·25	3·50

Nos. 340/343 have a short history of each regiment printed on the reverse side under the gum.

1975 (9 July). As Nos. 257/258 but W w **14** (sideways).

344	1p. multicoloured	1·60	2·25
	a. Pair. Nos. 344/345	3·00	4·50
345	1p. multicoloured	1·60	2·25

See note below No. 320.

105 Girl Guides' Badge   **106** Child at Prayer

(Des A. Ryman. Litho Harrison)

1975 (10 Oct). 50th Anniversary of Gibraltar Girl Guides. W w **12**. P 13×13½.

346	**105**	5p. gold, light blue and dull violet	25	55
		a. *Tête-bêche* (pair)	65	1·25
		w. Wmk inverted	40	70
347		7p. gold, sepia and light lake-brown	35	60
		a. *Tête-bêche* (pair)	90	1·40
		w. Wmk inverted	55	80
348	–	15p. silver, brownish black and yellow and brown	50	1·25
		a. *Tête-bêche* (pair)	1·25	2·75
		b. Silver omitted	£2500	
		w. Wmk inverted	80	1·50
346/348		*Set of 3*	1·00	2·25

No. 348 is as T **105** but shows a different badge.

Nos. 346/348 were each issued in sheets of 25 (5×5) with each horizontal row containing three upright stamps and two inverted.

(Des A. Ryman. Litho Walsall)

1975 (26 Nov). Christmas. T **106** and similar vert designs. Multicoloured. W w **14** (sideways*). P 14.

349	6p. Type **106**	40	60
	aw. Wmk Crown to right of CA	8·50	
	b. Sheetlet of 6. Nos. 349/354	2·10	3·25
	bw. Sheetlet of 6. Nos. 349aw/354aw	45·00	
350	6p. Angel with lute	40	60
	aw. Wmk Crown to right of CA	8·50	
351	6p. Child singing carols	40	60
	aw. Wmk Crown to right of CA	8·50	
352	6p. Three children	40	60
	aw. Wmk Crown to right of CA	8·50	
353	6p. Girl at prayer	40	60
	aw. Wmk Crown to right of CA	8·50	
354	6p. Boy and lamb	40	60
	aw. Wmk Crown to right of CA	8·50	
349/354	*Set of 6*	2·10	3·25

* The normal sideways watermark shows Crown to left of CA, *as seen from the back of the stamp.*

Nos. 349/354 were issued together *se-tenant* in sheetlets of 6 (3×2).

107 *Bruges Madonna*   **108** Bicentennial Emblem and Arms of Gibraltar

(Des Jennifer Toombs. Litho Walsall)

1975 (17 Dec). 500th Birth Anniversary of Michelangelo. T **107** and similar vert designs. Multicoloured.

(a) W w **14** *(sideways*). P 14*

355	6p. Type **107**	20	25
356	9p. *Taddei Madonna*	20	40
357	15p. *Pieta*	30	1·10
	w. Wmk Crown to right of CA	£150	
355/357	*Set of 3*	65	1·60

(b) No wmk. Imperf×roul 5†. Self-adhesive (from booklets)

358	6p. Type **107**	35	45
	a. Booklet pane Nos. 358/360 *se-tenant*	1·50	
	b. Booklet pane Nos. 358×2, 359×2 and 360×2	2·50	

359	9p. As No. 356		55	75
360	15p. As No. 357		80	1·25
358/360	Set of 3		1·50	2·25

* The normal sideways watermark shows Crown to left of CA, *as seen from the back of the stamp.*

† Nos. 358/360 were separated by various combinations of rotary knife (giving a straight edge) and roulette.

(Des A. Ryman. Litho Walsall)

1976 (28 May). Bicentenary of American Revolution. W w **14** (inverted). P 14.

361	**108** 25p. multicoloured		50	50
MS362	85×133 mm. No. 361×4		1·75	3·50

The edges of No. **MS**362 are rouletted.

(Des A. Ryman. Litho Walsall)

1976 (21 July). Military Uniforms (8th series). Multicoloured designs as T **77**. W w **14** (inverted). P 14.

363	1p. Suffolk Regt, 1795		15	20
364	6p. Northamptonshire Regt, 1779		30	30
365	12p. Lancashire Fusiliers, 1793		40	60
366	25p. Ordnance Corps, 1896		50	1·40
363/366	Set of 4		1·25	2·25

Nos. 363/366 have a short history of each regiment printed on the reverse side under the gum.

109 The Holy Family

110 Queen Elizabeth II, Royal Arms and Gibraltar Arms

(Des A. Ryman. Litho Questa)

1976 (3 Nov). Christmas. T **109** and similar vert designs showing stained glass windows in St Joseph's Church, Gibraltar. Multicoloured. W w **14**. P 14.

367	6p. Type **109**		15	15
368	9p. Madonna and Child		20	15
369	12p. St Bernard		30	45
370	20p. Archangel Michael		55	1·25
367/370	Set of 4		1·10	1·75

(Des A. Ryman. Litho J.W.)

1977 (7 Feb). Silver Jubilee. W w **14**. P 13½.

371	**110** 6p. multicoloured		15	20
372	£1 multicoloured		85	1·75
MS373	124×115 mm. Nos. 371/372. P 13		1·00	1·50

The outer edges of the miniature sheet are either guillotined or rouletted.

111 Toothed Orchid (*Orchis tridentata*)

112 Our Lady of Europa Stamp

(Des A. Ryman. Litho Questa)

1977 (1 Apr)–**82**. Multicoloured designs as T **111**. W w **14** (sideways* on horiz designs; inverted on £5). Chalk surfaced paper (15p., £5). Imprint date at foot. P 14.

374	½p. Type **111**		60	2·50
	a. Chalk-surfaced paper (22.2.82)		5·50	5·50
375	1p. Red Mullet (*Mullus surmuletus*) (*horiz*)		15	70
	w. Wmk Crown to right of CA		3·00	7·00
376	2p. *Maculinea arion* (Butterfly) (*horiz*)		30	1·75
377	2½p. Sardinian Warbler (*Sylvia melanocephala*)		1·75	2·75
378	3p. Giant Squill (*Scilla peruviana*)		20	10

379	4p. Grey Wrasse (*Crenilabrus cinereus*) (*horiz*)		30	10
	a. Inscription on reverse omitted		£100	
	b. Chalk-surfaced paper (21.4.81)		55	70
380	5p. *Vanessa atalanta* (Butterfly) (*horiz*)		50	1·00
381	6p. Black Kite (*Milvus migrans*)		2·25	55
	w. Wmk inverted		£180	
382	9p. Shrubby Scorpion-vetch (*Coronilla valentina*)		70	40
383	10p. John Dory (Fish) (*Zeus faber*) (*horiz*)		40	20
	a. Chalk-surfaced paper (21.4.81)		1·00	1·50
384	12p. *Colias crocea* (Butterfly) (*horiz*)		1·00	35
	a. Chalk-surfaced paper (21.4.81)		4·25	4·75
384b	15p. Winged Asparagus Pea (*Tetragonolobus purpureus*) (12.11.80)		1·50	55
	bw. Wmk inverted		£180	
385	20p. Audouin's Gull (*Larus audouinii*)		2·00	3·00
386	25p. Barbary Nut (iris) (*Iris sisyrinchium*)		1·00	1·75
	a. Chalk-surfaced paper		5·00	5·50
387	50p. Swordfish (*Xiphias gladius*) (*horiz*)		1·25	1·75
	a. Chalk-surfaced paper (21.4.81)		6·50	7·00
388	£1 *Papilio machaon* (Butterfly) (*horiz*)		2·75	4·00
389	£2 Hoopoe (*Upupa epops*)		6·00	10·00
389a	£5 Arms of Gibraltar (16.5.79)		6·50	10·00
374/389a	Set of 18		25·00	32·00

The ½p. to £2 values have a descriptive text printed on the reverse, beneath the gum. Examples are known with this text omitted.

* The normal sideways watermark shows Crown to left of CA, *as seen from the back of the stamp.*

Imprint dates: '1977' Nos. 374/384, 385/389; '1978', No. 382; '1979', No. 389a; '1980' No. 384b; '1981', Nos. 379b, 383a, 384a, 386a, 387a; '1982', No. 374a.

(Des J. Cooter. Litho Questa)

1977 (27 May). Amphilex 77 Stamp Exhibition, Amsterdam. T **112** and similar vert designs. Multicoloured. W w **14** (sideways on 6p.; inverted on 12p.). P 13½.

390	6p. Type **112**		10	20
391	12p. Europe Point stamp		15	30
	w. Wmk upright		28·00	
392	25p. EEC Entry stamp		20	50
	w. Wmk inverted		2·25	
390/392	Set of 3		40	90

113 The Annunciation (Rubens)

114 Aerial View of Gibraltar

(Des A. Ryman. Litho Enschedé)

1977 (2 Nov). Christmas and Rubens' 400th Birth Anniversary. T **113** and similar multicoloured designs. W w **14** (sideways on 12p.). P 13½.

393	3p. Type **113**		10	10
394	9p. *The Adoration of the Magi*		25	25
395	12p. *The Adoration of the Magi* (*horiz*)		30	50
396	15p. *The Holy Family under the Apple Tree*		30	55
393/396	Set of 4		85	1·25
MS397	110×200 mm. Nos. 393/396 (wmk upright)		2·25	3·50

(Des A. Ryman. Litho Enschedé)

1978 (3 May). Gibraltar from Space. P 13½.

398	**114** 12p. multicoloured		25	50
	a. Horiz pair imperf 3 sides		£5000	
MS399	148×108 mm. 25p.		80	80

Design: 25p. Aerial view of Straits of Gibraltar.

No. 398a occurs on the bottom pair from at least three sheets of ten (2×5) and shows the stamps perforated at top only.

115 Holyroodhouse

(Des and litho Walsall)

1978 (12 June). 25th Anniversary of Coronation. T **115** and similar horiz designs. Multicoloured.

(a) From sheets. P 13½×14

400	6p. Type **115**		20	15
401	9p. St James's Palace		25	15
402	12p. Sandringham		30	30
403	18p. Balmoral		40	1·10
400/403 *Set of 4*			1·00	1·50

(b) From booklets. Imperf×roul 5. Self-adhesive*

404	12p. As No. 402		25	90
	a. Booklet pane. Nos. 404/405, each×3		1·25	
405	18p. As No. 403		25	90
406	25p. Windsor Castle		1·00	2·00
	a. Booklet pane of 1		1·00	
404/406 *Set of 3*			1·40	3·50

* Nos. 404/405 were separated by various combinations of rotary knife (giving a straight edge) and roulette. No. 406 exists only with straight edges.

116 Short S.25 Sunderland, 1938–1958

117 *Madonna with Animals*

(Des A. Theobald. Litho Harrison)

1978 (6 Sept). 60th Anniversary of Royal Air Force. T **116** and similar horiz designs. Multicoloured. W w **14** (sideways). P 14.

407	3p. Type **116**		15	10
408	9p. Caudron G-3, 1918		35	40
409	12p. Avro Shackleton MR2, 1953–1966		40	55
410	16p. Hawker Hunter F.6, 1954–1977		45	1·00
411	18p. Hawker Siddeley HS.801 Nimrod MR1, 1969–1978		50	1·10
407/411 *Set of 5*			1·75	2·75

(Des A. Ryman. Litho Questa)

1978 (1 Nov). Christmas. Paintings by Dürer. T **117** and similar vert designs. Multicoloured. W w **14**. P 14.

412	5p. Type **117**		20	10
413	9p. *The Nativity*		25	10
414	12p. *Madonna of the Goldfinch*		30	30
415	15p. *Adoration of the Magi*		35	60
412/415 *Set of 4*			1·00	1·00

118 Sir Rowland Hill and 1d. Stamp of 1886

(Des A. Ryman. Litho Format)

1979 (7 Feb). Death Centenary of Sir Rowland Hill. T **118** and similar horiz designs. W w **14** (sideways*). P 13½×14.

416	3p. multicoloured		10	10
417	9p. multicoloured		15	15
418	12p. multicoloured		15	20
	w. Wmk Crown to right of CA		£110	
419	25p. black, dull claret and yellow		25	50
416/419 *Set of 4*			55	80

Designs: 3p. T **118**; 9p. Sir Rowland Hill and 1p. coil stamp of 1971; 12p. Sir Rowland Hill and Post Office Regulations document, 1840; 25p. Sir Rowland Hill and 'G' cancellation.

* The normal sideways watermark shows Crown to left of CA, *as seen from the back of the stamp.*

119 Posthorn, Dish Antenna and Early Telephone

120 African Child

(Des A. Ryman. Litho Format)

1979 (16 May). Europa. Communications. W w **14** (sideways). P 13½.

420	**119**	3p. green and pale green	15	10
421		9p. lake-brown and ochre	20	90
422		12p. ultramarine and dull violet-blue	25	1·25
420/422 *Set of 3*			50	2·00

(Des G. Hutchins. Litho Walsall)

1979 (14 Nov). Christmas. International Year of the Child. T **120** and similar vert designs. Multicoloured. W w **14** (sideways). P 14.

423	12p. Type **120**		20	30
	a. Block of 6. Nos. 423/428		1·10	1·60
424	12p. Asian child		20	30
425	12p. Polynesian child		20	30
426	12p. American Indian child		20	30
427	12p. Children of different races and Nativity scene		20	30
428	12p. European child		20	30
423/428 *Set of 6*			1·10	1·60

Nos. 423/428 were printed together, *se-tenant*, in blocks of six, with margin separating the two blocks in each sheet.

121 Early Policemen

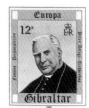

122 Peter Amigo (Archbishop)

(Des C. Abbott. Litho Questa)

1980 (5 Feb). 150th Anniversary of Gibraltar Police Force. T **121** and similar horiz designs. Multicoloured. W w **14** (sideways). P 14.

429	3p. Type **121**		20	10
430	6p. Policemen of 1895, early 1900s and 1980		20	15
431	12p. Policeman and police ambulance		25	20
432	37p. Policewoman and police motorcyclist		55	1·25
429/432 *Set of 4*			1·10	1·50

(Des A. Ryman. Litho Questa)

1980 (6 May). Europa. Personalities. T **122** and similar Vert designs. Multicoloured. W w **14** (inverted on No. 434). P 14½×14.

433	12p. Type **122**		15	30
434	12p. Gustavo Bacarisas (artist)		15	30
435	12p. John Mackintosh (philanthropist)		15	30
433/435 *Set of 3*			40	80

123 Queen Elizabeth the Queen Mother

124 *Horatio Nelson* (J. F. Rigaud)

(Des Harrison. Litho Questa)

1980 (4 Aug). 80th Birthday of Queen Elizabeth the Queen Mother. W w **14** (sideways). P 14.

436	**123**	15p. multicoloured	30	30

(Des BG Studio. Litho Questa)

1980 (20 Aug). 175th Death Anniversary of Nelson. Paintings. T **124** and similar multicoloured designs. W w **14** (sideways on 9 and 40p.). P 14.

437	3p. Type **124**		15	10
438	9p. *HMS Victory* (*horiz*)		20	25
439	15p. *Horatio Nelson* (Sir William Beechey)		20	35
440	40p. *HMS Victory being towed into Gibraltar* (Clarkson Stanfield) (*horiz*)		55	1·00
437/440 *Set of 4*			1·00	1·50
MS441 159×99 mm. No. 439			70	1·50

Examples of the 3p. value showing Nelson facing left in error were prepared, but not issued by the Gibraltar Post Office.

125 Three Kings

126 Hercules creating Mediterranean Sea

(Des A. Ryman. Litho Questa)

1980 (12 Nov). Christmas. T **125** and similar horiz design, each in deep brown and orange-yellow. W w **14** (sideways). P 14½.

442	15p. Type **125**		25	35
	a. Horiz pair. Nos. 442/443		50	70
443	15p. Nativity scene		25	35

Nos. 442/443 were printed together, *se-tenant*, in horizontal pairs throughout the sheet.

(Des G. Vasarhelyi. Litho Enschedé)

1981 (24 Feb). Europa. Folklore. T **126** and similar Vert design. Multicoloured. W w **14**. P 13½×13.

444	9p. Type **126**		20	15
445	15p. Hercules and Pillars of Hercules (Straits of Gibraltar)		25	35

127 Dining-room

128 Prince Charles and Lady Diana Spencer

(Des A. Ryman. Litho Harrison)

1981 (22 May). 450th Anniversary of The Convent (Governor's Residence). T **127** and similar square designs. Multicoloured. W w **14** (sideways). P 14½×14.

446	4p. Type **127**		10	10
447	14p. King's Chapel		15	15
448	15p. The Convent		15	15
449	55p. Cloister		60	80
446/449 *Set of 4*			85	1·00

(Des A. Ryman. Litho Questa)

1981 (27 July). Royal Wedding. W w **14** (sideways). P 14½.

450	**128**	£1 multicoloured	1·00	1·25

129

130 Paper Aeroplane

(Des A. Ryman. Litho Questa)

1981 (2 Sept). W w **14**. P 13½×14.

451	**129**	1p. black	40	60
		a. Booklet pane. Nos. 451/452 and 453×3 plus printed label	1·50	
		b. Booklet pane. Nos. 451/452×2 and 453×6 plus two printed labels	2·75	

452	4p. Prussian blue		40	50
453	15p. light green		30	40
451/453 *Set of 3*			1·00	1·40

Nos. 451/453 were only issued in 50p. and £1 stamp booklets.

(Des A. Ryman. Litho Walsall)

1981 (29 Sept*). 50th Anniversary of Gibraltar Airmail Service. T **130** and similar horiz designs. Multicoloured. W w **14** (sideways). P 14½×14.

454	14p. Type **130**		15	15
455	15p. Airmail letters, post box and aircraft tail fin		15	15
456	55p. Jet airliner circling globe		60	80
454/456 *Set of 3*			80	1·00

* This is the local release date. The Crown Agents released the stamps on 21 September.

131 Carol Singers

132 IYDP Emblem and Stylised Faces

(Des Clive Torres (15p.); Peter Parody (55p.); adapted G. Vasarhelyi. Litho Questa)

1981 (19 Nov). Christmas. Children's Drawings. T **131** and similar multicoloured design. W w **14** (sideways on 15p.). P 14.

457	15p. Type **131**		25	15
458	55p. Post Box (*Vert*)		75	85

(Des A. Ryman. Litho Questa)

1981 (19 Nov). International Year For Disabled Persons. W w **14** (sideways). P 14×14½.

459	**132**	14p. multicoloured	30	30

133 Douglas DC-3

134 Crest, HMS *Opossum*

(Des A. Theobald. Litho J.W.)

1982 (10 Feb). Aircraft. Horiz designs as T **133**. Multicoloured. W w **14**. Imprint date at foot. P 14.

460	1p. Type **133**		25	2·00
461	2p. Vickers Viking 1B		30	2·00
462	3p. Airspeed AS.57 Ambassador		30	1·75
463	4p. Vickers Viscount 800		40	20
464	5p. Boeing 727-100		90	60
465	10p. Vickers 953 Vanguard		1·75	50
466	14p. Short S.45A Solent 2		2·25	4·75
467	15p. Fokker F.27 Friendship		2·75	4·00
468	17p. Boeing 737		1·00	75
469	20p. BAC 1-11		2·25	65
470	25p. Lockheed Constellation		4·00	5·50
471	50p. Hawker Siddeley Comet 4B		4·00	1·75
472	£1 Saro A.21 Windhover		5·50	1·75
473	£2 Hawker Siddeley Trident 2E		6·50	5·00
474	£5 de Havilland DH.89A Dragon Rapide		7·00	14·00
460/474 *Set of 15*			35·00	40·00

Imprint dates: '1982', Nos. 460/74; '1982' and '1985', No. 469.
For 2p. and 5p. values watermarked w **16** see Nos. 549 and 552.

(Des A. Ryman. Litho Questa)

1982 (14 Apr). Naval Crests (1st series). T **134** and similar Vert designs. Multicoloured. W w **14**. P 14.

475	½p. Type **134**		10	30
476	15½p. HMS *Norfolk*		30	40
477	17p. HMS *Fearless*		30	30
478	60p. HMS *Rooke*		70	2·50
	w. Wmk inverted		50·00	
475/478 *Set of 4*			1·25	3·25

See also Nos. 493/496, 510/513, 522/525, 541/544, 565/568, 592/595, 616/619, 638/641 and 651/654.

135 Hawker Hurricane Mk 1 and Supermarine Spitfires at Gibraltar

136 Gibraltar Chamber of Commerce Centenary

(Des A. Ryman. Litho Questa)

1982 (11 June). Europa. Operation Torch. T **135** and similar horiz design. Multicoloured. W w **14** (sideways). P 14.

479	14p. Type **135**	25	70
480	17p. General Giraud, General Eisenhower and Gibraltar	35	80

(Des A. Ryman. Litho Questa)

1982 (22 Sept). Anniversaries. T **136** and similar vert designs. Multicoloured. W w **14** (sideways). P 14½.

481	½p. Type **136**	10	65
482	15½p. British Forces Postal Service centenary	35	25
483	60p. 75th Anniversary of Gibraltar Scout Association	65	1·25
481/483 *Set of 3*		1·00	1·90

137 Printed Circuit forming Map of World

138 Gibraltar illuminated at Night and Holly

(Des A. Ryman. Litho Harrison)

1982 (1 Oct). International Direct Dialling. W w **14** (sideways). P 14½.

484	**137**	17p. black, pale blue and bright orange.	35	35

(Des A. Ryman. Litho Questa)

1982 (18 Nov). Christmas. T **138** and similar horiz design. Multicoloured. W w **14** (sideways). P 14×14½.

485	14p. Type **138**	50	30
486	17p. Gibraltar illuminated at night and Mistletoe	50	35

139 Yacht Marina

140 St George's Hall Gallery

(Des Olympia Reyes. Litho Questa)

1983 (14 Mar). Commonwealth Day. T **139** and similar multicoloured designs. W w **14** (sideways on 4, 14p.). P 14.

487	4p. Type **139**	10	10
488	14p. Scouts and Guides Commonwealth Day Parade	20	15
489	17p. Flag of Gibraltar (vert)	25	20
490	60p. Queen Elizabeth II (from photo by Tim Graham) (vert)	70	1·00
487/490 *Set of 4*		1·00	1·25

(Des A. Ryman. Litho Harrison)

1983 (21 May). Europa. T **140** and similar horiz design. W w **14** (sideways). P 13½×13.

491	16p. black and brown-ochre	35	50
492	19p. black and pale blue	40	75

Designs: 16p. T **140**; 19p. Water catchment slope.

(Des A. Ryman. Litho Questa)

1983 (1 July). Naval Crests (2nd series). Vert designs as T **134**. Multicoloured. W w **14**. P 14.

493	4p. HMS *Faulknor*	35	10
494	14p. HMS *Renown*	70	35

495	17p. HMS *Ark Royal*	75	40
496	60p. HMS *Sheffield*	1·25	1·50
	w. Wmk inverted	50·00	
493/496 *Set of 4*		2·75	2·10

141 Landport Gate, 1729

(Des Olympia Reyes. Litho Enschedé)

1983 (13 Sept). Fortress Gibraltar in the 18th-century. T **141** and similar horiz designs. Multicoloured. W w **14** (sideways*). P 13×13½.

497	4p. Type **141**	10	10
498	17p. Koehler Gun, 1782	25	30
499	77p. King's Bastion, 1779	75	1·25
497/499 *Set of 3*		1·00	1·50
MS500 97×145 mm. Nos. 497/499		2·00	1·50

* The normal sideways watermark shows Crown to right of CA on Nos. 497/499 and Crown to left on No. **MS**500, *all as seen from the back of the stamp.*
Examples of No. 498 are also known from sheets with the Crown to left.

142 *Adoration of the Magi* (Raphael)

143 1932 2d. Stamp and Globe

(Des A. Ryman. Litho Questa)

1983 (17 Nov). Christmas. 500th Birth Anniversary of Raphael. T **142** and similar multicoloured designs. W w **14** (sideways on 4p.). P 14.

501	4p. Type **142**	15	10
502	17p. *Madonna of Foligno* (vert)	45	35
503	60p. *Sistine Madonna* (vert)	1·25	1·40
501/503 *Set of 3*		1·60	1·60

(Des E. Field. Litho Walsall)

1984 (6 Mar). Europa. Posts and Telecommunications. T **143** and similar vert design. Multicoloured. W w **14**. P 14½×14.

504	17p. Type **143**	45	50
505	23p. Circuit board and globe	55	1·00
	w. Wmk inverted	£110	

144 Hockey

145 Mississippi River Boat Float

(Des A. Ryman. Litho Walsall)

1984 (25 May). Sports. T **144** and similar horiz designs. Multicoloured. W w **14** (sideways). P 14×14½.

506	20p. Type **144**	45	70
507	21p. Basketball	45	70
508	26p. Rowing	35	80
509	29p. Football	35	1·00
506/509 *Set of 4*		1·40	3·00

(Des A. Ryman. Litho Walsall)

1984 (21 Sept). Naval Crests (3rd series). Vert designs as T **134**. Multicoloured. W w **14**. P 13½×13.

510	20p. HMS *Active*	1·25	2·00
511	21p. HMS *Foxhound*	1·25	2·25
512	26p. HMS *Valiant*	1·75	2·25
513	29p. HMS *Hood*	1·75	2·50
	w. Wmk inverted	22·00	
510/513 *Set of 4*		5·50	8·00

(Des A. Ryman. Litho Questa)

1984 (7 Nov). Christmas. Epiphany Floats. T **145** and similar horiz design. Multicoloured. W w **14** (sideways). P 14×14½.

514	20p. Type **145**		25	25
515	80p. Roman Temple float		1·00	2·25

146 Musical Symbols, and Score from Beethoven's *9th (Choral) Symphony*

147 Globe and Stop Polio Campaign Logo

(Des Olympia Reyes. Photo Courvoisier)

1985 (26 Feb). Europa. European Music Year. T **146** and similar horiz design. Multicoloured. Granite paper. P 12½.

516	**146**	20p. multicoloured	30	30
517	–	29p. multicoloured	40	1·50

The 29p. is as T **146** but shows different symbols.

(Des E. Field. Litho J.W.)

1985 (3 May). Stop Polio Campaign. Vert designs as T **147**. Multicoloured. W w **14** (inverted). P 13×13½.

518	26p. multicoloured (Type **147**)		70	1·10
	a. Horiz strip of 4. Nos. 518/521		2·50	4·00
519	26p. multicoloured ('ST' visible)		70	1·10
520	26p. multicoloured ('STO' visible)		70	1·10
521	26p. multicoloured ('STOP' visible)		70	1·10
518/521	Set of 4		2·50	4·00

Nos 518/521 were printed in horizontal *se-tenant* strips of four within the sheet. Each design differs in the position of the logo across the centre of the globe. On the left hand stamp in the strip only the letter 'S' is visible, on the next 'ST', on the next 'STO' and on the last 'STOP'.

Other features of the design also differ, so that the word 'Year' moves towards the top of the stamp and on No. 521 the upper logo is omitted.

(Des A. Ryman. Litho Questa)

1985 (3 July). Naval Crests (4th series). Vert designs as T **134**. Multicoloured. W w **16**. P 14.

522	4p. HMS *Duncan*		50	10
523	9p. HMS *Fury*		90	35
524	21p. HMS *Firedrake*		1·75	1·50
525	80p. HMS *Malaya*		3·50	6·00
522/525	Set of 4		6·00	7·00

148 IYY Logo

149 St Joseph

(Des Olympia Reyes. Litho Walsall)

1985 (6 Sept). International Youth Year. T **148** and similar horiz designs. Multicoloured. W w **14** (sideways). P 14×14½.

526	4p. Type **148**		25	10
527	20p. Hands passing diamond		1·10	1·10
528	80p. 75th Anniversary logo of Girl Guide Movement		2·25	3·75
526/528	Set of 3		3·25	4·50

(Des A. Ryman (4p.), Olympia Reyes (80p.). Litho Cartor)

1985 (25 Oct). Christmas. Centenary of St Joseph's Parish Church. T **149** and similar vert designs. Multicoloured. W w **16**. P 13½*.

529	4p. Type **149**		50	90
	a. Vert pair. Nos. 529/530		1·00	1·75
530	4p. St Joseph's Parish Church		50	90
531	80p. Nativity crib		4·00	5·00
529/531	Set of 3		4·50	6·00

* Nos. 529/530 were printed together in panes of 25; No. 529 on rows 1, 3 and 5, and No. 530 on rows 2 and 4. *Se-tenant* vertical pairs from rows 1/2 and 3/4, forming composite designs, have the stamps separated by a line of roulettes instead of perforations. Examples of No. 529 from row 5 have perforations on all four sides.

150 *Papilio machaon* (Butterfly) and The Convent

151 1887 Queen Victoria 6d. Stamp

(Des E. Field. Litho Walsall)

1986 (10 Feb). Europa. Nature and the Environment. T **150** and similar horiz design. Multicoloured. W w **16** (sideways). P 13×13½.

532	22p. Type **150**		50	40
533	29p. Herring Gull and Europa Point		75	3·25

(Des A. Ryman. Litho Walsall)

1986 (26 Mar). Centenary of First Gibraltar Postage Stamps. T **151** and similar vert designs showing stamps. Multicoloured. W w **16**. P 14×13½ (44p.) or 13½×13 (others).

534	4p. Type **151**		25	10
535	22p. 1903 Edward VII 2½d.		70	50
536	32p. 1912 George V 1d.		1·00	1·75
537	36p. 1938 George VI £1		1·10	2·00
538	44p. 1953 Coronation ½d. (29×46 *mm*)		1·40	3·00
534/538	Set of 5		4·00	6·50
MS539	102×73 mm. 29p. 1886 'GIBRALTAR' overprint on Bermuda 1d.		2·75	4·00
	w. Wmk inverted		£300	

152 Queen Elizabeth II in Robes of Order of the Bath

153 Prince Andrew and Miss Sarah Ferguson

(Des A. Ryman. Litho Walsall)

1986 (22 May). 60th Birthday of Queen Elizabeth II. W w **16**. P 14×13½.

540	**152**	£1 multicoloured	1·25	2·50

(Des A. Ryman. Litho Questa)

1986 (28 Aug). Naval Crests (5th series). Vert designs as T **134**. Multicoloured. W w **16**. P 14.

541	22p. HMS *Lightning*		1·75	1·00
542	29p. HMS *Hermione*		2·00	1·75
543	32p. HMS *Laforey*		2·25	3·25
544	44p. HMS *Nelson*		2·75	5·50
541/544	Set of 4		8·00	10·50

(Des A. Ryman. Litho Questa)

1986 (28 Aug). Royal Wedding. Sheet 115×85 mm. W w **16**. P 14½.

MS545	**153** 44p. multicoloured		1·40	2·25

154 Three Kings and Cathedral of St Mary the Crowned

155 Neptune House

(Des M. Infante. Litho Walsall)

1986 (14 Oct). Christmas. International Peace Year. T **154** and similar vert design. Multicoloured. W w **16**. P 14.

546	18p. Type **154**	75	50
547	32p. St Andrew's Church	1·25	3·00

(Litho Questa)

1986 (12 Dec)–**87**. As Nos. 461 and 464, but W w **16** (sideways). With '1986' imprint date. P 14.

549	2p. Vickers Viking 1B	2·00	3·75
552	5p. Boeing 727-100 (2.1.87)	2·00	3·75

(Des M. Infante. Litho Questa)

1987 (17 Feb). Europa. Architecture. T **155** and similar horiz design. Multicoloured. W w **16**. P 14½.

563	22p. Type **155**	75	35
564	29p. Ocean Heights	1·25	3·25

(Des A. Ryman. Litho Walsall)

1987 (15 Apr). Naval Crests (6th series). Vert designs as T **134**. Multicoloured. W w **16**. P 13½×13.

565	18p. HMS *Wishart* (destroyer)	1·60	75
566	22p. HMS *Charybdis* (cruiser)	1·75	1·10
567	32p. HMS *Antelope* (destroyer)	2·50	3·50
568	44p. HMS *Eagle* (aircraft carrier)	3·00	4·50
565/568 *Set of 4*		8·00	9·00

156 13-inch Mortar, 1783   **157** Victoria Stadium

(Des A. Ryman. Litho Format)

1987 (1 June). Guns. T **156** and similar horiz designs. Multicoloured. W w **14**. P 12½.

569	1p. Type **156**	20	70
570	2p. 6-inch coastal gun, 1909	30	70
571	3p. 8-inch howitzer, 1783	40	1·50
572	4p. Bofors L40/70 AA gun, 1951	40	10
573	5p. 100 ton rifled muzzle-loader, 1882	40	1·00
	w. Wmk inverted	†	
574	10p. 5.25–inch heavy AA gun, 1953	40	70
575	18p. 25–pounder gun-how, 1943	65	1·50
576	19p. 64–pounder rifled muzzle-loader, 1873	70	1·25
577	22p. 12–pounder gun, 1758	70	50
578	50p. 10–inch rifled muzzle-loader, 1870	1·40	3·00
579	£1 Russian 24–pounder gun, 1854	2·50	2·00
580	£3 9.2–inch MK. 10 coastal gun, 1935	3·00	13·00
581	£5 24–pounder gun, 1779	5·00	14·00
569/581 *Set of 13*		14·50	35·00

One sheet of the £5 value is known showing 12-pounder gun, 1758 (the vignette used for the 22p. stamp). The provenance of this item is unknown. See also No. 659.

(Des A. Ryman. Litho Walsall)

1987 (16 Sept). Bicentenary of Royal Engineers' Royal Warrant. T **157** and similar vert designs. Multicoloured. W w **14**. P 14½.

582	18p. Type **157**	1·25	65
583	32p. Freedom of Gibraltar scroll and casket	1·75	3·25
584	44p. Royal Engineers' badge	2·50	4·50
582/584 *Set of 3*		5·00	7·50

158 The Three Kings

(Des Olympia Reyes. Litho Walsall)

1987 (12 Nov). Christmas. T **158** and similar horiz designs. Multicoloured. W w **16** (sideways). P 14½.

585	4p. Type **158**	20	10
586	22p. The Holy Family	90	70
587	44p. The Shepherds	1·60	3·50
585/587 *Set of 3*		2·40	3·75

159 *Canberra* (liner) passing Gibraltar

(Des Olympia Reyes. Litho Format)

1988 (16 Feb). Europa. Transport and Communications. T **159** and similar horiz designs. Multicoloured. W w **14**. P 14½×14×roul between *se-tenant* pairs.

588	22p. Type **159**	1·25	2·25
	a. Horiz pair. Nos. 588/589	2·50	4·50
589	22p. *Gibline I* (ferry), dish aerial and Boeing 737	1·25	2·25
590	32p. Horse-drawn carriage and modern coach	1·50	2·75
	a. Horiz pair. Nos. 590/591	3·00	5·50
591	32p. Rover SD1 saloon (1976), telephone and Rock of Gibraltar	1·50	2·75
588/591 *Set of 4*		5·00	9·00

The two designs for each value were printed in sheets of ten, each containing five horizontal *se-tenant* pairs in which the stamps were rouletted between vertically.

(Des A. Ryman. Litho Walsall)

1988 (7 Apr). Naval Crests (7th series). Vert designs as T **134**. W w **16**. P 13½×13.

592	18p. multicoloured	1·25	50
593	22p. black, brownish black and gold	1·75	80
594	32p. multicoloured	2·00	2·75
595	44p. multicoloured	2·75	4·75
592/595 *Set of 4*		7·00	8·00

Designs: 18p. HMS *Clyde*; 22p. HMS *Foresight*; 32p. HMS *Severn*; 44p. HMS *Rodney*.

160 European Bee-eater

(Des Olympia Reyes. Litho B.D.T.)

1988 (15 June). Birds. T **160** and similar horiz designs. Multicoloured. W w **14** (sideways). P 13½.

596	4p. Type **160**	75	20
597	22p. Atlantic Puffin	1·75	90
598	32p. Honey Buzzard	2·25	2·50
599	44p. Blue Rock Thrush	2·75	4·00
596/599 *Set of 4*		6·75	7·00

161 *Zebu* (brigantine)   **162** Snowman (Rebecca Falero)

(Des A. Ryman. Litho B.D.T.)

1988 (14 Sept). Operation Raleigh. T **161** and similar horiz designs. Multicoloured. W w **14**. P 13.

600	19p. Type **161**	65	60
601	22p. Miniature of Sir Walter Raleigh and logo	75	70
602	32p. *Sir Walter Raleigh* (expedition ship) and world map	1·10	2·00
600/602 *Set of 3*		2·25	3·00
MS603 135×86 mm. 22p As No. 601; 44p. *Sir Walter Raleigh* (expedition ship) passing Gibraltar		3·00	5·00

(Des A. Ryman. Litho Questa)

1988 (2 Nov). Christmas. Children's Paintings. T **162** and similar multicoloured designs. W w **16** (sideways). P 14½ (44p.) or 14 (others).

604	4p. Type **162**	15	10
605	22p. The Nativity (Dennis Penalver)	55	60
606	44p. Father Christmas (Gavin Key) (23×31 *mm*)	1·00	2·40
604/606 *Set of 3*		1·50	2·75

163 Soft Toys and Toy Train

(Des Olympia Reyes. Litho Walsall)

1989 (15 Feb). Europa. Children's Toys. T **163** and similar horiz design. Multicoloured. W w **16** (sideways). P 13×13½.

607	25p. Type **163**	75	50
608	32p. Soft toys, toy boat and doll's house	1·00	2·25

164 Port Sergeant with Keys   **165** Nurse and Baby

(Des A. Ryman. Litho Walsall)

1989 (28 Apr). 50th Anniversary of Gibraltar Regiment. T **164** and similar vert designs. Multicoloured. W w **14**. P 13½×13.

609	4p. Type **164**	40	10
610	22p. Regimental badge and colours	1·10	70
611	32p. Drum major	1·75	3·50
609/611	Set of 3	3·00	3·75

MS612 124×83 mm. 22p. As No. 610; 44p. Former Gibraltar Defence Force badge. .... 4·25   6·00

(Des E. Field. Litho Questa)

1989 (7 July). 125th Anniversary of International Red Cross. T **165** and similar vert designs. W w **16**. P 15×14½.

613	25p. black, bright scarlet and grey-brown	75	50
614	32p. black, bright scarlet and grey-brown	1·00	1·50
615	44p. black, bright scarlet and grey-brown	1·25	3·00
613/615	Set of 3	2·75	4·50

Designs: 25p. T **165**; 32p. Famine victims; 44p. Accident victims.

(Des A. Ryman. Litho B.D.T.)

1989 (7 Sept). Naval Crests (8th series). Vert designs as T **134**. W w **16**. P 14×13½.

616	22p. multicoloured	1·25	60
617	25p. black and gold	1·25	1·00
618	32p. gold, black and bright scarlet	1·50	2·75
619	44p. multicoloured	2·50	5·50
616/619	Set of 4	6·00	9·00

Designs: 22p. HMS *Blankney*; 25p. HMS *Deptford*; 32p. HMS *Exmoor*; 44p. HMS *Stork*.

166 One Penny Coin

(Des A. Ryman. Litho Questa)

1989 (11 Oct). New Coinage. T **166** and similar vert designs in two miniature sheets. W w **16** (sideways). P 14½.

MS620 72×94 mm. 4p. bronze, black and dull vermilion (Type **166**); 4p. bronze, black and deep brown (two pence); 4p. silver, black and greenish yellow (ten pence); 4p. silver, black and emerald (five pence) .... 1·25   2·25

MS621 100×95 mm. 22p. silver, black and reddish orange (fifty pence); 22p. gold, black and ultramarine (five pounds); 22p. gold, black and orange-brown (two pounds); 22p. gold, black and bright emerald (one pound); 22p. gold, black and bright reddish violet (obverse of coin series); 22p. silver, black and pale violet-blue (twenty pence) .... 4·75   7·50

167 Father Christmas in Sleigh   **168** General Post Office Entrance

(Des M. Infante. Litho Questa)

1989 (11 Oct). Christmas. T **167** and similar horiz designs. Multicoloured. W w **16** (sideways). P 14½.

622	4p. Type **167**	15	10
623	22p. Shepherds and sheep	70	50
624	32p. The Nativity	1·00	1·25
625	44p. The Three Wise Men	1·60	3·75
622/625	Set of 4	3·00	5·00

(Des Olympia Reyes. Litho Questa)

1990 (6 Mar). Europa. Post Office Buildings. T **168** and similar vert designs. Multicoloured. P 14½×roul between *se-tenant* pairs.

626	22p. Type **168**	1·00	1·75
	a. Horiz pair. Nos. 626/627	2·00	3·50
627	22p. Interior of General Post Office	1·00	1·75
628	32p. Interior of South District Post Office	1·25	2·50
	a. Horiz pair. Nos. 628/629	2·50	5·00
629	32p. South District Post Office	1·25	2·50
626/629	Set of 4	4·00	7·75

Nos. 626/627 and 628/629 were printed in *se-tenant* horizontal pairs within separate sheets of eight, the stamps in each pair being divided by a line of roulettes.

169 19th-century Firemen   **170** Henry Corbould (artist) and Penny Black

(Des D. González. Litho Questa)

1990 (2 Apr). 125th Anniversary of Gibraltar Fire Service. T **169** and similar multicoloured designs. P 14½×14 (vert) or 14×14½ (horiz).

630	4p. Type **169**	1·00	15
631	20p. Early fire engine (*horiz*)	2·50	1·10
632	42p. Modern fire engine (*horiz*)	3·00	4·25
633	44p. Fireman in breathing apparatus	3·00	4·25
630/633	Set of 4	8·50	8·75

(Des A. Ryman. Litho Questa)

1990 (3 May). 150th Anniversary of the Penny Black. T **170** and similar vert designs. Multicoloured. P 13½×14.

634	19p. Type **170**	1·10	1·00
635	22p. Bath Royal Mail coach	1·25	1·00
636	32p. Sir Rowland Hill and Penny Black	2·50	4·50
634/636	Set of 3	4·25	6·00

MS637 145×95 mm. 44p. Penny Black with Maltese Cross cancellation. P 14½×14 .... 4·00   6·00

(Des A. Ryman. Litho Questa)

1990 (10 July). Naval Crests (9th series). Vert designs as T **134**. Multicoloured. P 14.

638	22p. HMS *Calpe*	1·75	70
639	25p. HMS *Gallant*	1·90	1·75
640	32p. HMS *Wrestler*	2·50	3·25
641	44p. HMS *Greyhound*	3·00	6·50
638/641	Set of 4	8·25	11·00

171 Model of Europort Development

172 Candle and Holly

(Des A. Ryman. Litho Questa)

1990 (10 Oct). Development Projects. T **171** and similar horiz designs. Multicoloured. P 14½.

642	22p. Type **171**	60	65
643	23p. Construction of building material		
	factory	60	1·25
644	25p. Land reclamation	80	1·25
642/644 Set of 3		1·75	2·75

(Des D. González. Litho B.D.T.)

1990 (10 Oct). Christmas. T **172** and similar vert designs. Multicoloured. P 13½.

645	4p. Type **172**	15	10
646	22p. Father Christmas	65	40
647	42p. Christmas Tree	1·25	2·25
648	44p. Nativity crib	1·25	2·25
645/648 Set of 4		3·00	4·50

173 Space Laboratory and Spaceplane (Colombus Development Programme)

174 Shag

(Des D. González. Litho B.D.T.)

1991 (26 Feb). Europa. Europe in Space. T **173** and similar horiz design. Multicoloured. P 13½×13.

649	25p. Type **173**	75	75
650	32p. ERS-1 earth resources remote sensing		
	satellite	1·00	2·25

(Des A. Ryman. Litho Walsall)

1991 (9 Apr). Naval Crests (10th series). Vert designs as T **134**. P 13½×13.

651	4p. black, new blue and gold	60	10
652	21p. multicoloured	1·75	1·25
653	22p. multicoloured	1·75	1·25
654	62p. multicoloured	3·75	7·00
651/654 Set of 4		7·00	8·75

Designs: 4p. HMS *Hesperus*; 21p. HMS *Forester*; 22p. HMS *Furious*; 62p. HMS *Scylla*.

(Des Olympia Reyes. Litho B.D.T.)

1991 (30 May). Endangered Species. Birds. T **174** and similar horiz designs. Multicoloured. P 13½.

655	13p. Type **174**	1·40	1·60
	a. Block of 4. Nos. 655/658	5·00	5·75
656	13p. Barbary Partridge	1·40	1·60
657	13p. Egyptian Vulture	1·40	1·60
658	13p. Black Stork	1·40	1·60
655/658 Set of 4		5·00	5·75

Nos. 655/658 were printed together, *se-tenant*, in differently arranged blocks of four throughout the sheet of 16.

(175)   **£1.05**

176 North View of Gibraltar (Gustavo Bacarisas)

1991 (30 May). No. 580 surch with T **175**.

659	£1.05 on £3 9.2-inch Mk.10 coastal gun, 1935	3·25	1·60

(Des A. Ryman. Litho B.D.T.)

1991 (10 Sept). Local Paintings. T **176** and similar multicoloured designs. P 14×15 (42p.) or 15×14 (others).

660	22p. Type **176**	85	50
661	26p. *Parsons Lodge* (Elena Mifsud)	1·00	1·00
662	32p. *Governor's Parade* (Jacobo Azagury)	1·50	2·25
663	42p. *Waterport Wharf* (Rudesindo Mannia)		
	(vert)	2·25	4·50
660/663 Set of 4		5·00	7·50

177 Once in Royal David's City

178 Donnaus chrysippus

(Des D. González. Litho Questa)

1991 (15 Oct). Christmas. Carols. T **177** and similar horiz designs. Multicoloured. P 14×14½.

664	4p. Type **177**	25	10
665	24p. *Silent Night*	80	40
666	25p. *Angels We have Heard on High*	80	65
667	49p. *O Come All Ye Faithful*	1·50	4·50
664/667 Set of 4		3·00	5·00

(Des A. Ryman. Litho Questa)

1991 (15 Nov). Phila Nippon '91 International Stamp Exhibition, Tokyo. Sheet 116×91 mm. P 14½.

MS668 **178** £1.05 multicoloured		2·50	4·00

179 Columbus and *Santa Maria*

(Des Olympia Reyes. Litho Walsall)

1992 (6 Feb). Europa. 500th Anniversary of Discovery of America by Columbus. T **179** and similar horiz designs. Multicoloured. P 14½.

669	24p. Type **179**	1·25	2·00
	a. Horiz pair. Nos. 669/670	2·50	4·00
670	24p. Map of Old World and *Nina*	1·25	2·00
671	34p. Map of New World and *Pinta*	1·50	2·50
	a. Horiz pair. Nos. 671/672	3·00	5·00
672	34p. Map of Old World and look-out	1·50	2·50
669/672 Set of 4		5·00	8·00

The two designs of each value were printed together, *se-tenant*, in sheets of eight, the background to each horizontal pair forming a composite design.

179a Gibraltar from North

180 Compass Rose, Sail and Atlantic Map

(Des D. Miller. Litho Questa (54p), B.D.T. (others))

1992 (6 Feb). 40th Anniversary of Queen Elizabeth II's Accession. Horiz designs as T **179a**. Multicoloured. W w **14** (sideways). P 14.

673	4p. Type **179a**	15	10
674	20p. HMS *Arrow* (frigate) and Gibraltar from		
	South	60	50
675	24p. Southport Gates	65	55
676	44p. Three portraits of Queen Elizabeth	80	1·00
677	54p. Queen Elizabeth II	90	1·90
673/677 Set of 5		2·75	3·50

(Des E. Field. Litho B.D.T.)

1992 (15 Apr). Round the World Yacht Rally. T **180** and similar multicoloured designs, each incorporating compass rose and sail. P 13½.

678	21p. Type **180**	50	65
679	24p. Map of Indonesian Archipelago (*horiz*)...	60	1·25
680	25p. Map of Indian Ocean (*horiz*)	60	1·50
678/680 Set of 3		1·50	3·00
MS681 108×72 mm. 21p Type **180**; 49p. Map of Mediterranean and Red Sea		1·25	2·75

181 Holy Trinity Cathedral

182 Sacred Heart of Jesus Church

(Des M. Infante. Litho Questa)

1992 (21 Aug). 150th Anniversary of Anglican Diocese of Gibraltar in Europe. T **181** and similar multicoloured designs. P 14.

682	4p. Type **181**	20	10
683	24p. Diocesan crest and map (*horiz*)	1·00	65
684	44p. Construction of Cathedral and Sir George Don (*horiz*)	1·75	3·00
685	54p. Bishop Tomlinson	2·00	3·50
682/685 Set of 4		4·50	6·50

(Des W. Stagnetto. Litho B.D.T.)

1992 (10 Nov). Christmas. Churches. T **182** and similar vert designs. Multicoloured. P 14×13½.

686	4p. Type **182**	35	10
687	24p. Cathedral of St Mary the Crowned	1·50	55
688	34p. St Andrew's Church of Scotland	1·75	2·50
689	49p. St Joseph's Church	2·25	5·50
686/689 Set of 4		5·25	7·75

183 Drama and Music

(Des E. Field. Litho Questa)

1993 (2 Mar). Europa. Contemporary Art. T **183** and similar vert designs. Multicoloured. P 14½×14.

690	24p. Type **183**	1·00	1·50
	a. Horiz pair. Nos. 690/691	2·00	3·00
691	24p. Sculpture, Art and Pottery	1·00	1·50
692	34p. Architecture	1·25	2·25
	a. Horiz pair. Nos. 692/693	2·50	4·50
693	34p. Printing and Photography	1·25	2·25
690/693 Set of 4		4·00	6·50

Nos. 690/691 and 692/693 were printed together, *se-tenant*, as horizontal pairs in sheetlets of eight with decorative margins.

184 HMS *Hood* (battle cruiser)

185 Landport Gate

(Des D. Miller. Litho B.D.T.)

1993 (27 Apr). Second World War Warships (1st series). Sheet 120×79 mm containing T **184** and similar horiz designs. Multicoloured. P 14.

MS694 24p. Type **184**; 24p. HMS *Ark Royal* (aircraft carrier, 1937); 24p. HMAS *Waterhen* (destroyer); 24p. USS *Gleaves* (destroyer)	11·00	11·00

See also Nos. **MS**724, **MS**748, **MS**779 and **MS**809.

(Des Olympia Reyes. Litho and thermography Cartor (£5), litho Cartor (6, 7, 8, 9, 20, 30, 40p. and £2) or B.D.T. (others))

1993 (28 June)–**95**. Architectural Heritage. T **185** and similar multicoloured designs. P 13.

695	1p. Type **185**	30	1·25
696	2p. St Mary the Crowned Church (*horiz*)	50	1·25
697	3p. Parsons Lodge Battery (*horiz*)	50	1·75
698	4p. Moorish Castle (*horiz*)	65	1·25
699	5p. General Post Office	55	30
699a	6p. House of Assembly (1.9.95)	2·00	1·50
699b	7p. Bleak House (*horiz*) (1.9.95)	2·00	1·50
699c	8p. General Eliott Memorial (1.9.95)	2·00	1·50
699d	9p. Supreme Court Building (*horiz*) (1.9.95)..	2·00	1·50
700	10p. South Barracks (*horiz*)	50	60
700a	20p. The Convent (*horiz*) (1.9.95)	3·00	1·50
701	21p. American War Memorial	1·00	80
702	24p. Garrison Library (*horiz*)	1·10	80
703	25p. Southport Gates	1·10	80
704	26p. Casemates Gate (*horiz*)	1·10	80
704a	30p. St Bernard's Hospital (1.9.95)	4·00	1·50
704b	40p. City Hall (*horiz*) (1.9.95)	4·00	2·25
705	50p. Central Police Station (*horiz*)	2·50	2·25
706	£1 Prince Edward's Gate	2·25	2·75
706a	£2 Church of the Sacred Heart of Jesus (1.9.95)	9·00	9·50
707	£3 Lighthouse, Europa Point	12·00	11·00
708	£5 Coat of Arms and Fortress keys (6.6.94)	10·00	16·00
695/708 Set of 22		55·00	55·00

186 £sd and Decimal British Coins (25th Anniversary of Decimal Currency)

187 Mice decorating Christmas Tree

(Des W. Stagnetto. Litho Cartor)

1993 (21 Sept). Anniversaries. T **186** and similar horiz designs. Multicoloured. P 13.

709	21p. Type **186**	1·00	65
710	24p. RAF crest with Handley Page 0/400 biplane and Panavia Tornado F Mk 3 fighter (75th Anniversary)	1·75	75
711	34p. Garrison Library badge and building (Bicentenary)	1·60	2·25
712	49p. Sir Winston Churchill and air raid (50th anniversary of visit)	4·00	5·00
709/712 Set of 4		7·50	7·75

(Des Josie Evans. Litho Cartor)

1993 (16 Nov). Christmas. T **187** and similar horiz designs. Multicoloured. P 13½.

713	5p. Type **187**	25	10
714	24p. Mice pulling cracker	1·10	70
715	44p. Mice singing carols	2·00	2·50
716	49p. Mice building snowman	2·50	3·75
713/716 Set of 4		5·25	6·25

188 Exploding Atom (Lord Penney)

(Des M. Braunewell. Litho Cartor)

1994 (1 Mar). Europa. Scientific Discoveries. T **188** and similar horiz designs. Multicoloured. P 13½.

717	24p. Type **188**	1·00	1·50
	a. Horiz pair. Nos. 717/718	2·00	3·00
718	24p. Polonium and radium experiment (Marie Curie)	1·00	1·50
719	34p. First oil engine (Rudolph Diesel)	1·25	2·00
	a. Horiz pair. Nos. 719/720	2·50	4·00
720	34p. Early telescope (Galileo)	1·25	2·00
717/720 Set of 4		4·00	6·25

Nos. 717/718 and 719/720 were each printed together, *se-tenant*, in horizontal pairs in sheetlets of eight with decorative margins.

189 World Cup and Map of USA

190 Pekingese

(Des M. Braunewell. Litho Cartor)

1994 (19 Apr). World Cup Football Championship, USA. T **189** and similar multicoloured designs. P 13½.

721	26p. Type **189**	60	30
722	39p. Players and pitch in shape of USA	85	1·25
723	49p. Player's legs (*vert*)	1·10	2·00
721/723	*Set of 3*	2·25	3·25

(Des D. Miller. Litho Cartor)

1994 (6 June). Second World War Warships (2nd series). Sheet 112×72 mm containing horiz designs as T **184**. Multicoloured. P 13.

MS724 5p. HMS *Penelope* (cruiser); 25p. HMS *Warspite* (battleship); 44p. USS *McLanahan* (destroyer); 49p. *Isaac Sweers* (Dutch destroyer) ... 10·00 11·00

(Des M. Braunewell. Litho B.D.T.)

1994 (16 Aug). Philakorea '94 International Stamp Exhibiton, Seoul. Sheet 102×76 mm. P 13.

MS725 **190** £1·05 multicoloured ... 2·00 3·50

191 Golden Star Coral

192 Throwing the Discus and Centenary Emblem

(Des M. Whyte. Litho Walsall)

1994 (27 Sept). Marine Life. T **191** and similar square designs. Multicoloured. P 14½×14.

726	21p. Type **191**	55	30
727	24p. Star Fish	65	35
728	34p. Gorgonian Sea-fan	75	1·00
729	49p. Peacock Wrasse ('Turkish Wrasse')	1·25	3·00
726/729	*Set of 4*	3·00	4·25

(Des S. Perera. Litho Walsall)

1994 (22 Nov). Centenary of International Olympic Committee. T **192** and similar horiz design. Multicoloured. P 14.

730	49p. Type **192**	1·25	1·75
731	54p. Javelin throwing and emblem	1·25	1·75

193 Great Tit

194 Austrian Flag, Hand and Star

(Des W. Stagnetto. Litho B.D.T.)

1994 (22 Nov). Christmas. Songbirds. T **193** and similar multicoloured designs. P 14×13½ (vert) or 13½×14 (horiz).

732	5p. Type **193**	80	10
733	24p. European Robin (*horiz*)	2·25	70
734	34p. Blue Tit (*horiz*)	2·50	1·50
735	54p. Goldfinch	3·25	5·50
732/735	*Set of 4*	8·00	7·00

(Des R. Ollington. Litho Questa)

1995 (3 Jan). Expansion of European Union. T **194** and similar horiz designs. Multicoloured. P 14.

736	24p. Type **194**	35	30
737	26p. Finnish flag, hand and star	35	30
738	34p. Swedish flag, hand and star	45	70
739	49p. Flags of new members and European Union emblem	80	2·50
736/739	*Set of 4*	1·75	3·50

195 Barbed Wire and Quote from Isaiah Ch 2.4

(Des Jennifer Toombs. Litho B.D.T.)

1995 (28 Feb). Europa. Peace and Freedom. T **195** and similar horiz designs. Multicoloured. P 13½.

740	24p. Type **195**	1·10	1·40
	a. Horiz pair. Nos. 740/741	2·10	2·75
741	24p. Rainbow and hands releasing Peace Dove	1·10	1·40
742	34p. Shackles on wall and quote from Isaiah ch 61.1	1·25	2·00
	a. Horiz pair. Nos. 742/743	2·50	4·00
743	34p. Hands and Mediterranean Gulls	1·25	2·00
740/743	*Set of 4*	4·25	6·00

Nos. 740/741 and 742/743 were each printed together, *se-tenant*, as horizontal pairs in sheetlets of eight with decorative margins.

196 Fairey Swordfish, I Class Destroyer and Rock of Gibraltar

(Des A. Theobald. Litho B.D.T.)

1995 (8 May). 50th Anniversary of End of Second World War. Sheet 101×66 mm. P 13½.

MS744 **196** £1·05 multicoloured ... 3·25 4·25

197 Laser Dinghy

198 Bee Orchid

(Des Stephen Perera. Litho B.D.T.)

1995 (8 May). Island Games '95. T **197** and similar vert designs. Multicoloured. P 14×13½.

745	24p. Type **197**	55	45
	a. Booklet pane. No. 745×3, with margins all round	1·90	
	b. Booklet pane. Nos. 745/747, with margins all round	3·00	
746	44p. Athlete on starting blocks	1·00	2·00
	a. Booklet pane. No. 746×3, with margins all round	3·25	
747	49p. Swimmer at start of race	1·00	2·00
	a. Booklet pane. No. 747×3, with margins all round	3·25	
745/747	*Set of 3*	2·25	4·00

(Des D. Miller. Litho Questa)

1995 (6 June). Second World War Warships (3rd series). Sheet 133×85 mm containing horiz designs as T **184**. Multicoloured. P 13½×14.

MS748 5p. HMS *Calpe* (destroyer); 24p. HMS *Victorious* (aircraft carrier); 44p. USS *Weehawken* (attack transport); 49p. *Savorgan de Brazza* (French destroyer) ... 10·00 11·00

(Des Roger Gorringe. Litho B.D.T.)

1995 (1 Sept). Singapore '95 International Stamp Exhibition. Orchids. T **198** and similar vert designs. Multicoloured. P 14×14½.

749	22p. Type **198**	1·40	1·60
	a. Horiz strip of 5. Nos. 749/753	6·25	7·25
750	23p. Brown Bee Orchid	1·40	1·60
751	24p. Pyramidal Orchid	1·40	1·60
752	25p. Mirror Orchid	1·40	1·60
753	26p. Sawfly Orchid	1·40	1·60
749/753	*Set of 5*	6·25	7·25

Nos. 749/753 were printed together, *se-tenant*, in horizontal strips of five.

199 Handshake and United Nations Emblem

200 Marilyn Monroe

(Des Stephen Perera. Litho B.D.T.)

1995 (24 Oct). 50th Anniversary of United Nations. T **199** and similar horiz design. Multicoloured. P 13½.

754	34p. Type **199**	1·50	1·10
755	49p. Peace Dove and UN emblem	1·75	3·00

(Des Mark Whyte. Litho Questa)

1995 (13 Nov). Centenary of Cinema. T **200** and similar horiz designs showing film stars. Multicoloured. P 14½×14.

MS756 Two sheets each 116×80 mm. (a) 5p. Type **200**; 25p. Romy Schneider; 28p. Yves Montand; 38p. Audrey Hepburn. (b) 24p Ingrid Bergman; 24p. Vittorio de Sica; 24p. Marlene Dietrich; 24p. Laurence Olivier *Set of 2 sheets* .... 2·50 3·00

201 Father Christmas

202 Shih Tzu

(Des Mark Whyte. Litho B.D.T.)

1995 (27 Nov). Christmas. T **201** and similar square designs. Multicoloured. P 14.

757	5p. Type **201**	25	10
758	24p. Toys in sack	75	30
759	34p. Reindeer	1·25	80
760	54p. Sleigh over houses	2·25	4·00
757/760 *Set of 4*		4·00	4·75

(Des Doreen McGuinness. Litho B.D.T.)

1996 (24 Jan). Puppies. T **202** and similar horiz designs. Multicoloured. P 14.

761	5p. Type **202**	40	85
	a. Sheetlet of 6. Nos. 761/766	4·00	6·00
762	21p. Dalmatians	75	95
763	24p. Cocker Spaniels	80	1·10
764	25p. West Highland White Terriers	80	1·10
765	34p. Labrador	90	1·25
766	35p. Boxer	90	1·25
761/766 *Set of 6*		4·00	6·00

Nos. 761/766 were printed together, *se-tenant*, in sheetlets of six.

No. 762 is inscr 'Dalmation' in error.

203 Princess Anne

204 West German Player, 1980

(Des Robin Ollington. Litho B.D.T.)

1996 (9 Feb). Europa. Famous Women. T **203** and similar horiz designs. P 13½.

767	**203**	24p. black and yellow	80	1·25
768	–	24p. black and deep turquoise-green	80	1·25
769	–	34p. black and vermilion	1·10	1·75
770	–	34p. black and purple	1·10	1·75
767/770 *Set of 4*			3·50	5·50

Designs: No. 768, Princess Diana; No. 769, Queen Elizabeth II; No. 770, Queen Elizabeth the Queen Mother.

Nos. 767/770 were each printed in sheets of ten with inscribed margins all round.

(Des Steven Noon. Litho Walsall)

1996 (2 Apr). European Football Championship, England. T **204** and similar vert designs showing players from previous winning teams. Multicoloured. P 13.

771	21p. Type **204**	35	30
772	24p. French player, 1984	40	35
773	34p. Dutch player, 1988	60	60
774	£1·20 Danish player, 1992	1·75	3·25
771/774 *Set of 4*		2·75	4·00
MS775 135×91 mm. As Nos. 771/774. P 13×13½		3·00	5·00

205 Ancient Greek Athletes

206 Asian Children

(Des Keith Bassford. Litho Walsall)

1996 (2 May). Centenary of Modern Olympic Games. T **205** and similar horiz designs. P 13½.

776	34p. black, deep reddish purple and bright orange	55	35
777	49p. black and grey-brown	80	1·10
778	£1·05 multicoloured	2·00	3·75
776/778 *Set of 3*		3·00	4·75

Designs: 34p. T **205**; 49p. Start of early race; £1·05 Start of modern race.

(Des Derek Miller. Litho Walsall)

1996 (8 June). Second World War Warships (4th series). Sheet, 118×84 mm containing horiz designs as T **184**. Multicoloured. P 14.

MS779 5p. HMS *Starling* (sloop); 25p. HMS *Royalist* (cruiser); 49p. USS *Philadelphia* (cruiser); 54p. HMCS *Prescott* (corvette) .... 7·50 8·50

(Des Steven Noon. Litho Walsall)

1996 (8 June). 50th Anniversary of UNICEF. T **206** and similar horiz designs showing children from different continents. P 13½×13.

780	21p. multicoloured	60	80
	a. Horiz strip of 4. Nos. 780/783	3·50	5·50
781	24p. multicoloured	70	90
782	49p. multicoloured	1·25	2·00
783	54p. multicoloured	1·40	2·25
780/783 *Set of 4*		3·50	5·50

Nos. 780/783 were printed together, *se-tenant*, in horizontal strips of four throughout the sheet.

207 Red Kites in Flight

(Des Roger Gorringe. Litho Walsall)

1996 (30 Sept). Endangered Species. Red Kite. T **207** and similar horiz designs. Multicoloured. P 14½.

784	34p. Type **207**	1·60	1·90
	a. Block of 4. Nos. 784/787	5·75	7·00
785	34p. Red Kite on ground	1·60	1·90
786	34p. On rock	1·60	1·90
787	34p. Pair at nest	1·60	1·90
784/787 *Set of 4*		5·75	7·00

Nos. 784/787 were printed together, *se-tenant*, in blocks of four throughout the sheet.

208 Christmas Pudding

209 Mary Celeste passing Gibraltar

(Des Keith Bassford. Litho Questa)

1996 (27 Nov). Christmas. T **208** and similar horiz designs created from Lego blocks. Multicoloured. P 14×14½.

788	5p. Type **208**		15	15
789	21p. Snowman face		40	25
790	24p. Present		45	30
791	34p. Father Christmas face		60	60
792	54p. Candle		1·00	2·50
788/792 Set of 5			2·40	3·50

(Des S. Tarabay. Litho Questa)

1997 (12 Feb). Europa. Tales and Legends. The *Mary Celeste*. T **209** and similar square designs. Multicoloured. P 14.

793	28p. Type **209**		1·10	1·10
794	28p. Boarding the *Mary Celeste*		1·10	1·10
795	30p. Crew leaving *Mary Celeste*		1·10	1·25
796	30p. *Mary Celeste* found by *Dei Gratis*		1·10	1·25
793/796 Set of 4			4·00	4·25

210 American Shorthair Silver Tabby

211 *Anthocharis belia euphenoides*

(Des Colleen Corlett. Litho B.D.T.)

1997 (12 Feb). Kittens. T **210** and similar horiz designs. Multicoloured. P 13½×14.

797	5p. Type **210**		40	1·00
	a. Booklet pane. Nos. 797, 799 and 801 with margins all round	1·75		
	b. Booklet pane. Nos. 797/798 and 801/802 with margins all round	2·50		
798	24p. Rumpy Manx Red Tabby		75	1·25
	a. Booklet pane. Nos. 798/800 with margins all round	2·00		
799	26p. Blue Point Birmans		75	1·25
	a. Booklet pane. Nos. 799/802 with margins all round	3·00		
800	28p. Red Self Longhair		80	1·25
801	30p. British Shorthair Tortoiseshell and White		80	1·25
802	35p. British Bicolour Shorthairs		90	1·40
797/802 Set of 6			4·00	6·75
MS803 132×80 mm. Nos. 797/802 with HONG KONG '97 International Stamp Exhibition logo at bottom left		5·00	8·00	
	a. Booklet pane. As No. **MS**803, but without HONG KONG '97 logo and with additional line of roulettes at left	7·00	8·00	

Nos. 797/802 were only issued in £5 stamp booklets or miniature sheet No. **MS**803.

(Des Roger Gorringe. Litho Enschedé)

1997 (7 Apr). Butterflies. T **211** and similar vert designs. Multicoloured. P 14×13½.

804	23p. Type **211**		55	35
805	26p. *Charaxes jasius*		65	40
806	30p. *Vanessa cardui*		75	70
807	£1·20 *Iphiclides podalirius*		2·75	4·50
804/807 Set of 4			4·25	5·50
MS808 135×90 mm. Nos. 804/807			4·25	6·00

(Des Derek Miller. Litho Cartor)

1997 (9 June). Second World War Warships (5th series). Sheet, 117×82 mm, containing horiz designs as T **184**. Multicoloured. P 13½.

MS809 24p. HMS *Enterprise* (cruiser); 26p. HMS *Cleopatra* (cruiser); 38p. USS *Iowa* (battleship); 50p. *Orkan* (Polish destroyer) ... 4·00 5·00

212 Queen Elizabeth and Prince Philip at Carriage-driving Trials

(Des Clive Abbott. Litho Questa)

1997 (10 July). Golden Wedding of Queen Elizabeth and Prince Philip. T **212** and similar horiz design. Multicoloured. P 13½.

810	£1·20 Type **212**		4·00	5·00
	a. Horiz pair. Nos. 810/811		8·00	10·00
811	£1·40 Queen Elizabeth in Trooping the Colour uniform		4·00	5·00

Nos. 810/811 were printed together, *se-tenant*, in horizontal pairs throughout the sheet.

213 Christian Dior Evening Dress

214 Our Lady and St Bernard (St Joseph's Parish Church)

(Des M. Whyte. Litho B.D.T.)

1997 (24 Oct). Christian Dior Spring/Summer '97 Collection designed by John Galliano. T **213** and similar vert designs. Multicoloured. P 13½.

812	30p. Type **213**		65	1·25
	a. Horiz pair. Nos. 812 and 814		1·25	2·50
813	35p. Tunic top and skirt		65	1·25
	a. Horiz pair. Nos. 813 and 815		1·25	2·50
814	50p. Ballgown		65	1·25
815	62p. Two-piece suit		65	1·25
812/815 Set of 4			2·40	5·00
MS816 110×90 mm. £1·20 Ballgown (*different*)		1·60	2·75	

Nos. 812 with 814 and 813 with 815 were each printed together, *se-tenant*, in sheets of eight with enlarged illustrated right-hand margin.

(Des Stephen Perera. Litho Cartor)

1997 (18 Nov). Christmas. Stained Glass Windows. T **214** and similar vert designs. Multicoloured. P 13½.

817	5p. Type **214**		20	10
818	26p. The Epiphany (Our Lady of Sorrows Church)		70	30
819	38p. St Joseph (Our Lady of Sorrows Church)		90	60
820	50p. The Holy Family (St Joseph's Parish Church)		1·10	1·75
821	62p. The Miraculous Medal (St Joseph's Parish Church)		1·40	3·00
817/821 Set of 5			3·75	5·00

215 Sir Joshua Hassan

216 Wales v Brazil (1958)

(Des Stephen Perera. Litho Cartor)

1997 (15 Dec). Sir Joshua Hassan (former Chief Minister) Commemoration. P 13.

822	**215** 26p. black		1·25	75

(Des Lee Montgomery. Litho Cartor)

1998 (23 Jan). World Football Championship, France (1998). T **216** and similar vert designs. Multicoloured. P 13.

823	5p. Type **216**		15	10
824	26p. Northern Ireland v France (1958)		55	25
825	38p. Scotland v Holland (1978)		65	50
826	£1·20 England v West Germany (1966)		1·40	3·50
823/826 Set of 4			2·50	4·00
MS827 153×96 mm. Nos. 823/826			2·50	4·00

216a Princess Diana wearing Jacket with White Fur Collar, 1988

216b Saro London (flying boat)

(Des Derek Miller. Litho Questa)

1998 (31 Mar). Diana, Princess of Wales Commemoration. Sheet 145×70 mm containing vert designs as T **216a**. Multicoloured. P 14½×14.

MS828	26p. Wearing jacket with white fur collar, 1988; 26p. Wearing pink checked suit and hat; 38p. Wearing black jacket, 1995; 38p. Wearing blue jacket with gold embroidery, 1987 (*sold at* £1·28+20p. *charity premium*)		1·25	3·00

(Des A. Theobald. Litho B.D.T.)

1998 (1 Apr). 80th Anniversary of Royal Air Force. Horiz designs as T **216b**. Multicoloured. P 14.

829	24p. Type **216b**		70	55
830	26p. Fairey Fox		75	60
831	38p. Handley Page Halifax GR.VI		95	1·25
832	50p. Hawker Siddeley Buccaneer S.2B		1·25	2·50
829/832	Set of 4		3·25	4·50
MS833	110×77 mm. 24p. Sopwith 1½ Strutter; 26p. Bristol M.1B; 38p. Supermarine Spitfire XII; 50p. Avro York		3·50	4·50

217 Miss Gibraltar saluting

218 Striped Dolphin

(Des Stephen Perera. Litho Cartor)

1998 (22 May). Europa. Festivals. National Day. T **217** and similar vert designs showing Miss Gibraltar in various costumes. Multicoloured. P 13½×13.

834	26p. Type **217**		60	90
835	26p. In black bodice and long red skirt		60	90
836	38p. In black bodice and short red skirt, with Gibraltar flag		80	1·25
837	38p. In Genoese-style costume		80	1·25
834/837	Set of 4		2·50	3·75

Nos. 834/837 were each printed in sheets of ten with enlarged illustrated right-hand margins.

(Des Lee Montgomery. Litho Questa)

1998 (22 May). International Year of the Ocean. Sheet 155×64 mm containing T **218** and similar multicoloured designs. P 14.

MS838	5p. Type **218**; 5p Common Dolphin (*vert*); 26p. Killer Whale (*vert*); £1·20 Blue Whale		5·50	6·50

219 Nileus (dog) with Hat and Telescope

220 "Love comforts like Sunshine after Rain" (William Shakespeare)

(Des Martin Hargreaves. Litho Cartor)

1998 (1 Aug). Bicentenary of Battle of the Nile. T **219** and similar multicoloured designs. P 13½.

839	12p. Type **219**		1·00	1·25
	a. Booklet pane. Nos. 839/841 with margins all round		3·25	

	b. Booklet pane. Nos. 839/843 with margins all round		6·50	
840	26p. Rear-Admiral Sir Horatio Nelson		1·00	80
	a. Booklet pane. No. 840 with margins all round		1·00	
	b. Booklet pane. Nos. 840×2 and 842/843 with margins all round		5·00	
	c. Booklet pane. Nos. 840 and 842/843 with margins all round		4·00	
841	28p. Frances Nisbet, Lady Nelson		1·75	2·00
842	35p. HMS *Vanguard* (ship of the line)		1·75	2·25
843	50p. Battle of the Nile (47×29 mm)		1·75	3·25
839/843	Set of 5		6·50	8·50

(Des Mark Whyte. Litho Questa)

1998 (6 Oct). Famous Quotations. T **220** and similar horiz designs. Multicoloured. P 14½.

844	26p. Type **220**		90	1·00
845	26p. "The price of greatness is responsibility" (Sir Winston Churchill)		90	1·00
846	38p. "Hate the sin, love the sinner" (Mahatma Gandhi)		1·10	1·50
847	38p. "Imagination is more important than knowledge" (Albert Einstein)		1·10	1·50
844/847	Set of 4		3·50	4·50

Nos. 844/847 were each issued in sheets of six stamps and six half stamp-size labels showing the quotations in different languages.

221 The Nativity

222 Barbary Macaque

(Des Petula Stone. Litho Walsall)

1998 (10 Nov). Christmas. T **221** and similar vert designs. Multicoloured. P 13½.

848	5p. Type **221**		35	10
849	26p. Star and stable		1·25	70
850	30p. King with gold		1·40	75
851	35p. King with myrrh		1·40	1·25
852	50p. King with frankincense		1·75	3·25
848/852	Set of 5		5·50	5·50

(Des Roger Gorringe. Litho Cartor)

1999 (4 Mar). Europa. Parks and Gardens. Upper Rock Nature Reserve. T **222** and similar vert designs. Multicoloured. P 13½×13.

853	30p. Type **222**		1·75	1·50
854	30p. Dartford Warbler		2·00	1·50
855	42p. Dusky Grouper		2·00	2·50
856	42p. River Kingfisher		2·25	2·50
853/856	Set of 4		7·25	7·25

223 Queen Elizabeth II

224 Roman Marine and Galley

(Des Stephen Perera. Litho B.D.T.)

1999 (4 Mar)–**2001**.

(a) P 14 (50p., £1, £1·20, £1·40, £3) or 13½×13 (others)

857	**223**	1p. reddish purple	10	80
858		2p. olive-sepia	15	1·25
859		4p. light greenish blue	25	80
860		5p. emerald	25	30
861		10p. orange	50	30
862		12p. rosine	55	40
863		20p. turquoise-green	1·25	45
864		28p. magenta	1·50	60
865		30p. reddish orange	1·75	50
866		40p. deep olive-grey	2·25	85
867		42p. deep grey-green	2·25	90
868		50p. bistre	2·50	1·25
869		£1 brownish black	3·75	2·75
869a		£1·20 bright carmine (1.6.01)	5·00	4·50

| 869*b* | £1·40 bright blue (1.6.01) | 5·00 | 4·75 |
| 870 | £3 bright blue | 9·00 | 12·00 |

(b) Self-adhesive. P 9½

| 871 | **223** | (1st) reddish orange | 1·00 | 60 |
| 857/871 | | *Set of* 15 | 32·00 | 29·00 |

Nos. 868/871 are larger, 25×30 mm.

No. 871 was printed in rolls of 100, on which the surplus self adhesive paper around each stamp was retained, and was initially *sold at* 26p.

(Des Simon Williams. Litho Cartor)

1999 (19 Mar). Maritime Heritage. T **224** and similar square designs. Multicoloured. P 12½.

872	5p. Type **224**	25	10
873	30p. Arab sailor, medieval galley house and dhow	95	65
874	42p. Marine officer and British ship of the line (1779–1783)	1·50	1·50
875	£1·20 Naval rating, Queen Alexandra Dry Dock and HMS *Berwick* (cruiser) (1904)	3·25	4·25
872/875	*Set of 4*	5·50	6·00
MS876	116×76 mm. Nos. 872/875	6·00	7·00

No. **MS**876 includes the Australia '99 International Stamp Exhibition, Melbourne, emblem on the sheet margin.

225 John Lennon (musician)

226 Postal Van at Dockside, 1930s

(Des Stephen Perera. Litho Cartor)

1999 (20 Mar). 30th Wedding Anniversary of John Lennon and Yoko Ono. T **225** and similar vert designs showing John Lennon. P 13½×13.

877	20p. multicoloured	1·00	55
878	30p. black and pale turquoise-blue	1·25	90
879	40p. multicoloured	1·50	1·90
877/9	*Set of 3*	3·25	3·00
MS880	Two sheets, each 62×100 mm. (a) £1 black and deep slate-blue. (b) £1 multicoloured *Set of 2 sheets*	8·50	8·50

Designs: 20p. With flower over left eye; 30p. T **225**; 40p. Wearing orange glasses; £1 (No. **MS**880(a)), Holding marriage certificate; £1 (No. **MS**880(b)), Standing on aircraft steps.

Nos. 877/879 were each printed in small sheets of ten with enlarged illustrated right margins.

(Des N. Walton. Litho Cartor)

1999 (20 Mar). 125th Anniversary of Universal Postal Union. T **226** and similar square design. Multicoloured. P 12½.

| 881 | 5p. Type **226** | 50 | 50 |
| 882 | 30p. Space shuttle and station | 1·00 | 1·25 |

227 EF-2000 Eurofighter

228 Prince Edward and Sophie Rhys-Jones

(Des Stephen Perera (30p.), Mike Atkinson (42p.). Litho Cartor)

1999 (7 June). Wings of Prey (1st series). Birds of Prey and RAF Fighter Aircraft. T **227** and similar horiz designs. Multicoloured. P 13×13½.

883	30p. Type **227**	1·25	1·40
	a. Horiz pair. Nos. 883 and 886	2·50	3·00
884	30p. Panavia Tornado F3	1·25	1·40
	a. Horiz pair. Nos. 884 and 887	2·50	3·00
885	30p. BAe Harrier II GR7	1·25	1·40
	a. Horiz pair. Nos. 885 and 888	2·50	3·00
886	42p. Lesser Kestrel	1·40	1·60
887	42p. Peregrine Falcon	1·40	1·60
888	42p. Common Kestrel	1·40	1·60
883/888	*Set of 6*	7·00	8·00
MS889	Two sheets, each 105×86 mm. (a) Nos. 883/885. (b) Nos. 886/888 *Set of 2 sheets*	8·00	8·50

Nos. 883 with 886, 884 with 887 and 885 with 888 were each printed together, *se-tenant*, as horizontal pairs in sheets of ten with enlarged illustrated margins at right and foot.

See also Nos. 943/**MS**948 and 982/**MS**988.

(Des Stephen Perera. Litho Cartor)

1999 (19 June–11 Oct). Royal Wedding. T **228** and similar multicoloured designs. P 13×13½ (horiz) or 13½×13 (vert).

890	30p. Type **228**	1·25	65
891	42p. Prince Edward and Sophie Rhys-Jones holding hands (*vert*)	1·60	1·00
892	54p. In carriage on wedding day (11.10)	2·00	2·50
893	66p. On Chapel steps after wedding (*vert*) (11.10)	2·50	3·00
890/893	*Set of 4*	6·50	6·50

Nos. 890/893 were printed in sheets with illustrated gutter margins.

229 Football   **230** 'Seasons Greetings'

(Des Jon Sayer. Litho Cartor)

1999 (2 July). Local Sporting Centenaries. T **229** and similar vert designs. Multicoloured. P 13½×13.

894	30p. Type **229**	50	40
895	42p. Rowing	70	60
896	£1·20 Cricket	3·00	4·25
894/896	*Set of 3*	3·75	4·75

(Des Simon Williams. Litho B.D.T.)

1999 (11 Nov). Christmas. T **230** and similar square designs. Multicoloured. P 14.

897	5p. Type **230**	15	10
898	5p. 'Happy Christmas'	15	10
899	30p. 'Happy Millennium'	70	70
900	30p. 'Happy Christmas' and Santa with reindeer	70	70
901	42p. Santa Claus in chimney	1·00	1·40
902	54p. Santa Claus leaving presents	1·10	2·25
897/902	*Set of 6*	3·50	4·75

231 People travelling with Environmentally-friendly Jet-packs (Colin Grech)

232 Dutch Football Player and Flag, 1988

(Litho Questa)

2000 (28 Jan). Stampin' the Future (children's stamp design competition). T **231** and similar horiz designs. Multicoloured. P 14½×14.

903	30p. Type **231**	1·25	1·75
	a. Strip of 4. Nos. 903/906	4·50	6·25
904	42p. Robotic Postman (Kim Barea)	1·25	1·75
905	54p. Living on the Moon (Stephan Williamson-Fa)	1·25	1·75
906	66p. Jet-powered Cars (Michael Podesta)	1·25	1·75
903/906	*Set of 4*	4·50	6·25

Nos. 903/906 were printed together, *se-tenant*, as vertical or horizontal strips of four in sheets of 16.

(Des Lee Montgomery and Anselmo Torres. Litho Cartor)

2000 (17 Apr). European Football Championship, Netherlands. T **232** and similar square designs. Multicoloured. P 12½.

907	30p. Type **232**	60	70
908	30p. French player and flag, 1984	60	70
909	42p. German player scoring and flag, 1996	80	1·10
910	42p. Danish player and flag, 1992	80	1·10
907/910	*Set of 4*	2·50	3·25
MS911	Two sheets, each 115×85 mm. (a) 54p.×4, English player and flag. (b) Nos. 907/910 *Set of 2 sheets*	11·00	13·00

Nos. 907/910 were each printed in sheets of ten (5×2) with enlarged illustrated right margins showing national newspapers reports of football matches.

233 Fountain of Stars

234 3000 Metre Waterfall between Gibraltar and North African Coast, 5 Million BC

(Des Jon Sayer. Litho Cartor)

2000 (17 Apr). Europa. T **233** and similar vert designs. Multicoloured. P 13½×13.

912	30p. Type **233**	75	70
913	40p. Exchanging star	1·00	1·25
914	42p. Stars and aeroplane	1·00	1·25
915	54p. Stars and end of rainbow	1·25	2·00
912/915 Set of 4		3·50	4·75

Nos. 912/915 were each printed in sheets of ten (5×2) with enlarged illustrated right margins.

(Des Christian Hook and Stephen Perera. Litho Questa)

2000 (9 May). New Millennium. History of Gibraltar. T **234** and similar square designs. Multicoloured (except Nos. 926/930). P 14.

916	5p. Type **234**	30	50
	a. Sheetlet of 16. Nos. 916/931	9·50	12·50
	b. Booklet pane. No. 916×2	60	
917	5p. Sabre-tooth Tiger, 2 million BC	30	50
	b. Booklet pane. No. 917×2	60	
918	5p. Neanderthal hunting Goat, and skull, 30,000 BC	30	50
	b. Booklet pane. No. 918×2	60	
919	5p. Phoenician traders and galley, 700 BC	30	50
	b. Booklet pane. No. 919×2	60	
920	5p. Roman warship, 100 BC	30	50
	b. Booklet pane. No. 920×2	60	
921	5p. Tarik-il-in-Zayad, Ape and Moorish Castle, 711 AD	30	50
	b. Booklet pane. No. 921×2	60	
922	5p. Coat of Arms, 1502	30	50
	b. Booklet pane. No. 922×2	60	
923	5p. Admiral George Rooke and Union Jack 1704	30	50
	b. Booklet pane. No. 923×2	60	
924	30p. General Eliott at The Great Siege, 1779–1783	1·00	1·25
	b. Booklet pane. No. 924×2	2·00	
925	30p. HMS *Victory*, 1805	1·00	1·25
	b. Booklet pane. No. 925×2	2·00	
926	30p. Queen Alexandra in horse-drawn carriage, 1903 (reddish brown, silver and black)	1·00	1·25
	b. Booklet pane. No. 926×3	2·75	
927	30p. 100 ton gun, 1870s (olive-grey, silver and black)	1·00	1·25
	b. Booklet pane. No. 927×3	2·75	
928	30p. Evacuees, 1940 (deep dull purple, silver and black)	1·00	1·25
	b. Booklet pane. No. 928×3	2·75	
929	30p. Tank and anti-aircraft gun 1940s (bistre-brown, silver and black)	1·00	1·25
	b. Booklet pane. No. 929×3	2·75	
930	30p. Queen Elizabeth II in carriage, 1954 (violet-grey, silver and black)	1·00	1·25
	b. Booklet pane. No. 930×3	2·75	
931	30p. Aerial view of office district, 2000	1·00	1·25
	b. Booklet pane. No. 931×3	2·75	
916/931 Set of 16		9·50	12·50

Nos. 916/931 were printed together, *se-tenant*, in sheetlets of 16.

The booklet panes contain two or three stamps within larger illustrations. Some of the 30p. stamps from the booklet differ slightly in shade from those in the sheetlet.

One booklet has been reported with all panes imperforate.

235 Princess Diana holding Prince William, 1982

236 Lady Elizabeth Bowes-Lyon signing Book

(Des Anselmo Torres. Litho Cartor)

2000 (21 June). 18th Birthday of Prince William. T **235** and similar square designs. Multicoloured. P 12½.

932	30p. Type **235**	60	40
933	42p. Prince William as a toddler	80	70
934	54p. Prince William with Prince Charles	1·00	1·75
935	66p. Prince William at 18	1·25	2·50
932/935 Set of 4		3·25	4·75
MS936 115×75 mm. Nos. 932/935		4·00	6·00

Nos. 932/935 were each printed in sheets of 80 containing two panes separated by a large vertical gutter, showing further photographs extending to the height of two vertical rows.

(Des Stephen Perera. Litho Cartor)

2000 (4 Aug). Queen Elizabeth the Queen Mother's 100th Birthday. T **236** and similar square designs. P 12½.

937	30p. black and Prussian blue	60	40
938	42p. black and sepia	80	70
939	54p. multicoloured	1·00	1·75
940	66p. multicoloured	1·25	2·50
937/940 Set of 4		3·25	4·75
MS941 115×75 mm. Nos. 937/940		4·00	6·00

Designs: 30p. T **236**; 42p. Duke and Duchess of York; 54p. Queen Mother with bouquet; 66p. Queen Mother in orange coat and hat.

Nos. 937/940 were printed in similar sheet format to Nos. 932/935.

237 Moorish Castle

238 Infant Jesus

(Eng Czeslaw Slania. Recess and photo Stamp Printing Office, Belgium)

2000 (15 Sept). P 11½.

942	**237**	£5 black, silver and gold†	13·00	14·00

† The Queen's head on this stamp is printed in optically variable ink which changes colour from gold to green when viewed from different angles.

(Des Stephen Perera (30p.), Roger Gorringe (42p.). Litho Questa)

2000 (15 Sept). Wings of Prey (2nd series). Birds of Prey and RAF Second World War Aircraft. Horiz designs as T **227**. Multicoloured. P 14½×14.

943	30p. Supermarine Spitfire MkIIA *Gibraltar*		1·75	1·75
	a. Horiz pair. Nos. 943 and 946		3·75	3·75
944	30p. Hawker Hurricane MkIIC		1·75	1·75
	a. Horiz pair. Nos. 944 and 947		3·75	3·75
945	30p. Avro Lancaster BI-III *City of Lincoln*		1·75	1·75
	a. Horiz pair. Nos. 945 and 948		3·75	3·75
946	42p. Merlin (male)		2·00	2·00
947	42p. Merlin (female)		2·00	2·00
948	42p. Bonelli's Eagle		2·00	2·00
943/948 Set of 6			10·00	10·00
MS949 Two sheets, each 105×85 mm. (a) Nos. 943/945. (b) Nos. 946/948 Set of 2 sheets			10·00	11·00
	ab. Lower stamp (No. 944) imperf on three sides		£1200	
	ba. Lower stamp (No. 947) imperf on three sides		£1200	

Nos. 943/948 were printed in a similar *se-tenant* format as Nos. 883/888.

(Des Christian Hook. Litho Questa)

2000 (13 Nov). Christmas. T **238** and similar square designs. Multicoloured. P 14.

950	5p. Type **238**	20	15
951	30p. Virgin Mary with infant Jesus	75	65
952	30p. Journey to Bethlehem	75	65
953	40p. Mary and Joseph with innkeeper	90	1·00
954	42p. The Nativity	90	1·25
955	54p. Visit of the Wise Men	1·40	2·25
950/955 Set of 6		4·50	5·50

239 Wedding of Queen Victoria and Prince Albert

240 Grass Snake

(Des Anselmo Torres. Litho Cartor)

2001 (22 Jan). Death Centenary of Queen Victoria. T **239** and similar square designs. P 12½.

956	30p. deep violet-blue, deep violet and black..	1·00	65
957	42p. myrtle-green, blackish green and black .	1·40	1·00
958	54p. blackish purple, scarlet and black	2·00	2·50
959	66p. olive-brown, gold and black	2·25	3·25
956/959 *Set of 4*		6·00	6·75

Designs: 30p. T **239**; 42p. Victoria as Empress of India; 54p. Queen Victoria in carriage; 66p. Queen Victoria standing by chair.

Nos. 956/959 were printed in similar sheet format to Nos. 932/935.

(Des Roger Gorringe and Anselmo Torres. Litho Questa)

2001 (1 Feb). Snakes. T **240** and similar multicoloured designs. P 14.

960	5p. Type **240**	25	40
961	5p. Ladder Snake	25	40
962	5p. Montpellier Snake	25	40
963	30p. Viperine Snake	75	1·00
964	30p. Southern Smooth Snake	75	1·00
965	30p. False Smooth Snake	75	1·00
966	66p. Horseshoe Whip Snake (30×62 *mm*)	1·50	2·50
960/966 *Set of 7*		4·00	6·00
MS967 155×87 mm. Nos. 960/966		4·75	6·50

No. **MS**967 also commemorates the Chinese New Year Year of the Snake. Nos. 962 and **MS**967 are inscribed MONTPELIER in error.

241 Long-snouted Seahorse

242 Queen Elizabeth II as a Baby

(Des Anselmo Torres. Litho Cartor)

2001 (1 Feb). Europa. Water and Nature. T **241** and similar vert designs. Multicoloured. P 13.

968	30p. Type **241**	1·00	65
969	40p. Snapdragon	1·50	1·00
970	42p. Herring Gull	2·75	1·50
971	54p. Goldfish	2·00	4·50
968/971 *Set of 4*		6·50	7·00

Nos. 967/971 were each printed in sheets of ten with enlarged illustrated and inscribed right margins. The margin of the 54p. sheet includes the Hong Kong 2001 Stamp Exhibition logo.

(Des Stephen Perera. Litho Questa)

2001 (20 Apr). 75th Birthday of Queen Elizabeth II. T **242** and similar designs. P 14.

972	30p. brownish black and magenta	60	65
973	30p. brownish black and bluish violet	60	65
974	42p. brownish black and vermilion	80	1·25
975	42p. brownish black and reddish violet	80	1·25
976	54p. multicoloured	1·00	2·00
972/976 *Set of 5*		3·50	5·00
MS977 101×89 mm. £2 multicoloured. P 13½		3·50	5·00

Designs: Square—No. 972, T **242**; No. 973, Queen Elizabeth as teenager; No. 974, On wedding day, 1947; No. 975, After Coronation, 1953; No. 976, Queen Elizabeth in blue hat. Vert (35×49 *mm*)—No. **MS**977, Queen Elizabeth II, 2001 (photo by Fiona Hanson).

Nos. 972/976 were printed in a similar sheet format to Nos. 932/935.

No. **MS**977 marks a successful attempt on the record for the fastest produced stamp issue. The miniature sheet was on sale in Gibraltar 10 hours and 24 minutes after the artwork was approved at Buckingham Palace.

243 Battle of Trafalgar, 1805

244 Snoopy as Father Christmas with Woodstock

(Des Stephen Perera. Litho Questa)

2001 (21 May). Bicentenary of *The Gibraltar Chronicle* (newspaper). T **243** and similar vert designs. Each black. P 14×14½.

978	30p. Type **243**	1·50	65

979	42p. Invention of the Telephone, 1876	1·25	90
980	54p. Winston Churchill (Victory in Second World War, 1945)	2·50	2·50
981	66p. Footprint on Moon (Moon landing, 1969)	2·50	3·75
978/981 *Set of 4*		7·00	7·00

(Des Stephen Perera (Nos. 982, 984, 986). Mike Atkinson (others). Litho Questa)

2001 (3 Sept). Wings of Prey (3rd series). Birds of Prey and Modern Military Aircraft. Horiz designs as T **227**. Multicoloured. P 14½×14.

982	40p. Royal Navy Sea Harrier FA MK.2	1·25	1·50
	a. Horiz pair. Nos. 982/983	2·50	3·00
983	40p. Western Marsh Harrier	1·25	1·50
984	40p. RAF Hawk T MK1	1·25	1·50
	a. Horiz pair. Nos. 984/985	2·50	3·00
985	40p. Northern Sparrow Hawk	1·25	1·50
986	40p. RAF Jaguar GR1B	1·25	1·50
	a. Horiz pair. Nos. 986/987	2·50	3·00
987	40p. Northern Hobby	1·25	1·50
982/987 *Set of 6*		6·75	8·00
MS988 Two sheets, each 103×84 mm. (a) Nos. 982, 984 and 986. (b) Nos. 983, 985 and 987		6·50	7·00

Nos. 982/987 were printed in a similar, *se-tenant* format to Nos. 883/888.

(Des Anselmo Torres. Litho Questa)

2001 (12 Nov). Christmas. *Peanuts* (cartoon characters by Charles Schulz). T **244** and similar square designs. Multicoloured. P 14.

989	5p. Type **244**	25	15
990	30p. Charlie Brown and Snoopy with Christmas tree	85	65
991	40p. Snoopy asleep in wreath	1·10	1·00
992	42p. Snoopy with plate of biscuits	1·25	1·25
993	54p. Snoopy asleep on kennel	1·75	2·50
989/993 *Set of 5*		4·75	5·00
MS994 140×85 mm. Nos. 989/993		4·75	5·50

245 One Cent Coin

245a Princess Elizabeth and Princess Margaret making Radio Broadcast, 1940

(Des Anselmo Torres. Litho and thermography Cartor)

2002 (1 Jan). Introduction of Euro Currency by European Union. Coins. Sheet, 165×105 mm, containing T **245** and similar square designs showing coins. Multicoloured. P 13.

MS995 5p. Type **245**; 12p. 2 cents; 30p. 5 cents; 35p. 10 cents; 40p. 20 cents; 42p. 50 cents; 54p. 1 Euro; 66p. 2 Euros		3·75	6·50

(Des Andrew Robinson. Litho Questa)

2002 (6 Feb). Golden Jubilee. T **245a** and similar designs. W w **14** (sideways Nos. 996/999). P 13½ (75p.) or 14½ (others).

996	30p. brownish black, rosine and gold	70	90
997	30p. agate, rosine and gold	70	90
998	30p. multicoloured	70	90
999	30p. multicoloured	70	90
1000	75p. multicoloured	1·40	2·25
996/1000 *Set of 5*		3·75	5·00
MS1001 162×95 mm. Nos. 996/1000. Wmk sideways		3·75	5·00

Designs: Horiz—No. 996, T **245a**; No. 997, Princess Elizabeth in Girl Guide uniform, 1942; No. 998, Queen Elizabeth in evening dress, 1961; No. 999, Queen Elizabeth in Chelsea, 1993. Vert (38×51 *mm*)—No. 1000, Queen Elizabeth after Annigoni.

Nos. 996/1000 were each printed together, in sheets of 80, the two panes (each 4×10), separated by a gutter showing further photographs extending to a height of two horizontal rows.

246 Joshua Grimaldi

247 Bobby Moore holding Jules Rimet Trophy, 1966

(Des Anselmo Torres. Litho Cartor)

2002 (4 Mar). Europa. Circus. Famous Clowns. T **246** and similar vert designs. Multicoloured. P 13½×13.

1002	30p. Type **246**	70	65
1003	40p. Karl Wettach (Grock)	1·00	1·25
1004	42p. Nicolai Polakovs (Coco)	1·00	1·25
1005	54p. Charlie Cairoli	1·25	2·50
1002/1005 *Set of 4*		3·50	5·00

Nos. 1002/1005 were each printed in sheets of ten with enlarged illustrated and inscribed right margins.

(Des Anselmo Torres. Litho Cartor)

2002 (29 Apr). World Cup Football Championship, Japan and Korea (2002). England's Victory, 1966. T **247** and similar vert designs. Multicoloured. P 13½×13.

1006	30p. Type **247**	50	30
1007	42p. Kissing Trophy	70	55
1008	54p. Bobby Moore with Queen Elizabeth II	1·00	1·50
1009	66p. Bobby Moore in action	1·25	2·50
1006/1009 *Set of 4*		3·25	4·25
MS1010 135×90 mm. Nos. 1006/1009		3·25	4·50

Nos. 1006/1009 were each printed in sheets of eight with enlarged illustrated and inscribed right margins.

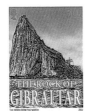

248 Barbary Macaque

249 Gibraltar from the North

(Des Roger Guilline and Anselmo Torres. Litho B.D.T.)

2002 (6 June). Wildlife. T **248** and similar multicoloured designs. P 14.

1011	30p. Type **248**	70	80
1012	30p. Red Fox (*horiz*)	70	80
1013	40p. White-toothed Shrew (*horiz*)	90	85
1014	£1 Rabbit	2·25	4·00
1011/1014 *Set of 4*		4·00	5·50
MS1015 125×100 mm. Nos. 1011/1014		5·00	7·50

(Des Anselmo Torres. Litho and themography Cartor)

2002 (15 Sept). Views of the Rock of Gibraltar. T **249** and similar multicoloured designs. P 13½×13.

1016	30p. Type **249**	1·25	1·25
	a. Horiz strip of 4. Nos. 1016/1019	7·25	8·50
1017	30p. View from the south	1·25	1·25
1018	£1 View from the east (50×40 *mm*)	2·75	3·50
1019	£1 View from the west (50×40 *mm*)	2·75	3·50
1016/1019 *Set of 4*		7·25	8·50

Nos. 1016/1019 were printed together, horizontally *se-tenant*, in sheets of 24 (2 panes, 4×3) with powdered particles of the Rock sintered to their surface using thermography.

250 Princess Diana holding Prince Harry

(Des Anselmo Torres. Litho Cartor)

2002 (31 Oct). 18th Birthday of Prince Harry. T **250** and similar square designs. Multicoloured. P 12½.

1020	30p. Type **250**	90	65
1021	42p. Prince Harry waving	1·25	90
1022	54p. Prince Harry skiing	1·50	1·60
1023	66p. Wearing dark suit	1·90	2·75
1020/1023 *Set of 4*		5·00	5·25
MS1024 115×75 mm. Nos. 1120/1123		5·50	6·50

Nos. 1020/1023 were each printed in sheets of 80, the two panes (each 4×10) separated by a gutter showing further photographs extending to the height of two vertical rows.

251 Crib, Cathedral of St Mary the Crowned

(Des Anselmo Torres. Litho B.D.T.)

2002 (13 Nov). Christmas. Cribs from Gibraltar Cathedrals and Churches. T **251** and similar horiz designs. Multicoloured. P 13½×13.

1025	5p. Type **251**	35	10
1026	30p. St Joseph's Parish Church	1·25	65
1027	40p. St Theresa's Parish Church	1·50	95
1028	42p. Our Lady of Sorrows Church	1·50	1·00
1029	52p. St Bernard's Church	1·75	2·75
1030	54p. Cathedral of the Holy Trinity	1·75	2·75
1025/1030 *Set of 6*		7·25	7·25

Nos. 1025/1030 were each printed in sheets of 40 containing two panes separated by a horizontal gutter showing the featured cathedral or church.

252 Archbishop of Canterbury crowning Queen Elizabeth II

253 Young Prince William with Princess Diana

(Des Stephen Perera. Litho Cartor)

2003 (20 Feb). 50th Anniversary of the Coronation. T **252** and similar square designs, each black, grey and brown-purple. P 12½.

1031	30p. Type **252**	60	60
1032	30p. Queen Elizabeth II in Coronation robes	60	60
1033	40p. Queen Elizabeth holding the Orb and Sceptre	70	60
1034	£1 Queen Elizabeth in Coronation Coach	2·00	3·00
1031/1034 *Set of 4*		3·50	4·25
MS1035 116×76 mm. Nos. 1131/1134		3·50	5·00

Nos. 1031/1034 were each printed in sheets of 80, the two panes of 40 (4×10) separated by a gutter showing further photographs extending to the height of two horizontal rows.

(Des Stephen Perera. Litho Cartor)

2003 (20 Feb). 21st Birthday of Prince William of Wales. T **253** and similar square designs. Each black, grey and bluish violet. P 12½.

1036	30p. Type **253**	1·00	80
1037	30p. Prince William at Eton College	1·00	80
1038	40p. Prince William	1·25	80
1039	£1 Prince William in Operation Raleigh sweatshirt	2·00	3·75
1036/1039 *Set of 4*		4·75	5·50
MS1040 115×75 mm. Nos. 1136/1139		4·75	6·00

254 Drama Festival Poster

255 Wright Brothers' *Flyer I*, 1903

(Des Stephen Perera. Litho De La Rue)

2003 (3 Mar). Europa. Poster Art. T **254** and similar vert designs. Multicoloured. P 14×14½.

1041	30p. Type **254**	60	60
1042	40p. Spring Festival poster	75	90
1043	42p. Art Festival poster	75	90
1044	54p. Dance Festival poster	1·10	2·00
1041/1044 *Set of 4*		3·00	4·00

Nos. 1041/1044 were each printed in sheets of ten with enlarged, illustrated right margins.

(Des Anselmo Torres. Litho Cartor)

2003 (31 Mar). Centenary of Powered Flight. T **255** and similar designs showing aircraft. P 13.

1045	30p. multicoloured	90	65
1046	40p. black and agate	1·25	1·25
1047	40p. black and dull blue	1·25	1·25
1048	42p. black and greenish blue	1·25	1·25
1049	44p. multicoloured	1·40	1·40
1050	66p. multicoloured	2·00	3·25
1045/1050 *Set of 6*		7·25	8·00
MS1051 140×110 mm. Nos. 1140/1145. P 12½		7·75	8·50

Designs: Horiz (37×28 *mm*)—30p. T **255**; 40p. (No. 1046) Charles Lindbergh and *Spirit of St Louis* (first Transatlantic solo flight, 1927); 40p. (No. 1047) Boeing 314 *Yankee Clipper* flying boat (first Transatlantic scheduled air service, 1939). (77×28 *mm*)—42p. Saunders Roe Saro A 21 Windhover amphibian (first scheduled air service between Gibraltar and Tangier, 1931); 44p. British Airways Concorde (first supersonic airliner, 1976). Vert (37×58 *mm*)—66p. Space shuttle *Columbia* (first shuttle flight in Space orbit, 1981)

Nos. 1045/1050 were each printed in sheets of five with enlarged, illustrated margins.

256 Flag of St George

257 Big Ben, Swift and Rock of Gibraltar

(Des Christian Hook and Anselmo Torres. Litho Questa)

2003 (23 Apr). 1700th Death Anniversary of St George. T **256** and similar multicoloured designs. P 13½.

1052	30p. Type **256**	60	40
1053	40p. Cross of Military Constantinian Order of St George	70	55
1054	£1·20 St George and the Dragon (stained glass window, St Joseph's Church, Gibraltar) (32×63 *mm*)	2·50	4·25
1052/1054 *Set of 3*		3·50	4·75
MS1055 150×100 mm. Nos. 1052/1054		3·50	6·00

(Des Anselmo Torres. Eng Geslaw Slania. Recess and photo Stamp Printing Office, Belgium)

2003 (21 June). P 11½.

1056	**257**	(£3) multicoloured†	8·00	9·50

No. 1056 is inscribed 'UK express' and was initially *sold at* £3.

† The Queen's head on this stamp is printed in optically variable ink which changes colour from gold to green when viewed from different angles.

258 Wood Blewit (*Lepista nuda*)

259 Daisy (Latvia), Cornflower (Estonia) and Rue (Lithuania)

(Des Roger Gorringe and Anselmo Torres. Litho D.L.R.)

2003 (15 Sept). Mushrooms of Gibraltar. T **258** and similar square designs. Multicoloured. P 14½.

1057	30p. Type **258**	75	75
1058	30p. Blue-green Funnel-cap (*Clitocybe odora*)	75	75
1059	30p. Sulphur Tuft (*Hypholoma fasciculare*)	75	75
1060	£1·20 Field Mushrooms (*Agaricus campestris*)	3·00	4·50
1057/1060 *Set of 4*		4·75	6·00
MS1061 105×90 mm. Nos. 1057/1060		5·50	7·50

(Des Antonia Eenthoven. Litho D.L.R.)

2003 (15 Sept). Enlargement of the European Union (2004). T **259** and similar square designs showing the National Flowers of new member countries. Multicoloured. P 14.

1062	30p. Type **259**	80	70
1063	40p. Rose (Cyprus) and Maltese Centaury (Malta)	90	80
1064	42p. Tulip (Hungary), Carnation (Slovenia) and Dog Rose (Slovakia)	90	80

1065	54p. Corn Poppy (Poland) and Scented Thyme (Czech Republic)	1·25	3·00
1062/1065 *Set of 4*		3·50	4·75

Nos. 1062/1065 were each printed in small sheets of ten with enlarged illustrated right-hand margins showing outline maps of new member countries.

260 Baby Jesus Crib Figure, Our Lady of Sorrows Church

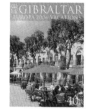

261 Street Café

(Des Anselmo Torres. Litho Walsall)

2003 (17 Nov). Christmas. T **260** and similar multicoloured designs. P 14.

1066	5p. Type **260**	20	10
1067	30p. Children making crib	90	65
1068	40p. Three Kings Cavalcade	1·25	1·00
1069	42p. Children's provisions for Santa and Reindeer	1·25	1·00
1070	54p. Cathedral of St Mary the Crowned lit for Christmas Eve Midnight Mass	1·75	3·50
1066/1070 *Set of 5*		4·75	5·50
MS1071 100×80 mm. £1 Cartoon characters from *Peanuts* carol singing around Christmas tree (50×40 *mm*). P 13		4·25	5·50

(Des Stephen Perera. Litho D.L.R.)

2004 (20 Feb). Europa. Holidays. T **261** and similar vert designs. Multicoloured. P 14×14½.

1072	40p. Type **261**	1·00	1·25
1073	40p. St Michael's Cave	1·00	1·25
1074	54p. Dolphins	1·40	2·25
1075	54p. Harbourside restaurant	1·40	2·25
1072/1075 *Set of 4*		4·25	6·25

Nos. 1072/1075 were each printed in sheets of ten (2×5) with enlarged illustrated right-hand margins.

262 Arms

263 Queen Elizabeth holding Bouquet

(Des Stephen Perera. Litho Cartor)

2004 (24 Apr). 300th Anniversary of British Gibraltar (1st series). T **262** and similar horiz designs. Multicoloured. P 13×13½.

1076	8p. Type **262**	65	65

MS1077 144×114 mm. 30p. *Royal Katarine* flying Red Ensign, 1704; 30p. Landing party, 1704; 30p. Soldiers of 1704; 30p. Arms of Gibraltar on military uniform; 30p. Royal Gibraltar police helmet and red phone box; 30p. Post Office Arms and red pillar box; 30p. Graduates and University of Cambridge examination certificate; 30p. Crowd waving Union Jacks and Gibraltar flags; £1 Union Jack ... 13·00 15·00

See also Nos. **MS**1093.

(Des Anselmo Torres. Litho Cartor)

2004 (4 May). 50th Anniversary of Visit of Queen Elizabeth II. T **263** and similar square designs. P 12½.

1078	38p. multicoloured	80	60
1079	40p. black and yellow	80	60
1080	47p. multicoloured	1·00	1·00
1081	£1 black	2·50	3·75
1078/1081 *Set of 4*		4·50	5·50
MS1082 95×110 mm. £1·50 black		3·75	4·50

Designs: 38p. T **263**; 40p. Queen Elizabeth holding out keys; 47p. Queen and Duke of Edinburgh in car; £1 Queen, Prince Charles and Princess Anne with members of British armed forces; £1·50 Queen waving with Duke of Edinburgh.

264 Scoring a Goal

265 Landing at St Aubin, 1944

(Des Lee Montgomery. Litho Cartor)

2004 (6 June). European Football Championship 2004, Portugal. T **264** and similar square designs. Multicoloured. P 12½.

1083	30p. Type **264**	50	30
1084	40p. Two defenders blocking a goal attempt.	65	75
1085	40p. Overhead kick	65	75
1086	£1 Player performing header	1·75	3·00
1083/1086 *Set of 4*		3·25	4·25

MS1087 Two sheets. (a) 102×77 mm. £1·50 Player celebrating with arms in air (51×39 *mm*) P 13. (b) 105×105 mm. (circular). Nos. 1083/1086 *Set of 2 sheets*.. 4·75 7·00

(Des Anselmo Torres. Litho Cartor)

2004 (6 June). 60th Anniversary of D-Day Landings. T **265** and similar horiz designs. Each black, brownish-black and red. P 13×13½.

1088	38p. Type **265**	1·40	85
1089	40p. Cruiser tank Mk VIII Cromwell	1·40	85
1090	47p. Handley Page Halifax aeroplane	1·60	1·60
1091	£1 HMS *Belfast*	3·00	4·00
1088/1091 *Set of 4*		6·50	7·00

MS1092 170×100 mm. Nos. 1088/1091 6·50 7·00

266 Union Flag

267 Mallow-leaved Bindweed

(Des Stephen Perera. Litho Cartor)

2004 (10 Sept). 300th Anniversary of British Gibraltar (2nd series). Elton John Tercentenary Concert. Circular sheet 105×105 mm. P 13×13½.

MS1093 **266** £1·20 multicoloured 3·00 3·50
The stamp in No. **MS**1093 is similar in design to the £1·20 stamp in No. **MS**1077.

(Des Stephen Perera (3p., 15p., 53p., £1·60), or Antonia Eenthoven and Anselmo Torres (others). Litho B.D.T.)

2004 (10 Sept)–**06**. Wild Flowers. T **267** and similar vert designs. Multicoloured. P 13½.

1094	1p. Type **267**	15	65
	a. Booklet pane. No. 1094 with margins all round	15	
1095	2p. Gibraltar Sea Lavender	25	65
	a. Booklet pane. No. 1095 with margins all round	25	
1095*b*	3p. Gibraltar Restharrow (20.2.06)	75	1·25
1096	5p. Gibraltar Chickweed	30	40
	a. Booklet pane. No. 1096 with margins all round	30	
1097	(7p.) Romulea	45	20
	a. Booklet pane. No. 1097 with margins all round	45	
1098	10p. Common Centaury	60	30
	a. Booklet pane. No. 1098 with margins all round	60	
1099	(12p.) Pyramidal Orchid	75	75
	a. Booklet pane. No. 1099 with margins all round	75	
1099*b*	15p. Paper-white Narcissus (20.2.06)	1·50	75
1100	(28p.) Friars Cowl	1·25	60
	a. Booklet pane. No. 1100 with margins all round	1·25	
1101	(38p.) Corn Poppy	1·40	85
	a. Booklet pane. No. 1101 with margins all round	1·40	
1102	(40p.) Giant Tangier Fennel	1·40	65
	a. Booklet pane. No. 1102 with margins all round	1·40	
1103	(47p.) Snapdragon	1·75	1·10
	a. Booklet pane. No. 1103 with margins all round	1·75	

1104	50p. Common Gladiolus	1·75	1·75
	a. Booklet pane. No. 1104 with margins all round	1·75	
1104*b*	53p. Gibraltar Campion (20.2.06)	3·00	3·25
1105	£1 Yellow Horned Poppy	3·50	4·00
	a. Booklet pane. No. 1105 with margins all round	3·50	
1105*b*	£1·60 Sea Daffodil (20.2.06)	6·50	7·00
1106	£3 Gibraltar Candytuft	9·50	12·00
	a. Booklet pane. No. 1106 with margins all round	9·50	
1094/1106 *Set of 17*		30·00	32·00

Nos. 1094/1095, 1096/1099, 1100/1104, 1105 and 1106 were available as single stamps and also from £6·40 stamp booklets, No. SB14.
Nos. 1095*b*, 1099*b*, 1104*b* and 1105*b* are sheet stamps.
Nos. 1097 and 1099/1103 are inscribed 'G', 'G1', 'S', 'UK', 'E' and 'U' and were initially sold for 7p., 12p., 28p., 38p., 40p. and 47p. respectively.

268 Father Christmas

(Des Stephen Perera. Litho Cartor)

2004 (12 Nov). Christmas. Decorations. T **268** and similar square designs. Multicoloured. P 13.

1107	7p. Type **268**	30	20
1108	28p. Cherub	1·25	60
1109	38p. Red star	1·40	80
1110	40p. Gold conical tree	1·40	85
1111	47p. Red bauble	1·60	1·00
1112	53p. Gold star	1·90	4·00
1107/1112 *Set of 6*		7·00	7·00

269 Ferrari F2003 GA

(Des Stephen Perera. Litho B.D.T.)

2004 (12 Nov). Ferrari. T **269** and similar horiz designs. Multicoloured. P 15×14.

1113	5p. Type **269**	30	40
1114	5p. F2004	30	40
1115	30p. F2001	60	80
1116	30p. F2002	60	80
1117	75p. F399	1·40	2·50
1118	75p. F1-2000	1·40	2·50
1113/1118 *Set of 6*		4·25	6·75

MS1119 161×116 mm. Nos. 1113/1118 4·25 6·75
Nos. 1113/1118 were each available in sheetlets of five with an enlarged, illustrated bottom margin.

270 Royal Marine guarding Nelson's Body

(Des John Batchelor. Litho Cartor)

2005 (31 Jan). Bicentenary of the Battle of Trafalgar (1st issue). T **270** and similar multicoloured designs. P 13½.

1120	38p. Type **270**	2·00	75
1121	40p. HMS *Entreprenante*	2·00	85
1122	47p. Admiral Nelson (*vert*)	2·00	1·50
1123	£1·60 HMS *Victory*	6·00	8·00
1120/1123 *Set of 4*		11·00	10·00

MS1124 120×80 mm. £2 HMS *Victory* (44×44 *mm*) 14·00 14·00
Nos. 1120/1123 were each printed in sheetlets of six with illustrated margins.
Nos. 1120/1124 contain traces of powdered wood from HMS *Victory*.
See also Nos. **MS**1144/**MS**1145.

271 Spinach Pie

272 Churchill giving Victory Salute

(Des Stephen Perrera. Litho B.D.T.)

2005 (31 Mar). Europa. Gastronomy. T **271** and similar vert designs. Multicoloured. P 14½×15.

1125	47p. Type **271**	1·75	2·00
1126	47p. Grilled Sea-Bass	1·75	2·00
1127	47p. Veal 'Birds'	1·75	2·00
1128	47p. Sherry Trifle	1·75	2·00
1125/1128 *Set of 4*		6·25	7·25

Nos. 1125/1128 were each printed in sheetlets of ten with enlarged illustrated right margins.

(Des Anselmo Torres. Litho B.D.T.)

2005 (8 May). 60th Anniversary of VE Day. T **272** and similar vert designs. Multicoloured. P 14×15.

1129	38p. Type **272**	1·40	90
1130	40p. Family with Union Jack flags	1·40	90
1131	47p. VE Day celebrations	1·60	1·50
1132	£1 Returning Gibraltar people on dockside	3·75	5·50
1129/1132 *Set of 4*		7·25	8·00
MS1133 150×100 mm. Nos. 1129/1132		7·25	8·00

Nos. 1129/1132 were also available in sheetlets of four with enlarged illustrated right margin, from a limited-edition pack.

273 *Circassia*

(Des Simon Williams and Anselmo Torres. Litho Cartor)

2005 (17 June). Cruise Ships (1st series). T **273** and similar horiz designs. Multicoloured. P 13×13½.

1134	38p. Type **273**	1·60	90
1135	40p. *Nevasa*	1·60	90
1136	47p. *Black Prince*	1·75	1·50
1137	£1 *Arcadia*	4·00	6·00
1134/1137 *Set of 4*		8·00	8·50
MS1138 150×85 mm. Nos. 1134/1137		8·00	8·50

See also Nos. 1180/**MS**1184, 1207/**MS**1211 and 1286/**MS**1290.

274 Early and Modern Police Officers

275 Pope John Paul II

(Des Stephen Perrera. Litho B.D.T.)

2005 (17 June). Anniversaries. T **274** and similar horiz designs. Multicoloured. P 15×14½.

1139	38p. Type **274** (175th Anniversary of Royal Gibraltar Police)	2·00	1·00
1140	47p. Skull, plate and ceramic Horses (75th Anniversary of Gibraltar Museum)	1·50	1·00
1141	£1 Charter of Justice (175th Anniversary)	3·75	5·50
1139/1141 *Set of 3*		6·50	6·75

The backs of Nos. 1139/1141 are printed with a brief description of the subject of the stamp.

(Des Andrew Robinson. Litho B.D.T.)

2005 (15 July). Pope John Paul II Commemoration. P 14½×15.

1142	**275** 75p. multicoloured	2·50	3·00

No. 1142 was printed in sheetlets of six stamps with an enlarged illustrated left margin.

276 Map of Europe and 1979 Europa 12p. Stamp

(Des Stephen Perrera. Litho and die-stamped B.D.T.)

2005 (30 Sept). 50th Anniversary of Europa Stamps. P 14½.

1143	**276** £5 multicoloured	10·00	14·00

277 *Death of Nelson* (William Devis)

278 Two Angels

(Des Anselmo Torres. Litho Cartor (No. **MS**1144) or Lowe-Martin (No. **MS**1145))

2005 (21 Oct). Bicentenary of the Battle of Trafalgar (2nd issue) and Death of Admiral Lord Nelson. T **277** and similar horiz designs. Multicoloured. P 13½.

MS1144 120×80 mm. £1 Type **277**	4·50	5·00
MS1145 170×75 mm. £1 As Type **277**, but 50×31 mm together with £1 stamp from Isle of Man No. **MS**1264	6·00	7·50

No. **MS**1145 was also issued by Isle of Man.

(Des Stephen Perrera. Litho Cartor)

2005 (21 Oct). Christmas. Angels. T **278** and similar vert designs. Multicoloured. P 13½×13.

1146	7p. Type **278**	25	20
1147	38p. Angel with children by Christmas tree	1·00	80
1148	40p. Angel with toys	1·00	80
1149	47p. Angel with hymn book and top of Christmas tree	1·50	1·50
1150	53p. Angel with basket of fruit	1·75	3·50
1146/1150 *Set of 5*		5·00	6·00
MS1151 168×86 mm. Nos. 1146/1150		5·00	7·00

279 Giant Devil Ray

280 Queen Elizabeth II

(Des Anselmo Torres. Litho Cartor)

2006 (20 Feb). Endangered Species. Giant Devil Ray (*Mobula mobular*). T **279** and similar horiz designs. Multicoloured. P 13×13½.

1152	38p. Type **279**	1·25	1·75
	a. Strip of 4. Nos. 1152/1155	6·25	8·50
1153	40p. Giant Devil Ray and trail of bubbles	1·40	1·75
1154	47p. Two Giant Devil Rays	1·75	2·00
1155	£1 Upperside of Giant Devil Ray	2·75	4·00
1152/1155 *Set of 4*		6·25	8·50

Nos. 1152/1155 were printed together, *se-tenant*, in horizontal and vertical strips of four stamps in sheets of 16.

(Des Stephen Perera. Litho B.D.T.)

2006 (31 Mar). 80th Birthday of Queen Elizabeth II. T **280** and similar horiz designs, each showing 1950s and more recent photograph. Multicoloured. P 15×14.

1156	38p. Type **280**	2·00	2·00
	a. Block of 4. Nos. 1156/1159	8·00	8·50
1157	40p. In evening dress, c. 1955 and wearing purple hat	2·00	2·00
1158	47p. Smelling carnation, c. 1955 and wearing yellow hat	2·00	2·00
1159	£1 Princess Elizabeth, c. 1950 and Queen wearing red and black hat	3·00	3·50
1156/1159 Set of 4		8·00	8·50
MS1160 Two sheets, each 142×82 mm. (a) Nos. 1156 and 1159. (b) Nos. 1157/1158 Set of 2 sheets		7·00	8·50

Nos. 1156/1159 were printed together, se-tenant, in sheetlets of eight stamps with enlarged illustrated left margins.

281 Uruguay

282 Children Making Model Building

(Des Stephen Perera. Litho B.D.T.)

2006 (4 May). World Cup Football Championship, Germany. T **281** and similar square designs showing children with flags painted on faces. Multicoloured. P 15.

1161	38p. Type **281**	75	1·10
	a. Sheetlet of 7. Nos. 1161/1167	4·75	7·00
1162	38p. Italy	75	1·10
1163	38p. Germany	75	1·10
1164	38p. Brazil	75	1·10
1165	38p. England	75	1·10
1166	38p. Argentina	75	1·10
1167	38p. France	75	1·10
1161/1167 Set of 7		4·75	7·00

Nos. 1161/1167 were printed together, se-tenant, in sheetlets of seven stamps with enlarged illustrated margins.

(Des Holli Conger and Stephen Perera. Litho B.D.T.)

2006 (30 June). Europa. Integration. T **282** and similar horiz designs. Multicoloured. P 13×13½.

1168	47p. Type **282**	1·50	1·75
1169	47p. Boy and girl	1·50	1·75
1170	47p. Children playing football	1·50	1·75
1171	47p. Children playing music	1·50	1·75
1168/1171 Set of 4		5·50	6·25

Nos. 1168/1171 were each printed in sheetlets of ten stamps with enlarged illustrated right margins.

283 Cornwallis

284 Saro A21 Windhover Flying Boat, 1931

(Des John Batchelor. Litho B.D.T.)

2006 (15 Sept). Bicentenary of the Gibraltar Packet Agency. T **283** and similar horiz designs showing packet ships of the 1800s. Multicoloured. P 15×14.

1172	8p. Type **283**	60	35
1173	40p. Meteor	2·00	1·25
1174	42p. Carteret	2·00	1·25
1175	68p. Prince Regent	3·00	6·00
1172/1175 Set of 4		7·00	8·00

(Des John Batchelor. Litho B.D.T.)

2006 (15 Sept). 75th Anniversary of Gibraltar Airmail Service. T **284** and similar horiz designs. Multicoloured. P 15×14.

1176	8p. Type **284**	75	30
1177	40p. Vickers Vanguard, 1959	2·50	90
1178	49p. Vickers Viscount	3·00	2·00
1179	£1·60 Boeing 737	7·50	10·00
1176/1179 Set of 4		12·50	12·00

285 Coral

286 St Nicholas and Christmas Tree

(Des Simon Williams. Litho Lowe-Martin, Canada)

2006 (15 Sept). Cruise Ships (2nd series). T **285** and similar horiz designs. Multicoloured. P 13.

1180	40p. Type **285**	1·75	1·25
1181	42p. Legend of the Seas	1·90	1·40
1182	66p. Saga Ruby	3·25	3·75
1183	78p. Costa Concordia	3·50	6·00
1180/1183 Set of 4		9·50	11·00
MS1184 100×80 mm. Nos. 1180/1183		9·50	11·00

(Des Stephen Perera. Litho Lowe-Martin, Canada)

2006 (1 Nov). Christmas. St Nicholas. T **286** and similar vert designs. Multicoloured. P 13.

1185	8p. Type **286**	40	15
1186	40p. St Nicholas (in red) carrying presents	1·50	80
1187	42p. St Nicholas giving present to young girl	1·60	85
1188	49p. St Nicholas (in green) carrying sack of toys	2·00	1·75
1189	55p. St Nicholas (in white) carrying sack and small Christmas tree	2·25	4·25
1185/1189 Set of 5		7·00	7·00
MS1190 165×80 mm. Nos. 1185/1189. P 13×12½		7·00	7·50

287 Navigational Instruments

288 Engagement, 1947

(Des Christian Hook and Stephen Perera. Litho Lowe-Martin, Canada)

2006 (1 Nov). 500th Death Anniversary of Christopher Columbus. T **287** and similar multicoloured designs. P 13.

1191	40p. Type **287**	1·50	1·25
1192	42p. Columbus writing report of voyage, 1492	1·50	1·25
1193	66p. Santa Maria	2·50	3·25
1194	78p. Columbus and Arawak chief	3·00	4·50
1191/1194 Set of 4		7·75	9·25
MS1195 95×74 mm. £1·60 Columbus' fleet, 1492 (47×47 mm). P 13½		6·50	7·50

Nos. 1191/1194 were each printed in separate sheetlets of six stamps with enlarged illustrated margins.

(Des Stephen Perera. Litho Lowe-Martin, Canada)

2007 (28 Feb). Diamond Wedding of Queen Elizabeth II and Prince Philip. T **288** and similar vert designs. Multicoloured. P 13½.

1196	40p. Type **288**	1·50	1·25
1197	42p. Wedding photograph, 1947	1·60	1·40
1198	66p. Silver Wedding anniversary, 1972	2·40	3·00
1199	78p. Ruby Anniversary, 1987	2·75	4·25
1196/1199 Set of 4		7·50	9·00
MS1200 105×105 mm. £1·60 Wedding photograph with bridesmaids and pageboys, 1947 (diamond shape, 84×83 mm). P 13½×13		5·75	7·00

Nos. 1196/1199 were each printed in sheetlets of three stamps with enlarged margins.

No. **MS**1200 is perforated 13½ on the two left-hand edges and 13 on the two right edges.

289 Flag of Belgium

(Des Stephen Perera. Litho B.D.T.)

2007 (28 Feb). 50th Anniversary of the Treaty of Rome. Sheet 137×100 mm containing T **289** and similar horiz designs showing National Flags. Multicoloured. P 15×14.
MS1201 40p.×6 Type **289**; Germany; France; Italy;
Luxembourg; Netherlands .... 3·75   6·00
The stamps within No. **MS**1201 were arranged in two vertical strips of three separated by a large illustrated gutter.

290 Princess Diana

(Des Stephen Perera. Litho Lowe-Martin, Canada)

2007 (31 Mar). Tenth Death Anniversary of Princess Diana. T **290** and similar square designs. Multicoloured. P 13½.
1202   8p. Type **290**................................... 40   25
1203   40p. Seen full-face, eyes looking sideways...... 1·10   90
1204   42p. In half profile, smiling................... 1·10   90
1205   £1·60 Seen full-face, smiling................... 4·00   5·75
1202/1205 Set of 4 .... 6·00   7·00
MS1206 165×92 mm. Nos. 1202/1204 .... 6·00   7·00
Nos. 1202/1205 were each printed in sheetlets of six stamps with enlarged margins.

(Des Simon Williams and Stephen Perera. Litho B.D.T.)

2007 (15 May). Cruise Ships (3rd series). Horiz designs as T **285**. Multicoloured. P 15×14.
1207   40p. Oriana .... 2·00   1·25
1208   42p. Oceana .... 2·00   1·40
1209   66p. Queen Elizabeth 2 .... 3·50   3·75
1210   78p. Queen Mary 2 .... 4·00   6·00
1207/1210 Set of 4 .... 10·50   11·00
MS1211 168×67 mm. Nos. 1207/1210 .... 10·50   11·00

291 Gibraltar Scout, 1908

292 Postcard from Fez, 1907

(Des Christian Hook and Stephen Perera. Litho Lowe-Martin, Canada)

2007 (30 June). Europa. Centenary of World Scouting. T **291** and similar vert designs. Multicoloured. P 13.
1212   8p. Type **291**.............................. 40   30
1213   40p. Scout, 1950s .... 1·10   1·00
1214   42p. Sea scout, 1980s .... 1·10   1·00
1215   £1 Modern scout .... 3·00   5·00
1212/1215 Set of 4 .... 5·00   6·50

(Des Anselmo Torres. Litho B.D.T.)

2007 (26 Sept). Gibraltar Postal Anniversaries. T **292** and similar horiz designs. Multicoloured. P 15×14.
1216   8p. Type **292** (Centenary of Gibraltar
         relinquishing control of British Postal
         Service in Morocco) 55   30
1217   40p. Gibraltar datestamp of Packet Agency,
         1857 (150th Anniversary of Gibraltar
         Post Office)................................ 2·00   1·25
1218   42p. Letter with British postage stamps
         cancelled 'G' (150th Anniversary of the
         introduction of British postage stamps
         in Gibraltar)............................... 2·00   1·40

1219   £1 Earliest known letter from Morocco
         via Gibraltar (150th Anniversary of first
         British Postal Agency in Morocco)............ 4·50   6·00
1216/1219 Set of 4 .... 8·00   8·00
Nos. 1216/1219 have information about the anniversaries commemorated printed on the reverse (gummed) side of the stamps.

293 Bear and Cub feeding on Dolphin   294 Stork ('New baby')

(Des Christian Hook and Stephen Perera. Litho Cartor)

2007 (26 Sept). Prehistoric Wildlife of Gibraltar. T **293** and similar vert designs. Multicoloured. P 13.
1220   8p. Type **293**.............................. 50   40
         a. Booklet pane. No. 1220 with margins all
            round 50
         b. Booklet pane. Nos. 1220/1225........... 16·00
1221   40p. Eagle Owl .... 2·00   1·50
         a. Booklet pane. No. 1221 with margins all
            round .... 2·00
1222   42p. Great Auk and Eagle .... 2·00   1·60
         a. Booklet pane. No. 1222 with margins all
            round .... 2·00
1223   55p. Red Deer and Boar .... 2·00   2·50
         a. Booklet pane. No. 1223 with margins all
            round .... 2·00
1224   78p. Wolf and Vulture feeding on Wild
            Horse................................... 3·00   5·00
         a. Booklet pane. No. 1224 with margins all
            round .... 3·00
1220/1224 Set of 5 .... 8·50   10·00
MS1225 154×100 mm. £2 Ibex......................... 8·50   9·50
         a. Booklet pane. As No. **MS**1225, but
            150×113 mm. .... 8·50
Booklet panes Nos. 1220a and 1221a/**MS**1225a contain a single stamp within a larger illustration.

(Des Holli Conger and Stephen Perera. Litho Lowe-Martin, Canada)

2007 (26 Sept). YouStamps. T **294** and similar square designs. Multicoloured. P 12½×13.
1226   (8p.) Type **294**............................ 40   50
1227   (8p.) Lion, Sheep and Dog wearing party hats
            ('Let's celebrate') 40   50
1228   (8p.) Crab finding heart written in beach sand
            ('With love') 40   50
1229   (8p.) Heart enclosed in wedding ring
            ('Commitment')......................... 40   50
1230   (8p.) Dolphins and Rock of Gibraltar ('Greetings
            from Gibraltar') 40   50
1231   (40p.) As Type **294** .... 1·40   1·60
1232   (40p.) As No. 1227 .... 1·40   1·60
1233   (40p.) As No. 1228 .... 1·40   1·60
1234   (40p.) As No. 1229 .... 1·40   1·60
1235   (40p.) As No. 1230 .... 1·40   1·60
1226/1235 Set of 10 .... 8·00   9·50
Nos. 1226/1230 are inscr 'G' and sold for 8p. each. Nos. 1231/1235 are inscr 'E' and sold for 40p. each.
Nos. 1226/1235 were each issued in sheets of 20 stamps, each stamp accompanied by a se-tenant greetings label. These stamps were also available with blank se-tenant labels to which personal photographs could be added.

295 Rock of Gibraltar   296 Joseph

(Des Stephen Perera. Litho Cartor)

2007 (1 Oct). Panoramic Views of Gibraltar. T **295** and similar horiz designs. Multicoloured. P 13½.

1236	40p. Type **295**	1·40	1·25
1237	42p. Beach and Rock of Gibraltar	1·60	1·40
1238	55p. Rock of Gibraltar at sunset	2·00	2·50
1239	78p. Town and Rock of Gibraltar	3·25	4·50
1236/1239 Set of 4		7·50	8·75
MS1240 114×67 mm. £1·70 Gibraltar Trinity Lighthouse (52×20 mm). P 13		7·50	8·00

No. 1236 is inscr 'sepac'.

(Des Stephen Perera. Litho Lowe-Martin, Canada)

2007 (2 Nov). Christmas. Porcelain Figurines. T **296** and similar vert designs. Multicoloured. P 13½×13.

1241	8p. Type **296**	40	25
1242	8p. Baby Jesus	40	25
1243	40p. Mary	1·25	80
1244	42p. King Melchoir	1·25	90
1245	49p. King Balthasar	1·40	1·75
1246	55p. King Gaspar	1·50	3·25
1241/1246 Set of 6		5·50	6·50
MS1247 124×105 mm. Nos. 1241/1246		5·50	7·00

Nos. 1241/1247 have biblical quotations printed on the reverse (gummed) side of the stamps.

297 Woodchat Shrike

298 Short 184 and Saro London

(Des Jonathan Pointer and Stephen Perera. Litho B.D.T. (Nos. 1252a, 1253a, 1254a, 1258a/1258b, 1259d/1259d) or Lowe-Martin, Canada (others))

2008 (15 Feb)–**12**. Birds of the Rock. T **297** and similar vert designs. Multicoloured. P 13 (1252a, 1253a, 1254a, 1258a/1258b, 1259, 1259b, 1259d, 1260), 13×13½ (1252a, 1259a, 1259c) or 13×12½ (others).

1248	1p. Type **297**	30	60
1249	2p. Balearic Shearwater (*Puffinus Mauretanicus*)	35	70
1250	5p. Eagle Owl (*Bubo Bubo*)	1·00	75
1251	(8p.) European Bee-eater (*Merops Apiaster*)	1·25	35
1252	10p. Razorbill (*Alca Torda*)	1·50	1·00
1252a	10p. Black Stork (*Ciconia Nigra*) (16.9.09)	1·00	1·00
1253	(30p.) Egyptian Vulture (*Neophron Percnopterus*)	2·00	85
1253a	(30p.) Red-necked Nightjar (*Caprimulgus Ruficollis*) (16.4.12)	2·00	85
1254	(40p.) Blue Rock Thrush (*Monticola Solitarius*)	2·50	1·10
1254a	(42p.) Little Owl (*Athene Noctua*) (16.4.12)	2·75	1·25
1255	(42p.) Hoopoe (*Upupa Epops*)	2·75	1·25
1256	(49p.) Bonelli's Eagle (*Hieraaëtus Fasciatus*)	2·75	1·25
1257	50p. Greater Flamingo (*Phoenicopterus Roseus*)	2·75	1·50
1258	55p. Mediterranean Shag (*Phalacrocorax Aristotelis Desmarestii*)	2·75	1·50
1258a	59p. Barbary Partridge (*Alectoris Barbara*) (20.10.10)	2·75	2·25
1258b	76p. Ortolan Bunting (*Emberiza Hortulana*) (20.10.10)	3·00	3·00
1259	£1 Honey Buzzard (*Pernis Apivorus*) (34×47 mm)	5·00	4·00
1259a	£2 Northern Gannet (*Morus Bassanus*) (35×48 mm) (16.9.09)	6·50	8·00
1259b	£2 Pallid Swift (*Apus Pallidus*) (20.10.10)	6·50	8·00
1259c	£3 Osprey (*Pandion Haliaetus*) (35×38 mm) (16.9.09) 100	10·00	12·00
1259d	£3·44 Spotted Flycatcher (*Muscicapa striata*) (16.4.12)	12·00	14·00
1260	£5 Lesser Kestrel (*Falco naumanni*) (34×47 mm)	16·00	17·00
1248/1260 Set of 22		75·00	75·00

No. 1251 was inscribed 'G' (for Gibraltar Postage) and was originally sold for 8p.

Nos. 1253/1253a were inscribed 'S' (for Surface Mail International) and were originally sold for 30p.

Nos. 1254/1254a were inscribed 'UK' (for United Kingdom) and were originally sold for 40p. (No. 1254) or 42p. (No. 1254a).

No. 1255 was inscribed 'E' (for Europe) and was originally sold for 42p.

No. 1256 was inscribed 'U' (for mail outside Europe) and was originally sold for 49p.

See also Nos. 1545/1546.

(Des John Bachelor or Stephen Perera. Litho B.D.T.)

2008 (15 Mar). 90th Anniversary of the Royal Air Force. T **298** and similar vert designs. Multicoloured. P 14×15.

1261	40p. Type **298**	3·25	2·50
1262	40p. Spitfire IV and Hurricane IIc	3·25	2·50
1263	42p. Beaufighter II and Lancaster TS III	3·25	2·50
1264	42p. Hunter Mk.6 and Shackleton MR2	3·25	2·50
1265	49p. Vulcan and Mosquito	3·25	3·25
1266	49p. Tornado GR4 and Jaguar GR3	3·25	2·50
1261/1266 Set of 6		18·00	15·00
MS1267 107×75 mm. £2 Felixstowe F.3 of No. 265 Squadron on anti-submarine patrol, Gibraltar, 1918		13·00	13·00

299 HMS *Minerve*

300 Sir Winston Churchill

(Des John Bachelor and Stephen Perera. Litho B.D.T.)

2008 (15 Mar). 250th Birth Anniversary of Admiral Lord Nelson. T **299** and similar multicoloured designs. P 14×15.

1268	40p. Type **299**	2·50	2·50
1269	40p. HMS *Agamemnon*	2·50	2·50
1270	42p. HMS *Vanguard*	2·50	2·50
1271	42p. HMS *Captain*	2·50	2·50
1272	49p. HMS *Victory*	2·50	3·00
1273	49p. HMS *Amphion*	2·50	3·00
1268/1273 Set of 6		13·50	14·50
MS1274 120×80 mm. £2 Birthplace at Burnham Thorpe, Norfolk (*horiz*). P 15×14		8·00	9·00

Nos. 1268/1273 were each printed in sheetlets of six stamps with enlarged illustrated margins.

(Des Robert Papp and Stephen Perera. Litho B.D.T.)

2008 (1 June). Europa. Writing Letters. T **300** and similar vert designs. Multicoloured. P 14×14½.

1275	10p. Type **300**	75	50
1276	42p. Lord Nelson	1·75	1·25
1277	44p. President John F. Kennedy	1·75	1·50
1278	£1 Mahatma Gandhi	5·50	6·50
1275/1278 Set of 4		8·75	8·75

301 *Christ the Redeemer* Statue, Rio de Janeiro, Brazil

302 Launch of *Apollo 11*

(Des Stephen Perera. Litho B.D.T.)

2008 (1 June). The New Seven Wonders of the World. T **301** and similar vert designs. Multicoloured. P 14×14½.

1279	8p. Type **301**	50	35
1280	8p. Colosseum, Rome, Italy	50	35
1281	38p. Petra, Jordan	1·75	1·75
1282	38p. The Great Wall of China	1·75	1·75
1283	40p. Machu Picchu, Peru	1·75	1·75
1284	40p. Chichen Itza	1·75	1·75
1285	66p. Taj Mahal, India	6·00	6·00
1279/1285 Set of 7		12·50	12·50

(Des Simon Williams and Stephen Perera. Litho Lowe-Martin)

2008 (15 Sept). Cruise Ships (4th series). Horiz designs as T **285**. Multicoloured. P 13.

1286	40p. *Century*	2·00	1·25
1287	42p. *Grand Princess*	2·00	1·25
1288	66p. *Queen Victoria*	3·00	3·75
1289	78p. *Costa Mediterranea*	4·00	5·50
1286/1289 Set of 4		10·00	10·50
MS1290 168×66 mm. Nos. 1286/1289		10·00	11·00

(Des Stephen Perera. Litho Lowe-Martin, Canada)

2008 (15 Sept). 50th Anniversary of NASA (US National Aeronautics and Space Administration). Sheet 144×98 mm containing T **302** and similar square designs. Multicoloured. P 13.
MS1291 10p. Type **302**; 17p. The Earth seen from the
Moon; 42p. Lunar module; £2 US flag on the Moon ....   9·50   10·00

303 Gibraltar Volunteer Corps, World War I

304 *When Santa got stuck in a Chimney*

(Des Jonathan Pointer and Stephen Perera. Litho B.D.T.)

2008 (11 Nov). Royal Gibraltar Regiment. T **303** and similar vert designs. Multicoloured. P 14×14½.

1292	10p. Type **303**	60	60
1293	10p. Gibraltar Defence Force, World War II	60	60
1294	10p. Buena Vista Barracks (National Service)	60	60
1295	42p. Thomson's Battery 1958–1991 (Gibraltar Regiment)	1·50	1·50
1296	42p. Infantry Company 1958–1999 (Gibraltar Regiment)	1·50	1·50
1297	44p. Air Defence Troop 1958–1991 (Gibraltar Regiment)	1·50	1·50
1298	44p. 'Guarding the Rock' (Royal Gibraltar Regiment)	1·50	1·50
1299	51p. Training African Peacekeepers (Royal Gibraltar Regiment)	2·00	2·25
1300	51p. Operations in Iraq (Royal Gibraltar Regiment)	2·00	2·25
1301	£2 Operations in Afghanistan (Royal Gibraltar Regiment)	7·00	9·00
1292/1301 *Set of 10*		17·00	19·00

(Des Olympia Reyes and Stephen Perera. Litho Cartor)

2008 (11 Nov). Christmas. Christmas Songs and Carols. T **304** and similar square designs. Multicoloured. P 12½.

1302	10p. Type **304**	45	20
1303	42p. *Rudolph the Red-nosed Reindeer*	1·50	1·25
1304	44p. *Oh Christmas Tree*	1·50	1·25
1305	51p. *Away in a Manger*	1·90	1·90
1306	59p. *Jingle Bells*	2·25	3·75
1302/1306 *Set of 5*		7·00	7·50

305 Catherine of Aragon

306 Virgin and Child (shrine of Our Lady of Europe at Europa Point, Gibraltar)

(Des Martin Hargreaves and Stephen Perera. Litho Lowe-Martin, Canada)

2009 (30 Jan). 500th Anniversary of the Coronation of King Henry VIII. T **305** and similar square designs. Multicoloured. P 12½.

1307	10p. Type **305**	85	75
1308	10p. Anne Boleyn	85	75
1309	42p. Jane Seymour	2·25	2·00
1310	42p. Anne of Cleves	2·25	2·00
1311	44p. Catherine Howard	2·25	2·00
1312	44p. Katherine Parr	2·25	2·00
1313	51p. King Henry VIII	2·75	3·25
1314	51p. *Mary Rose* (galleon)	2·75	3·25
1307/1314 *Set of 8*		14·50	14·50
MS1315 120×80 mm. £2 King Henry VIII and Hampton Court Palace		8·50	9·00

(Des Stephen Perera. Litho B.D.T.)

2009 (10 Feb). 700th Anniversary of Our Lady of Europe. P 14×14½.
1316	**306**	61p. multicoloured	3·50	3·75

No. 1316 was printed in sheetlets of four stamps with enlarged illustrated right margins.
Stamps of a similar design were issued by Vatican City.

307 Short S27

308 Peter Phillips

(Des Jon Bachelor and Stephen Perera. Litho B.D.T.)

2009 (15 Mar). Centenary of Naval Aviation. T **307** and similar vert designs. Multicoloured. P 14×14½.

1317	42p. Type **307**	3·00	2·75
1318	42p. Morane-Saulnier Type L and Zeppelin LZ 37	3·00	2·75
1319	42p. Short Type 184 seaplane	3·00	2·75
1320	42p. SS Type Non Rigid Airship	3·00	2·75
1321	42p. Caudron Gill	3·00	2·75
1322	42p. Avro 504	3·00	2·75
1317/1322 *Set of 6*		16·00	15·00
MS1323 120×80 mm. £2 Short Type 184 seaplane hoisted over stern of First World War seaplane carrier and Hawker Siddeley Sea Harrier on ramp of modern Invincible Class CVS aircraft carrier		11·00	12·00

The stamp within No. **MS**1323 has text printed on the back describing the aircraft and ships depicted on the miniature sheet.

(Des Stephen Perera. Litho Lowe-Martin, Canada)

2009 (1 May). Queen Elizabeth II's Grandchildren. T **308** and similar horiz designs. Multicoloured. P 12½.

1324	42p. Type **308**	1·75	1·75
1325	42p. Zara Phillips	1·75	1·75
1326	42p. Prince William of Wales	1·75	1·75
1327	42p. Prince Henry of Wales	1·75	1·75
1328	42p. Princess Beatrice of York	1·75	1·75
1329	42p. Princess Eugenie of York	1·75	1·75
1330	42p. Lady Louise Windsor	1·75	1·75
1331	42p. Viscount Severn	1·75	1·75
1324/1331 *Set of 8*		12·50	12·50

309 Aristotle (early Greek philosopher and scientist)

310 Road to the Frontier

(Des Robert Papp and Stephen Pereira. Litho Lowe-Martin)

2009 (1 June). Europa. International Year of Astronomy. T **309** and similar vert designs. Multicoloured. P 13×12½.

1332	10p. Type **309**	40	30
1333	42p. Galileo Galilei (astronomer, mathematician and philosopher)	1·75	1·25
1334	44p. Nicolaus Copernicus (astronomer)	2·75	1·90
1335	£1·50 Sir Isaac Newton (scientist and mathematician)	4·50	7·00
1332/1335 *Set of 4*		8·50	9·50

(Des Stephen Perera. Litho B.D.T.)

2009 (16 Sept). Old Views of Gibraltar (1st series). T **310** and similar horiz designs showing scenes from postcards. Multicoloured. P 14×15.

1336	10p. Type **310**	50	30
1337	42p. Catalan Bay village	1·75	1·40
1338	44p. The Rock of Gibraltar	1·75	1·40
1339	51p. The Moorish Castle	2·25	2·25
1340	59p. South Barracks	2·50	4·00
1336/1340 *Set of 5*		8·00	8·50
MS1341 163×79 mm. 10p. Garrison Library; 42p. The Piazza; 44p. The Piazza Casemates; £1 Main Street		7·25	8·00

See also Nos. 1470/**MS**1475, 1500/**MS**1505, 1508*a* and 1571/**MS**1576.

310a Charles Darwin, *Zoology of the Beagle* and *Voyages of the Adventure and Beagle*

311 Santa Tree Decoration

(Des Stephen Perera. Litho Lowe-Martin, Canada)

2009 (12 Nov). Birth Bicentenary of Charles Darwin (naturalist and evolutionary theorist). T **310a** and similar vert designs showing portraits of Charles Darwin and extracts from his books. Multicoloured. P 14×14½.

1341*a*	10p. Type **310a**	60	30
1341*b*	42p. Charles Darwin and *The Descent of Man*	1·75	1·25
1341*c*	44p. Charles Darwin and *Animals and Plants under Domestication*	1·75	1·40
1341*d*	£2 Charles Darwin and *On the Origin of Species*	7·50	9·50
1341*a*/1341*d* Set of 4		10·50	11·00
MS1341*e* 126×86 mm. £2·42 Charles Darwin, The Mount, Shrewsbury (his birthplace) and *On the Origin of Species*		10·00	11·00

(Des Stephen Perera. Litho Cartor)

2009 (12 Nov). Christmas. T **311** and similar vert designs. Multicoloured. P 13½×13.

1342	10p. Type **311**	50	30
1343	42p. Angel	1·75	1·25
1344	44p. Teddy bear	1·75	1·40
1345	51p. Filigree Christmas tree	2·00	1·60
1346	£2 Bells and baubles	6·75	9·00
1342/1346 Set of 5		11·50	12·00

312 100 Ton Gun, Napier of Magdala Battery, Gibraltar, 1880

313 Hawker Hurricane

(Des John Batchelor. Litho Printex Ltd., Malta)

2010 (19 Feb). 100 Ton Guns. Sheet 118×102 mm containing T **312** and similar horiz designs. Multicoloured. P 13½.

MS1347 75p.×4 Type **312**; 100 ton gun, Napier of Magdala Battery, Gibraltar, 1880; 100 ton gun, Fort Rinella, Malta, 2010; 100 ton gun, Fort Rinella, Malta, 1882	11·00	13·00

A miniature sheet containing the same designs was issued by Malta.

(Des Westminster Collection. Litho B.D.T.)

2010 (21 Feb). 70th Anniversary of the Battle of Britain. T **313** and similar horiz designs. Multicoloured. P 14.

1348	50p. Type **313**	3·50	3·25
1349	50p. Miles Master	3·50	3·25
1350	50p. Bristol Blenheim	3·50	3·25
1351	50p. Boulton Paul Defiant	3·50	3·25
1352	50p. Gloster Gladiator	3·50	3·25
1353	50p. Supermarine Spitfire	3·50	3·25
1348/1353 Set of 6		19·00	18·00
MS1354 110×70 mm. £2 Douglas Bader (*vert*)		8·50	8·50

314 King George V, Queen Mary and Family

315 *Charlie and the Chocolate Factory*

(Des Martin Hargreaves and Stephen Perera. Litho Lowe-Martin, Canada)

2010 (26 Mar). Centenary of Accession of King George V. T **314** and similar horiz designs. Multicoloured. P 13.

1355	10p. Type **314**	1·00	30
1356	42p. King George V with his stamp collection	2·50	1·25
1357	44p. King George V on horseback inspecting soldiers	2·50	1·40
1358	£2 King George V in navy uniform and gun battery	11·00	14·00
1355/1358 Set of 4		15·00	15·00

(Des Stephen Perera. Litho Lowe-Martin, Canada)

2010 (4 May). Europa. Children's Books. T **315** and similar horiz designs showing illustrations by Quentin Blake from books by Roald Dahl. Multicoloured. P 13.

1359	10p. Type **315**	55	30
1360	42p. *Matilda*	2·00	1·25
1361	44p. *The Twits*	2·00	1·40
1362	£1·50 *The BFG*	5·00	7·00
1359/1362 Set of 4		8·50	9·00

316 Emblem

317 Second Tower, San Marino

(Des Stephen Perera. Litho and die stamped B.D.T.)

2010 (30 June). Miss Gibraltar 2009 (Kaiane Aldorino) is Miss World. Sheet 140×84 mm. P 14×14½.

MS1363 **316** £2 gold and black		7·00	8·00
	a. Gold omitted		

(Des R&AR, Litho B.D.T.)

2010 (30 June). Gibraltar and San Marino. Sheet 147×105 mm containing T **317** and similar horiz designs. Multicoloured. P 14½×14.

MS1364 75p.×4 Type **317**; Moorish Castle, Gibraltar; Mount Titano, San Marino; The Rock of Gibraltar	10·00	12·00

A miniature sheet containing the same designs was issued by San Marino.

318 Elise Deroche (inscr 'Baroness Raymonde de Laroche') flying Voisin Biplane, 8 March 1910

319 Rainbow

(Des John Batchelor and Stephen Perera. Litho B.D.T.)

2010 (20 Aug). Aviation Centenaries. T **318** and similar horiz designs. Multicoloured. P 14½×14.

1365	10p. Type **318** (first woman with pilot's licence)	65	30
1366	42p. DELAG's Zeppelin LZ7 (first fare paying passengers), 21 June 1910	1·75	1·25
1367	49p. Hubert Latham sets altitude record at 4,541 ft in *Antoinette VII*, 7 July 1910	2·25	1·75
1368	£2 Clément-Bayard No. 2 (first airship flight across English Channel, 16 October 1910	7·50	9·00
1365/1368 Set of 4		11·00	11·00
MS1369 163×75 mm. 10p. Henri Fabre flies *Le Canard*, 28 March 1910; 42p. Supermarine S.6B Schneider Trophy winner, 1931; 49p. Short Sunderland, 204 Squadron, Gibraltar, 1941; £2 Saunders-ROE Princess, 22 August 1952 (centenary of seaplanes)		14·00	15·00

(Des Stephen Perera. Litho B.D.T.)

2010 (20 Oct). Centenary of Girlguiding. T **319** and similar horiz designs showing uniforms. Multicoloured. P 13½.

1370	10p. Type **319**	50	30
1371	42p. Brownie	1·60	1·25
1372	44p. Guide	1·60	1·40
1373	£2 Senior	6·75	9·00
1370/1373 Set of 4		9·50	11·00

320 Emblem

321 Interior of Cathedral of St Mary the Crowned

(Des Stephen Perera. Litho B.D.T.)

2010 (20 Oct). Commonwealth Games, Delhi. Sheet 90×103 mm. P 14×14½.

MS1374	**320**	£2 multicoloured	8·50	9·00

(Des Stephen Perera. Litho B.D.T.)

2010 (16 Nov). Centenary of Diocese of Gibraltar. Sheet 114×80 mm. P 14½×14.

MS1375	**321**	£2 multicoloured	7·00	7·50

322 Christmas Stocking, Wrapped Presents and Decorations

(Des Stephen Perera. Litho B.D.T.)

2010 (26 Nov). Christmas. T **322** and similar horiz designs. Multicoloured. P 13×13½.

1376	10p.	Type **322**	45	30
1377	42p.	Christmas stockings hanging from mantelpiece	1·50	1·25
1378	44p.	Santa's sleigh flying over snowy landscape	1·60	1·40
1379	51p.	Three snowmen as musicians with accordion, fiddle and cymbals	2·00	3·00
1376/1379 Set of 4			5·00	5·50

323 Prince William and Miss Catherine Middleton

324 World War I ('Reflection')

2011 (21 Jan). Royal Engagement. Sheet 90×97 mm. P 15×14.

MS1380	**323**	£2 multicoloured	9·00	9·00

(Des Stephen Perera. Litho Lowe-Martin, Canada)

2011 (21 Jan). Royal British Legion. T **324** and similar horiz designs. Multicoloured. P 13×13½ (No. **MS**1389) or 13 (others).

1381	50p.	Type **324**	2·00	2·00
1382	50p.	World War II ('Hope')	2·00	2·00
1383	50p.	Northern Ireland ('Selflessness')	2·00	2·00
1384	50p.	The Falklands ('Comradeship')	2·00	2·00
1385	50p.	The Gulf War ('Welfare')	2·00	2·00
1386	50p.	The Balkans ('Service')	2·00	2·00
1387	50p.	Iraq ('Representation')	2·00	2·00
1388	50p.	Afghanistan ('Remembrance')	2·00	2·00
1381/1388 Set of 8			14·00	14·00
MS1389 120×80 mm. £2 Statue and poppies			7·00	8·00

325 Queen Elizabeth II

(Des Westminster Collection. Litho B.D.T.)

2011 (6 Feb). Queen Elizabeth II and Prince Philip. Lifetime of Service. T **325** and similar diamond-shaped designs. Multicoloured. P 13.

1390	10p.	Queen Elizabeth II and Prince Philip	60	30
1391	42p.	Queen Elizabeth II and Prince Philip, 1960s	1·75	1·25
1392	44p.	Queen Elizabeth II (wearing purple) and Prince Philip, c. 2010	1·75	1·40
1393	51p.	Queen Elizabeth II and Prince Philip, c. 1952	2·25	2·25
1394	55p.	Queen Elizabeth II (wearing tiara) and Prince Philip, c. 1965	2·25	2·50
1395	£2	Prince Philip, c. 1970	7·00	8·50
1390/1395 Set of 6			14·00	14·50
MS1396 174×164 mm. Nos. 1390/1395 and two stamp-size labels			15·00	16·00
MS1397 110×70 mm. £3 Princess Elizabeth and Duke of Edinburgh on wedding day, 1947			15·00	16·00

Nos. 1390/1395 were printed in separate sheetlets of eight stamps.

No. **MS**1396 forms a diamond-shape but with the left, right and top corners removed.

326 The Alps

327 1886 Gibraltar overprint on Bermuda Queen Victoria 1s. Stamp

328 Prince William and Miss Catherine Middleton

(Des Stephen Perera. Litho Lowe-Martin, Canada)

2011 (4 Apr). Europa. Year of Forests. T **326** and similar vert designs. Multicoloured. P 12½.

1398	10p.	Type **326**	45	30
1399	42p.	The Amazon	1·50	1·00
1400	44p.	Yosemite National Park, California	1·60	1·25
1401	£1·50	Plitvice National Park, Croatia	6·00	7·00
1398/1401 Set of 4			8·50	8·50

(Des Stephen Perera. Litho B.D.T.)

2011 (15 Apr). 125th Anniversary of Gibraltar Stamps. T **327** and similar vert designs. Multicoloured. P 13.

1402	10p.	Type **327**	60	35
1403	42p.	1903 King Edward VII £1 stamp	1·75	1·25
1404	44p.	1925 King George V £5 stamp	1·90	1·40
1405	55p.	1938 King George VI £1 stamp	2·50	2·50
1406	£1·50	1953 Coronation ½d. stamp	7·00	8·00
1402/1406 Set of 5			12·50	12·00

(Des Stephen Perera. Litho B.D.T.)

2011 (15 July). Royal Wedding. Sheet 90×97 mm. P 14½×14.

MS1407	**328**	£3 multicoloured	11·00	12·00

329 Asian Elephant (*Elephas maximus*)

(Des Jon Pointer and Stephen Perera. Litho B.D.T.)

2011 (31 July). Endangered Animals (1st series). T **329** and similar horiz designs. Multicoloured. P 14×14½.

1408	42p. Type **329**	2·50	2·25
1409	42p. Bengal Tiger (*Panthera tigris tigris*)	2·50	2·25
1410	42p. Black Rhinoceros (*Diceros bicornis*)	2·50	2·25
1411	42p. Giant Panda (*Ailuropoda melanoleuca*)	2·50	2·25
1412	42p. Polar Bear (*Ursus maritimus*)	2·50	2·25
1413	42p. Sumatran Orangutan (*Pongo abelii*)	2·50	2·25
1408/1413 *Set of 6*		13·50	12·00
MS1414 161×105 mm. Nos. 1408/1413		13·50	13·50

See also Nos. 1476/MS1482 and 1531/MS1537.

330 Barbary Macaque   **331** Supermarine Spitfire K5054 modified to Mk I Standard

(Des Jonathan Pointer and Stephen Perera. Litho B.D.T.)

2011 (28 Sept). Barbary Macaque (*Macaca sylvanus*). T **330** and similar vert designs. Multicoloured. P 15×14.

1415	10p. Type **330**	45	30
1416	42p. Barbary Macaque, peak of Rock of Gibraltar in background	1·50	1·00
1417	44p. Barbary Macaque in tree at water's edge	1·60	1·10
1418	51p. Barbary Macaque, cliffs in background	2·00	1·40
1419	59p. Barbary Macaque sitting on rock	2·25	2·50
1420	£1.50 Two adult Macaques and baby	6·00	8·50
1415/1420 *Set of 6*		12·50	13·00

No. 1416 was inscr'sepac'.

(Des John Batchelor and Stephen Perera. Litho B.D.T.)

2011 (28 Sept). 75th Anniversary of the Supermarine Spitfire. T **331** and similar horiz designs. Multicoloured. P 14½×14.

1421	10p. Type **331**	80	40
1422	42p. First flight of the Supermarine Spitfire, March 5th 1936	2·25	1·25
1423	49p. Ground testing before the first flight	2·50	1·75
1424	£2 Supermarine Spitfire Prototype K5054 under construction	8·00	10·00
1421/1424 *Set of 4*		12·00	12·00
MS1425 129×85 mm. £2 RAF 92 Squadron Spitfire Mk 1B		7·50	8·50

332 Invading Muslim Army approaching Gibraltar   **333** Nativity (Giorgione (Giorgio Barbarelli da Castelfranco))

(Des Christian Hook and Stephen Perera. Litho B.D.T.)

2011 (7 Nov). 1300th Anniversary of Landing of Tariq ibn Ziyad at Gibraltar and Islamic Conquest of Spain. T **332** and similar horiz designs. Multicoloured. P 13.

1426	42p. Type **332**	1·50	70
1427	44p. Landing of Tariq ibn Ziyad's army at Gibraltar, 711 AD	1·60	80
1428	66p. Tariq ibn Ziyad and his army in Gibraltar	2·50	3·00
1429	£2 Battle between Tariq ibn Ziyad and the Visigothic King Roderick	7·00	9·50
1426/1429 *Set of 4*		11·50	12·50

(Des Stephen Perera. Litho B.D.T.)

2011 (7 Nov). Christmas. Nativity Art. T **333** and similar square designs. Multicoloured. P 14.

1430	10p. Type **333**	45	20
1431	42p. Nativity (Lorenzo Lotto)	1·60	60

1432	44p. Nativity (Charles Le Brun)	1·75	75
1433	51p. Nativity (Agnolo di Cosimo)	2·00	1·40
1434	£2 Nativity (Gerard van Honthorst)	7·00	9·50
1430/1434 *Set of 5*		11·00	11·00

334 Grand Master Viktor Bologan v GM Pia Cramling Move 49   **335** Fitting of *Titanic* completed, 31st March 1912

(Des Stephen Perera. Litho B.D.T.)

2012 (22 Jan). Tenth Anniversary of the Gibraltar International Chess Festival. Chessboards from Games in Progress. T **334** and similar vert designs. Multicoloured. P 13.

1435	2p. Type **334**	30	60
1436	30p. GM Michael Adams v GM Natalia Zhukova Move 52	1·75	70
1437	75p. GM Fabiano Caruana v GM Viktor Korchnoi Move 46	4·25	4·00
1438	£2 GM Vassily Ivanchuk v GM Nigel Short Move 63	9·50	10·00
1435/1438 *Set of 4*		14·00	14·00

(Des John Batchelor and Stephen Perera. Litho B.D.T.)

2012 (31 Jan). Centenary of the Sinking of the *Titanic*. T **335** and similar vert designs. Multicoloured. P 13½.

1439	10p. Type **335**	75	40
1440	42p. Titanic sets sail on her maiden voyage, 10 April 1912	2·25	1·25
1441	44p. Iceberg strikes starboard bow, 14 April 1912, 23.40 hrs	2·25	1·40
1442	54p. First lifeboats lowered, 15 April 1912, 00.45 hrs	3·00	2·75
1443	66p. Stern rises and Titanic starts sinking, 15 April 1912, 02.10 hrs	3·75	5·50
1439/1443 *Set of 5*		11·00	10·00

336 Queen Elizabeth II

(Des Westminster Collection. Litho B.D.T.)

2012 (27 Feb). Diamond Jubilee. T **336** and similar diamond-shaped designs. Multicoloured. P 13½.

1444	10p. Type **336**	50	30
1445	42p. Queen Elizabeth II wearing tiara, c. 2005	1·50	75
1446	44p. Queen Elizabeth II wearing flowered hat, c. 1970	1·50	90
1447	51p. Queen Elizabeth II, c. 1970	2·00	1·50
1448	55p. Princess Elizabeth, c. 1942	2·25	2·50
1449	£2 Queen Elizabeth II wearing Garter robes, c. 1980	7·00	9·00
1444/1449 *Set of 6*		13·50	13·50
MS1450 174×165 mm. Nos. 1444/1449		13·50	13·50
MS1451 111×71 mm. £3 Portrait of Queen Elizabeth II, c. 1953		9·50	11·00

Nos. 1444/1449 were printed in separate sheetlets of eight stamps.

No. MS1450 forms a diamond-shape but with the left, right and top corners removed.

337 Westland WS-61 Sea King Helicopter, 22 Squadron

338 Musical Instruments

(Des John Batchelor and Stephen Perera. Litho B.D.T.)

2012 (16 Apr). Royal Air Force Squadrons (1st series). T **337** and similar multicoloured designs. P 13½.

1452	10p. Type **337**	1·00	45
1453	42p. Gloster Javelin FAW 7 Mk IV, 89 Squadron	2·50	70
1454	76p. Panavia Tornado, 111 Squadron	4·25	4·00
1455	£2 Bristol Type 156 Beaufighter, 248 Squadron	9·00	10·00
1452/1455 Set of 4		15·00	13·50

MS1456 129×102 mm. Squadron blazer badges: 10p. No. 22 Squadron; 42p. No. 89 Squadron; 76p. No. 111 Squadron; £2 No. 248 Squadron (all 36×36 mm)......... 15·00 14·00

See also Nos. 1495/**MS**1499, 1606/**MS**1610 and 1652/**MS**1656.

(Des Stephen Perera. Litho Cartor)

2012 (15 June). International Jazz Festival. P 13×13½.

| 1457 | **338** | 75p. multicoloured | 2·75 | 3·00 |

339 Aerial View of Gibraltar

340 Countess of Wessex

(Des Stephen Pereira. Litho Cartor)

2012 (15 June). Europa. Visit Gibraltar. T **339** and similar square designs. Multicoloured. P 13½.

1458	10p. Type **339**	55	35
1459	42p. Tower of Homage (built 711 AD), Moorish Castle, Upper Rock Nature Reserve	1·75	90
1460	44p. Aerial view of Gibraltar (different)	1·75	1·10
1461	51p. St Michael's Cave, Upper Rock Nature Reserve	2·25	1·50
1462	54p. Trinity Lighthouse, Europa Point	4·00	3·50
1463	66p. Eliott's Column, Alameda Botanical Gardens	2·75	4·25
1458/1463 Set of 6		11·50	10·50

(Des Stephen Perera. Litho Cartor)

2012 (14 Sept). Royal Visit, June 2012. Sheet, 134×85 mm, containing T **340** and similar vert designs. Multicoloured. P 13×13½.

MS1464 £1×3 Type **340**; Earl and Countess of Wessex unveiling plaque at new airport terminal building; Earl of Wessex...... 10·00 11·00

341 Charles Dickens and *David Copperfield*

342 Santa Claus and Gifts

(Des Stephen Perera. Litho B.D.T.)

2012 (14 Sept). Birth Bicentenary of Charles Dickens (writer). T **341** and similar vert designs. Multicoloured. P 14×14½.

| 1465 | 10p. Type **341** | 50 | 30 |

1466	42p. Charles Dickens and *Oliver Twist*	1·75	90
1467	44p. Charles Dickens and *A Tale of Two Cities*	1·75	1·10
1468	£2 Charles Dickens and *A Christmas Carol*	7·50	9·50
1465/1468 Set of 4		10·50	10·50

MS1469 129×89 mm. £2 Charles Dickens...... 7·00 8·50

(Des Stephen Perera. Litho Cartor)

2012 (14 Sept). Old Views of Gibraltar (2nd series). Scenes from Postcards. Horiz designs as T **310** but smaller, 48×30 mm. Multicoloured. P 13½.

1470	10p. The Old Moorish Castle	55	30
1471	30p. Grand Casemates Square, awaiting the Arrival of King George V and Queen Mary	1·25	60
1472	61p. Landing Pier	2·50	2·50
1473	78p. Waterport	3·25	3·50
1474	£1·75 Alameda Gardens	7·00	8·50
1470/1474 Set of 5		13·00	14·00

MS1475 165×80 mm. 10p. Sand Hill Road, arrival of Troops to be inspected by King George V; 42p. South Port Gates; 50p. Victoria Monument; £1 Hargraves Barracks...... 7·00 8·00

(Des Jonathan Pointer and Stephen Perera. Litho Cartor)

2012 (2 Nov). Endangered Animals (2nd series). Horiz designs as T **329**. Multicoloured. P 13.

1476	42p. Arabian Oryx (*Oryx leucoryx*)	2·50	2·25
1477	42p. Asian One-horned Rhinoceros (*Rhinoceros unicornis*)	2·50	2·25
1478	42p. European Wolf (*Canis lupus lupus*)	2·50	2·25
1479	42p. Iberian Lynx (*Lynx pardinus*)	2·50	2·25
1480	42p. Snow Leopard (*Panthera uncia*)	2·50	2·25
1481	42p. Western Lowland Gorilla (*Gorilla gorilla gorilla*)	2·50	2·25
1476/1481 Set of 6		13·50	12·00

MS1482 160×105 mm. Nos. 1476/1481...... 13·50 13·00

(Des nokee art and Stephen Perera. Litho Cartor)

2012 (2 Nov). Christmas. Santa Claus. T **342** and similar horiz designs. Multicoloured. P 13×13½.

1483	10p. Type **342**	45	20
1484	42p. Santa carrying lamp and sack of toys	1·50	60
1485	44p. Snowman and Christmas tree	1·50	75
1486	51p. Santa in sleigh	2·00	1·40
1487	£2 Santa ringing bell, Reindeer and elf	7·50	9·00
1483/1487 Set of 5		11·50	11·00

343 Snake's Head

344 Coronation Photograph

(Des Stephen Perera. Litho and embossed Cartor)

2013 (30 Jan). Chinese New Year. Year of the Snake. T **343** and similar square design. Multicoloured. P 12½.

1488	42p. Type **343**	2·25	1·75
	a. Horiz pair. Nos. 1488/1489	5·50	6·50
1489	£1 Snake	3·25	4·75

Nos. 1488/1489 were printed together, *se-tenant*, as horizontal pairs in sheetlets of ten (2×5).

(Des Stephen Perera. Litho Cartor)

2013 (30 Jan). 60th Anniversary of Coronation. T **344** and similar vert designs. Multicoloured. P 13.

1490	10p. Type **344**	50	30
1491	42p. Coronation photograph (wearing crown)	1·60	80
1492	44p. Coronation photograph (wearing diadem)	1·75	1·25
1493	£1·50 Queen Elizabeth II leaving golden State Coach on Coronation Day	6·50	8·00
1490/1493 Set of 4		9·25	9·25

MS1494 96×96 mm. £3 Portrait of Queen Elizabeth II wearing crown and silver-grey dress, c. 1952...... 11·00 12·00

(Des John Batchelor and Stephen Perera. Litho Cartor)

2013 (25 Mar). Royal Air Force Squadrons (2nd series). Multicoloured designs as T **337**. P 13 (Nos. 1495/14958) or 13½ (No. **MS**1499).

1495	10p. VS Spitfire 5C, 43 Squadron	85	35
1496	42p. Hawker Hurricane, 87 Squadron	2·50	65
1497	76p. Consolidated PBY Catalina IV A, 210 Squadron	4·00	3·75

1498	£2 Avro Shackleton MR2, 224 Squadron.......	9·00	10·00
1495/1498 Set of 4..		15·00	13·50

MS1499 128×102 mm. Squadron badges: 10p. No. 43 Squadron; 42p. No. 87 Squadron; 76p. No. 210 Squadron; £2 No. 224 Squadron .... 15·00   14·00

(Des Stephen Perera. Litho Cartor)

2013 (3 May). Old Views of Gibraltar (3rd series). Scenes from Postcards. Horiz designs as T **310** but smaller, 48×30 mm. Multicoloured. P 13½.

1500	10p. Moorish Castle and Landport	50	30
1501	30p. Casemates Square...................................	1·25	60
1502	61p. The Rock from Victoria Gardens................	2·50	2·50
1503	78p. Main Street...	3·00	3·25
1504	£1·75 Casemates Barracks	7·00	8·00
1500/1504 Set of 5..		13·00	13·00

MS1505 163×79 mm. 10p. The Rock from North Front Camp; 42p. Rosia Bay; 50p. Kingsway Walk, Alameda Gardens; £1 Spanish water sellers drawing water from Rain Water Fountain, Gunner's Parade .... 8·50   9·00

345 Books

346 Arms of Gibraltar Football Association

(Des Stephen Perera. Litho Lowe-Martin)

2013 (3 May). Gibraltar International Literary Festival. T **345** and similar horiz designs. Multicoloured. P 13×13½.

1506	10p. Type **345**..	50	30
1507	42p. Braille..	1·60	60
1508	£2 e-book reader and open book....................	7·00	8·50
1506/1508 Set of 3..		8·25	8·50

(Litho)

2013 (26 May). Tel Aviv 2013 Multinational Stamp Exhibition, Israel. Sheet 149×106 mm. P 14×15.

MS1508*a* As No. 1338 but 'sepac' inscr omitted.............. 3·50   3·50

(Des Stephen Perera. Litho B.D.T.)

2013 (31 May). Gibraltar, 54th Member of UEFA. P 14½×14.

1509	**346**	54p. multicoloured	1·90	2·25

347 1970 Replica of 1911 Dennis 2 Ton Mail Van used on London Contract Services LE304

348 Union Flag

(Des John Batchelor (illustration) and Stephen Perera. Litho Cartor)

2013 (20 June). Europa. Postal Vehicles. T **347** and similar horiz designs. Multicoloured. P 13×13½.

1510	10p. Type **347**..	60	30
1511	42p. Horse-drawn mail cart, 1897–1920s.........	1·75	1·00
1512	44p. Rover Motorcycle Combination DU 5660, 1914...	1·90	1·25
1513	£1·75 Electromobile 1-ton battery-electric van YX7649, 1928	7·00	8·50
1510/1513 Set of 4..		10·00	11·50

(Des Stephen Perera. Litho Cartor)

2013 (20 June). 300th Anniversary of the Treaty of Utrecht (gave Gibraltar to Great Britain). T **348** and similar square design. Multicoloured. P 12½.

1514	10p. Type **348**..	75	75
	a. Horiz pair. Nos. 1514/1515	2·25	2·25

1515	42p. "for ever, without any exception or impediment whatsoever"............................	1·50	1·50

Nos. 1514/1515 were printed together, *se-tenant*, as horizontal pairs throughout the sheets.

T **349** is vacant.

350 Cargo and Passenger Wharves

(Des Stephen Perera. Litho Lowe-Martin)

2013 (18 July). 60th Anniversary of Gibraltar Queen Elizabeth II Definitive Stamps. Designs as Types **24/37** but revalued in decimal currency as T **350**. P 12½.

1516	**350**	2p. indigo and grey-green.......................	20	50
1517	**25**	10p. bluish green....................................	50	30
1518	**26**	16p. black...	75	55
1519	**27**	20p. deep olive-brown............................	90	70
1520	**28**	22p. carmine	90	70
1521	**29**	30p. light blue	1·25	70
1522	**30**	42p. maroon	1·75	70
1523	**31**	44p. ultramarine	1·90	70
1524	**32**	50p. black and pale blue.........................	2·25	1·75
1525	**33**	58p. pale blue and red-brown...................	2·50	2·00
1526	**34**	60p. orange and reddish violet	2·75	2·75
1527	**35**	£2 deep brown	8·00	8·50
1528	**36**	£3 reddish brown and ultramarine	11·00	13·00
1529	**37**	£5 scarlet and orange-yellow.................	14·00	17·00
1516/1529 Set of 14			42·00	45·00

351 Duke and Duchess of Cambridge with Prince George

352 'MERRY CHRISTMAS'

(Des Stephen Perera. Litho B.D.T.)

2013 (16 Aug). Birth of Prince George of Cambridge. P 14×14½.

1530	**351**	£2 multicoloured	7·00	7·50

(Des Jonathan Pointer (illustrations) and Stephen Perera. Litho Lowe-Martin)

2013 (14 Sept). Endangered Animals (3rd series). Horiz designs as T **329**. P 13 (No. **MS**1537) or 12½×13 (others).

1531	42p. African Penguin (*Spheniscus demersus*)..	2·50	2·25
1532	42p. Atlantic Bluefin Tuna (*Thunnus thynnus*)...	2·50	2·25
1533	42p. Asiatic Cheetah (*Acinonyx jubatus venaticus*)...	2·50	2·25
1534	42p. Chinese Alligator (*Alligator sinensis*).........	2·50	2·25
1535	42p. Red-crowned Crane (*Grus japonensis*)..	2·50	2·25
1536	42p. Leatherback Sea Turtle (*Dermochelys coriacea*)..	2·50	2·25
1531/1536 Set of 6..		13·50	12·00

MS1537 160×105 mm. Nos. 1531/1536............ 13·50   13·50

No. 1532 was inscr 'sepac'.

(Des Stephen Perera. Litho Enschedé)

2013 (2 Nov). Christmas. T **352** and similar horiz designs. Multicoloured. P 14×13½.

1538	12p. Type **352**..	40	20
1539	50p. Rocking horse, teddy and wrapped parcels around Christmas tree....................	1·50	60
1540	54p. Santa in sleigh	1·60	1·00
1541	64p. Wrapped present	2·00	1·75
1542	£2·50 Christmas baubles.................................	7·50	9·50
1538/1542 Set of 5..		11·50	11·50

MS1543 140×92 mm. Nos. 1538/1542 .... 11·50   12·00

353 Flag of Governor
of Gibraltar and Keys

(354)

(Des Stephen Perera. Litho B.D.T.)

2013 (2 Nov). Ceremony of the Keys. P 13.
1544 **353** £1 multicoloured .... 3·25 3·50
No. 1544 was printed in sheetlets of five stamps and ten *se-tenant* labels, with the labels at left showing the Governor of Gibraltar from 2009 to 2013 Vice Admiral Sir Adrian Johns and the labels at right showing the Port Sergeant. The stamp and labels form a composite design showing the Governor and Port Sergeant holding the Keys.

2013 (2 Nov). Nos. 1250 and 1254*a* surch as T **354**, No. 1254*a* in silver.
1545 14p. Little Owl (*Athene noctua*) .... 2·00 1·75
1546 28p. on 5p. Eagle Owl (*Bubo bubo*) .... 3·75 3·25

355 Queen
Elizabeth II

356 Horse's Head

(Des Stephen Perera. Litho Cartor)

2014 (31 Jan). Queen Elizabeth II (1st series). T **355** and similar vert designs. P 14×13½.
1547 **355** 2p. chestnut 15 30
1548 4p. maroon 20 40
1549 6p. violet 30 50
1550 8p. grey-black 35 50
1551 10p. dull blue-green 35 50
1552 (12p.) deep turquoise-blue and new
blue 40 20
1553 14p. carmine-red 50 35
1554 20p. bronze-green 70 70
1555 28p. deep reddish violet 90 70
1556 40p. sepia .... 1·40 90
1557 50p. turquoise-green .... 1·75 1·00
1558 54p. rose-red .... 1·90 1·25
1559 64p. bistre .... 2·50 2·00
1560 70p. chalky blue .... 2·75 2·25
1561 £2 emerald .... 7·00 7·50
1562 £2·50 deep magenta .... 8·00 9·00
1547/1562 *Set of 16* .... 26·00 25·00
Nos. 1547/1562 depict the inset portrait of Queen Elizabeth II from the 1953–1959 definitives, Nos. 145/158.
No. 1552 was inscr 'G' and originally sold for 12p.
See also Nos. 1639/1643.

(Des Stephen Perera. Litho Cartor)

2014 (31 Jan). Chinese New Year. Year of the Horse. T **356** and similar square design. Multicoloured. P 12½.
1563 50p. Type **356** .... 1·75 1·75
a. Horiz pair. Nos. 1563/1564 .... 4·75 4·75
1564 £1 Horse .... 3·00 3·00
Nos. 1563/1564 were printed together, *se-tenant*, as horizontal pairs in sheetlets of ten (2×5).

357 Poster of Lord Kitchener
('Your Country Wants You')

(Litho B.D.T.)

2014 (19 Feb). Centenary of World War I (1st issue). T **357** and similar horiz designs. Multicoloured. P 14.
1565 12p. Type **357** 60 30
1566 40p. Joining up .... 1·75 60
1567 50p. Leaving family .... 1·90 1·10
1568 64p. Kit .... 2·75 2·75
1569 68p. Training .... 2·75 3·00
1570 £1 Embarkation .... 3·75 4·50
1565/1570 *Set of 6* .... 12·00 11·00
See also Nos. 1628/1633.

(Des Stephen Perera. Litho Cartor)

2014 (20 Mar). Old Views of Gibraltar (4th series). Horiz designs as T **310** but smaller, 48×30 mm. Multicoloured. P 13½.
1571 12p. Waterport Wharf 50 30
1572 40p. Eliott's Monument, ... 1·40 60
1573 50p. Entrance to the Town .... 1·75 1·25
1574 64p. Sandpits .... 2·50 2·75
1575 70p. Alameda Gardens .... 2·75 4·00
1571/1575 *Set of 5* .... 8·00 8·00
MS1576 163×79 mm. 12p. Waterport Street (Main Street); 40p. The Wharfs; 50p. The Market; £1 The Cascade .... 7·00 8·00

358 Red Arrows Jet (BAE Hawk T1)

359 Band and Corps of Drums of Royal Gibraltar Regiment at Buckingham Palace

(Des Stephen Perera. Litho Lowe-Martin)

2014 (20 Mar). 50th Anniversary of the Red Arrows. T **358** and similar horiz designs. Multicoloured. P 13.
1577 50p. Type **358** .... 2·00 1·10
1578 54p. Two Red Arrows .... 2·00 1·25
1579 64p. Red Arrow (front view) .... 2·75 2·50
1580 70p. Red Arrow (rear view) .... 3·00 2·75
1581 £2 Red Arrow (flying to upper right) .... 7·50 9·00
1577/1581 *Set of 5* .... 15·00 15·00

(Des Stephen Perera. Litho Cartor)

2014 (2 May). Europa. National Musical Instruments. T **359** and similar vert design. Multicoloured. P 13.
1582 50p. Type **359** .... 2·00 1·25
1583 £1 Drums of Royal Gibraltar Regiment .... 3·50 4·25

360 Common Dolphin
(*Delphinus delphis*)

361 Shakespeare and
'Whats done Cannot be
undone' (*Macbeth*)

(Des Jonathan Pointer (illustration) and Stephen Perera. Litho Cartor)

2014 (2 May). Dolphins. T **360** and similar horiz designs. Multicoloured. P 13×13½.
1584 68p. Type **360** .... 2·75 2·75
1585 84p. Striped Dolphin (*Stenella coeruleoalba*) .. 3·25 3·75
1586 £2·50 Bottlenose Dolphin (*Tursiops truncatus*).. 8·25 10·00
1584/1586 *Set of 3* .... 13·00 15·00

(Des Stephen Perera. Litho Cartor)

2014 (2 June). 450th Birth Anniversary of William Shakespeare (poet and playwright). T **361** and similar square designs. Multicoloured. P 12½.
1587 12p. Type **361** 60 30
1588 40p. Shakespeare and 'To be, or not to be, that is the question' (*Hamlet*) .... 1·75 60

1589	64p. Shakespeare and 'Love looks not with the eyes, but with the mind' (*A Midsummer Night's Dream*)	2·75	2·75
1590	£2 Shakespeare and 'O Romeo, Romeo, wherefore art thou Romeo?' (*Romeo and Juliet*)	8·00	9·00
1587/1590 *Set of 4*		11·50	11·50

MS1591 123×83 mm. £2 Statue of Shakespeare and 'If music be the food of love, play on'.................. 7·50 8·50

362 Gibraltar Saxifrage (*Saxifraga globulifera* Desfr. *gibraltarica* Ser.)

(Des Stephen Pereira. Litho Cartor)

2014 (15 July). Endemic Flowers. T **362** and similar horiz designs. Multicoloured. P 13½.

1592	10p. Type **362**	50	30
1593	12p. Gibraltar Restharrow (*Ononis natrix* L. subsp. *ramosissima* (Desf.) Batt. var. ramosissima)	55	30
1594	50p. Gibraltar Chickweed (*Cerastium gibraltaricum* Boiss.)	2·00	1·25
1595	54p. Gibraltar Candytuft (*Iberis gibraltarica* L.)	2·25	1·75
1596	64p. Gibraltar Campion (*Silene tomentosa* Otth. (*S. gibraltarica* Boiss.))	2·75	2·75
1597	70p. Gibraltar Thyme (*Thymus willdenowii* Boiss.)	3·00	3·25
1598	£2 Gibraltar Sea Lavender (*Limonium emarginatum* (Willd.) Kuntze)	7·50	9·00
1592/1598 *Set of 7*		17·00	17·00

363 Evacuees disembarking from Ship

364 Gibraltar Sea Scouts

(Des Stephen Perera. Litho Cartor)

2014 (10 Sept). 75th Anniversary of the Evacuation of Civilians from Gibraltar. T **363** and similar horiz designs. Multicoloured. P 13½.

1599	12p. Type **363**	55	30
1600	50p. Family reunion	1·75	1·25
1601	54p. Evacuation of children	1·90	1·60
1602	£1 Evacuation of adults	3·00	3·50
1603	£2 Figures of man, woman and child from Gibraltar Evacuees Memorial Sculpture and text giving history of the evacuation	6·00	7·00
1599/1603 *Set of 5*		12·00	12·00

(Des Stephen Perera. Litho Cartor)

2014 (13 Sept). Centenary of Gibraltar Sea Scouts. T **364** and similar vert design. Multicoloured. P 13.

1604	40p. Type **364**	1·50	1·25
1605	64p. Pipes and drums of Gibraltar Sea Scouts	2·25	2·50

(Des John Batchelor and Stephen Perera. Litho BDT)

2014 (15 Sept). Royal Air Force Squadrons (3rd series). Multicoloured designs as T **337**. Multicoloured. P 14½×14 (Nos. 1606/1609) or 13½ (No. **MS**1610).

1606	54p. British Aerospace Hawk, 100 Squadron	1·90	1·25
1607	64p. Short Saro London, 202 Squadron	2·25	1·75
1608	70p. Buccaneer S2s, 208 Squadron	2·50	2·00
1609	£2 Lockheed Hudson V, 233 Squadron	6·00	7·00
1606/1609 *Set of 4*		11·50	11·50

MS1610 129×102 mm. Squadron badges: 54p. No. 100 Squadron; 64p. No. 202 Squadron; 70p. No. 208 Squadron; £2 No. 233 Squadron (all 36×36 *mm*)......... 11·50 11·50

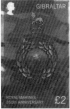

365 Royal Marines Badge

366 Father Christmas

(Des Stephen Perera. Litho Cartor)

2014 (25 Oct). 350th Anniversary of the Royal Marines. P 13.

1611	**365**	£2 multicoloured	5·00	5·50

(Des Stephen Perera. Litho Cartor)

2014 (3 Nov). Christmas. International Day of People with Disability. T **366** and similar square designs. Multicoloured. P 12½.

1612	(22p.) Type **366**	55	20
1613	40p. Stars	1·00	40
1614	64p. Toys	1·75	1·25
1615	70p. Three Wise Men	2·00	2·00
1616	80p. Decorated tree	2·25	2·75
1612/1616 *Set of 5*		6·75	6·00

MS1617 160×98 mm. £3 Portion of Christmas collage ... 7·00 7·50
No. 1612 was inscr 'G' and originally sold for 22p.
Nos. 1612/1616 show portions of a Christmas collage made by service users at the St Bernadette Resource Centre, and the stamp and margins of No. **MS**1617 show the complete collage.

367 Head of Goat

(Des Stephen Perera. Litho Cartor)

2015 (30 Jan). Chinese New Year. Year of the Goat. T **367** and similar square design. Multicoloured. P 12½.

1618	50p. Type **367**	1·50	1·75
	a. Horiz pair. Nos. 1618/1619	4·00	4·75
1619	£1 Goat	2·50	3·00

Nos. 1618/1619 were printed together, *se-tenant*, as horizontal pairs in sheetlets of ten (2×5).

368 Firefighters

(Des Stephen Perera and Nicholas Ferrary (illustration). Litho Lowe-Martin)

2015 (11 Feb). 150th Anniversary of Gibraltar Fire and Rescue Service. T **368** and similar horiz designs. Multicoloured. P 13.

1620	10p. Type **368**	30	30
1621	12p. Using foam making equipment	35	30
1622	40p. Rescue of casualty from tower crane	1·40	80
1623	50p. Firefighter's helmet	1·75	1·25
1624	54p. Sub-aqua rescue training	1·90	1·40
1625	64p. Removing car door to release person trapped in vehicle	2·50	1·75
1626	70p. Firefighters in gas-tight suits dealing with chemical hazard	2·75	2·50
1627	£2 Firefighters attending vehicle fire	7·00	8·00
1620/1627 *Set of 8*		16·00	15·00

(Litho Lowe-Martin)

2015 (18 Feb). Centenary of World War I (2nd issue). Horiz designs as T **357**. Multicoloured. P 13.

1628	22p. Machine guns	65	30
1629	40p. Warships	1·25	60
1630	64p. Soldiers in trench wearing gas masks	2·00	1·50
1631	70p. Aircraft	2·25	2·25
1632	80p. Soldiers with bayonets	2·50	2·50
1633	£1·20 Tank	3·25	3·75
1628/1633 *Set of 6*		11·00	10·00

369 Winston Churchill aboard HMS *Prince of Wales* off Newfoundland, 1941

370 Queen Elizabeth II

(Des Stephen Perera. Litho BPost, Belgium)

2015 (20 Mar). 50th Death Anniversary of Winston Churchill (British Prime Minister 1940–1945, 1951–1955). T **369** and similar vert designs. Multicoloured. P 12.

1634	22p. Type **369**	65	30
1635	64p. Winston Churchill by jeeps on tour of France, 12 June 1944	1·90	1·90
1636	70p. Wearing helmet during air raid warning, 1940	2·40	2·50
1637	80p. Inspecting bomb damage to Parliament building, 1941	2·50	2·75
1634/1637 *Set of* 4		6·75	6·75
MS1638 118×76 mm. £3 Winston Churchill giving V for Victory salute		8·00	8·00

(Des Stephen Perera. Litho Cartor)

2015 (24 Apr). Queen Elizabeth II (2nd series). Self-adhesive. T **370** (£1) or designs as T **355** but self-adhesive (others). Self-adhesive. Die-cut (£1) or die-cut perf 14×13½ (others).

1639	**355**	12p. yellowish-green	40	20
1640	**355**	18p. yellow-brown	60	25
1641	**355**	80p. deep dull blue	2·25	1·75
1642	**370**	£1 black	2·75	2·75
1643	**355**	£3 reddish brown and light brown	8·25	9·00
1639/1643 *Set of* 5			13·00	12·50

371 Penny Blacks

372 Toy Soldier

(Des Stephen Perera. Litho B.D.T.)

2015 (24 Apr). 175th Anniversary of the Penny Black. Sheet 125×80 mm. P 13½.

MS1644 **371** £3 multicoloured	7·00	7·50

(Des Stephen Perera. Litho B.D.T.)

2015 (5 May). Europa. Old Toys. T **372** and similar vert designs. Multicoloured. P 14×14½.

1645	14p. Type **372**	30	20
1646	22p. Toy merry-go-round	55	30
1647	64p. Spinning top	1·75	1·40
1648	70p. Teddy bear	2·00	2·00
1649	80p. Yoyo	2·25	2·25
1650	£1·20 Toy train	3·25	3·75
1645/1650 *Set of* 6		9·00	9·00

373 Queen Elizabeth II (photo by Cecil Beaton), 1955

374 Moorish Castle

(Des Stephen Perera. Litho Lowe-Martin Group)

2015 (30 May). Queen Elizabeth II. Britain's Longest Reigning Monarch. P 13.

1651	**373**	£10 multicoloured	23·00	24·00

(Des John Batchelor (illustration) and Stephen Perera. Litho B.D.T.)

2015 (31 Aug). Royal Air Force Squadrons (4th series). Multicoloured designs as T **337**. P 14½×14 (Nos. 1652/1655) or 13½ (No. **MS**1656).

1652	54p. Handley Page Halifax Mk V, 520 Squadron	1·75	1·25
1653	64p. Vickers Wellington Mk IV, 544 Squadron	2·25	2·00
1654	70p. Bristol Blenheim Mk IV, 600 Squadron	2·50	2·25
1655	£2 de Havilland Vampire Mk V, 608 Squadron	6·00	7·00
1652/1655 *Set of* 4		11·00	11·00
MS1656 128×102 mm. Squadron badges: 54p. No. 520 Squadron; 64p. No. 544 Squadron; 70p. No. 600 Squadron; £2 No. 608 Squadron (all 36×36 *mm*)		11·00	11·00

(Des Stephen Perera. Litho B.D.T.)

2015 (7 Sept). YouStamps. T **374** and similar square designs. Multicoloured. P 14.

1657	(22p.) Type **374**	60	50
1658	(22p.) Rock of Gibraltar	60	50
1659	(22p.) Hands wearing wedding rings and white Roses	60	50
1660	(70p.) Type **374**	1·75	2·00
1661	(70p.) As No. 1658	1·75	2·00
1662	(70p.) As No. 1659	1·75	2·00
1657/1662 *Set of* 6		6·25	6·75

Nos. 1657/1659 were each inscr. 'G' and originally sold for 22p.
Nos. 1660/1662 were each inscr. 'E' and originally sold for 70p.

375 Arms

376 Christmas Tree

(Des Stephen Perera. Litho B.D.T.)

2015 (21 Sept). Opening of University of Gibraltar. P 13½.

1663	**375**	80p. multicoloured	1·90	1·90

(Des Stephen Perera. Litho B.D.T.)

2015 (2 Nov). Christmas. T **376** and similar square designs. Multicoloured. P 14.

1664	(22p.) Type **376**	55	20
1665	40p. Red ribbon bow and Holly	1·00	30
1666	64p. Wrapped present	1·75	1·75
1667	70p. Reindeer	2·00	2·25
1668	80p. 'Merry CHRISTMAS & Happy New Year'	2·25	2·50
1665/1668 *Set of* 5		6·75	6·25

No. 1664 was inscr 'G' and originally sold for 22p.

377 Portion of *Magna Carta* Document

378 Monkey (close-up, three quarter length)

(Des Stephen Perera. Litho Cartor)

2015 (13 Nov). 800th Anniversary of the *Magna Carta*. Sheet 129×83 mm containing T **377** and similar horiz design. Multicoloured. P 13.

MS1669 £2 Type **377**; £2 Portion of *Magna Carta* document (light brown border at left)	10·00	11·00

(Des Stephen Perera. Litho Cartor)

2016 (30 Jan). Chinese New Year. Year of the Monkey. T **378** and similar square design. Multicoloured. P 12½.

1670	£2 Type **378**	5·00	5·50
	a. Horiz pair. Nos. 1670/1671	10·00	11·00
1671	£2 Monkey (full length)	5·00	5·50

Nos. 1670/1671 were printed together, *se-tenant*, as horizontal pairs in sheetlets of ten (2×5), each pair forming a composite design.

379 Baby Princess Elizabeth

380 Roller painting Contaminated Landscape Green

(Des Stephen Perera. Litho Lowe-Martin)

2016 (19 Feb). 90th Birthday of Queen Elizabeth II. T **379** and similar square designs. Multicoloured. P 13 (£5) or 12½ (others).

1672	12p. Type **379**	40	25
1673	18p. Princess Elizabeth as Girl Guide	60	30
1674	22p. Princess Elizabeth, c. 1946	65	30
1675	40p. Queen Elizabeth II, 1960s	1·10	60
1676	50p. Queen Elizabeth II, 1970s	1·40	80
1677	64p. Queen Elizabeth II (in profile), 1970s	1·75	1·40
1678	70p. Queen Elizabeth II, 1980s	2·00	1·75
1679	80p. Queen Elizabeth II in recent years, looking through curtain	2·25	2·25
1680	£1 Queen Elizabeth II in recent years	3·00	3·25
1681	£5 Formal portrait of Queen Elizabeth II, c. 1952 (39×39 mm)	10·00	12·00
1672/1681 Set of 10		21·00	21·00

(Des Doxia Sergidou (illustrator No. 1682), Giordano Aita (illustrator No. 1683) and Stephen Perera. Litho B.D.T.)

2016 (30 Mar). Europa. Think Green. T **380** and similar horiz design. Multicoloured. P 14.

1682	£1·50 Type **380**	4·00	4·25
1683	£1·50 Human brain as canopy of tree foliage	4·00	4·25

381 Soldiers and Poppies ('I will never forget the first of July')

382 Duke and Duchess of Cambridge

(Des Stephen Pereira. Litho Cartor)

2016 (16 May). Centenary of the Battle of the Somme. T **381** and similar horiz designs. Multicoloured. P 13½.

1684	22p. Type **381**	75	30
1685	64p. Soldiers with bayonets and Poppies ('...In the greatest fight ever seen')	2·00	1·25
1686	70p. Two soldiers running and Poppies ('...When we started our great push')	2·25	2·00
1687	80p. Soldiers and Poppies ('...And our gallant lads in the trenches')	2·50	2·25
1688	£2 Soldiers running and Poppies ('...Over the top like a flash and rush')	6·00	7·00
1684/1688 Set of 5		12·00	12·00

(Des Stephen Pereira. Litho B.D.T.)

2016 (16 May). Fifth Wedding Anniversary of Duke and Duchess of Cambridge. Sheet 90×96 mm. P 14½×14.

MS1689 **382** £2 multicoloured	5·50	6·00

383 Ragged Staff Gates

(Des Leslie Gaduzo and Stephen Perera. Litho LMG)

2016 (25 July). Historic Gates. T **383** and similar horiz designs. Multicoloured. P 13.

1690	22p. Type **383**	60	30
1691	64p. Prince Edward's Gate	1·75	1·25

1692	70p. Landport Gate	2·00	2·00
1693	80p. Grand Casemates Gates	2·25	2·25
1694	£1 Old Waterport Gates	3·00	3·25
1695	£2 Southport Gates	5·50	6·50
1690/1695 Set of 6		13·50	14·00

384 Russian Guns and the Heathfield Steps at Garden Entrance

(Des Jonathan Pointer and Stephen Perera. Litho LMG)

2016 (25 July). Bicentenary of the Alameda Gardens. T **384** and similar horiz designs. Multicoloured. P 12½×13.

1696	64p. Type **384**	1·75	1·25
1697	70p. *Aloe pseudorubroviolacea* and Prince of Wales' Summer House (bandstand)	2·00	2·00
1698	80p. Bust of landscape designer Giuseppe Codali and bougainvillea covered old bridge over The Dell	2·25	2·25
1699	£1 The Dell or Italian Garden	3·00	3·25
1700	£2 Bust of General George Augustus Eliott (Governor of Gibraltar 1779–1783), howitzer, Candelabra Aloes, Stone Pines and Dragon Trees	5·50	6·50
1696/1700 Set of 5		13·00	14·00

385 Moonrise at Gorham's Cave

386 Queen Victoria Pillar Box

(Des Stephen Perera. Litho B.D.T.)

2016 (20 Sept). UNESCO World Heritage Site Gorham's Cave Complex. T **385** and similar square designs. Multicoloured. P 14.

1701	22p. Type **385**	60	30
1702	64p. Excavation at Gorham's Cave	1·75	1·25
1703	70p. South-eastern face of Rock of Gibraltar with entrances to caves	2·00	2·00
1704	80p. Neanderthal adult with child	2·25	2·25
1705	£2 Neanderthal engraving on rock wall	5·50	6·50
1701/1705 Set of 5		11·00	11·00

(Des Stephen Perera. Litho Cartor)

2016 (10 Oct). Pillar Boxes. T **386** and similar vert designs. Multicoloured. P 13½.

1706	22p. Type **386**	70	30
1707	64p. King Edward VII pillar box	2·00	1·25
1708	70p. King George V pillar box	2·25	2·00
1709	80p. King George VI pillar box	2·50	2·25
1710	£2 Queen Elizabeth II pillar box	6·00	7·00
1706/1710 Set of 5		12·00	11·50

387 'CANNON LANE'

388 Santa

(Des Stephen Perera. Litho Cartor)

2016 (10 Oct). Historic Streets of Gibraltar. Street Signs. T **387** and similar horiz designs. Multicoloured. P 13½.

1711	22p. Type **387**	60	30
1712	40p. 'CASTLE STREET'	1·25	80

1713	50p. 'GEORGE'S LANE'		1·40	1·10
1714	54p. 'CLOISTER RAMP'		1·50	1·25
1715	64p. 'ENGINEER LANE'		1·75	1·50
1716	70p. 'MAIN STREET'		2·00	2·00
1717	80p. 'FLAT BASTION ROAD'		2·25	2·25
1718	£2 'CONVENT PLACE'		5·50	6·50
1711/1718 *Set of 8*			14·50	14·00

(Des Stephen Perera. Litho Lowe-Martin Group)

2016 (2 Nov). Christmas. Christmas Biscuits. T **388** and similar square designs. Multicoloured. P 12½.

1719	(22p.) Type **388**		60	20
1720	40p. Reindeer		1·10	40
1721	64p. Bell		1·75	1·50
1722	70p. Christmas tree		2·00	2·00
1723	80p. Red and white biscuits with snowflake decorations		2·25	2·25
1724	£2 Snowman		5·50	6·50
1719/1724 *Set of 6*			12·00	11·50

No. 1719 was inscr 'G' and originally sold for 22p.

389 Head of Rooster   **390** Queen Elizabeth II

(Des Stephen Perera. Litho Cartor)

2017 (30 Jan). Chinese New Year. Year of the Rooster. T **389** and similar square design. Multicoloured. P 12½.

1725	£2 Type **389**		5·50	6·00
	a. Horiz pair. Nos. 1725/1726		11·00	12·00
1726	£2 Rooster		5·50	6·00

Nos. 1725/1726 were printed together, *se-tenant*, as horizontal pairs in sheetlets of ten (2×5), each pair forming a composite background design.

(Des Stephen Perera. Litho Cartor)

2017 (6 Feb). 65th Anniversary of Accession of Queen Elizabeth II. T **390** and similar square designs. Multicoloured. P 13½.

1727	22p. Type **390**		60	20
1728	64p. Queen Elizabeth II, wearing Coronation dress and diadem, coming through curtain		1·75	1·25
1729	70p. Queen Elizabeth II wearing kimono, 1950s		2·00	1·75
1730	80p. Queen Elizabeth II seated in chair, wearing Imperial Crown		2·25	2·00
1731	£2 Queen Elizabeth II during Coronation ceremony, holding Orb		5·50	6·50
1732	£3 Queen Elizabeth II, wearing white coat and diadem, waving		7·50	8·50
1727/1732 *Set of 6*			18·00	18·00
MS1733 159×64 mm. £3 Queen Elizabeth II wearing white dress, blue sash and diadem			7·50	8·50

391 Moorish Castle, Gibraltar   **392** Arrival of Princess Elizabeth at her Wedding

(Des Stephen Perera. Litho Lowe-Martin Group, Canada)

2017 (6 Feb). Europa. Castles. T **391** and similar horiz design. Multicoloured. P 12½.

1734	£1·50 Type **391**		3·75	4·00
1735	£1·50 Moorish Castle and walls		3·75	4·00

(Des Stephen Perera. Litho Cartor)

2017 (25 May). 70th Wedding Anniversary of Queen Elizabeth II and Prince Philip, Duke of Edinburgh. T **392** and similar vert designs. Multicoloured. P 13×13½.

1736	22p. Type **392**		60	20
1737	40p. Wedding ceremony, 20 November 1947		1·25	75
1738	50p. Princess Elizabeth and Prince Philip, Duke of Edinburgh		1·40	90
1739	64p. Princess Elizabeth and Prince Philip, Duke of Edinburgh leaving Westminster Abbey after their wedding		1·75	1·40
1740	70p. Princess Elizabeth and Prince Philip, Duke of Edinburgh waving from Buckingham Palace balcony after wedding		2·00	1·75
1741	80p. Wedding portrait photo of Princess Elizabeth and Prince Philip, Duke of Edinburgh		2·25	2·00
1742	£1·50 Princess Elizabeth holding wedding bouquet		4·25	4·75
1743	£2 Wedding portrait photo of Princess Elizabeth		5·50	6·50
1736/1743 *Set of 8*			17·00	16·00
MS1744 150×89 mm. £3 Princess Elizabeth and her father King George VI in Irish State Coach on way to wedding			7·50	8·50

393 HMS *Gibraltar*, Edgar-class Cruiser, 1892   **394** King George V

(Des John Batchelor (illustration) and Stephen Perera. Litho Cartor)

2017 (25 May). HMS *Gibraltar*. T **393** and similar horiz designs. Multicoloured. P 13½.

1745	22p. Type **393**		60	25
1746	54p. HMS *Gibraltar*, 101-Gun Screw First Rate, 1860		1·60	1·10
1747	64p. HMS *Gibraltar*, 80-Gun Fenix		1·75	1·40
1748	70p. HMS *Gibraltar*,14-Gun Brig, 1779		2·00	1·75
1749	80p. HMS *Gibraltar*, 45,000 Ton Aircraft Carrier, 1943 (ordered but never delivered)		2·25	2·00
1750	£1 HMS *Gibraltar*, 20-Gun Sixth Rate, 1711		3·00	3·25
1751	£3 HMS *Gibraltar*, 20-Gun Sixth Rate, 1754		7·50	8·50
1745/1751 *Set of 7*			17·00	16·00

(Des Stephen Perera. Litho Lowe-Martin)

2017 (19 June). Centenary of House of Windsor. T **394** and similar square designs. Multicoloured. P 12½.

MS1752 104×103 mm. 64p. Type **394**; 70p. King Edward VIII; 80p. King George VI; £2 Queen Elizabeth II			10·00	11·00

395 Union Jack Flag, Flag over Street and Worn by Children   **396** Queen Elizabeth II

(Des Stephen Perera. Litho Lowe-Martin)

2017 (26 June). 50th Anniversary of the 1967 Referendum (1st issue). T **395** and similar square designs. Multicoloured. P 12½.

MS1753 159×72 mm. 22p. Type **395**; 64p. Union Jack, man and boy with Union Jack T-shirts and flag on wall; 70p. Union Jack and Coat of Arms over street; £2 Union Jack, flag over street and red, white and blue bunting over street			9·00	9·50

(Des Stephen Perera. Litho Lowe-Martin)

2017 (26 June). 50th Anniversary of the 1967 Referendum (2nd issue). P 13.

1754	**396**	£5 multicoloured	12·00	13·00

397 The Convent **398** Princess Diana

(Des Leslie Gaduzo (illustration) and Stephen Perera. Litho Cartor)

2017 (25 July). Gibraltar Military Heritage. T **397** and similar horiz designs. Multicoloured. P 13.

1755	18p. Type **397**	50	25
1756	22p. Cross of Sacrifice	60	25
1757	40p. 100 Ton Victorian Gun	1·10	60
1758	50p. War Memorial	1·40	90
1759	64p. Nelson's Anchorage	1·75	1·50
1760	70p. Parson's Lodge	2·00	2·00
1761	80p. Garrison Library	2·25	2·25
1762	£1 Battle of Trafalgar Cemetery	2·75	3·00
1763	£3 American War Memorial	7·50	8·50
1755/1763	Set of 9	18·00	17·00

(Des Stephen Perera. Litho Cartor)

2017 (31 Aug). 20th Death Anniversary of Princess Diana. T **398** and similar square designs. Multicoloured. P 12½.

1764	64p. Type **398**	1·75	1·25
1765	70p. Princess Diana wearing black dress with patterned collar and cuff	2·00	1·75
1766	£1 Princess Diana with head resting on hand	2·75	3·00
1767	£2 Princess Diana facing left	5·50	6·50
1764/1767	Set of 4	11·00	11·00

399 Windsor Bridge **400** Cupcake with Rock Ape Decoration

(Des Stephen Perera. Litho Bpost Security Printers)

2017 (30 Sept). Upper Rock Nature Reserve. T **399** and similar horiz designs. Multicoloured. P 12.

1768	22p. Type **399**	60	25
1769	50p. Great Siege Tunnels	1·25	90
1770	64p. Apes Den	1·75	1·50
1771	70p. Cable Car	2·00	2·00
1772	80p. St Michael's Cave	2·25	2·25
1773	£1 Mediterranean Steps	2·75	3·00
1774	£2 Moorish Castle	5·50	6·50
1768/1774	Set of 7	14·50	15·00

(Des Stephen Perera. Litho Lowe-Martin Group)

2017 (2 Nov). Christmas Cupcakes. T **400** and similar vert designs. Multicoloured. P 13.

1775	22p. Type **400**	60	20
1776	40p. Cupcake with Pan Dulce-a cake decoration	1·00	40
1777	64p. Cupcake with snowman decoration	1·75	1·25
1778	70p. Cupcake with Rock of Gibraltar shaped Christmas tree decoration	2·00	1·75
1779	80p. Cupcake with Penguin decoration	2·25	2·25
1780	£2 Cupcake with Santa decoration	5·50	6·50
1775/1780	Set of 6	12·00	11·00

401 Schreiber's Bent-winged Bat (*Miniopterus schreibersii*) **402** Dog

(Des Jonathan Pointer (illustration) and Stephen Perera. Litho Bpost Security Printers)

2017 (30 Nov). Endangered Species. Bats of Gibraltar. T **401** and similar horiz designs. Multicoloured. P 13.

1781	70p. Type **401**	2·25	2·50
	a. Strip of 4. Nos. 1781/1784	11·00	12·00
1782	80p. European Free-tailed Bat (*Tadarida teniotis*)	2·50	2·75
1783	£1 Greater Noctule Bat (*Nyctalus lasiopterus*)	2·75	3·00
1784	£2 Isabelline Serotine Bat (*Eptesicus isabellinus*)	4·75	5·00
1781/1784	Set of 4	11·00	12·00

Nos. 1781/1784 were printed together, *se-tenant*, as horizontal and vertical strips of four stamps in sheetlets of 16.

(Des Stephen Perera. Litho Cartor)

2018 (30 Jan). Chinese New Year. Year of the Dog. T **402** and similar square designs. Multicoloured. P 12½.

1785	£2 Type **402**	3·75	4·00
	a. Horiz pair. Nos. 1785/1786	7·50	8·00
1786	£2 Dog (yellow scrolls in background)	3·75	4·00

Nos. 1785/1786 were printed together, *se-tenant*, as horizontal pairs in sheetlets of ten (2×5), each pair forming a composite background design.

403 Corral Road Bridge **404** 5.25 HAA, 1953

(Des Leslie Gaduzo (illustration) and Stephen Perera. Litho Bpost Security Printers)

2018 (6 Feb). Europa. Bridges. T **403** and similar horiz designs. Multicoloured. P 12.

1787	70p. Type **403**	1·60	1·60
1788	70p. Landport Bridge	1·60	1·60
1789	£1·50 Montagu Curtain	3·00	3·50
1790	£1·50 Windsor Bridge	3·00	3·50
1787/1790	Set of 4	8·25	9·25

(Des Leslie Gaduzo (illustration) and Stephen Perera. Litho Bpost Security Printers)

2018 (5 Mar). Gibraltar Cannons. T **404** and similar horiz designs. Multicoloured. P 12.

1791	10p. Type **404**	35	25
1792	12p. 6 inch Coast, 1909	35	25
1793	18p. 8 inch Howitzer, 1783	50	30
1794	22p. 9.2 inch Coast MK 10, 1935	55	30
1795	40p. 10 inch RML, 1870	1·00	70
1796	50p. 12 Pounder, 1758	1·25	90
1797	64p. 24 Pounder, 1779	1·75	1·40
1798	70p. 13 inch Mortar, 1783	2·00	1·75
1799	80p. 25 Pounder Gun-How, 1943	2·00	1·75
1800	£1 64 Pounder RML, 1873	2·75	3·00
1801	£2 Bofors L40-70, 1951	5·00	6·00
1802	£3 Russian 24 PR, 1854	7·00	8·00
1791/1802	Set of 12	22·00	22·00

405 Prince Harry and Ms. Meghan Markle

(Des Stephen Perera. Litho Cartor)

2018 (5 Mar). Royal Engagement. P 13.

MS1803 71×77 mm. **405** £3 multicoloured ... 7·00 7·50

An imperforate proof of this miniature sheet was sold by the Gibraltar bureau on the original printer card with a certificate of authenticity for £19·95.

406 HMS *Queen Elizabeth* arrives in Gibraltar for First Overseas Port Visit, 9 February 2018

(Des Stephen Perera. Litho Bpost Security Printers)

2018 (10 May). New Aircraft Carrier HMS *Queen Elizabeth*. P 12.
MS1804 100×49 mm. **406** £3 multicoloured..................... 7·50   8·50

407 Coronation Portrait of Queen Elizabeth II by Sir Cecil Beaton

408 Supermarine Spitfire V

(Des Stephen Perera. Litho Bpost Security Printers)

2018 (10 May). 65th Anniversary of Coronation of Queen Elizabeth II. P 12.
| 1805 | **407** | £4 multicoloured............................ | 10·00 | 12·00 |

(Des Stephen Perera. Litho Lowe-Martin)

2018 (15 May). Cryptocurrency. Sheet containing 4×50p. stamps as No. 1658. Multicoloured. P 14.
MS1806 50p.×4 Rock of Gibraltar...
No. **MS**1806 contains four 50p. stamps and was sold at face value (£2). It also has four identical QR codes, which when scanned with a smartphone or tablet links to a website giving instructions on how to claim 200 QRG of cryptocurrency tokens/coins per sheet.

(Des Stephen Perera. Litho Bpost Security Printers)

2018 (18 May). Centenary of the RAF (Royal Air Force). Aircraft stationed in Gibraltar. T **408** and similar vert designs. Multicoloured. P 12.
1807	22p. Type **408**	55	35
1808	64p. Hawker Sea Hurricane I	1·60	1·25
1809	70p. Consolidated Catalina I	1·75	1·40
1810	80p. Short Sunderland I	2·00	2·00
1811	£2 Vickers Wellington IC	5·00	6·00
1812	£3 Lockheed Hudson III	7·50	8·50
1807/1812 Set of 6		17·00	18·00

MS1813 131×105 mm. 64p. Eurofighter Typhoon T.1; 70p. Hawker Siddeley Buccaneer S.2; 80p. Hawker Siddeley Nimrod MR.1; £3 Boeing C-17A...................... 13·00   15·00

409 View towards Old Town with Moorish Castle

410 Prince Charles as Boy

(Des Benjamin Hassan (illustration) and Stephen Perera. Litho Cartor)

2018 (31 July). Views of the Rock. T **409** and similar horiz designs. Multicoloured. P 13.
1814	22p. Type **409**	55	35
1815	64p. View to south with eastern slopes of the Rock	1·60	1·25
1816	70p. View of eastern side towards Spain	1·75	1·40
1817	80p. Catalan Bay	2·00	2·00
1818	£1 Western side of the Rock (77×27 *mm*)	2·50	3·00
1819	£2 Trinity Lighthouse, Europa Point in stormy weather (77×27 *mm*)	5·00	6·00
1814/1819 Set of 6		12·00	12·50

MS1820 170×70 mm. Nos. 1814/1819.............................. 13·50   16·00

(Des Stephen Perera. Litho Lowe-Martin)

2018 (21 Sept). 70th Birthday of the Prince of Wales. T **410** and similar horiz designs. Multicoloured. P 12½.
1821	22p. Type **410**	55	35
1822	64p. Prince Charles, *c.* 1969	1·60	1·25
1823	70p. Prince Charles, *c.* 1969	1·75	1·40
1824	80p. Prince Charles, *c.* 1980	2·00	2·00
1825	£2 Prince Charles, *c.* 2000	5·00	6·00
1826	£3 Prince Charles in recent years	7·50	8·50
1821/1826 Set of 6		17·00	18·00

411 Soldiers crossing Trench

(Des Stephen Perera. Litho Lowe-Martin)

2018 (21 Sept). Centenary of the End of World War I. T **411** and similar square designs. Multicoloured. P 12½.
MS1827 158×72 mm. 70p. Type **411**; 80p. Silhouettes of ten soldiers walking; £1 Silhouettes of six soldiers walking; £3 Silhouette of soldier pointing the way and others standing.. 14·00   16·00
MS1828 72×72 mm. £3 Gibraltar Arboretum War Memorial... 7·50   8·50

412 *Adoration of the Magi* (Bernardino Luini), 1520–1525

(Des Stephen Perera. Litho Bpost Security Printers)

2018 (2 Nov). Christmas. Birth and Adoration of Jesus Christ. T **412** and similar vert designs. Multicoloured. P 12.
1829	22p. Type **412**	55	35
1830	40p. *Nativity* (Fra Angelico), 1437–1445	1·00	80
1831	64p. *Nativity* (Gentile da Fabriano) (detail), 1423	1·60	1·25
1832	70p. *Nativity and Annunciation to the Shepherds* (Bernardino Luini), 1520–1525	1·75	1·50
1833	80p. *Adoration of the Magi* (Gentile da Fabriano) (detail), 1423	2·00	2·00
1834	£2 *Adoration of the Magi* (Giotto), 1303–1305	5·00	6·00
1835	£3 *Holy Family* (Johann Martin Metz), 1790.	7·50	8·50
1829/1835 Set of 7		17·00	18·00

MS1836 135×100 mm. Nos. 1829/1835........................ 19·00   20·00

413 Calpe House, London

(Des Leslie Gaduzo (illustration) and Stephen Perera. Litho Bpost Security Printers)

2018 (2 Nov). Calpe House. T **413** and similar horiz design. Multicoloured. P 12.
MS1837 130×74 mm. £1·50 Type **413**; £1·50 Houses of Parliament, London (*sold for £3·50*)........................ 9·00   10·00
No. **MS**1837 was sold for £3·50, a 50c. charity premium for Calpe House, which provides accommodation for hospital patients sent from Gibraltar to London for treatment.

GIBRALTAR Design Index

POST & GO STAMPS

In 2015 the issue was announced of Post & Go stamps depicting the Gibraltar flag, available in six different service options. In spite of the fact that first day covers dated 13 May 2015 were available from the Gibraltar Philatelic Bureau, we understand that no Post & Go service is available in the post office in Gibraltar, so they do not fulfil the criteria required for listing in this catalogue.

STAMP BOOKLETS

1906 (Oct). Black on red cover. Stapled.
SB1   2s.0½d. booklet containing 24×½d. and 12×1d.
      (Nos. 56a, 67) in blocks of 6...

1912 (17 July). Black on red cover. Stapled.
SB2   2s.0½d. booklet containing 24×½d. and 12×1d.
      (Nos. 76/77) in blocks of 6 .... £7500

B **1**

1974 (2 May). Centenary of Universal Postal Union. Multicoloured cover, 152×79 mm, as T B **1**. Stitched.
SB3   46p. booklet containing *se-tenant* panes of 3 (No. 328a)
      and 6 (No. 328b).. 5·00

B **1a** Michelangelo

1975 (17 Dec). 500th Birth Anniversary of Michelangelo. Multicoloured cover, 165×91 mm, as T B **1a**, Stitched.
SB4   90p. booklet containing *se-tenant* panes of 3 (No. 358a)
      and 6 (No. 358b).. 4·00

B **1b** Buckingham Palace

1978 (12 June). 25th Anniversary of Coronation. Multicoloured cover, 165×92 mm, as T B **1b**. Stitched.
SB5   £1·15 booklet containing *se-tenant* pane of 6 (No. 404a)
      and pane of 1 (No. 406a)................................ 2·25

B **2**

1981 (2 Sept). Black and vermilion (No. SB6) and black and ultramarine (No. SB7) covers, 76×51 mm, as T B **2**. Stamps attached by selvedge.
SB6   50p. booklet containing *se-tenant* pane of 5 and 1 label
      (No. 451a) .... 1·50
SB7   £1 booklet containing *se-tenant* pane of 10 and 2
      labels (No. 451b).. 2·75

B **3** Moorish Castle

1993 (21 Sept). Multicoloured covers, 53×40 mm, as T B **3**. Stamps affixed by selvedge.
SB8   20p. booklet containing 5p. (No. 699) in strip of 4......... 2·00
SB9   £1·20 booklet containing 24p. (No. 702) in strip of 5 .... 5·00

B **4** Rock of Gibraltar and Games Events

1995 (8 May). Island Games '95. Multicoloured cover, 175×97 mm, as T B **4**. Stitched.
SB10   £4·68 booklet containing four panes of 3 (Nos. 745a/745b,
      746a and 747a).. 11·00

B **5** Kitten

1997 (12 Feb). Kittens. Multicoloured cover, 150×80 mm, as T B **5**. Stitched.
SB11   £5 booklet containing five *se-tenant* panes
      (Nos. 797a/797b, 798a, 799a and **MS**803a)............. 14·00

B **6** Battle of the Nile

1998 (1 Aug). Bicentenary of Battle of the Nile. Multicoloured cover, 145×102 mm, as T B **6**. Stitched.
SB12   £5 booklet containing five panes (Nos. 839a/839b
      and 840a/840c) .... 18·00

B **7**

2000 (9 May). New Millennium. History of Gibraltar. Bright red, yellow-orange and black cover, 144×102 mm, as T B **7** showing the Gibraltar Coat of Arms. Booklet contains text and illustrations on panes and interleaving pages. Stitched.
SB13 £7·40 booklet containing panes Nos. 916b/931b .... 22·00

B **8** Flowers on Coastline

2004 (10 Sept). Wild Flowers. Multicoloured cover, 160×98 mm, as T B **8**. Booklet contains text and illustrations on each pane. Stitched.
SB14 £6·40 booklet containing 13 panes (Nos. 1094a/1106a) 22·00

B **9** East Side of Rock of Gibraltar

2007 (26 Sept). Prehistoric Wildlife of Gibraltar. Multicoloured cover, 155×114 mm, as T B **9**. Booklet contains text and illustrations on panes and first page. Stitched.
SB15 £8·46 booklet containing seven panes (Nos. 1220a/1220b and 1221a/**MS**1225a)................................ 30·00

STAMP SACHETS

Booklet covers with the stamps loose inside, contained in clear plastic sachets, were issued for a number of definitive sets from 1978 onwards. They are outside the scope of this catalogue.

POSTAGE DUE STAMPS

D **1**

D **2**

D **3** Gibraltar Coat of Arms

Normal

Large 'd.' (R. 9/6, 10/6)

4d. Ball of 'd' broken and serif at top damaged (R. 9/5). Other stamps in 5th vertical row show slight breaks to ball of 'd'.

(Typo D.L.R.)
1956 (1 Dec). Chalk-surfaced paper. Wmk Mult Script CA. P 14.

D1	D **1**	1d. green	1·50	4·25
D2		2d. sepia	2·25	2·75
		a. Large 'd' (R. 9/6, 10/6)	28·00	40·00
D3		4d. blue	1·75	5·00
		a. Broken 'd'	40·00	
D1/D3 *Set of 3*			5·00	11·00

1971 (15 Feb). As Nos. D1/D3 but inscr in decimal currency. W w **12**. P 17½×18.

D4	D **1**	½p. green	25	80
D5		1p. sepia	25	70
D6		2p. blue	25	1·00
D4/D6 *Set of 3*			65	2·25

(Des A. Ryman. Litho Questa)
1976 (13 Oct). W w **14**. P 14×13½.

D7	D **2**	1p. light red-orange	15	60
D8		3p. bright blue	15	75
D9		5p. orange-vermilion	20	75
D10		7p. reddish violet	20	75
D11		10p. greenish slate	25	75
D12		20p. green	45	1·00
D7/D12 *Set of 6*			1·25	4·25

(Des A. Ryman. Litho B.D.T.)
1984 (2 July). W w **14** (sideways). P 15×14.

D13	D **3**	1p. black	20	60
D14		3p. vermilion	30	60
D15		5p. ultramarine	35	60
D16		10p. new blue	50	60
D17		25p. deep mauve	75	1·00
D18		50p. reddish orange	1·00	1·75
D19		£1 blue-green	1·50	3·25
D13/D19 *Set of 7*			4·25	7·75

D **4** Water Port Gates

(Des Olympia Reyes. Litho B.D.T.)
1996 (30 Sept). Gibraltar Landmarks. T D **4** and similar vert designs. P 14½×14.

D20	1p. black, emerald and bright yellow-green	20	75
D21	10p. black and bluish grey	50	70
D22	25p. black, red-brown and chestnut	1·00	1·25
D23	50p. black and reddish lilac	1·75	2·25
D24	£1 black, olive-brown and chestnut	2·75	3·75
D25	£2 black and light blue	4·50	6·50
D20/D25 *Set of 6*		9·50	14·00

Designs: 1p. T D **4**; 10p. Naval Dockyard; 25p. Military Hospital; 50p. Governor's Cottage; £1 Swans on the Laguna; £2 Catalan Bay.

D **5** Greenfinch

(Des Roger Gorringe and Anselmo Torres. Litho Cartor)
2002 (6 June). Gibraltar Finches. T D **5** and similar vert designs. Multicoloured. P 13×13½.

D26	5p. Type D **5**	20	40
D27	10p. Serin	35	50
D28	20p. Siskin	60	80
D29	50p. Linnet	1·40	1·60
D30	£1 Chaffinch	2·25	2·75
D31	£2 Goldfinch	4·00	5·50
D26/D31 *Set of 6*		8·00	10·50

MOROCCO AGENCIES
(British Post Offices)

With the growth of trade and commerce during the 19th-century European powers opened post offices or postal agencies in various ports along the Moroccan coast from the early 1850's onwards. French and, in the north, Spanish influence eventually became predominant, leading to the protectorates of 1912. The British, who had inaugurated a regular postal service between Gibraltar and Tangier or Tetuan in May 1778, established their first postal agency in 1857. German offices followed around the turn of the century.

Before 1892 there was no indigenous postal service and those towns where there was no foreign agency were served by a number of private local posts which continued to flourish until 1900. In November 1892 the Sultan of Morocco established the Cherifian postal service, but this was little used until after its reorganisation at the end of 1911. The Sultan's post was absorbed by the French postal service on 1 October 1913. Issues of the local posts and of the Sultan's post can occasionally be found used on cover in combination with stamps of Gibraltar or the Morocco Agencies.

On 1 April 1857 the first British postal agency was established at Tangier within the precincts of the Legation and was run by the official interpreter. From 1 March 1858 all letters for Great Britain sent via the British mail packets from Gibraltar required franking with Great Britain stamps.

In 1872 the Tangier office was relocated away from the Legation and the interpreter was appointed British Postal Agent and supplied with a stock of British postage stamps which would be cancelled on arrival in Gibraltar with the 'A26' obliterator. Such stamps used in Morocco can therefore only be identified when on cover or large piece, also showing the Tangier datestamp. British stamps known to have been used in Morocco are the ½d. of 1870, 1880 and 1884; 1d. of 1864 and 1881; 2d. of 1858; 2½d. of 1876, 1880, 1881 and 1884; 4d. of 1865 and 6d. stamps of 1856, 1865 and 1872. At the same time the agency was placed under the control of the Gibraltar postmaster.

When the colonial posts became independent of the British GPO on 1 January 1886 Gibraltar retained responsibility for the Morocco Agencies. Further offices, each under the control of the local Vice-Consul, were opened from 1886 onwards.

I. GIBRALTAR USED IN MOROCCO

Details of the various agencies are given below. Type C, the 'A26' killer, is very similar to postmarks used at Gibraltar during this period. In addition to the town name, postmarks at Types A, B and D from Fez, Mazagan, Saffi and Tetuan were also inscribed 'MOROCCO'.

Postmark Types used on Gibraltar issues.

Type A Circular datestamp    Type C 'A26' killer

Type B Duplex cancellation

Type D Registered oval

BISECTS. The 1886-1887 1d. and the 10c., 40c. and 50c. values of the 1889 surcharges and the 1889–1896 issue are known bisected and used for half their value from various of the Morocco Agencies (price *on cover* from £500). These bisects were never authorised by the Gibraltar Post Office.

CASABLANCA

The British postal agency opened on 1 January 1887 and was initially supplied with ½d., 4d. and 6d. stamps from the Gibraltar 1886 overprinted on Bermuda issue and 1d., 2d. and 2½d. values from the 1886–1887 set.

Stamps of GIBRALTAR cancelled with Types A (without code or code 'C'), B (without code or code 'A') or D.

1886. Optd on Bermuda (Nos. 1/7).

Z1	½d. dull green	£150
Z2	4d. orange-brown	£550
Z3	6d. deep lilac	£550

1886–87. Queen Victoria £sd issue (Nos. 8/14).

Z4	½d. dull green	80·00
Z5	1d. rose	65·00
Z6	2d. brown-purple	£150
Z7	2½d. blue	80·00
Z8	4d. orange-brown	£225
Z10	1s. bistre	£600

1889. Surch in Spanish currency (Nos. 15/21).

Z11	5c. on ½d. green	£100
Z12	10c. on 1d. rose	90·00
Z13	25c. on 2d. brown-purple	£130
Z14	25c. on 2½d. bright blue	80·00
Z15	40c. on 4d. orange-brown	£275
Z16	50c. on 6d. bright lilac	£225
Z17	75c. on 1s. bistre	£300

1889–96. Queen Victoria Spanish currency issue (Nos. 22/33).

Z18	5c. green	25·00
Z19	10c. carmine	22·00
Z20	20c. olive-green and brown	70·00
Z21	20c. olive-green	£225
Z22	25c. ultramarine	22·00
Z23	40c. orange-brown	70·00
Z24	50c. bright lilac	55·00
Z25	75c. olive-green	£190
Z26	1p. bistre	£160
Z28	1p. bistre and ultramarine	80·00
Z29	2p. black and carmine	£110

FEZ

The British postal agency in this inland town opened on 13 February 1892 and was initially supplied with stamps up to the 50c. value from the Gibraltar 1889–1896 issue.

Stamps of GIBRALTAR cancelled with Types A (without code) or D.

1889–96. Queen Victoria Spanish currency issue (Nos. 22/33).

Z31	5c. green	55·00
Z32	10c. carmine	45·00
Z33	20c. olive-green and brown	£150
Z35	25c. ultramarine	70·00
Z36	40c. orange-brown	£170
Z37	50c. bright lilac	£150

LARAICHE

The British postal agency at Laraiche opened on 3 April 1886, although the first postmark, an 'A26' killer, was not supplied until May.

Stamps of GIBRALTAR cancelled with Types B (without code) or D.

1886. Optd on Bermuda (Nos. 1/7).

Z39	½d. dull green	
Z40	1d. rose-red	
Z41	2½d. ultramarine	

1886–87. Queen Victoria £sd issue (Nos. 8/14).

Z42	½d. dull green	£200
Z43	1d. rose	£190
Z45	2½d. blue	£200

1889. Surch in Spanish currency (Nos. 15/21).

Z47	5c. on ½d. green	£170
Z48	10c. on 1d. rose	
Z49	25c. on 2½d. bright blue	

It is believed that the other surcharges in this series were not supplied to Laraiche.

1889–96. Queen Victoria Spanish currency issue (Nos. 22/33).

Z50	5c. green	70·00
Z51	10c. carmine	75·00
Z52	20c. olive-green and brown	£180
Z54	25c. ultramarine	75·00
Z55	40c. orange-brown	£180
Z56	50c. bright-lilac	£180
Z57	1p. bistre and ultramarine	

MAZAGAN

This was the main port for the inland city of Marrakesh. The British postal agency opened on 1 March 1888 and was initially supplied with stamps from the Gibraltar 1886–1887 series.

Stamps of GIBRALTAR cancelled with Types A (codes 'A' or 'C')
or D (without code, code 'A' or code 'C').

1886–87. Queen Victoria £sd issue (Nos. 8/14).

Z58	½d. dull green		65·00
Z59	1d. rose		75·00
Z60	2d. brown-purple		
Z61	2½d. blue		80·00
Z62	4d. orange-brown		£275
Z63	6d. lilac		£325

1889. Surch in Spanish currency (Nos. 15/21).

Z64	5c. on ½d. green		£120
Z65	10c. on 1d. rose		
Z66	25c. on 2½d. bright blue		

It is believed that the other surcharges in this series were not supplied to Mazagan.

1889–96. Queen Victoria Spanish currency issue (Nos. 22/33).

Z67	5c. green		30·00
Z68	10c. carmine		26·00
Z69	20c. olive-green and brown		£120
Z70	25c. ultramarine		60·00
Z71	40c. orange-brown		£140
Z72	50c. bright lilac		£170
Z74	1p. bistre and ultramarine		£190
Z75	2p. black and carmine		£190

MOGADOR

The British postal agency at this port opened on 1 June 1887 and was initially supplied with stamps from the Gibraltar 1886–1887 series.

Stamps of GIBRALTAR cancelled with Types A (code 'C'),
B (code 'C') or D.

1886. Optd on Bermuda (Nos. 1/7).

Z75d	4d. orange-brown		£550

1886–87. Queen Victoria £sd issue (Nos. 8/14).

Z76	½d. dull green		60·00
Z77	1d. rose		85·00
Z78	2d. brown-purple		£170
Z79	2½d. blue		70·00
Z79b	6d. lilac		£300

1889. Surch in Spanish currency (Nos. 15/21).

Z80	5c. on ½d. green		£100
Z81	10c. on 1d. rose		95·00
Z82	25c. on 2½d. bright blue		85·00

It is believed that the other surcharges in this series were not supplied to Mogador.

1889–96. Queen Victoria Spanish currency issue (Nos. 22/33).

Z83	5c. green		25·00
Z84	10c. carmine		25·00
Z85	20c. olive-green and brown		£110
Z87	25c. ultramarine		29·00
Z88	40c. orange-brown		£120
Z89	50c. bright lilac		90·00
Z89a	1p. bistre		£180
Z90	1p. bistre and ultramarine		£120
Z91	2p. black and carmine		£150

RABAT

The British postal agency at this port on the north-west coast of Morocco opened on 6 April 1886, although the first cancellation, an 'A26' killer, was not supplied until May. The initial stock of stamps was from the Gibraltar 1886 overprinted on Bermuda issue.

Stamps of GIBRALTAR cancelled with Types B (code 'O') or D.

1886. Optd on Bermuda (Nos. 1/7).

Z92	½d. dull green		
Z93	1d. rose-red		
Z94	2½d. ultramarine		£325

1886–87. Queen Victoria £sd issue (Nos. 8/14).

Z95	½d. dull green		75·00
Z96	1d. rose		70·00
Z97	2d. brown-purple		£150
Z98	2½d. blue		80·00
Z101	1s. bistre		£700

1889. Surch in Spanish currency (Nos. 15/21).

Z102	5c. on ½d. green		£110
Z103	10c. on 1d. rose		90·00
Z104	25c. on 2½d. bright blue		95·00

It is believed that the other surcharges in this series were not supplied to Rabat.

1889–96. Queen Victoria Spanish currency issue (Nos. 22/33).

Z105	5c. green		30·00
Z106	10c. carmine		27·00
Z107	20c. olive-green and brown		£130
Z108	25c. ultramarine		29·00
Z109	40c. orange-brown		£130
Z110	50c. bright lilac		95·00
Z110a	1p. bistre and ultramarine		£150

SAFFI

The British postal agency at this port opened on 1 July 1891 and was supplied with stamps from the Gibraltar 1889–1896 series.

Stamps of GIBRALTAR cancelled with Types B (code 'C') or D (code 'C')*.

1889–96. Queen Victoria Spanish currency issue (Nos. 22/33).

Z111	5c. green		45·00
Z112	10c. carmine		40·00
Z113	20c. olive-green and brown		£110
Z115	25c. ultramarine		48·00
Z116	40c. orange-brown		£150
Z117	50c. bright lilac		£110
Z118	1p. bistre and ultramarine		£140
Z119	2p. black and carmine		£160

* Stamps of this issue can also be found with double-circle datestamps of the French Post Office at Saffi. These are worth less than prices quoted.

TANGIER

The British postal agency in Tangier opened on 1 April 1857 and from 1 March of the following year letters from it sent via the packet service to Great Britain required franking with Great Britain stamps.

No identifiable postmark was supplied to Tangier until 1872 and all earlier mail was cancelled with one of the Gibraltar marks. In April 1872 a postmark as Type A was supplied on which the 'N' of 'TANGIER' was reversed. A corrected version, with code letter 'A', followed in 1878, but both were used as origin or arrival marks and the Great Britain stamps continued to be cancelled with Gibraltar obliterators. The Type A postmarks generally fell into disuse after 1880 and very few identifiable marks occur on mail from Tangier until the introduction of Gibraltar stamps on 1 January 1886.

Type E Horizontal
'A26' killer

New cancellers were not ready on 1 January and, as a temporary measure, the old horizontal 'A26' killer, which was very worn by this time, was sent from Gibraltar. Strikes of this handstamp on the overprinted Bermuda stamps tend to be blurred but are indicative of use in Tangier. Use of Type E lasted until 4 May, when it was replaced by Type C.

Stamps of GIBRALTAR cancelled with Types A (codes 'A' or 'C'),
B (code 'A'), D or E.

1886. Optd on Bermuda (Nos. 1/7).

Z120	½d. dull green		75·00
Z121	1d. rose-red		£100
Z122	2d. purple-brown		£225
Z123	2½d. ultramarine		95·00
Z124	4d. orange-brown		£300
Z125	6d. deep lilac		£300
Z126	1s. yellow-brown		£650

1886–87. Queen Victoria £sd issue (Nos. 8/14).

Z127	½d. dull green		25·00
Z128	1d. rose		25·00
Z129	2d. brown-purple		80·00
Z130	2½d. blue		32·00
Z131	4d. orange-brown		£130
Z132	6d. lilac		£200
Z133	1s. bistre		£400

1889. Surch in Spanish currency (Nos. 15/21).

Z134	5c. on ½d. green		50·00
Z135	10c. on 1d. rose		32·00
Z136	25c. on 2d. brown-purple		65·00
Z137	25c. on 2½d. bright blue		48·00
Z138	40c. on 4d. orange-brown		£180
Z139	50c. on 6d. bright lilac		£170
Z140	75c. on 1s. bistre		£225

1889–96. Queen Victoria Spanish currency issue (Nos. 22/33).

Z141	5c. green		7·00
Z142	10c. carmine		6·00
Z143	20c. olive-green and brown		26·00

Z144	20c. olive-green	£140
Z145	25c. ultramarine	9·00
Z146	40c. orange-brown	14·00
Z147	50c. bright lilac	13·00
Z148	75c. olive-green	95·00
Z149	1p. bistre	85·00
Z150	1p. bistre and ultramarine	32·00
Z151	2p. black and carmine	60·00
Z152	5p. slate-grey	£130

TETUAN

The British postal agency in this northern town opened on 4 May 1890 and was supplied with stamps from the Gibraltar 1889–1896 series.

Stamps of GIBRALTAR cancelled with Types A (code 'C'),
B (code 'C' often inverted) or D (code 'C').

1889–96. Queen Victoria Spanish currency issue (Nos. 22/33).

Z153	5c. green	45·00
Z154	10c. carmine	45·00
Z155	20c. olive-green and brown	£100
Z157	25c. ultramarine	48·00
Z158	40c. orange-brown	£120
Z159	50c. bright lilac	£120
Z161	1p. bistre and ultramarine	£160
Z162	2p. black and carmine	£170
Z163	5p. slate-grey	£200

Gibraltar stamps, Nos. 22/28 and 31/32 were issued, overprinted 'Marocco Agencies' on 1 June 1898.

Heligoland

Stamps of HAMBURG (see *Germany* catalogue) were used in Heligoland until 16 April 1867. The Free City of Hamburg ran the Heligoland postal service between 1796 and 1 June 1866. Its stamps continued in use on the island until replaced by Heligoland issues.

PRICES FOR STAMPS ON COVER
Nos. 1/19   *from* × 3

PRINTERS. All the stamps of Heligoland were typographed at the Imperial Printing Works, Berlin.

REPRINTS. Many of the stamps of Heligoland were subsequently reprinted at Berlin (between 1875 and 1885), Leipzig (1888) and Hamburg (1892 and 1895). Of these only the Berlin productions are difficult to distinguish from the originals so separate notes are provided for the individual values. Leipzig reprints can be identified by their highly surfaced paper and those from Hamburg by their 14 perforation. All of these reprints are worth much less than the original stamps priced below.

There was, in addition, a small reprinting of Nos. 13/19, made by the German government in 1890 for exchange purposes, but examples of this printing are far scarcer than the original stamps.

Forgeries, printed by lithography instead of typography, also exist for Nos. 1/4, 6 and 8 perforated 12½ or 13. Forged cancellations can also be found on originals and, on occasion, genuine postmarks on reprints.

1

(Currency. 16 schillings = 1 mark)

Three Dies of Embossed Head for Types **1** and **2**:

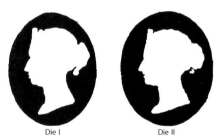

Die I   Die II

Die III

Die I.   Blob instead of curl beneath the chignon. Outline of two jewels at top of diadem.
Die II. Curl under chignon. One jewel at top of diadem.
Die III. Shorter curl under chignon. Two jewels at top of diadem.

(Des Wedding. Die eng E. Schilling)

1867 (21 Mar)–**68**. Head Die I embossed in colourless relief. Roul.
1	**1**	½sch. blue-green and rose	£350	£850
		a. Head Die III (7.68)	£800	£1200
2		1sch. rose and blue-green	£180	£200
3		2sch. rose and grass-green	20·00	65·00
4		6sch. green and rose	21·00	£275

For Nos. 1/4 the second colour given is that of the spandrels on the ½ and 1sch., and of the spandrels and central background for the 2 and 6sch.

All four values exist from the Berlin, Leipzig and Hamburg reprintings. The following points are helpful in identifying originals from Berlin reprints; for Leipzig and Hamburg reprints see general note above:

½sch. –   Reprints are all in yellowish green and show Head Die II
1sch. –   All reprints are Head Die III
2sch. –   Berlin reprints are in dull rose with a deeper blue-green
6sch. –   Originals show white specks in green. Berlin reprints have a more solid bluish green

1869 (Apr)–**73**. Head embossed in colourless relief. P 13½×14½.
5	**1**	¼sch. rose and green (background) (I) (*quadrillé paper*) (8.73)	35·00	£1600
		a. Error. Green and rose (background) (9.73)	£190	£3250
		b. Deep rose and pale green (background) (11.73)	95·00	£1600
6		½sch. blue-green and rose (II)	£225	£250
		a. Yellow green and rose (7.71)	£160	£225
		b. Quadrillé paper (6.73)	£110	£170
7		¾sch. green and rose (I) (*quadrillé paper*) (12.73)	50·00	£1200
8		1sch. rose and yellow-green (11.71)..	£160	£200
		a. Quadrillé paper. Rose and pale blue-green (6.73)	£140	£200
9		1½sch. green and rose (I) (*quadrillé paper*) (9.73)	95·00	£275

For Nos. 5/9 the second colour given is that of the spandrels on the ½ and 1sch., of the central background on the ¼ and 1½sch., and of the central background, side labels and side marginal lines of the ¾sch.

No. 5a was a printing of the ¼sch. made in the colour combination of the 1½sch. by mistake.

A further printing of the ½sch. (Head die I) in deep rose-red and yellowish green (background), on non-*quadrillé* paper, was made in December 1874, but not issued (*Price £15, unused*).

All five values exist from the Berlin, Leipzig and Hamburg reprintings. The following points are helpful in identifying originals from Berlin reprints; for Leipzig and Hamburg reprints see general note above:

¼sch. –   All Berlin and some Hamburg reprints are Head Die II
½sch. –   Berlin reprints on thinner paper with solid colour in the spandrels
¾sch. –   Berlin reprints on thinner, non-quadrillé paper
1sch. –   Berlin reprints are on thinner paper or show many breaks in the rose line beneath 'SCHILLING' at the top of the design or in the line above it at the foot
1½sch. – All Berlin and some Hamburg reprints are Head Die II

Berlin, Leipzig and Hamburg reprints also exist of the 2 and 6sch., but these values do not come as perforated originals.

(New Currency. 100 pfennig = 1 mark)

2    **3**    **4**

5

(Des H. Gätke. Die eng E. Schilling (T **2**), A. Schiffner (others))

1875 (Feb)–**90**. Head Die II on T **2** embossed in colourless relief. P 13½×14½.
10	**2**	1pf. (¼d.) deep green and rose	20·00	£550
11		2pf. (½d.) deep rose and deep green	20·00	£650
12	**3**	3pf. (⅝d.) pale green, red and yellow (6.76)	£250	£1200
		a. Green, red and orange (6.77)	£170	£900
13	**2**	5pf. (¾d.) deep yellow-green and rose ..	23·00	20·00
		a. Deep green and rose (6.90)	27·00	55·00
14		10pf. (1½d.) deep rose and deep green ..	42·00	23·00
		a. Scarlet and pale blue-green (5.87)	17·00	24·00
15	**3**	20pf. (2½d.) rose, green and yellow (6.76)	£275	£120
		a. Rose-carmine, deep green and orange (4.80)	£180	55·00
		b. Dull red, pale green and lemon (7.88)	26·00	30·00
		c. Aniline vermilion, bright green and lemon (6.90)	16·00	55·00

16	**2**	25pf. (3d.) deep green and rose	24·00	29·00
17		50pf. (6d.) rose and green............................	26·00	42·00
18	**4**	1m. (1s.) deep green, scarlet and black		
		(8.79)	£170	£200
		a. Perf 11½	£1400	
		b. *Deep green, aniline rose and black*		
		(5.89)	£170	£200
19	**5**	5m. (5s.) deep green, aniline rose, black		
		and yellow (8.79).....................................	£225	£950
		a. Perf 11½	£1400	
		ab. Imperf between (horiz pair)	£6000	

For stamps as T **2** the first colour is that of the central background and the second that of the frame. On the 3pf. the first colour is that of the frame and the top band of the shield, the second is the centre band and the third the shield border. The 20pf. is similar, but has the centre band in the same colour as the frame and the upper band on the shield in the second colour.

The 1, 2 and 3pf. exist from the Berlin, Leipzig and Hamburg reprintings. There were no such reprints for the other values. The following points are helpful in identifying originals from Berlin reprints; for Leipzig and Hamburg reprints see general note above:

1pf.	–	Berlin printings show a peculiar shade of pink
2pf.	–	All reprints are much lighter in shade than the deep rose and deep green of the originals
3pf.	–	Berlin reprints either show the band around the shield in brownish orange, or have this feature in deep yellow with the other two colours lighter

Heligoland was ceded to Germany on 9 August 1890.

Ionian Islands

The British occupation of the Ionian Islands was completed in 1814 and the archipelago was placed under the protection of Great Britain by the Treaty of Paris of 9 November 1815. The United States of the Ionian Islands were given local self-government, which included responsibility for the postal services. Crowned-circle handstamps were, however, supplied in 1844, although it is believed these were intended for use on prepaid mail to foreign destinations.

Examples of the Great Britain 1855 1d. red-brown stamp are known used at Corfu, cancelled as No. CC2, but it is believed that these originate from mail sent by the British garrison.

CEPHALONIA
CROWNED-CIRCLE HANDSTAMPS

CC1	CC **1**	CEPHALONIA (19.4.1844)................*Price on cover*	£1800

CORFU
CROWNED-CIRCLE HANDSTAMPS

CC2	CC **1**	CORFU (19.4.1844) ....*Price on cover*	£650
CC3	CC **1**	CORFU (G. or B.) (1844) ....*Price on cover*	—

ZANTE
CROWNED-CIRCLE HANDSTAMPS

CC4	CC **1**	ZANTE (G. or B.) (19.4.1844) ....*Price on cover*	£1400

Nos. CC1/CC2 were later, *circa* 1860/1861, struck in green (Cephalonia) or red (Corfu).

It is believed that examples of No. CC4 in black are from an unauthorised use of this handstamp which is now on display in the local museum. A similar handstamp, but without 'PAID AT' was introduced in 1861.

PRICES FOR STAMPS ON COVER TO 1945	
Nos. 1/3	*from* × 10

PERKINS BACON 'CANCELLED'. For notes on these handstamps, showing 'CANCELLED' between horizontal bars forming an oval, see Catalogue Introduction.

1

(Eng C. Jeens. Recess Perkins Bacon & Co)

1859 (15 June). Imperf.

1	**1**	(½d.) orange (no wmk) (H/S 'CANCELLED'		
		in oval £12000)	£140	£750
2		(1d.) blue (wmk '2') (H/S 'CANCELLED' in		
		oval £12000)...	35·00	£300
3		(2d.) carmine (wmk '1') (H/S		
		'CANCELLED' in oval £12000)	28·00	£300

On 30 May 1864, the islands were ceded to Greece, and these stamps became obsolete.

Great care should be exercised in buying used stamps, on or off cover, as forged postmarks are plentiful.

Malta

Early records of the postal services under the British Occupation are fragmentary, but it is known that an Island Postmaster was appointed in 1802. A British Packet Agency was established in 1806 and it later became customary for the same individual to hold the two appointments together. The inland posts continued to be the responsibility of the local administration, but the overseas mails formed part of the British GPO system.

The stamps of Great Britain were used on overseas mails from September 1857. Previously during the period of the Crimean War letters franked with Great Britain stamps from the Crimea were cancelled at Malta with a wavy line obliterator. Such postmarks are known between April 1855 and September 1856.

The British GPO relinquished control of the overseas posts on 31 December 1884 when Great Britain stamps were replaced by those of Malta.

Z 1   Z 2

1855–56. Stamps of GREAT BRITAIN cancelled with wavy lines obliteration, T Z **1**.

Z1	1d. red-brown (1854), Die I, wmk Small Crown, perf 16	£1000
Z2	1d. red-brown (1855), Die II, wmk Small Crown, perf 14	£1000
	a. Very blued paper	
Z3	1d. red-brown (1855), Die II, wmk Large Crown, perf 16	£1000
Z3a	1d. red-brown (1855), Die II, wmk Large Crown, perf 14	£1000
Z4	2d. (1854), wmk Large Crown, perf 14 Plate No. 5	£4500
Z5	6d. (1854) embossed	£4500
Z6	1s. (1847) embossed	£5000

It is now established that this obliterator was sent to Malta and used on mail in transit emanating from the Crimea.

1857 (18 Aug)–**59.** Stamps of GREAT BRITAIN cancelled 'M', T Z **2**.

Z7	1d. red-brown (1841), imperf	£2500
Z8	1d. red-brown, Die I, wmk Small Crown, perf 16	£160
Z9	1d. red-brown, Die II, wmk Small Crown, perf 16	£950
Z10	1d. red-brown, Die II (1855), wmk Small Crown, perf 14	£250
Z11	1d. red-brown, Die II (1855), wmk Large Crown, perf 14	80·00
Z11a	1d. rose-red (1857) wmk Large Crown, perf 16	
Z12	1d. rose-red (1857), wmk Large Crown, perf 14	22·00
Z13	2d. blue (1841), imperf	£3750
Z14	2d. blue (1854) wmk Small Crown, perf 16 Plate No. 4	£850
Z15	2d. blue (1855), wmk Large Crown, perf 14 ...... From Plate Nos. 5, 6.	65·00
Z16	2d. blue (1858), wmk Large Crown, perf 16 Plate No. 6.	£350
Z17	2d. blue (1858) (Plate Nos. 7, 8, 9) .... From	45·00
Z18	4d. rose (1857)	40·00
	a. Thick glazed paper	£225
Z19	6d. violet (1854), embossed	£5000
Z20	6d. lilac (1856)	42·00
	a. Thick paper	£250
Z21	6d. lilac (1856) (blued paper)	£900
Z22	1s. green (1856)	£130
	a. Thick paper	£200

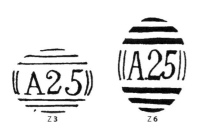

Z 3   Z 6

Z 4

Z 5

Z 7

1859–84. Stamps of GREAT BRITAIN cancelled 'A25' as in Types Z **3**/Z **7**.

Z23	½d. rose-red (1870 1879) .... From	32·00
	Plate Nos. 4, 5, 6, 8, 9, 10, 11, 12, 13, 14, 15, 19, 20	
Z24	1d. red-brown (1841), imperf	£3250
Z25	1d. red-brown (1854), wmk Small Crown, perf 16	£373
Z26	1d. red-brown (1855), wmk Large Crown, perf 14	85·00
Z27	1d. rose-red (1857), wmk Large Crown, perf 14	9·00
Z28	1d. rose-red (1861), Alphabet IV	£475
Z30	1d. rose-red (1864–1879) .... From	19·00
	Plate Nos, 71, 72, 73, 74, 76, 78, 79, 80, 81, 82, 83, 84, 85, 86, 87, 88, 89, 90, 91, 92, 93, 94, 95, 96, 97, 98, 99, 100, 101, 102, 103, 104, 105, 106, 107, 108, 109, 110, 111, 112, 113, 114, 115, 116, 117, 118, 119, 120, 121, 122, 123, 124, 125, 127, 129, 130, 131, 132, 133, 134, 135, 136, 137, 138, 139, 140, 141, 142, 143, 144, 145, 146, 147, 148, 149, 150, 151, 152, 153, 154, 155, 156, 157, 158, 159, 160, 161, 162, 163, 164, 165, 166, 167, 168, 169, 170, 171, 172, 173, 174, 175, 176, 177, 178, 179, 180, 181, 182, 183, 184, 185, 186, 187, 188, 189, 190, 191, 192, 193, 194, 195, 196, 197, 198, 199, 200, 201, 202, 203, 204, 205, 206, 207, 208, 209, 210, 211, 212, 213, 214, 215, 216, 217, 218, 219, 220, 221, 222, 223, 224.	
Z31	1½d. lake-red (1870–1879) (Plate Nos. 1, 3)........... From	£600
Z32	2d. blue (1841), imperf	£4500
Z33	2d. blue (1855) wmk Large Crown perf 14	80·00
Z34	2d. blue (1858–1869)................................ From Plate Nos. 7, 8, 9, 12, 13, 14, 15.	19·00
Z35	2½d. rosy mauve (1875) (blued paper) ....From Plate Nos. 1, 2.	80·00
Z36	2½d. rosy mauve (1875–1876) .... From Plate Nos. 1, 2, 3.	35·00
Z37	2½d. rosy mauve (Error of Lettering)...................	£3500
Z38	2½d. rosy mauve (1876–1879) .... From Plate Nos. 3, 4, 5, 6, 7, 8, 9, 10, 11, 12, 13, 14, 15, 16, 17.	17·00
Z39	2½d. blue (1880–1881)............................... From Plate Nos. 17, 18, 19, 20.	11·00
Z40	2½d. blue (1881) (Plate Nos. 21, 22, 23)............ From	8·00
Z41	3d. carmine-rose (1862)	£130
Z42	3d. rose (1865) (Plate No. 4)	80·00
Z43	3d. rose (1867–1873) .... From Plate Nos. 4, 5, 6, 7, 8, 9, 10.	32·00
Z44	3d. rose (1873–1876) .... From Plate Nos. 11, 12, 14, 15, 16, 17, 18, 19, 20.	38·00
Z45	3d. rose (1881) (Plate Nos. 20, 21) .... From	£1000
Z46	3d. on 3d. lilac (1883)	£550
Z47	4d. rose (or rose-carmine) (1857)	40·00
	a. Thick glazed paper	£150
Z48	4d. red (1862) (Plate Nos. 3, 4) .... From	35·00
Z49	4d. vermilion (1865–1873) .... From Plate Nos. 7, 8, 9, 10, 11, 12, 13, 14.	18·00
Z50	4d. vermilion (1876) (Plate No. 15)	£225

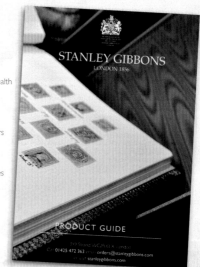

Z51	4d. sage-green (1877) (Plate Nos. 15, 16)............ *From*	£110
Z52	4d. grey-brown (1880) wmk Large Garter .... Plate No. 17.	£180
Z53	4d. grey-brown (1880) wmk Crown .... *From* Plate Nos. 17, 18..	55·00
Z54	6d. violet (1854), embossed..	£3750
Z55	6d. lilac (1856)...	48·00
	a. Thick paper	
Z56	6d. lilac (1862) (Plate Nos. 3, 4).................................*From*	40·00
Z57	6d. lilac (1865–1867) (Plate Nos. 5, 6) ....*From*	30·00
Z58	6d. lilac (1865–1867) (Wmk error)..............................	£1300
Z59	6d. lilac (1867) (Plate No. 6).......................................	38·00
Z60	6d. violet (1867–1870) (Plate Nos. 6, 8, 9) ....*From*	26·00
Z61	6d. buff (1872–1873) (Plate Nos. 11, 12)..................*From*	£100
Z62	6d. chestnut (1872) (Plate No. 11)..............................	35·00
Z63	6d. grey (1873) (Plate No. 12).....................................	75·00
Z64	6d. grey (1873–1880) ....*From* Plate Nos. 13, 14, 15, 16, 17.	35·00
Z65	6d. grey (1881–1882) (Plate Nos. 17, 18) ....*From*	80·00
Z66	6d. on 6d. lilac (1883)...	£150
Z67	8d. orange (1876)...	£475
Z68	9d. straw (1862)...	£700
Z69	9d. bistre (1862)...	£650
Z70	9d. straw (1865)...	£650
Z71	9d. straw (1867)...	£800
Z72	10d. red-brown (1867)..	£130
Z73	1s. (1847), embossed..	£4000
Z74	1s. green (1856)..	80·00
Z75	1s. green (1856) (*thick paper*)................................	£275
Z76	1s. green (1862)..	70·00
Z77	1s. green ('K' variety)...	£2250
Z78	1s. green (1865) (Plate No. 4)..................................	48·00
Z79	1s. green (1867–1873) (Plate Nos. 4, 5, 6, 7) ....*From*	32·00
Z80	1s. green (1873–1877) ....*From* Plate Nos. 8, 9, 10, 11, 12, 13.	45·00
Z81	1s. orange-brown (1880) (Plate No. 13)...................	£300
Z82	1s. orange-brown (1881) ....*From* Plate Nos. 13, 14.	90·00
Z83	2s. blue (*shades*) (1867)..*From*	£160
Z84	2s. brown (1880)...	£3250
Z85	5s. rose (1867–1874) (Plate Nos. 1, 2)..................*From*	£425
Z86	5s. rose (1882) (Plate No. 4), *blued paper*............	£2500
Z87	5s. rose (1882) (Plate No. 4), *white paper*	£1800
Z88	10s. grey-green (1878)..	£3500

1880.

Z89	½d. deep green..	16·00
Z90	½d. pale green..	16·00
Z91	1d. Venetian red..	16·00
Z92	1½d. Venetian red..	£500
Z93	2d. pale rose...	40·00
Z94	2d. deep rose..	42·00
Z95	5d. indigo..	75·00

1881.

Z96	1d. lilac (*14 dots*)..	35·00
Z97	1d. lilac (*16 dots*)..	9·00

1883–84.

Z98	½d. slate-blue...	20·00
Z99	1½d. lilac...	
Z100	2d. lilac...	£110
Z101	2½d. lilac...	13·00
Z102	3d. lilac...	
Z103	4d. dull green..	£180
Z104	5d. dull green..	£150
Z105	6d. dull green..	£400
Z106	9d. dull green..	
Z107	1s. dull green..	£400
Z108	5s. rose (*blued paper*)...	£2000
Z109	5s. rose (*white paper*)...	£1100

POSTAL FISCALS

Z109a	1d. reddish lilac (Type F **8**) (1867) wmk Anchor	
Z110	1d. purple (Type F **12**) (1871) wmk Anchor..................	£850
Z111	1d. purple (Type F **12**) (1881) wmk Orb......................	£650

PRICES FOR STAMPS ON COVER TO 1945	
Nos. 1/3	*from* × 5
Nos. 4/17	*from* × 6
Nos. 18/19	*from* × 12
Nos. 20/29	*from* × 6
No. 30	—
Nos. 31/33	*from* × 4
Nos. 34/37	*from* × 10
Nos. 38/88	*from* × 4
Nos. 92/93	*from* × 5
Nos. 97/103	*from* × 3
Nos. 104/105	—
Nos. 106/120	*from* × 3
No. 121	—
Nos. 122/138	*from* × 3
Nos. 139/140	—

PRICES FOR STAMPS ON COVER TO 1945	
Nos. 141/172	*from* × 4
Nos. 173/209	*from* × 3
Nos. 210/231	*from* × 2
Nos. D1/D10	*from* × 30
Nos. D11/D20	*from* × 15

CROWN COLONY

PRINTERS. Nos. 1/156. Printed by De La Rue; typographed *except where otherwise stated.*

1

Type **1**

The first Government local post was established on 10 June 1853 and, as an experiment, mail was carried free of charge. During 1859 the Council of Government decided that a rate of ½d. per ½ ounce should be charged for this service and stamps in T **1** were ordered for this purpose. Both the new rate and the stamps were introduced on 1 December 1860. Until 1 January 1885 the ½d. stamps were intended for the local service only; mail for abroad being handled by the British Post Office on Malta, using GB stamps.

Specialists now recognise 29 printings in shades of yellow and one in green during the period to 1884. These printings can be linked to the changes in watermark and perforation as follows:

Ptg 1—Blued paper without wmk. P 14.
Ptgs 2 and 3—White paper without wmk. P 14.
Ptgs 4 to 9, 11, 13 to 19, 22 to 24—Crown CC wmk. P 14.
Ptg 10—Crown CC wmk. P 12½ (rough).
Ptg 12—Crown CC wmk. P 12½ (clean-cut).
Ptgs 20 and 21—Crown CC wmk. P 14×12½.
Ptgs 25 to 28, 30—Crown CA wmk. P 14.
Ptg 29—In green (No. 20).

PRICES. The prices quoted for Nos. 1/19 are for examples in very fine condition, with fresh colour. Unused examples should have original gum, used examples should have neat clear cancels. The many surviving stamps which do not meet these criteria are usually worth only a fraction of the prices quoted, with stamps of poor colour being virtually worthless.

(Des E. Fuchs)

1860 (1 Dec)–**63**. No wmk. P 14.

(a) Blued paper

1	½d. buff (1.12.60)	£1300	£650

(b) Thin, hard white paper

2	½d. brown-orange (11.61)	£1300	£500
3	½d. buff (1.63)	£850	£400
	a. Pale buff...	£850	£400

No. 1 is printed in fugitive ink. It is known imperforate but was not issued in that state (*Price* £12000 *unused*).

The printing on No. 2 gives a very blurred and muddy impression; on Nos. 3/3a the impression is clear.

Specks of carmine can often be detected with a magnifying glass on Nos. 2/3a, and also on No. 4. Examples also exist on which parts of the design are in pure rose, due to defective mixing of the ink.

1863–81. Wmk Crown CC.

(a) P 14

4	½d. buff (6.63) (*shades*)	£120	75·00
	w. Wmk inverted	£500	£450
	x. Wmk reversed	£1700	
5	½d. bright orange (11.64)	£900	£250
	w. Wmk inverted	£1700	£400
6	½d. orange-brown (4.67)	£425	£110
7	½d. dull orange (4.70)	£300	90·00
	w. Wmk inverted	†	£700
	x. Wmk reversed	£2000	
8	½d. orange-buff (5.72)	£190	80·00
9	½d. golden yellow (aniline) (10.74)	£350	£400
10	½d. yellow-buff (9.75) (*shades*)	85·00	60·00
11	½d. pale buff (3.77)	£190	75·00
	w. Wmk inverted	£1200	£600
12	½d. bright orange-yellow (4.80)	£275	£120
13	½d. yellow (4.81)	£150	75·00
	w. Wmk inverted	†	£600

(b) P 12½ rough (No. 14) or clean-cut (No. 15)

14	½d. buff-brown (11.68)	£160	£110
15	½d. yellow-orange (5.71)	£400	£180

(c) P 14×12½

16	½d. yellow-buff (7.78)	£200	£100
	w. Wmk inverted	†	£1700
17	½d. yellow (2.79)	£275	£110

Examples of No. 4 from the 1863 printing are on thin, surfaced paper; later printings in the same shade were on unsurfaced paper.

The ink used for No. 5 is mineral and, unlike that on No. 9, does not stain the paper.

Some variations of shade on No. 6 may be described as chestnut. The ink of No. 6 is clear and never muddy, although some examples are over-inked. Deeper shades of No. 4, with which examples of No. 6 might be confused, have muddy ink.

Nos. 7/8 and 11 are distinctive shades which should not be confused with variants of No. 10.

It is believed that there are no surviving pairs of the buff-brown imperforate between variety previously listed.

The Royal Collection contains an unused horizontal pair of the yellow-buff perforated 12½×14.

1882 (Mar)–**84**. Wmk Crown CA. P 14.

18		½d. orange-yellow	40·00	35·00
19		½d. red-orange (9.84)	18·00	50·00

2

3

4

5

1885 (1 Jan)–**90**. Wmk Crown CA. P 14.

20	**1**	½d. green	5·50	50
		w. Wmk inverted	£170	£110
21	**2**	1d. rose	85·00	26·00
		w. Wmk inverted	£2250	
22		1d. carmine (*shades*) (1890)	13·00	35
		w. Wmk inverted	†	£1400
23	**3**	2d. grey	13·00	2·50
24	**4**	2½d. dull blue	65·00	3·00
25		2½d. bright blue	50·00	1·00
26		2½d. ultramarine	50·00	1·00
27	**3**	4d. brown	11·00	3·00
		a. Imperf (pair)	£5500	£6500
		w. Wmk inverted	£2500	
28		1s. violet	50·00	12·00
29		1s. pale violet (1890)	60·00	21·00
		w. Wmk inverted	£1100	£350
20/28 *Set of 6*			£120	17·00
20s/28s Optd 'SPECIMEN' *Set of 6*			£4750	

Although not valid for postage until 1 January 1885 these stamps were available at the GPO, Valletta from 27 December 1884.

Three unused examples of the ½d. green, No. 20, are known line perforated 12. These originated from proof books, the stamp not being issued for use with this perforation.

The Royal Philatelic Collection includes an example of the 1d. carmine printed on the gummed side.

1886 (1 Jan). Wmk Crown CC. P 14.

30	**5**	5s. rose	£110	80·00
		s. Optd 'SPECIMEN'	£1000	
		w. Wmk inverted	£160	£130

6 Harbour of Valletta

7 Gozo Fishing Boat

8 Galley of Knights of St John

9 Emblematic figure of Malta

10 Shipwreck of St Paul

(Types **6/10** recess)

1899 (4 Feb)–**1901**. P 14.

(a) Wmk Crown CA (sideways* on ¼d.)

31	**6**	¼d. brown (4.1.01)	9·00	2·75
		a. Red-brown	1·50	40
		b. Wmk upright	£3000	
		bx. Wmk upright (reversed)	†	£3000
		w. Wmk Crown to left of CA	2·50	75
		ws. Optd 'SPECIMEN'	80·00	
		x. Wmk sideways reversed	48·00	25·00
		y. Wmk Crown to left of CA and reversed	80·00	32·00
		ys. Optd 'SPECIMEN'	£275	
32	**7**	4½d. sepia	27·00	16·00
		x. Wmk reversed	£1000	
33	**8**	5d. vermilion	48·00	19·00
		x. Wmk reversed	£225	£225

(b) Wmk Crown CC

34	**9**	2s.6d. olive-grey	45·00	17·00
		x. Wmk reversed	£1500	
35	**10**	10s. blue-black	£100	65·00
		x. Wmk reversed	—	£1200
		y. Wmk inverted and reversed	£900	£700
31/35 *Set of 5*			£190	£100
31s/35s Optd 'SPECIMEN' *Set of 5*			£300	

* The normal sideways watermark shows Crown to right of CA, *as seen from the back of the stamp.*

One Penny

(11)

12

1902 (4 July). Nos. 24 and 25 surch locally at Govt Ptg Office with T **11**.

36		1d. on 2½d. dull blue	2·00	2·50
		a. Surch double	£16000	£3750
		b. 'One Pnney' (R. 9/2)	32·00	55·00
		ba. Surch double, with 'One Pnney'	£42000	
		s. Optd 'SPECIMEN'	70·00	
		w. Wmk inverted	—	£2000
37		1d. on 2½d. bright blue	1·50	2·50
		a. 'One Pnney' (R. 9/2)	32·00	55·00

(Des E. Fuchs)

1903 (12 Mar)–**04**. Wmk Crown CA. P 14.

38	**12**	½d. green	11·00	85
39		1d. blackish brown and red (7.5.03)	15·00	40
40		2d. purple and grey	29·00	6·00
41		2½d. maroon and blue (1903)	32·00	4·50
42		3d. grey and purple (26.3.03)	2·00	50
43		4d. blackish brown and brown (19.5.04)	26·00	19·00
44		1s. grey and violet (6.4.03)	35·00	9·00
38/44 *Set of 7*			£130	35·00
38s/44s Optd 'SPECIMEN' *Set of 7*			£190	

Broken Crown (Lower right pane. R. 7/3)

1904–**14**. Wmk Mult Crown CA (sideways* on ¼d.). P 14.

45	**6**	¼d. red-brown (10.10.05)	9·00	2·50
		a. Deep brown (1910)	9·50	10
		w. Wmk Crown to left of CA	29·00	1·50
		x. Wmk reversed	£350	
		y. Wmk Crown to left of CA and reversed	£250	
47	**12**	½d. green (6.11.04)	5·50	30
		aw. Wmk inverted		
		b. Deep green (1909)	6·00	10
		bw. Wmk inverted		
48		1d. black and red (24.4.05)	26·00	20
		c. Broken Crown	£550	50·00
49		1d. red (2.4.07)	3·50	10
50		2d. purple and grey (22.2.05)	18·00	3·75
51		2d. grey (4.10.11)	6·50	7·00
		c. Broken Crown	£250	£250
52		2½d. maroon and blue (8.10.04)	40·00	60
		c. Broken Crown	£750	70·00
53		2½d. bright blue (15.1.11)	5·50	4·25
		c. Broken Crown	£200	£150

54		4d. black and brown (1.4.06)	11·00	8·50
		c. Broken Crown	£325	
		w. Wmk inverted		
55		4d. black and red/*yellow* (21.11.11)........	4·75	5·50
		c. Broken Crown	£180	£200
57	**7**	4½d. brown (27.2.05)	40·00	8·50
		w. Wmk inverted	£550	£375
58		4½d. orange (6.3.12†)	4·75	4·50
59	**8**	5d. vermilion (20.2.05)..........................	48·00	8·00
60		5d. pale sage-green (1910)	4·75	4·25
		a. *Deep sage-green* (1914)	11·00	14·00
		y. Wmk inverted and reversed	†	£1100
61	**12**	1s. grey and violet (14.12.04)................	50·00	2·00
		c. Broken Crown	—	£100
62		1s. black/*green* (15.3.11).....................	7·50	4·25
		c. Broken Crown	£275	£160
63		5s. green and red/*yellow* (22.3.11)	65·00	75·00
		c. Broken Crown	£1100	
45/63 *Set of* 17			£300	£110

45*as*, 47*bs*, 49*s*, 51*s*, 53*s*, 55*s*, 58*s*, 60*s*, 62*s*/3*s* Optd
'SPECIMEN' *Set of* 10... £500

* The normal sideways watermark shows Crown to right of CA, *as seen from the back of the stamp.*

† This is the earliest known date of use.

13	**14**	**15**

Break in scroll (R. 1/12)

Broken crown and scroll (R. 2/12)

Nick in top right scroll (R. 3/12)
(some printings from 1920 onwards
show attempts at repair)

Break in lines below left scroll (R. 4/9. Ptgs
from May 1920)

Damaged leaf at bottom right (R. 5/6. Ptgs
from April 1918)

1914–21. Ordinary paper (¼d. to 2½d., 2s.6d.) or chalk-surfaced paper (others). Wmk Mult Crown CA. P 14.

69	**13**	¼d. brown (2.1.14)...............................	2·00	10
		a. *Deep brown* (1919)	3·25	1·75
		x. Wmk reversed	†	£1600
71		½d. green (20.1.14).............................	3·75	30
		aa. Wmk sideways.............................	†	£11000
		a. *Deep green* (1919)	7·50	1·50
		aw. Wmk inverted	†	£450
73		1d. carmine-red (15.4.14)....................	1·50	10
		a. Scarlet (1915)	3·75	40
		w. Wmk inverted	†	£500
		y. Wmk inverted and reversed	†	£1600
75		2d. grey (12.8.14)................................	15·00	8·50
		aw. Wmk inverted	†	£1400
		b. *Deep slate* (1919)	15·00	19·00
77		2½d. bright blue (11.3.14).....................	3·00	65
		w. Wmk inverted	†	£225
78	**14**	3d. purple/*yellow* (1.5.20)...................	2·50	22·00
		a. *On orange-buff*	75·00	50·00
		bs. On yellow, white back (opt. 'SPECIMEN')................................	£375	
79	**6**	4d. black (21.8.15)...............................	15·00	7·00
		a. *Grey-black* (28.10.16)	45·00	10·00
80	**13**	6d. dull and bright purple (10.3.14)	11·00	21·00
		a. *Dull purple and magenta* (1918)........	16·00	21·00
		w. Wmk inverted		
81	**14**	1s. black/*green* (white back) (2.1.14)	17·00	48·00
		a. On green, green back (1915)	13·00	27·00
		ab. Wmk sideways	†	£2500
		as. Optd 'SPECIMEN'...........................	70·00	
		b. On blue-green, olive back (1918)........	19·00	38·00
		c. On emerald surface (1920)	9·00	48·00
		d. On emerald back (1921)	42·00	90·00
86	**15**	2s. purple and bright blue/*blue* (15.4.14)	50·00	38·00
		a. Break in scroll	£375	
		b. Broken crown and scroll..................	£400	£400
		c. Nick in top right scroll....................	£375	£375
		f. Damaged leaf at bottom right............	£500	£500
		g. *Dull purple and blue/grey-blue* (1921)......................................	90·00	65·00
		ga. Break in scroll	£650	
		gb. Broken crown and scroll.................	£700	
		ge. Break in lines below left scroll..........	£700	
		gf. Damaged leaf at bottom right..........	£700	£700
87	**9**	2s.6d. olive-green (1919).........................	75·00	80·00
		a. *Olive-grey* (1920)	80·00	£110

88	**15**	5s. green and red/*yellow* (21.3.17)	£100	£110
		a. Break in scroll	£550	
		b. Broken crown and scroll	£600	£650
		c. Nick in top right scroll	£600	£650
		e. Break in lines below left scroll	£800	£800
		f. Damaged leaf at bottom right	£750	
69/88 *Set of* 12			£250	£275
69s/88s (*ex* 2s.6d.) Optd 'SPECIMEN' *Set of* 11			£550	

The design of Nos. 79/79*a* differs in various details from that of T **6**. We have only seen one example of No. 71aa; it is in used condition.

No. 78*bs*, the 3d. purple on yellow on white back, was prepared for use in 1914, and 'SPECIMEN' examples were distributed to UPU members, but the stamp was never issued.

An example of the 2s.6d. olive-grey with bottom margin attached exists with the 'A' omitted from 'CA' in the watermark on the margin.

WAR TAX
(16)   17    18

1917–18. Optd with T **16** by De La Rue.

92	**13**	½d. deep green (14.12.17*)	2·25	15
		w. Wmk inverted	£650	
		y. Wmk inverted and reversed	£950	
93	**12**	3d. grey and purple (15.2.18*)	3·50	16·00
92s/93s Optd 'SPECIMEN' *Set of* 2			£150	

* These are the earliest known dates of use.

(T **17** recess)

1919 (6 Mar). Wmk Mult Crown CA. P 14.

96	**17**	10s. black	£3250	£4750
		s. Optd 'SPECIMEN'	£1000	

Dark flaw on scroll (R. 2/4 1st state)   Lines omitted from scroll (R. 2/4 later state)

1921 (16 Feb)–**22**. Chalk-surfaced paper (6d., 2s.) or ordinary paper (others). Wmk Mult Script CA. P 14.

97	**13**	¼d. brown (12.1.22)	6·00	40·00
98		½d. green (19.1.22)	6·50	35·00
99		1d. scarlet (24.12.21)	7·00	2·75
		w. Wmk inverted	£1200	£500
100	**18**	2d. grey	12·00	1·75
101	**13**	2½d. bright blue (15.1.22)	7·00	48·00
102		6d. dull purple and bright purple (19.1.22)	35·00	85·00
		sa. Opt 'SPECIMEN' double	£750	
103	**15**	2s. purple and blue/*blue* (shades) (19.1.22)	70·00	£225
		a. Break in scroll	£350	£750
		b. Broken crown and scroll	£375	
		c. Dark flaw on scroll	£3500	
		d. Lines omitted from scroll	£550	
		e. Break in lines below left scroll	£400	
		f. Damaged leaf at bottom right	£400	
		g. Nick in top right scroll	£375	
104	**17**	10s. black (19.1.22)	£350	£800
97/104 *Set of* 8			£450	£1100
97s/104s Optd 'SPECIMEN' *Set of* 8			£475	

Examples of all values are known showing a forged GPO Malta postmark dated 'MY 10 22'.

SELF-GOVERNMENT
(19)   **SELF-GOVERNMENT**
(20)

1922 (12 Jan–Apr). Optd with Types **19** or **20** (large stamps), at Govt Printing Office, Valletta.

(a) On No. 35. Wmk Crown CC

105	**10**	10s. blue-black (R.)	£250	£400
		x. Wmk reversed	£1800	

(b) On Nos. 71, 77, 78a, 80, 81d, 86c, 87a and 88.
Wmk Mult Crown CA

106	**13**	½d. green	2·25	4·25
		w. Wmk inverted	£200	
107		2½d. bright blue	19·00	50·00
108	**14**	3d. purple/*orange-buff*	5·00	27·00
109	**13**	6d. dull and bright purple	7·00	42·00
		x. Wmk reversed	£1500	£1500
110	**14**	1s. black/*emerald*	7·00	30·00
111	**15**	2s. purple and blue/*blue* (R.)	£250	£500
		a. Break in scroll	£1100	
		b. Broken crown and scroll	£1100	
		c. Nick in top right scroll	£1300	
		e. Break in lines below left scroll	£1300	
		f. Damaged leaf at bottom right	£1300	
112	**9**	2s.6d. olive-grey	32·00	55·00
		a. 'C' of 'CA' missing from wmk	£1400	
113	**15**	5s. green and red/*yellow*	60·00	£100
		a. Break in scroll	£375	
		b. Broken crown and scroll	£375	
		c. Lines omitted from scroll	£375	
		e. Break in lines below left scroll	£475	
		f. Damaged leaf at bottom right	£475	
106/113 *Set of* 8			£350	£700

(c) On Nos. 97/104. Wmk Mult Script CA

114	**13**	¼d. brown	30	1·25
		w. Wmk inverted		
115		½d. green (29.4)	5·50	16·00
116		1d. scarlet	1·00	20
117	**18**	2d. grey	6·50	45
118	**13**	2½d. bright blue (15.1)	1·10	2·50
119		6d. dull and bright purple (19.4)	26·00	55·00
120	**15**	2s. purple and blue/*blue* (R.) (25.1)	50·00	95·00
		a. Break in scroll	£300	
		b. Broken crown and scroll	£300	
		c. Lines omitted from scroll	£425	
		e. Break in lines below left scroll	£375	
		f. Damaged leaf at bottom right	£375	£600
121	**17**	10s. black (R.) (9.3)	£140	£250
		x. Wmk reversed	£3250	
114/121 *Set of* 8			£200	£375

Examples of all values are known showing a forged GPO Malta postmark dated 'MY 10 22'.

One Farthing
(21)   **22**    **23**

1922 (15 Apr). No. 100 surch with T **21**, at Govt Printing Office, Valletta.

122	**18**	¼d. on 2d. grey	85	30
		a. Dot to 'i' of 'Farthing' omitted	£425	

No. 122a occurred on R. 4/4 of the lower left pane during part of the printing only. Small or faint dots are found on other positions.

(Des E. C. Dingli (T **22**) and G. Vella (T **23**))

1922 (1 Aug)–**26**. Wmk Mult Script CA (sideways* on T **22**, except No. 140). P 14.

(a) Typo. Chalk-surfaced paper

123	**22**	¼d. brown (22.8.22)	3·00	60
		a. Chocolate-brown	7·50	80
		w. Wmk Crown to right of CA	—	£160
124		½d. green	2·50	15
		w. Wmk Crown to right of CA	—	£160
125		1d. orange and purple	7·50	20
		w. Wmk Crown to right of CA	—	£120
126		1d. bright violet (25.4.24)	4·25	80
127		1½d. brown-red (1.10.23)	5·50	15
128		2d. bistre-brown and turquoise (28.8.22)	3·75	1·25
		w. Wmk Crown to right of CA	—	£190
129		2½d. ultramarine (16.2.26)	6·50	20·00
130		3d. cobalt (28.8.22)	9·50	3·25
		a. Bright ultramarine	7·50	3·00
131		3d. black/*yellow* (16.2.26)	5·50	26·00
132		4d. yellow and bright blue (28.8.22)	3·00	6·50
		w. Wmk Crown to right of CA	£375	
133		6d. olive-green and reddish violet	7·50	4·75
134	**23**	1s. indigo and sepia	17·00	4·50
135		2s. brown and blue	14·00	25·00
136		2s.6d. bright magenta and black (28.8.22)	13·00	15·00
137		5s. orange-yellow and bright ultramarine (28.8.22)	21·00	50·00
138		10s. slate-grey and brown (28.8.22)	65·00	£160

		(b) Recess			
139	**22**	£1 black and carmine-red (wmk sideways) (28.8.22)	£150	£350
140		£1 black and bright carmine (wmk upright) (14.5.25)	£110	£325
123/140	*Set of 17*		£250	£550
123s/139s	Optd 'SPECIMEN' *Set of 17*		£550	

* The normal sideways watermark shows Crown to left of CA, *as seen from the back of the stamp.*

Two pence halfpenny
(24)

POSTAGE
(25)

1925. Surch with T **24**, at Govt Printing Office, Valletta.

141	**22**	2½d. on 3d. cobalt (3.12)	3·00	9·50
142		2½d. on 3d. bright ultramarine (9.12)	1·75	7·50

1926 (1 Apr). Optd with T **25** at Govt Printing Office, Valletta.

143	**22**	¼d. brown	1·75	9·00
144		½d. green	70	15
		w. Wmk Crown to right of CA	£170	
145		1d. bright violet	1·00	25
146		1½d. brown-red	1·25	60
147		2d. bistre-brown and turquoise	75	2·50
148		2½d. ultramarine	1·25	2·25
149		3d. black/*yellow*	75	1·00
		a. Opt inverted	£170	£500
150		4d. yellow and bright blue	27·00	45·00
		w. Wmk Crown to right of CA	£350	
151		6d. olive-green and violet	2·75	8·00
152	**23**	1s. indigo and sepia	5·50	26·00
153		2s. brown and blue	55·00	£150
154		2s.6d. bright magenta and black	18·00	50·00
155		5s. orange-yellow and bright ultramarine	10·00	50·00
156		10s. slate-grey and brown	7·00	22·00
143/156	*Set of 14*		£110	£325

26

27 Valletta Harbour

28 St Publius

29 Mdina (Notabile)

30 Gozo fishing boat

31 Neptune

32 Neolithic temple, Mnajdra

33 St Paul

(T **26** typo, others recess Waterlow)

1926 (6 Apr)–**27**. Types **26/33**. Inscr 'POSTAGE'. Wmk Mult Script CA. P 15×14 (T **26**) or 12½ (others).

157	**26**	¼d. brown	80	15
158		½d. yellow-green (5.8.26)	60	15
		a. Printed on the gummed side	£1700	
		w. Wmk inverted	†	£1600
159		1d. rose-red (1.4.27)	3·00	2·00

160		1½d. chestnut (7.10.26)	2·00	10
161		2d. greenish grey (1.4.27)	4·50	16·00
162		2½d. blue (1.4.27)	4·00	3·00
162*a*		3d. violet (1.4.27)	4·25	6·50
163		4d. black and red	3·75	18·00
164		4½d. lavender and ochre	3·50	7·50
165		6d. violet and scarlet (5.5.26)	4·25	10·00
166	**27**	1s. black	7·00	13·00
167	**28**	1s.6d. black and green	8·00	23·00
168	**29**	2s. black and purple	8·50	28·00
169	**30**	2s.6d. black and vermilion	21·00	55·00
170	**31**	3s. black and blue	21·00	48·00
171	**32**	5s. black and green (5.5.26)	24·00	75·00
172	**33**	10s. black and carmine (9.2.27)	65·00	£110
157/172	*Set of 17*		£160	£350
157s/172s	Optd 'SPECIMEN' *Set of 17*		£400	

POSTAGE

AIR MAIL
(34)

POSTAGE AND REVENUE
(35)

POSTAGE AND REVENUE.
(36)

1928 (1 Apr). Air. Optd with T **34**.

173	**26**	6d. violet and scarlet	1·75	2·25

1928 (1 Oct–5 Dec). As Nos. 157/172, optd.

174	**35**	¼d. brown	1·50	10
175		½d. yellow-green	1·50	10
176		1d. rose-red	1·75	3·25
177		1d. chestnut (5.12.28)	4·50	10
178		1½d. chestnut	3·00	85
179		1½d. rose-red (5.12.28)	4·25	10
180		2d. greenish grey	4·25	9·00
181		2½d. blue	2·00	10
182		3d. violet	2·00	80
183		4d. black and red	2·00	1·75
184		4½d. lavender and ochre	2·25	1·00
185		6d. violet and scarlet	2·25	1·75
186	**36**	1s. black (R.)	5·50	2·50
187		1s.6d. black and green (R.)	15·00	12·00
188		2s. black and purple (R.)	27·00	70·00
189		2s.6d. black and vermilion (R.)	17·00	21·00
190		3s. black and blue (R.)	23·00	24·00
191		5s. black and green (R.)	38·00	70·00
192		10s. black and carmine (R.)	70·00	£100
174/192	*Set of 19*		£200	£275
174s/192s	Optd 'SPECIMEN' *Set of 19*		£425	

1930 (20 Oct). As Nos. 157/172, but inscr 'POSTAGE (&) REVENUE'.

193		¼d. brown	60	10
194		½d. yellow-green	60	10
195		1d. chestnut	60	10
196		1½d. rose-red	70	10
197		2d. greenish grey	1·25	50
198		2½d. blue	2·00	10
199		3d. violet	1·50	10
200		4d. black and red	1·25	8·00
201		4½d. lavender and ochre	3·25	1·25
202		6d. violet and scarlet	3·00	2·75
203		1s. black	10·00	25·00
204		1s.6d. black and green	8·50	35·00
205		2s. black and purple	15·00	27·00
206		2s.6d. black and vermilion	17·00	60·00
207		3s. black and blue	50·00	60·00
208		5s. black and green	55·00	75·00
209		10s. black and carmine	£110	£180
193/209	*Set of 17*		£225	£425
193s/209s	Perf 'SPECIMEN' *Set of 17*		£400	

1935 (6 May). Silver Jubilee. As Nos. 144/147 of Cyprus, but printed by B.W. P 11×12.

210		½d. black and green	50	70
		a. Extra flagstaff	26·00	50·00
		b. Short extra flagstaff	65·00	£150
		c. Lightning conductor	40·00	65·00
211		2½d. brown and deep blue	2·50	4·50
		a. Extra flagstaff	£140	£190
		b. Short extra flagstaff	£180	£250
		c. Lightning conductor	£160	£225
212		6d. light blue and olive-green	7·00	14·00
		a. Extra flagstaff	£180	£275
		b. Short extra flagstaff	£325	£375
		c. Lightning conductor	£200	£275
213		1s. slate and purple	19·00	30·00
		a. Extra flagstaff	£425	£550
		b. Short extra flagstaff	£450	£600
		c. Lightning conductor	£400	£550
210/213	*Set of 4*		26·00	45·00
210s/213s	Perf 'SPECIMEN' *Set of 4*		£180	

For illustrations of plate varieties see Gibraltar.

Sheets from the second printing of the ½d., 6d. and 1s. in November 1935 had the extra flagstaff partially erased from the stamp with a sharp point.

1937 (12 May). Coronation. As Nos. 148/150 of Cyprus, but printed by D.L.R. P 14.

214	½d. green	10	20
215	1½d. scarlet	1·50	65
	a. Brown-lake	£650	£650
216	2½d. bright blue	1·50	80
214/216 Set of 3		2·75	1·50
214s/216s Perf 'SPECIMEN' Set of 3		£160	

37 Grand Harbour, Valletta

38 HMS *St Angelo*

39 Verdala Palace

40 Hypogeum, Hal Saflieni

41 Victoria and Citadel, Gozo

42 De L'Isle Adam entering Mdina

43 St John's Co-Cathedral

44 Ruins at Mnajdra

45 Statue of Manoel de Vilhena

46 Maltese girl wearing faldetta

47 St Publius

48 Mdina Cathedral

49 Statue of Neptune

50 Palace Square, Valletta

51 St Paul

1½d. Broken cross (Right pane R. 5/7)

2d. Extra windows (R. 2/7) (corrected in 1945)

2d. Flag on citadel (R. 5/8)

Damaged value tablet (R. 4/9)

5s. Semaphore flaw (R. 2/7)

(Recess Waterlow)

1938 (17 Feb*)–**43**. Types **37/51**. Wmk Mult Script CA (sideways on No. 217). P 12½.

217	**37**	¼d. brown	10	10
218	**38**	½d. green	4·50	30
218a		½d. red-brown (8.3.43)	55	30
219	**39**	1d. red-brown	7·00	40
219a		1d. green (8.3.43)	60	10
220	**40**	1½d. scarlet	3·75	30
		a. Broken cross	£400	90·00
220b		1½d. slate-black (8.3.43)	30	30
		ba. Broken cross	80·00	70·00
221	**41**	2d. slate-black	3·75	2·00
		a. Extra windows	£190	
221b		2d. scarlet (8.3.43)	40	30
		ba. Extra windows	85·00	60·00
		bb. Flag on citadel	£130	£100
222	**42**	2½d. greyish blue	9·00	1·25
222a		2½d. dull violet (8.3.43)	60	10
223	**43**	3d. dull violet	6·50	80
223a		3d. blue (8.3.43)	30	20
224	**44**	4½d. olive-green and yellow-brown	50	30
225	**45**	6d. olive-green and scarlet	3·00	30
226	**46**	1s. black	3·00	30
227	**47**	1s.6d. black and olive-green	8·50	4·00
228	**48**	2s. green and deep blue	5·50	7·50
229	**49**	2s.6d. black and scarlet	9·00	6·00
		a. Damaged value tablet	£400	£250
230	**50**	5s. black and green	5·50	9·00
		a. Semaphore flaw	85·00	£170
231	**51**	10s. black and carmine	19·00	19·00
217/231 Set of 21			75·00	45·00
217s/231s Perf 'SPECIMEN' Set of 21			£700	

* This is the local date of issue but the stamps were released in London on 15 February.

1946 (3 Dec). Victory. As Nos. 164/165 of Cyprus, but inscr 'MALTA' between Maltese Cross and George Cross.

232	1d. green	15	10
	w. Wmk inverted	£1800	
233	3d. blue	75	2·00
232s/233s Perf 'SPECIMEN' Set of 2		£120	

SELF-GOVERNMENT

(52)

½d. and **5s.** 'NT' joined
(R. 4/10)

1½d. 'NT' joined (R. 4/6)

2d. Halation flaw (Pl 2
R. 2/5) (ptg of 8 Jan 1953)

2d. Cracked plate (Pl 2
R. 5/1) (ptg of 8 Jan 1953)

6d. Damaged 'F' (R. 3/1)

'F' repaired

(Optd by Waterlow)

1948 (25 Nov)–**53**. New Constitution. As Nos. 217/231 but optd as T **52**; reading up on ½d. and 5s., down on other values, and smaller on ¼d. value.

234	**37**	¼d. brown	30	20
235	**38**	½d. red-brown	30	10
		a. 'NT' joined	19·00	25·00
236	**39**	1d. green	30	10
236*a*		1d. grey (8.1.53)	75	10
237	**40**	1½d. blue-black (R.)	1·25	10
		aa. Broken cross	£170	75·00
		a. 'NT' joined (R. 4/6)		
237*b*		1½d. green (8.1.53)	30	10
		ba. Albino opt	†	£18000
238	**41**	2d. scarlet	1·25	10
		a. Extra windows	£200	£120
		b. Flag on citadel	£160	£110
238*c*		2d. yellow-ochre (8.1.53)	30	10
		ca. Halation flaw	£200	£225
		cc. Cracked plate	£190	£200
239	**42**	2½d. dull violet (R.)	80	10
239*a*		2½d. scarlet-vermilion (8.1.53)	75	1·50
240	**43**	3d. blue (R.)	3·25	15
		aa. 'NT' joined (R.4/6)		
240*a*		3d. dull violet (R.) (8.1.53)	50	15
241	**44**	4½d. olive-green and yellow-brown	2·75	1·00
241*a*		4½d. olive-green and deep ultramarine (R.) (8.1.53)	50	90
242	**45**	6d. olive-green and scarlet	3·25	15
		a. Damaged 'F'	£110	70·00
		b. 'F' repaired	95·00	70·00
243	**46**	1s. black	3·75	40
244	**47**	1s.6d. black and olive-green	2·50	50
245	**48**	2s. green and deep blue (R.)	9·50	2·50
246	**49**	2s.6d. black and scarlet	12·00	2·50
		a. Damaged value tablet	£2000	
247	**50**	5s. black and green (R.)	30·00	3·50
		a. 'NT' joined	£300	£150
		b. Semaphore flaw	—	£3750
248	**51**	10s. black and carmine	30·00	27·00
234/248 *Set of* 21			90·00	35·00

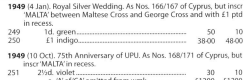

1949 (4 Jan). Royal Silver Wedding. As Nos. 166/167 of Cyprus, but inscr 'MALTA' between Maltese Cross and George Cross and with £1 ptd in recess.

249		1d. green	50	10
250		£1 indigo	38·00	48·00

1949 (10 Oct). 75th Anniversary of UPU. As Nos. 168/171 of Cyprus, but inscr 'MALTA' in recess.

251		2½d. violet	30	10
		a. 'A' of 'CA' omitted from wmk	£1200	£1200
252		3d. deep blue	3·00	1·00
		a. 'C' of 'CA' omitted from wmk	£1200	
		b. 'A' of 'CA' omitted from wmk	£1200	
253		6d. carmine-red	60	1·00
254		1s. blue-black	60	2·50
251/254 *Set of* 4			4·00	4·25

53 Queen Elizabeth II when Princess

54 Our Lady of Mount Carmel (attrib Palladino)

(T **53/54**. Recess B.W.)

1950 (1 Dec). Visit of Princess Elizabeth to Malta. Wmk Mult Script CA. P 12×11½.

255	**53**	1d. green	15	15
256		3d. blue	25	20
257		1s. black	1·00	3·00
255/257 *Set of* 3			1·25	3·00

1951 (12 July). Seventh Centenary of the Scapular. Wmk Mult Script CA. P 12×11½.

258	**54**	1d. green	20	30
259		3d. violet	50	10
260		1s. black	2·10	2·50
258/260 *Set of* 3			2·50	2·50

1953 (3 June). Coronation. As No. 172 of Cyprus.

261		1½d. black and deep yellow-green	70	10

55 St John's Co-Cathedral

56 Immaculate Conception (Caruana) (altarpiece, Cospicua)

(Recess Waterlow)

1954 (3 May). Royal Visit. Wmk Mult Script CA. P 12½.

262	**55**	3d. violet	45	10

(Photo Harrison)

1954 (8 Sept). Centenary of Dogma of the Immaculate Conception. Wmk Mult Script CA. Chalk-surfaced paper. P 14×14.

263	**56**	1½d. emerald	15	10
264		3d. bright blue	15	10
265		1s. grey-black	35	20
263/265 *Set of* 3			60	35

57 Monument of the Great Siege, 1565

58 Wignacourt aqueduct horse trough

59 Victory Church

60 Second World War Memorial

61 Mosta Church

62 Auberge de Castile

63 The King's Scroll

64 Roosevelt's Scroll

65 Neolithic temples Tarxien

66 Vedette (tower)

67 Mdina gate

68 Les Gavroches (statue)

69 Monument of Christ the King

70 Grand Master Cottener's monument

71 Grand Master Perello's monument

72 St Paul

73 Baptism of Christ

(Recess Waterlow (2s.6d. to £1). B.W. (others))

1956 (23 Jan)–**58**. Types **57**/**73**. Wmk Mult Script CA. P 14×13½ (2s.6d. to £1) or 11½ (others).

266	**57**	¼d. violet	20	10
267	**58**	½d. orange	50	10
268	**59**	1d. black (9.2.56)	3·25	10
269	**60**	1½d. bluish green (9.2.56)	30	10
270	**61**	2d. brown (9.2.56)	3·50	10
		a. Deep brown (26.2.58)	9·00	40
271	**62**	2½d. orange-brown	2·25	30
272	**63**	3d. rose-red (22.3.56)	1·50	10
		w. Wmk inverted	†	£1500
273	**64**	4½d. deep blue	2·50	1·00
274	**65**	6d. indigo (9.2.56)	1·50	10
		w. Wmk inverted	£325	
275	**66**	8d. bistre-brown	4·50	1·00
276	**67**	1s. deep reddish violet	1·75	10
277	**68**	1s.6d. deep turquoise-green	18·00	35
278	**69**	2s. olive-green	13·00	5·00
279	**70**	2s.6d. chestnut (22.3.56)	11·00	2·50
280	**71**	5s. green (11.10.56)	17·00	3·25
281	**72**	10s. carmine-red (19.11.56)	38·00	16·00
282	**73**	£1 yellow-brown (5.1.57)	38·00	35·00
266/282 *Set of* 17			£130	55·00

See also Nos. 314/315.

74 'Defence of Malta'

75 Searchlights over Malta

(Des E. Cremona. Photo Harrison)

1957 (15 Apr). George Cross Commemoration. Cross in silver. Types **74**/**75** and similar design. Wmk Mult Script CA. P 14½×14 (3d.) or P 14×14½ (others).

283	1½d. deep dull green	20	10
284	3d. vermilion	20	10
285	1s. reddish brown	20	10
283/285 *Set of* 3		55	25

Designs: Vert—1½d. T **74**; 1s. Bombed buildings. Horiz—3d. T **75**.

77 Design

(Des E. Cremona. Photo Harrison)

1958 (15 Feb). Technical Education in Malta. T **77** and similar designs. W w **12**. P 14×14½ (3d.) or 14½×14 (others).

286	1½d. black and deep green	25	10
287	3d. black, scarlet and grey	25	10
288	1s. grey, bright purple and black	30	10
286/288 *Set of* 3		70	25

Designs: Vert—3d. 'Construction'. Horiz—1½d. T **77**; 1s. Technical School, Paola.

80 Bombed-out Family

81 Sea Raid on Grand Harbour, Valletta

3d. White flaw on third gun from right appearing as larger gunflash (Pl. 1A R. 5/7)

(Des E. Cremona. Photo Harrison)

1958 (15 Apr). George Cross Commemoration. Cross in first colour, outlined in silver. Types **80/81** and similar design. W w **12**. P 14×14½ (3d.) or 14½×14 (others).

289	1½d. blue-green and black	25	10
290	3d. red and black	25	10
	a. 'Gunflash' flaw	4·75	
291	1s. reddish violet and black	35	10
	a. Silver (outline) omitted	£800	
289/291 Set of 3		75	25

Designs: Horiz—1½d. T **80**; 1s. Searchlight crew. Vert—3d. T **81**.

83 Air Raid Casualties

84 'For Gallantry'

(Des E. Cremona. Photo Harrison)

1959 (15 Apr). George Cross Commemoration. Types **83/84** and similar design. W w **12**. P 14½×14 (3d.) or 14×14½ (others).

292	1½d. grey-green, black and gold	30	10
293	3d. reddish violet, black and gold	30	10
294	1s. blue-grey, black and gold	1·40	1·75
292/294 Set of 3		1·75	1·75

Designs: Vert—1½d. T **83**; 1s. Maltese under bombardment. Horiz—3d. T **84**.

96 Shipwreck of St Paul (after Palombi)

97 Statue of St Paul, Rabat, Malta

8d. Two white flaws in 'PAUL' one giving the 'P' the appearance of 'R' and other a blob over the 'L' (Pl. 1A-1A R. 5/2).

(Des E. Cremona. Photo Harrison)

1960 (9 Feb). 19th Centenary of the Shipwreck of St Paul. Types **86/87** and similar designs. W w **12**.

295	1½d. blue, gold and yellow-brown	15	10
	a. Gold (dates and crosses) omitted	75·00	£110
296	3d. bright purple, gold and blue	15	10
	a. Printed on the gummed side		
297	6d. carmine, gold and pale grey	25	10
298	8d. black and gold	40	60
	a. 'RAUL' flaw	7·00	
299	1s. maroon and gold	30	10
300	2s.6d. blue, deep bluish green and gold	1·00	2·75
	a. Gold omitted	£1900	£750
295/300 Set of 6		2·00	3·25

Designs: Vert as T **86**—1½d. T **86**; 3d. Consecration of St Publius (first Bishop of Malta) (after Palombi); 6d. Departure of St Paul (after Palombi). Diamond shaped as T **87**—8d. T **87**; 1s. Angel with *Acts of the Apostles*; 2s.6d. St Paul with *Second Epistle to the Corinthians*.

92 Stamp of 1860

(Centre litho; frame recess. Waterlow)

1960 (1 Dec). Stamp Centenary. W w **12**. P 13½.

301	**92**	1½d. buff, pale blue and green	30	10
		a. *Buff, pale blue and myrtle* (white paper)	9·50	3·75
302		3d. buff pale blue and deep carmine	35	10
		a. Blank corner	£650	
303		6d. buff, pale blue and ultramarine	1·00	1·00
301/303 Set of 3			1·50	1·10

Examples of the 1½d. apparently with the blue omitted are from sheets with a very weak printing of this colour.

No. 302*a* shows the right-hand bottom corner of the 1860 stamp blank. It occurs on R. 4/7 from early trial plates and sheets containing the error should have been destroyed, but some were sorted into good stock and issued at a post office.

93 George Cross

(Photo Harrison)

1961 (15 Apr). George Cross Commemoration. T **93** and similar designs showing medal. W w **12**. P 15×14.

304	1½d. black, cream and bistre	30	10
305	3d. olive-brown and greenish blue	30	10
306	1s. olive-green, lilac and deep reddish violet	1·40	2·50
304/306 Set of 3		1·75	2·50

96 *Madonna Damascena*

(Photo Harrison)

1962 (7 Sept). Great Siege Commemoration. T **96** and similar vert designs. W w **12** P 13×12.

307	2d. bright blue	10	10
308	3d. red	10	10
309	6d. bronze-green	30	10
310	1s. brown-purple	30	40
307/310 Set of 4		70	60

Designs: 2d. T **96**; 3d. Great Siege Monument; 6d. Grand Master La Valette; 1s. Assault on Fort St Elmo.

1963 (4 June). Freedom from Hunger. As No. 174 of Gibraltar.
311   1s.6d. sepia .... 1·50   2·50

1963 (2 Sept). Red Cross Centenary. As Nos. 175/176 of Gibraltar.
312   2d. red and black 25   15
313   1s. 6d. red and blue .... 1·50   4·50

1963 (15 Oct)–**64**. As Nos. 268 and 270, but wmk. w **12**.
314   **59**   1d. black 50   30
315   **61**   2d. deep brown (11.7.64*) .... 1·50   4·25
* This is the earliest known date recorded in Malta.

100 Bruce, Zammit and Microscope   **101** Goat and Laboratory Equipment

(Des E. Cremona. Photo Harrison)
1964 (14 Apr). Anti-Brucellosis Congress. W w **12**. P 14.
316   **100**   2d. light brown, black and bluish
        green 10   10
       a. Black (microscope, etc) omitted £450
317   **101**   1s.6d. black and maroon .... 1·25   2·00

102 Nicole Cotoner tending Sick Man (M. Preti)

105 Maltese Cross (Upright)

In this illustration the points of the crosses meet in a vertical line. When the watermark is sideways they meet in a horizontal line.

(Des E. Cremona. Photo Harrison)
1964 (5 Sept). First European Catholic Doctors' Congress, Vienna. T **102** and similar horiz designs. (sideways). W **105**. P 13½×11½.
318   2d. red, black, gold and grey-blue 20   10
319   6d. red, black, gold and bistre 50   15
320   1s.6d. red, black, gold and reddish violet .... 1·10   1·90
318/320 *Set of 3* .... 1·60   1·90
Designs: 2d. T **102**; 6d. St Luke and Hospital; 1s.6d. Sacra Infermeria, Valletta.

INDEPENDENT

106 Dove and British Crown   **109** The Nativity

(Des E. Cremona. Photo Harrison)
1964 (21 Sept). Independence. T **106** and similar vert designs. W w **105**. P 14½×13½.
321   2d. olive-brown, red and gold 30   10
       a. Gold omitted .... 75·00
322   3d. brown-purple, red and gold 30   10
       a. Gold omitted .... 75·00
323   6d. slate, red and gold 60   15
324   1s. blue, red and gold 60   15
325   1s.6d. indigo, red and gold .... 1·25   1·00
326   2s.6d. deep violet-blue, red and gold .... 1·50   3·75
321/326 *Set of 6* .... 4·00   4·75
Designs: 2d, 1s. T **106**; 3d., 1s.6d. Dove and Pope's Tiara; 6d., 2s.6d. Dove and UN emblem.

4d. White flaw on Virgin's head-shawl appearing as earring (Pl. 1B-2B. R. 6/1)

(Des E. Cremona. Photo D.L.R.)
1964 (3 Nov). Christmas. W **105** (sideways). P 13×13½.
327   **109**   2d. bright purple and gold 10   10
328   4d. bright blue and gold 20   15
       a. 'Earring' flaw .... 3·00
329   8d. deep bluish green and gold 45   45
327/329 *Set of 3* 65   60

110 Neolithic era   **111** Punic era   **112** Roman era

113 Proto Christian era   **114** Saracenic era   **115** Siculo Norman era

116 Knights of Malta   **117** Galleys of Knights of St John   **117a** Fortifications

118 French occupation   **119** British rule

119a Naval arsenal

120 Maltese corps of the British army

121 International Eucharistic congress

122 Self-government

123 Gozo civic council

124 State of Malta

125 Independence

126 HAFMED (Allied forces, Mediterranean)

127 The Maltese Islands (map)

128 Patron saints

(Des E. Cremona. Photo Harrison)

1965 (7 Jan)–**70**. Types **110**/**128**. W **105**. Chalk-surfaced paper. P 14×14½ (vert) or 14½ (horiz).

330	**110**	½d. multicoloured	10	10
		a. '½d.' (white) printed twice†	10·00	
		ab. ditto, once inverted	†	£2250
		b. Rose-pink ('MALTA') printed twice	10·00	
		c. White (face value) omitted	85·00	
331	**111**	1d. multicoloured	10	10
		a. Gold (ancient lettering) omitted	£150	
		b. White (Greek lettering and 'PUNIC') omitted	£110	
		c. White ptg double	30·00	
		d. 'PUNIC' omitted	£160	
332	**112**	1½d. multicoloured	30	10
333	**113**	2d. multicoloured	10	10
		a. Gold omitted	26·00	
		b. Imperf (pair)	£275	
334	**114**	2½d. multicoloured	1·00	10
		a. Orange omitted*	£110	
		b. Gold ('SARACENIC') omitted	55·00	
		c. Salmon printed twice†	£110	
335	**115**	3d. multicoloured	10	10
		a. Gold (windows) omitted	£100	
		b. 'MALTA' (silver) omitted	26·00	
		c. 'MALTA' (silver) printed twice	£400	
		d. Bright lilac ('SICULO NORMAN') omitted	£425	
		e. Imperf (pair)	£300	
		f. Value omitted (vert pair with normal)	£1100	
336	**116**	4d. multicoloured	1·00	10
		a. 'KNIGHTS OF MALTA' (silver) omitted	45·00	
		b. 'MALTA' (silver) omitted	£120	
		c. Black (shield surround) omitted	70·00	
		d. Imperf (pair)	£170	
		e. Gold omitted	£150	
337	**117**	4½d. multicoloured	1·00	75
		a. Silver ('MALTA', etc) omitted	£1900	

337b	**117a**	5d. multicoloured (1.8.70)	30	20
		ba. 'FORTIFICATIONS' (gold) omitted	£140	
338	**118**	6d. multicoloured	30	10
		a. 'MALTA' (silver) omitted	45·00	
		b. Black omitted	£110	
339	**119**	8d. multicoloured	50	10
		a. Gold (centre) omitted	42·00	
		b. Gold (frame) omitted	65·00	
339c	**119a**	10d. multicoloured (1.8.70)	50	1·50
		ca. 'NAVAL ARSENAL' (gold) omitted	£325	
340	**120**	1s. multicoloured	30	10
		a. Gold (centre) omitted	£250	
		b. Gold (framework) omitted	48·00	
		c. Gold (framework) doubled	£250	
341	**121**	1s.3d. multicoloured	2·00	1·40
		a. Gold (centre) omitted	65·00	
		b. Gold (framework) omitted	£250	
		c. Imperf (pair)	£400	
342	**122**	1s.6d. multicoloured	60	20
		a. Head (black) omitted	£375	
		b. Gold (centre) omitted	55·00	
		c. Gold (frame) omitted	£150	
343	**123**	2s. multicoloured	70	10
		a. Gold (centre) omitted	£170	
		b. Gold (framework) omitted	70·00	
344	**124**	2s.6d. multicoloured	70	50
345	**125**	3s. multicoloured	1·00	75
		a. Gold (framework) omitted	45·00	
		b. Gold ('1964') omitted	£200	
346	**126**	5s. multicoloured	4·00	1·00
		a. Gold (HAFMED emblem) omitted	£180	
		b. Gold (framework) omitted	£180	
347	**127**	10s. multicoloured	2·00	5·00
		a. Gold (centre) omitted	£425	
348	**128**	£1 multicoloured	2·25	5·50
		a. Pink omitted	32·00	
330/348		Set of 21	16·00	15·00

* The effect of this is to leave the Saracenic pattern as a pink colour.

† On the ½d. the second impression is 6½ mm lower or 3 mm to the left, and on the 2½d. 1 mm lower so that it falls partly across 'MALTA' and '2½d.' Stamps with almost coincidental double impression are common. The ½d. and 1d. had white printing plates. Two silver plates were used on the 4d., one for 'KNIGHTS OF MALTA' and the other for 'MALTA'. Two gold plates were used for the 8d. to 10s., one for the framework and the other for the gold in the central part of the designs.

No. 335f comes from a sheet showing a major shift of the grey-black colour, so that stamps in the top horizontal row are without the face value.

No. 337a comes from a sheet on which the silver printing was so misplaced that it missed the top horizontal row entirely.

The ½d. to 4d., 1s. and 1s.6d. to 5s. values exist with PVA gum as well as gum arabic and the 5d. and 10d. have PVA gum only.

See also Nos. 475/477 and 575.

129 *Dante* (Raphael)

(Des E. Cremona. Photo Govt Ptg Works, Rome)

1965 (7 July). 700th Birth Anniversary of Dante. P 14.

349	**129**	2d. indigo	10	10
350		6d. bronze-green	25	10
351		2s. chocolate	1·10	1·50
349/351		Set of 3	1·25	1·50

130 Turkish Camp

131 Turkish Fleet

(Des E. Cremona. Photo Harrison)

1965 (1 Sept). 400th Anniversary of Great Siege. Types **130**/**131** and similar designs. W **105** (sideways). P 13 (6d., 1s.) or 14½×14 (others).

352		2d. olive-green, red and black	25	10
		a. Red (flag) omitted	£425	

353		3d. olive-green, red, black and light drab......	25	10
354		6d. multicoloured...	35	10
		a. Gold (framework and dates) omitted........	£375	
		b. Black (on hulls) omitted..........................	£375	
355		8d. red, gold, indigo and blue.........................	70	90
		a. Gold (flag and dates) omitted..................	£180	
356		1s. red, gold and deep grey-blue...................	35	10
357		1s.6d. ochre, red and black............................	70	30
358		2s.6d. sepia, black, red and yellow-olive.......	1·10	3·00
352/358 *Set of 7*...			3·25	4·00

Designs: Square (as T **130**)—2d. T **130**; 3d. Battle scene; 8d. Arrival of relief force; 1s.6d. 'Allegory of Victory' (from mural by M. Preti); 2s.8d. Victory medal. Vert (as T **131**)—6d. T **131**; 1s. Grand Master J. de La Valette's Arms.

137 The Three Kings   **138** Sir Winston Churchill

(Des E. Cremona. Photo Enschedé)

1965 (7 Oct). Christmas. W **105** (sideways). P 11×11½.

359	**137**	1d. slate-purple and red.............................	10	10
360		4d. slate-purple and blue............................	30	30
361		1s.3d. slate-purple and bright purple	30	30
359/361 *Set of 3*...			65	60

(Des E. Cremona. Photo Harrison)

1966 (24 Jan). Churchill Commemoration. T **138** and similar square design. W **105** (sideways). P 14½×14.

362	**138**	2d. black, red and gold................................	30	10
363	–	3d. bronze-green, yellow-olive and gold...	30	10
		a. Gold omitted..	£375	
364	**138**	1s. maroon, red and gold.............................	45	10
		a. Gold (shading) omitted..........................	£170	
365	–	1s.6d. chalky blue, violet-blue and gold....	65	1·10
362/365 *Set of 4*...			1·50	1·25

Design: 3d., 1s.6d. Sir Winston Churchill and George Cross.

140 Grand Master   **145** President Kennedy
La Valette   and Memorial

(Des E. Cremona. Photo State Ptg Works, Vienna)

1966 (28 Mar). 400th Anniversary of Valletta. T **140** and similar square designs. Multicoloured. W **105** (sideways). P 12.

366		2d. Type **140**...	10	10
367		3d. Pope Pius V...	15	10
		a. Gold omitted..	£850	
368		6d. Map of Valletta.......................................	20	10
369		1s. Francesco Laparelli (architect)................	20	10
370		2s.6d. Girolamo Cassar (architect)................	45	60
366/370 *Set of 5*...			1·00	80

(Des E. Cremona. Photo Harrison)

1966 (28 May). President Kennedy Commemoration. W **105** (sideways). P 15×14.

371	**145**	3d. olive, gold and black..............................	10	10
		a. Gold inscr omitted.................................	£300	
372		1s.6d. Prussian blue, gold and black	10	10

146 Trade

(Des E. Cremona. Photo D.L.R.)

1966 (16 June). Tenth Malta Trade Fair. W **105** (sideways). P 13½.

373	**146**	2d. multicoloured...	10	10
		a. Gold omitted..	80·00	
374		8d. multicoloured...	50	1·10
375		2s.6d. multicoloured.....................................	55	1·10
		a. Gold omitted..	85·00	
373/375 *Set of 3*...			1·00	2·00

147 The Child in the   **148** George
Manger   Cross

(Des E. Cremona. Photo D.L.R.)

1966 (7 Oct). Christmas. W **105**. P 13½.

376	**147**	1d. black, gold, turquoise-blue and slate-purple...	10	10
377		4d. black, gold, ultramarine and slate-purple...	10	10
378		1s.3d. black, gold, bright purple and slate purple..	10	10
		a. Gold omitted..	70·00	
376/378 *Set of 3*...			25	25

1967 (1 Mar). 25th Anniversary of George Cross Award to Malta. W **105** (sideways). P 14½×14.

379	**148**	2d. multicoloured...	10	10
380		4d. multicoloured...	10	10
381		3s. multicoloured...	20	40
379/381 *Set of 3*...			30	45

149 Crucifixion of
St Peter

150 Open Bible and Episcopal Emblems

(Des E. Cremona. Photo Harrison)

1967 (28 June). 1900th Anniversary of Martyrdom of Saints Peter and Paul. Types **149/150** and similar design. W **105** (sideways). P 13½×14½ (8d.) or 14½ (others).

382		2d. chestnut, orange and black....................	10	10
383		8d. yellow-olive, gold and black...................	15	10
384		3s. blue, light blue and black.......................	20	20
382/384 *Set of 3*...			40	30

Designs: Square as T **149**—2d. T **149**; 3s. Beheading of St Paul. Horiz—8d. T **150**.

152 *St Catherine of Siena*   **156** Temple Ruins,
Tarxien

(Des E. Cremona. Photo Enschedé)

1967 (1 Aug). 300th Death Anniversary of Melchior Gafà (sculptor). T **152** and similar horiz designs. Multicoloured. W **105** (sideways). P 13½×13.

385	2d. Type **152**		10	10
386	4d. *Thomas of Villanova*		10	10
387	1s.6d. *Baptism of Christ* (detail)		15	10
388	2s.6d. St John the Baptist (from *Baptism of Christ*)		25	20
385/388 *Set of 4*			40	35

(Des E. Cremona. Photo Harrison)

1967 (12 Sept). 15th International Historical Architecture Congress, Valletta. T **156** and similar square designs. Multicoloured. W **105**. P 15×14½.

389	2d. Type **156**		10	10
390	6d. Facade of Palazzo Falzon, Notabile		10	10
391	1s. Parish Church, Birkirkara		10	10
392	3s. Portal, Auberge de Castille		25	25
389/392 *Set of 4*			40	40

160 Angels   **161** Crib   **162** Angels

(Des E. Cremona. Photo D.L.R.)

1967 (20 Oct). Christmas. W **105** (sideways). P 14.

393	**160**	1d. multicoloured	10	10
		a. Horiz strip of 3 Nos. 393/395	45	25
		b. White stars (red omitted)	£120	
394	**161**	8d. multicoloured	20	10
395	**162**	1s.4d. multicoloured	20	10
393/395 *Set of 3*			45	25

Nos. 393/395 were issued in sheets of 60 of each value (arranged *tête-bêche*), and also in sheets containing the three values *se-tenant*, thus forming a triptych of the Nativity.

163 Queen Elizabeth II and Arms of Malta

(Des E. Cremona. Photo Harrison)

1967 (13 Nov). Royal Visit. T **163** and similar designs. W **105** (sideways on 2d., 3s.). P 14×15 (4d.) or 15×14 (others).

396	2d. multicoloured		10	10
	a. Grey-brown omitted*		£150	
397	4d. black, brown-purple and gold		10	10
398	3s. multicoloured		20	30
396/398 *Set of 3*			35	40

Designs: Vert—4d. Queen in Robes of Order of St Michael and St George. Horiz—2d. T **163**; 3s. Queen and outline of Malta.
* This affects the Queen's face.

166 Human Rights Emblem and People **167**

(Des E. Cremona. Photo Harrison)

1968 (2 May). Human Rights Year. W **105**. P 12½ (6d.) or 14½ (others).

399	**166**	2d. multicoloured	10	10
400	**167**	6d. multicoloured	10	10
401	–	2s. multicoloured	10	15
399/401 *Set of 3*			25	25

The design of the 2s. value is a reverse of T **166**.

169 Fair 'Products'

(Des E. Cremona. Photo Harrison)

1968 (1 June). Malta International Trade Fair. W **105** (sideways). P 14½×14.

402	**169**	4d. multicoloured	10	10
403		8d. multicoloured	10	10
404		3s. multicoloured	20	15
402/404 *Set of 3*			30	25

170 Arms of the Order of   **171** *La Valette*
St John and La Valette   (A. de Favray)

172 La Valette's Tomb   **173** Angels and
                     Scroll bearing
                     Date of Death

(Des E. Cremona. Photo Govt Printer, Israel)

1968 (1 Aug). Fourth Death Centenary of Grand Master La Valette. W **105** (upright, 1s.6d.; sideways, others). P 13×14 (1d., 1s.6d.) or 14×13 (others).

405	**170**	1d. multicoloured	10	10
406	**171**	8d. multicoloured	15	10
407	**172**	1s.6d. multicoloured	15	10
408	**173**	2s.6d. multicoloured	20	25
405/408 *Set of 4*			55	45

174 Star of Bethlehem and   **177** 'Agriculture'
Angel waking Shepherds

(Des E. Cremona. Photo Harrison)

1968 (3 Oct). Christmas. T **174** and similar shaped designs. Multicoloured. W **105** (sideways). P 14½×14.

409	1d. Type **174**		10	10
410	8d. Mary and Joseph with shepherd watching over cradle		15	10
411	1s.4d. Three Wise Men and Star of Bethlehem		15	20
409/411 *Set of 3*			35	35

The shortest side at top and the long side at the bottom both gauge 14½, the other three sides are 14. Nos. 409/411 were issued in sheets of 60 arranged in ten strips of six, alternately upright and inverted.

2s.6d. Large white flaw on chest (left pane,
R. 1/10)

(Des E. Cremona. Photo Enschedé)

1968 (21 Oct). Sixth Food and Agricultural Organisation Regional
Conference for Europe. T **177** and similar vert designs. Multicoloured.
W **105** (sideways). P 12½×12.

412		4d. Type **177**	10	10
413		1s. FAO emblem and coin	10	10
414		2s.6d. 'Agriculture' sowing seeds	20	15
		a. White chest	5·00	
412/414 Set of 3			30	30

180 Mahatma Gandhi

181 ILO Emblem

(Des E. Cremona. Photo Enschedé)

1969 (24 Mar). Birth Centenary of Mahatma Gandhi. W **105**. P 12×12½.

415	**180**	1s.6d. blackish brown, black and gold	65	10

(Des E. Cremona. Photo Harrison)

1969 (26 May). 50th Anniversary of International Labour Organisation.
W **105** (sideways). P 13½×14½.

416	**181**	2d. indigo, gold and turquoise	10	10
417		6d. sepia gold and chestnut	10	10

182 Robert Samut (birth centenary)

183 Dove of Peace, UN Emblem and
Sea-Bed (UN Resolution on Oceanic
Resources)

184 'Swallows' returning to Malta
(Maltese Migrants' Convention)

185 University Arms and Grand Master
de Fonseca (founder) (Bicentenary of
University)

(Des E. Cremona. Photo D.L.R.)

1969 (26 July). Anniversaries. W **105** (sideways). P 13.

418	**182**	2d. multicoloured	10	10
419	**183**	5d. multicoloured	10	10
420	**184**	10d. black, gold and yellow-olive	10	10
421	**185**	2s. multicoloured	15	20
418/421 Set of 4			25	25

186 1919 Monument   **187** Flag of Malta and Birds

(Des E. Cremona. Photo Enschedé)

1969 (20 Sept). Fifth Anniversary of Independence. Types **186/187** and
similar designs. W **105** (upright on 5d., sideways others). P 13½×12½
(2d.), 12×12½ (5d.), or 12½×12 (others).

422		2d. multicoloured	10	10
423		5d. black, red and gold	10	10
424		10d. black, turquoise-blue and gold	10	10
425		1s.6d. multicoloured	20	40
426		2s.6d. black, olive-brown and gold	25	50
422/426 Set of 5			50	1·00

Designs: 2d. T **186**; 5d. T **187**. Vert as T **187**—10d. 'Tourism'; 1s.6d. UN
and Council of Europe emblems; 2s.6d. 'Trade and Industry'.

191 Peasants playing
Tambourine and Bagpipes

(Des E. Cremona. Litho D.L.R.)

1969 (8 Nov). Christmas. Children's Welfare Fund. T **191** and similar horiz
designs. Multicoloured. W **105** (sideways). P 12½.

427		1d. +1d. Type **191**	10	20
		a. Gold omitted	£180	
		b. Horiz strip of 3. Nos. 427/429	35	75
428		5d. +1d. Angels playing trumpet and harp	15	20
429		1s.6d. +3d. Choirboys singing	15	45
427/429 Set of 3			35	75

Nos. 427/429 were issued in sheets of 60 of each value, and also in
sheets containing the three values *se-tenant*, thus forming the triptych
No. 427b.

194 The Beheading of St John (Caravaggio)

(Des E. Cremona. Photo Enschedé)

1970 (21 Mar). 13th Council of Europe Art Exhibition. T **194** and similar
multicoloured designs. W **105** (upright, 10d., 2s.; sideways, others).
P 14×13 (1d., 8d.), 12 (10d., 2s.) or 13×13½ (others).

430		1d. Type **194**	10	10
431		2d. *St John the Baptist* (M. Preti) (45×32 *mm*)	10	10
432		5d. Interior of St John's Co-Cathedral, Valletta (39×39 *mm*)	10	10
433		6d. *Allegory of the Order* (Neapolitan School) (45×32 *mm*)	15	10

434		8d.	*St Jerome* (Caravaggio)	15	50
435		10d.	Articles from the Order of St John in Malta (63×21 *mm*)	15	10
436		1s.6d.	*The Blessed Gerard receiving Godfrey de Bouillon* (A. de Favray) (45×35 *mm*)	25	40
437		2s.	Cape and Stolone (16th-century) (63×21 *mm*)	25	55
			a. Blue omitted	£300	
430/437 *Set of 8*				1·00	1·50

202 Artist's Impression of Fujiyama

(Des E. Cremona. Photo D.L.R.)

1970 (29 May). World Fair, Osaka. W **105** (sideways). P 15.

438	**202**	2d. multicoloured	10	10
439		5d. multicoloured	10	10
440		3s. multicoloured	15	15
438/440 *Set of 3*			30	30

203 'Peace and Justice' **204** Carol Singers, Church and Star

(Des J. Casha. Litho Harrison)

1970 (30 Sept). 25th Anniversary of United Nations. W **105**. P 14×14½.

441	**203**	2d. multicoloured	10	10
442		5d. multicoloured	10	10
443		2s.6d. multicoloured	15	15
441/443 *Set of 3*			30	30

(Des E. Cremona. Photo Govt Printer, Israel)

1970 (7 Nov). Christmas. T **204** and similar vert designs. Multicoloured. W **105** (sideways). P 14×13.

444		1d. +½d. Type **204**	10	10
445		10d. +2d. Church, star and Angels with Infant	15	20
446		1s.6d. +3d. Church, star and nativity scene	20	40
444/446 *Set of 3*			40	60

207 Books and Quill **208** Dun Karm, Books, Pens and Lamp

(Des H. Alden (1s.6d.), A. Agius (2s.). Litho D.L.R.)

1971 (20 Mar). Literary Anniversaries. Death Bicentenary (1970) of de Soldanis (historian) (1s.6d.) and Birth Centenary of Dun Karm (poet) (2s.). W **105** (sideways). P 13×13½.

447	**207**	1s.6d. multicoloured	10	10
448	**208**	2s. multicoloured	10	15

209 Europa Chain

(Des H. Haflidason; adapted E. Cremona. Litho Harrison)

1971 (3 May). Europa. W **105** (sideways). P 13½×14½.

449	**209**	2d. orange, black and yellow-olive	10	10
450		5d. orange, black and vermilion	10	10
451		1s.6d. orange, black and slate	60	1·10
449/451 *Set of 3*			70	1·10

210 *St Joseph, Patron of the Universal Church* (G. Cali) **211** *Centaurea spathulata*

(Des E. Cremona. Litho D.L.R.)

1971 (24 July). Centenary of Proclamation of St Joseph as Patron Saint of Catholic Church, and 50th Anniversary of the Coronation of the Statue of *Our Lady of Victories*. T **210** and similar horiz design. Multicoloured. W **105** (sideways). P 13×13½.

452		2d. Type **210**	10	10
453		5d. Statue of *Our Lady of Victories* and alley..	10	10
454		10d. Type **210**	15	10
455		1s.6d. As 5d.	30	40
452/455 *Set of 4*			45	50

(Des Reno Psaila. Litho Harrison)

1971 (18 Sept). National Plant and Bird of Malta. T **211** and similar horiz design. Multicoloured. W **105** (sideways on 5d. and 10d.). P 14½×14.

456		2d. Type **211**	10	10
457		5d. Blue Rock Thrush	20	10
458		10d. As 5d.	30	15
459		1s.6d. Type **211**	30	1·25
456/459 *Set of 4*			75	1·40

212 Angel

(Des E. Cremona. Litho Format)

1971 (8 Nov). Christmas. T **212** and similar horiz designs. Multicoloured. W **105** (sideways). P 13½×14.

460		1d. +½d. Type **212**	10	10
461		10d. +2d. Mary and the Child Jesus	15	25
462		1s.6d. +3d. Joseph lying awake	20	40
460/462 *Set of 3*			35	55
MS463 131×113 mm. Nos. 460/462. P 15			75	2·50

213 Heart and WHO Emblem **214** Maltese Cross

(Des A. Agius. Litho Format)

1972 (20 Mar). World Health Day. W **105**. P 13½×14.

464	**213**	2d. multicoloured	10	10
465		10d. multicoloured	15	10
466		2s.6d. multicoloured	40	80
464/466 *Set of 3*			55	85

(New Currency. 10 mile =1 cent; 100 cents =1 Maltese pound)

(Des G. Pace. Litho Format)

1972 (16 May). Decimal Currency. T **214** and similar vert designs showing decimal coins. Multicoloured. W **105**. P 14 (2m., 3m., 2c.), 14½×14 (5m., 1c., 5c.) or 13½ (10c., 50c.).

467		2m. Type **214**	10	10
468		3m. Bee on honeycomb	10	10
469		5m. Earthen lampstand	10	10
470		1c. George Cross	10	10
471		2c. Classical head	10	10
472		5c. Ritual altar	10	10
473		10c. Grandmaster's galley	20	10
474		50c. Great Siege Monument	1·00	1·25
467/474 *Set of 8*			1·25	1·25

Sizes: 2m., 3m. and 2c. as T **214**; 5m., 1c. and 5c. 22×27 mm; 10c. and 50c. 27×35 mm.

No. 467 exists imperforate from stock dispersed by the liquidator of Format International Security Printers Ltd.

$= \mathbf{1c3}$

(215)

216 Communications

1972 (30 Sept). Nos. 337*b*, 339 and 341 surch as T **215**, by Govt. Printing Works, Valletta.

475	1c.3, on 5d. multicoloured		10	10
	a. Gold ('FORTIFICATIONS') omitted		£150	
476	3c. on 8d. multicoloured		15	10
	a. Surch inverted		65·00	
	b. Gold (frame) omitted		£110	
477	5c. on 1s.3d. multicoloured		15	20
	a. Surch double		£110	
	b. Surch inverted		55·00	
	c. Gold (centre) omitted		£110	
475/477 *Set of 3*			30	35

PRINTERS. All stamps between Nos. 478 and 1093 were printed in lithography by Printex Ltd. Malta.

(Des P. Huovinen; adapted G. Pace)

1972 (11 Nov). Europa. W **105** (sideways). P 13.

478	**216**	1c.3, multicoloured	10	10
479		3c. multicoloured	10	10
480		5c. multicoloured	15	35
481		7c.5, multicoloured	20	75
478/481 *Set of 4*			50	1·10

Nos. 478/481 were each printed in sheets including two *se-tenant* stamp-size labels in the second and third positions of the top row.

217 Angel

(Des E. Cremona)

1972 (9 Dec). Christmas. T **217** and similar horiz designs. W **105** (sideways). P 13½.

482	8m. +2m. dull sepia, brownish grey and gold		10	10
483	3c. +1c. plum, lavender and gold		15	40
484	7c.5, +1c.5, indigo, azure and gold		20	50
482/484 *Set of 3*			35	85
MS485 137×113 mm. Nos. 482/484			1·75	3·50
	a. Imperf horizontally			

Designs: No.482, T **217**; No. 483, Angel with tambourine; No. 484, Singing Angel.
See also Nos. 507/510.

218 Archaeology   **219** Europa Posthorn

(Des E. Cremona)

1973 (31 Mar)–**76**. T **218** and similar designs. Multicoloured. W **105** (sideways). P 13½×14 (Nos. 500/500a) or 13½ (others).

486	**218**	2m. Type **218**	10	10
487		4m. History	10	10
		a. Gold (inscr and decoration) omitted	85·00	
		b. Imperf (pair)	£375	
488		5m. Folklore	10	10
489		8m. Industry	10	10
490		1c. Fishing industry	10	10
491		1c.3, Pottery	10	10
492		2c. Agriculture	10	10
493		3c. Sport	10	10
494		4c. Yacht marina	15	10
495		5c. Fiesta	15	10
496		7c.5, Regatta	25	10
497		10c. Voluntary service	25	10
498		50c. Education	2·00	50
499		£1 Religion	2·75	2·00
500		£2 Coat of Arms (*horiz*)	14·00	17·00
		a. Gold omitted		
500*b*		£2 National Emblem (*horiz*) (28.1.76)	5·00	11·00
486/500*b* *Set of 16*			22·00	27·00

Nos. 500/500*b* are larger, 32×27 mm.

(Des L. Anisdahl; adapted G. Pace)

1973 (2 June). Europa. W **105**. P 14.

501	**219**	3c. multcoloured	15	10
502		5c. multicoloured	15	35
503		7c.5, multicoloured	25	65
501/503 *Set of 3*			50	1·00

Nos. 501/503 were each printed in sheets containing two *se-tenant* stamp-size labels.

220 Emblem, and Woman holding Corn   **221** Girolamo Cassar (architect)

(Des H. Alden)

1973 (6 Oct). Anniversaries. T **220** and similar vert designs showing emblem and allegorical figures. W **105** (sideways). P 13½.

504	1c.3, multicoloured		10	10
505	7c.5, multicoloured		25	40
506	10c. multicoloured		30	50
504/506 *Set of 3*			55	85

Anniversaries: 1c.3, Tenth Anniversary of World Food Programme; 7c.5, 25th Anniversary of WHO; 10c. 25th Anniversary of Universal Declaration of Human Rights.

(Des E. Cremona)

1973 (10 Nov). Christmas. Horiz designs as T **217**. Multicoloured. W **105** (sideways). P 13½.

507	8m. +2m. Angels and organ pipes		15	10
508	3c. +1c. Madonna and Child		25	60
509	7c.5 +1c.5, Buildings and Star		45	1·50
507/509 *Set of 3*			75	2·00
MS510 137×112 mm. Nos. 507/509			4·75	7·50

(Des E. Cremona)

1974 (12 Jan). Prominent Maltese. T **221** and similar vert designs. W **105**. P 14.

511	1c.3, dull myrtle-green, dull grey-green and gold		10	10
512	3c. deep turquoise, grey-blue and gold		15	10
513	5c. dull sepia, deep slate-green and gold		20	15
514	7c.5, slate-blue, light slate-blue and gold		20	30
515	10c. purple, dull purple and gold		20	40
511/515 *Set of 5*			70	85

Designs: 1c.3, T **221**; 3c. Giuseppe Barth (ophthalmologist); 5c. Nicolo' Isouard (composer); 7c.5, John Borg (botanist); 10c. Antonio Sciortino (sculptor).

222 Air Malta Emblem

(Des E. Cremona)

1974 (30 Mar). Air. T **222** and similar horiz design. Multicoloured. W **105** (sideways). P 13½.

516	3c. Type **222**		10	10
517	4c. Boeing 720B		15	10
518	5c. Type **222**		15	10
519	7c.5, As 4c.		15	10
520	20c. Type **222**		25	40
521	25c. As 4c.		25	40
522	35c. Type **222**		35	1·00
516/522 *Set of 7*			1·25	1·90

223 Prehistoric Sculpture

(Des E. Cremona)

1974 (13 July). Europa. T **223** and similar designs. W **105** (sideways) on Nos. 523 and 525). P 13½.

523	1c.3, slate-blue, grey-black and gold		15	10
524	3c. light bistre-brown, grey-black and gold		20	15
525	5c. purple, grey-black and gold		25	50
526	7c.5c. dull green, grey-black and gold		35	1·00
523/526 Set of 4			85	1·60

Designs: Vert—3c. Old Cathedral Door, Mdina; 7c.5, *Vetlina* (sculpture by A. Sciortino). Horiz—1c.3, T **223**; 5c. Silver Monstrance.

Nos. 523/526 were each printed in sheets including two *se-tenant* stamp-size labels.

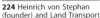

224 Heinrich von Stephan (founder) and Land Transport

225 Decorative Star and Nativity Scene

(Des S. and G. Sullivan)

1974 (20 Sept). Centenary of Universal Postal Union. T **224** and similar horiz designs. W **105**. P 13½×14.

527	1c.3, blue-green, light violet-blue and yellow and orange	30	10
528	5c. brown, dull vermilion and yellow-green	30	10
529	7c.5, deep dull blue, light violet-blue and yellow-green	35	20
530	50c. purple, dull vermilion and yellow-orange	1·00	1·25
527/530 Set of 4		1·75	1·50
MS531 126×91 mm. Nos. 527/530		4·25	5·50

Designs (each containing portrait as T **224**): 1c.3, T **224**; 5c. *Washington* (paddle-steamer) and *Royal Viking Star* (liner); 7c.5, Balloon and Boeing 747-100; 50c. UPU Buildings, 1874 and 1974.

(Des E. Cremona)

1974 (22 Nov). Christmas. T **225** and similar vert designs, each with decorative star. Multicoloured. W **105** (sideways). P 14.

532	8m. +2m. Type **225**	10	10
533	3c. +1c. Shepherds	15	20
534	5c. +1c. Shepherds with gifts	20	35
535	7c.5 +1c.5, The Magi	30	45
532/535 Set of 4		65	1·00

REPUBLIC

226 Swearing-in of Prime Minister

(Des E. Cremona)

1975 (31 Mar). Inauguration of Republic. T **226** and similar horiz designs. W **105** (sideways). P 14.

536	1c.3, multicoloured	10	10
537	5c. rose-red and grey-black	20	10
538	25c. multicoloured	60	1·00
536/538 Set of 3		75	1·10

Designs: 1c.3, T **226**; 5c. National Flag; 25c. Minister of Justice, President and Prime Minister.

227 Mother and Child (Family Life)

(Des D. Friggieri)

1975 (30 May). International Women's Year. T **227** and similar horiz design. W **105**. P 13½×14.

539	**227**	1c.3, light violet and gold	15	10
540	–	3c. light blue and gold	15	10
541	**227**	5c. dull olive-sepia and gold	20	15
542	–	20c. chestnut and gold	60	2·50
539/542 Set of 4			1·00	2·50

Design: 3c., 20c. Office secretary (Public Life).

228 *Allegory of Malta* (Francesco de Mura)

(Des E. Cremona)

1975 (15 July). Europa. T **228** and similar horiz design. Multicoloured. W **105**. P 14×13½.

543	5c. Type **228**	30	10
544	15c. *Judith and Holofernes* (Valentin de Boulogne)	50	75

The 15c. is a smaller design than the 5c. (47×23 *mm*), though the perforated area is the same.

Nos. 543/544 were each printed in sheets including two *se-tenant* stamp-size labels.

229 Plan of Ggantija Temple

(Des R. England)

1975 (16 Sept). European Architectural Heritage Year. T **229** and similar horiz designs. W **105** (sideways). P 13½.

545	1c.3, brownish black and light orange-red	10	10
546	3c. dull purple, light orange-red and blackish brown	15	10
547	5c. blackish brown and light orange-red	25	25
548	25c. dull grey-olive, light orange-red and brownish black	90	2·75
545/548 Set of 4		1·25	2·75

Designs: 1c.3, T **229**; 3c. Mdina skyline; 5c. View of Victoria, Gozo; 25c. Silhouette of Fort St Angelo.

230 Farm Animals

231 The Right to Work

(Des E. Cremona)

1975 (4 Nov). Christmas. T **230** and similar multicoloured designs. W **105** (sideways). P 13½.

549	8m. +2m. Type **230**	25	25
	a. Horiz strip of 3. Nos. 549/551	1·00	2·25
550	3c. +1c. Nativity scene (50×23 *mm*)	40	75
551	7c.5 +1c.5, Approach of the Magi	45	1·40
549/551 Set of 3		1·00	2·25

Nos. 549/551 were issued in sheets of 50 of each value, and also in sheets containing the three values horizontally *se-tenant*, thus forming the triptych No. 549a which is a composite design of *The Nativity* by Master Alberto.

(Des A. de Giovanni)

1975 (12 Dec). First Anniversary of Republic. T **231** and similar vert designs. W **105**. P 14.

552	1c.3, multicoloured	10	10
553	5c. multicoloured	20	10
554	25c. deep rose, light steel-blue and black	70	1·10
552/554 Set of 3		80	1·10

Designs: 1c.3, T **231**; 5c. Safeguarding the Environment; 25c. National Flag.

232 'Festa Tar-Rahal'

233 Water Polo

(Des M. Camilleri)

1976 (26 Feb). Maltese Folklore. T **232** and similar multicoloured designs. W **105** (sideways on 5c. and 7c.5). P 14.

555	1c.3, Type **232**		10	10
556	5c. 'L-Imnarja' (*horiz*)		15	10
557	7c.5, 'Il-Karnival' (*horiz*)		35	70
558	10c. 'Il-Gimgha L-Kbira'		55	1·40
555/558 *Set of 4*			1·00	2·00

(Des H. Alden)

1976 (28 Apr). Olympic Games, Montreal. T **233** and similar horiz designs. Multicoloured. W **105**. P 13½×14.

559	1c.7, Type **233**		10	10
560	5c. Sailing		25	10
561	30c. Athletics		85	1·50
559/561 *Set of 3*			1·10	1·50

234 Lace-making

(Des F. Portelli)

1976 (8 July). Europa. T **234** and similar horiz design. Multicoloured. W **105** (sideways). P 13×14.

562	7c. Type **234**		20	35
563	15c. Stone carving		25	60

Nos. 562/563 were each printed in sheets including two *se-tenant* stamp-size labels.

235 Nicola Cotoner

(Des E. Cremona)

1976 (14 Sept). 300th Anniversary of School of Anatomy and Surgery. T **235** and similar horiz designs. Multicoloured. W **105** (sideways). P 13½.

564	2c. Type **235**		10	10
565	5c. Arm		15	10
566	7c. Giuseppe Zammit		20	10
567	11c. Sacra Infermeria		35	65
564/567 *Set of 4*			70	75

1c7

236 St John the Baptist and St Michael	**237** Jean de la Valette's Armour	(**238**)

(Des E. Cremona)

1976 (23 Nov). Christmas. Designs showing portions of *Madonna and Saints* by Domenico di Michelino. Multicoloured. W **105** (sideways on No. 571). P 13½×14 (No. 571) or 13½ (others).

568	1c. +5m. Type **236**		10	20
569	5c. +1c. Madonna and Child		15	60
570	7c. +1c.5, St Christopher and St Nicholas		20	60
571	10c. +2c. Complete painting (32×27 *mm*)		30	1·25
568/571 *Set of 4*			65	2·50

(Des J. Briffa)

1977 (20 Jan). Suits of Armour. T **237** and similar vert designs. Multicoloured. W **105**. P 13½.

572	2c. Type **237**		10	10
573	7c. Aloph of Wignacourt's armour		20	10
574	11c. Jean Jacques de Verdelin's armour		25	50
572/574 *Set of 3*			45	60

1977 (24 Mar). No. 336 surch with T **238** by Govt Printing Press, Malta.

575	**116**	1c.7 on 4d. multicoloured	25	25
		a. 'KNIGHTS OF MALTA' (silver) omitted	£110	

239 Annunciation	**240** Map and Radio Aerial

(Des E. Cremona)

1977 (30 Mar). 400th Birth Anniversary of Rubens. Flemish tapestries (1st series) showing his paintings as T **239**. Multicoloured. W **105** (sideways). P 14.

576	2c. Type **239**		10	10
577	7c. *Four Evangelists*		20	10
578	11c. *Nativity*		35	45
579	20c. *Adoration of the Magi*		55	1·00
576/579 *Set of 4*			1·00	1·50

See also Nos. 592/595, 615/618 and 638/**MS**640.

(Des H. Borg)

1977 (17 May). World Telecommunication Day. T **240** and similar design. W **105** (sideways on 1 and 6c.). P 14×13½ (1 and 6c.) or 13½×14 (others).

580	**240**	1c. black, green and vermilion	10	10
581		6c. black, grey-blue and vermilion	20	10
582	–	8c. black, chestnut and vermilion	30	10
583	–	17c. black, dull mauve and vermilion	60	40
580/583 *Set of 4*			1·00	55

Design: Horiz—8 and 17c. Map, aerial and aeroplane tail-fin.

241 Ta' L-Isperanza	**242** Aid to Disabled Workers (detail from Workers' Monument)

(Des G. French)

1977 (5 July). Europa. T **241** and similar horiz design. Multicoloured. W **105** (sideways). P 13½.

584	7c. Type **241**		30	15
585	20c. Is-Salini		35	1·00

Nos. 584/585 were each printed in sheets including two *se-tenant* stamp-size labels.

(Des A. Agius)

1977 (12 Oct). Maltese Worker Commemoration. T **242** and similar designs. W **105** (sideways on 20c.). P 13½.

586	2c. orange-brown and light brown		10	10
587	7c. chestnut and brown		15	10
588	20c. multicoloured		40	60
586/588 *Set of 3*			55	60

Designs: Vert—2c. T **242**; 7c. Stoneworker, modern industry and ship building (monument detail). Horiz—20c. Mother with Dead Son and Service Medal.

243 The Shepherds	**244** Young Lady on Horseback and Trooper

(Des E. Cremona)

1977 (16 Nov). Christmas. T **243** and similar horiz designs. Multicoloured. W **105** (sideways). P 13½×14.

589	1c. +5m. Type **243**	10	35
	a. Vert strip of 3. Nos. 589/591	40	1·40
590	7c. +1c. The Nativity	15	55
591	11c. +1c.5, Flight into Egypt	20	70
589/591	Set of 3	40	1·40

Nos. 589/591 were issued in sheets of 50 of each value, and also in sheets containing the three values *se-tenant*.

(Des E. Cremona)

1978 (26 Jan). Flemish Tapestries (2nd series). Horiz designs similar to T **239**. Multicoloured. W **105** (sideways). P 14.

592	2c. *The Entry into Jerusalem* (artist unknown)	10	10
593	7c. *The Last Supper* (after Poussin)	20	10
594	11c. *The Raising of the Cross* (after Rubens)	25	25
595	25c. *The Resurrection* (after Rubens)	60	80
592/595	Set of 4	1·00	1·10

(Des A. Camilleri)

1978 (7 Mar). 450th Death Anniversary of Albrecht Dürer. T **244** and similar vert designs. W **105**. P 14.

596	1c.7, black, vermilion and deep blue	10	10
597	8c. black, vermilion and slate	15	10
598	17c. black, vermilion and deep slate	40	45
	a. Vermilion (monogram) omitted	£180	
596/598	Set of 3	55	55

Designs: 1c.7, T **244**; 8c. *The Bag-piper*; 17c. *The Virgin and Child with a Monkey*.

245 Monument to Grand Master Nicola Cotoner (Foggini)

246 Goalkeeper

(Des E. Cremona)

1978 (26 Apr). Europa. Monuments. T **245** and similar vert design. Multicoloured. W **105**. P 14×13½.

599	7c. Type **245**	15	10
600	25c. Monument to Grand Master Racoon Perellos (Mazzuoli)	35	90

Nos. 599/600 were each printed in sheets including two *se-tenant* stamp-size labels.

(Des A. de Giovanni)

1978 (6 June). World Cup Football Championship, Argentina. T **246** and similar vert designs. Multicoloured. W **105** (sideways). P 14×13½.

601	2c. Type **246**	10	10
	a. Red omitted		
602	11c. Players heading ball	15	10
603	15c. Tackling	25	35
601/603	Set of 3	45	45
MS604	125×90 mm. Nos. 601/603	1·25	2·50

247 Boeing 707 over Megalithic Temple

(Des R. Caruana)

1978 (3 Oct). Air. Horiz designs as T **247**. Multicoloured. W **105** (sideways). P 13½.

605	5c. Type **247**	25	10
606	7c. Air Malta Boeing 720B	25	10
607	11c. Boeing 747 taking off from Luqa Airport	35	10
608	17c. Type **247**	45	30
609	20c. As 7c.	45	45
610	75c. As 11c.	1·00	2·50
605/610	Set of 6	2·50	3·25

248 Folk Musicians and Village Church

249 Luzzu and Aircraft Carrier

(Des E. Cremona)

1978 (9 Nov). Christmas. T **248** and similar multicoloured designs. W **105** (sideways). P 13½ (11c.) or 14 (others).

611	1c. +5m. Type **248**	10	10
612	5c. +1c. Choir of Angels	15	20
613	7c. +1c.5, Carol singers	20	35
614	11c. +3c. Folk musicians, church, Angels and carol singers (58×23 *mm*)	25	45
611/611	Set of 4	60	1·00

The 1, 5 and 7c. values depict details of the complete design shown on the 11c. value.

(Des E. Cremona)

1979 (24 Jan). Flemish Tapestries (3rd series). Horiz designs as T **239** showing paintings by Rubens. Multicoloured. W **105** (sideways). P 14.

615	2c. *The Triumph of the Catholic Church*	10	10
616	7c. *The Triumph of Charity*	20	10
617	11c. *The Triumph of Faith*	30	25
618	25c. *The Triumph of Truth*	95	80
615/618	Set of 4	1·40	1·10

(Des E. Cremona)

1979 (31 Mar). End of Military Facilities Agreement. T **249** and similar vert designs. Multicoloured. W **105** (sideways). P 13½.

619	2c. Type **249**	10	10
620	5c. Raising the flag ceremony	10	10
621	7c. Departing soldier and Olive sprig	15	10
622	8c. Type **249**	30	30
623	17c. As 5c.	40	45
624	20c. As 7c.	40	45
619/624	Set of 6	1·25	1·25

250 Speronara (fishing boat) and Tail of Air Malta Airliner

251 Children on Globe

(Des E. Cremona)

1979 (9 May). Europa. Communications. T **250** and similar vert design. Multicoloured. W **105** (sideways). P 14.

625	7c. Type **250**	20	10
626	25c. Coastal watch tower and radio link towers	40	75

Nos. 625/626 were each printed in sheets including two *se-tenant* stamp-size labels.

(Des A. Bonnici (2c.), A. Pisani (7c.), M. French (11c.))

1979 (13 June). International Year of the Child. T **251** and similar multicoloured designs. W **105** (sideways). P 14×13½ (2c.) or 14 (others).

627	2c. Type **251**	10	10
628	7c. Children flying kites (27×33 *mm*)	15	10
629	11c. Children in circle (27×33 *mm*)	20	35
627/629	Set of 3	35	45

252 Shells (*Gibbula nivosa*) **253** *The Nativity* (detail)

(Des R. Pitré)

1979 (10 Oct). Marine Life. T **252** and similar horiz designs. Multicoloured. W **105**. P 13½.

630	2c. Type **252**	10	10
631	5c. Loggerhead Turtle (*Caretta carena*)	20	10
632	7c. Dolphinfish (*Coryphaena hippurus*)	20	10
633	25c. Noble Pen Shell (*Pinna nobilis*)	70	1·25
630/633 *Set of 4*		1·00	1·25

(Des E. Cremona)

1979 (14 Nov). Christmas. Paintings by G. Cali. T **253** and similar horiz designs. Multicoloured. W **105**. P 14×13½.

634	1c. +5m. Type **253**	10	10
635	5c. +1c. *The Flight into Egypt* (detail)	15	15
636	7c. +1c.5, *The Nativity*	20	20
637	11c. +3c. *The Flight into Egypt*	30	50
634/637 *Set of 4*		65	85

(Des E. Cremona)

1980 (30 Jan). Flemish Tapestries (4th series). Horiz designs as T **239** taken from paintings. Multicoloured. W **105** (sideways). P 14.

638	2c. *The Institution of Corpus Domini* (Rubens)	10	10
639	8c. *The Destruction of Idolatry* (Rubens)	20	20
MS640 114×86 mm. 50c. *Grand Master Perellos with St Jude and St Simon* (unknown Maltese artist) (*vert*)		80	1·60

254 Hal Saflieni Hypogeum, Paola

255 Dun Gorg Preca

1980 (15 Feb). International Restoration of Maltese Monuments Campaign. T **254** and similar multicoloured designs. W **105** (sideways on 8 and 12 c.). P 14.

641	2c.5, Type **254**	10	15
642	6c. Vilhena Palace, Mdina	15	20
643	8c. Victoria Citadel, Gaza (*horiz*)	20	40
644	12c. Fort St Elmo, Valletta (*horiz*)	30	60
641/644 *Set of 4*		65	1·25

(Des R. Pitré)

1980 (12 Apr). Birth Centenary of Dun Gorg Preca (founder of Society of Christian Doctrine). W **105** (sideways). P 14×13½.

645	**255** 2c.5, black and grey	10	10

256 Ruzar Briffa (poet)

257 *Annunciation*

(Des V. Apap)

1980 (29 Apr). Europa. Personalities. T **256** and similar horiz design. W **105** (sideways). P 13½×14.

646	8c. black, brown-ochre and bronze-green ...	15	10
647	30c. brown, brown-olive and brown-lake	45	1·25

Designs: 8c. T **256**; 30c. Nikiol Anton Vassalli (scholar and patriot). Nos. 646/647 were each printed in sheets including two *se-tenant* stamp-size labels.

(Des R. Pitré)

1980 (7 Oct). Christmas. Paintings by A. Inglott. T **257** and similar multicoloured designs. W **105** (sideways on 12c.). P 14 (12c.) or 13½ (others).

648	2c. +5m. Type **257**	10	10
649	6c. +1c. *Conception*	20	20
650	8c. +1c.5, *Nativity*	25	40

651	12c. +3c. *Annunciation, Conception* and *Nativity* (47×38 mm)	30	70
648/651 *Set of 4*		75	1·25

The paintings from the 2, 6 and 8c. values are united to form the triptych on the 12c. value.

258 Rook and Pawn

259 Barn Owl (*Tyto alba*)

(Des H. Borg)

1980 (20 Nov). 24th Chess Olympiad and International Chess Federation Congress, Malta. T **258** and similar multicoloured designs. W **105** (sideways on 30c.) P 14×13½ (30c.) or 13½×14 (others).

652	2c.5, Type **258**	15	20
653	8c. Bishop and Pawn	35	20
654	30c. King, Queen and Pawn (*vert*)	60	1·25
652/654 *Set of 3*		1·00	1·50

(Des M. Burlò)

1981 (20 Jan). Birds. T **259** and similar vert designs. Multicoloured. W **105** (sideways). P 13½.

655	3c. Type **259**	30	25
656	8c. Sardinian Warbler (*Sylvia melanocephala*)	40	25
657	12c. Woodchat Shrike (*Lanius senator*)	50	80
658	23c. British Storm Petrel (*Hydrobates pelagicus*)	80	1·75
655/658 *Set of 4*		1·75	2·75

260 Traditional Horse Race

261 Stylised '25'

(Des H. Borg)

1981 (28 Apr). Europa. Folklore. T **260** and similar vert design. Multicoloured. W **105** (sideways). P 14.

659	8c. Type **260**	20	10
660	30c. Attempting to retrieve flag from end of 'gostra' (greasy pole)	40	65

The two values were each printed in sheets including two *se-tenant* stamp-size labels.

(Des A. de Giovanni)

1981 (12 June). 25th Maltese International Trade Fair. W **105** (sideways). P 13½.

661	**261** 4c. multicoloured	15	15
662	25c. multicoloured	50	60

262 Disabled Artist at Work

263 Wheat Ear in Conical Flask

(Des A. Camilleri)

1981 (17 July). International Year for Disabled Persons. T **262** and similar vert design. Multicoloured. W **105**. P 13½.

663	3c. Type **262**	20	10
664	35c. Disabled child playing football	90	75

(Des R. Caruana)

1981 (16 Oct). World Food Day. W **105** (sideways). P 14.

665	**263** 8c. multicoloured	15	15
666	23c. multicoloured	60	50

264 Megalithic Building

265 Children and Nativity Scene

(Des F. Portelli).

1981 (31 Oct). History of Maltese Industry. Horiz designs as T **264**. Multicoloured. W **105**. P 14.

667	5m. Type **264**	10	85
668	1c. Cotton production	10	10
669	2c. Early ship-building	85	10
670	3c. Currency minting	30	10
671	5c. 'Art'	30	25
672	6c. Fishing	1·25	25
673	7c. Agriculture	30	1·50
674	8c. Stone quarrying	1·00	35
675	10c. Grape pressing	35	50
676	12c. Modern ship-building	2·00	2·25
677	15c. Energy	70	2·00
678	20c. Telecommunications	70	75
679	25c. 'Industry'	1·00	2·25
680	50c. Drilling for water	3·00	2·75
681	£1 Sea transport	5·00	7·50
682	£3 Air transport	11·00	18·00
667/682 *Set of 16*		24·00	35·00

(Des A. Bugeja)

1981 (18 Nov). Christmas. T **265** and similar multicoloured designs. W **105** (sideways). P 14.

683	2c. +1c. Type **265**	25	10
684	8c. +2c. Christmas Eve procession (*horiz*)	35	20
685	20c. +3c. Preaching midnight sermon	50	1·10
683/685 *Set of 3*		1·00	1·25

266 Shipbuilding

267 Elderly Man and Has-Serh (home for elderly)

(Des N. Attard)

1982 (29 Jan). Shipbuilding Industry. T **266** and similar vert designs showing different scenes. W **105** (sideways). P 13½.

686	3c. multicoloured	15	10
687	8c. multicoloured	25	15
688	13c. multicoloured	40	35
689	27c. multicoloured	1·00	1·25
686/689 *Set of 4*		1·60	1·60

(Des R. Pitré)

1982 (16 Mar). Care of Elderly. T **267** and similar horiz design. Multicoloured. W **105**. P 14×13½.

690	8c. Type **267**	25	20
691	30c. Elderly woman and Has-Zmien (hospital for elderly)	75	1·40

268 Redemption of Islands by Maltese, 1428

(Des F. Portelli)

1982 (29 Apr). Europa. Historical Events. T **268** and similar horiz design. Multicoloured. W **105**. P 14×13½.

692	8c. Type **268**	40	20
693	30c. Declaration of rights by Maltese, 1802	70	1·40

Nos. 692/693 were each printed in sheets containing two *se-tenant* stamp-size labels.

269 Stylised Footballer

270 Angel appearing to Shepherds

(Des R. Caruana)

1982 (11 June). World Cup Football Championship, Spain. T **269** and similar horiz designs showing stylised footballers. W **105**. P 14.

694	3c. multicoloured	15	10
695	12c. multicoloured	45	55
696	15c. multicoloured	50	65
694/696 *Set of 3*		1·00	1·25
MS697 125×90 mm. Nos. 694/696		3·50	4·50

(Des J. Mallia)

1982 (8 Oct). Christmas. T **270** and similar multicoloured designs. W **105** (sideways). P 14 (No. 700) or 13½ (others).

698	2c. +1c. Type **270**	15	20
699	8c. +2c. Nativity and Three Wise Men bearing gifts	40	60
700	20c. +3c. Nativity scene (*larger 45×37 mm*)	80	75
698/700 *Set of 3*		1·25	1·90

The designs from the 2c. and 8c. values are united to form the design of the 20c. stamp.

271 *Ta' Salvo Serafino* (oared brigantine), 1531

(Des N. Attard)

1982 (13 Nov). Maltese Ships (1st series). T **271** and similar horiz designs. Multicoloured. W **105**. P 14×13½.

701	3c. Type **271**	20	10
702	8c. *La Madonna del Rosaries* (tartane), 1740	40	15
703	12c. *San Paulo* (xebec), 1743	50	40
704	20c. *Ta' Pietro Saliba* (xprunara), 1798	70	80
701/704 *Set of 4*		1·60	1·25

See also Nos. 725/728, 772/775, 792/795 and 809/812.

272 Locomotive *Manning Wardle*, 1883

(Des R. Caruana)

1983 (21 Jan). Centenary of Malta. Railway. T **272** and similar horiz designs. Multicoloured. W **105**. P 14×13½.

705	3c. Type **272**	35	15
706	13c. Locomotive *Black Hawthorn*, 1884	75	1·00
707	27c. Beyer Peacock locomotive, 1895	1·25	3·25
705/707 *Set of 3*		2·10	4·00

273 Peace Doves leaving Malta

(Des C. Cassar)

1983 (14 Mar). Commonwealth Day. T **273** and similar multicoloured designs. W **105** (sideways on vert designs). P 14×13½. (8, 12c.) or 13½×14 (others).

708	8c. Type **273**	20	30
709	12c. Tourist landmarks	30	60
710	15c. Holiday beach (*vert*)	35	75
711	23c. Ship-building (*vert*)	55	1·00
708/711 *Set of 4*		1·25	2·40

274 Ggantija Megalithic Temples, Gozo

(Des T. Bugeja (8c.), R. Caruana (30c.))

1983 (5 May). Europa. T **274** and similar horiz design. Multicoloured. W **105**. P 14×13½.

712	8c. Type **274**	40	40
713	30c. Fort St Angelo	70	2·40

Nos. 712/713 were each printed in sheets including two *se-tenant* stamp-size labels.

275 Dish Aerials (World Communications Year)

(Des D. Friggieri)

1983 (14 July). Anniversaries and Events. T **275** and similar horiz designs. Multicoloured. W **105** (sideways). P 13½×14.

714	3c. Type **275**	20	15
715	7c. Ships' prows and badge (25th Anniversary of IMO Convention)	40	55
716	13c. Container lorries and badge (30th Anniversary of Customs Co-operation Council)	75	90
717	20c. Stadium and emblem (Ninth Mediterranean Games)	65	2·25
714/717 *Set of 4*		1·75	3·50

276 Monsignor Giuseppe de Piro

277 Annunciation

(Des E. Barthet)

1983 (1 Sept). 50th Death Anniversary of Monsignor Giuseppe de Piro. W **105** (sideways). P 14.

718	**276** 3c. multicoloured	15	15

(Des N. Attard)

1983 (6 Sept). Christmas. T **277** and similar vert designs. Multicoloured. W **105** (sideways). P 13½×14.

719	2c. +1c. Type **277**	30	15
720	8c. +2c. The Nativity	70	60
721	20c. +3c. Adoration of the Magi	1·25	2·25
719/721 *Set of 3*		2·00	2·75

278 Workers at Meeting

(Des F. Portelli)

1983 (5 Oct). 40th Anniversary of General Workers' Union. T **278** and similar horiz designs. Multicoloured. W **105**. P 14×13½.

722	3c. Type **278**	15	10
723	8c. Worker with family	35	40
724	27c. Union HQ Building	1·00	1·75
722/724 *Set of 3*		1·40	2·00

(Des N. Attard)

1983 (17 Nov). Maltese Ships (2nd series). Horiz designs as T **271**. Multicoloured. W **105**. P 14×13½.

725	2c. *Strangier* (full-rigged ship), 1813	30	25
726	12c. *Tigre* (topsail schooner) 1839	80	1·25
727	13c. *La Speranza* (brig), 1844	80	1·25
728	20c. *Wignacourt* (barque), 1844	1·25	2·75
725/728 *Set of 4*		2·75	5·00

279 Boeing 737

(Des R. Caruana)

1984 (26 Jan). Air. T **279** and similar horiz designs. Multicoloured. W **105**. P 14×13½.

729	7c. Type **279**	50	30
730	8c. Boeing 720B	60	35
731	16c. Vickers 953 Vanguard	1·25	70
732	23c. Vickers Viscount 700	1·50	70
733	27c. Douglas DC-3	1·75	80
734	38c. Armstrong Whitworth AW.15 Atalanta *Artemis*	2·25	2·75
735	75c. Marina Fiat MF.5 flying boat	3·25	5·00
729/735 *Set of 7*		10·00	9·50

280 CEPT 25th Anniversary Logo

281 Early Policeman

(Des J. Larrivière and L. Borg)

1984 (27 Apr). Europa. W **105**. P 13½.

736	**280** 8c. green, black and gold	35	35
737	30c. carmine-lake, black and gold	1·00	1·25

Nos. 736/737 were each printed in sheets including two *se-tenant* stamp-size labels.

(Des T. Bugeja)

1984 (14 June). 170th Anniversary of Malta Police Force. T **281** and similar vert designs. Multicoloured. W **105**. P 14×13½.

738	3c. Type **281**	65	15
739	8c. Mounted police	1·25	65
	a. Pale Venetian red (background) omitted	£275	
740	11c. Motorcycle policeman	1·50	2·00
741	25c. Policeman and fireman	2·25	3·75
738/741 *Set of 4*		5·00	6·00

282 Running

283 The Visitation (Pietru Caruana)

(Des L. Micallef)

1984 (26 July). Olympic Games, Los Angeles. T **282** and similar vert designs. Multicoloured. W **105** (sideways). P 14.

742	7c. Type **282**	25	30
743	12c. Gymnastics	50	70
744	23c. Swimming	85	1·25
742/744 *Set of 3*		1·50	2·00

(Des L. Micallef)

1984 (5 Oct). Christmas. Paintings from Church of Our Lady of Porto Salvo, Valletta. T **283** and similar multicoloured designs. W **105** (sideways on horiz designs). P 14.

745	2c. +1c. Type **283**	45	65
746	8c. +2c. *The Epiphany* (Rafel Caruana) (*horiz*)	80	1·40
747	20c. +3c. *Jesus among the Doctors* (Rafel Caruana) (*horiz*)	1·75	4·00
745/747 *Set of 3*		2·75	5·50

284 Dove on Map

285 1885 ½d. Green Stamp

(Des L. Micallef)

1984 (12 Dec). Tenth Anniversary of Republic. T **284** and similar vert designs. Multicoloured. W **105** (sideways). P 14.

748	3c. Type **284**	30	20
749	8c. Fort St Angelo	60	65
750	30c. Hands	2·10	4·75
748/750 *Set of 3*		2·75	5·00

(Des N. Attard)

1985 (2 Jan). Centenary of Malta Post Office. T **285** and similar vert designs showing stamps of 1885. Multicoloured. W **105**. P 14.

751	3c. Type **285**	45	15
752	8c. 1885 1d. rose	65	45
753	12c. 1885 2½d. dull blue	90	1·40
754	20c. 1885 4d. brown	1·40	3·00
751/754 *Set of 4*		3·00	4·50
MS755 165×90 mm. Nos. 751/754. Wmk sideways		3·75	6·50

286 Boy, and Hands planting Vine

(Des T. Bugeja)

1985 (7 Mar). International Youth Year. T **286** and similar multicoloured designs. W **105** (sideways on 13c.). P 14.

756	2c. Type **286**	15	15
757	13c. Young people and flowers (*vert*)	70	60
758	27c. Girl holding flame in hand	1·40	1·40
756/758 *Set of 3*		2·00	1·90

287 Nicolo Baldacchino (tenor)

288 Guzeppi Bajada and Manwel Attard (victims)

(Des L. Micallef)

1985 (25 Apr). Europa. European Music Year. T **287** and similar vert design. Multicoloured. W **105**. P 14.

759	8c. Type **287**	1·00	50
760	30c. Francesco Azopardi (composer)	2·00	4·50

Nos. 759/760 were each printed in sheets including two *se-tenant* stamp-size labels.

(Des L. Micallef)

1985 (7 June). 66th Anniversary of 7 June 1919 Demonstrations. T **288** and similar multicoloured designs. W **105** (sideways on 3c., 7c.). P 14.

761	3c. Type **288**	30	15
762	7c. Karmnu Abela and Wenzu Dyer (victims)	60	40
763	35c. Model of projected Demonstration monument by Anton Agius (*vert*)	1·90	2·75
761/763 *Set of 3*		2·50	3·00

289 Stylised Birds

290 Giorgio Mitrovich (nationalist) (Death Centenary)

(Des D. Friggieri)

1985 (26 July). 40th Anniversary of United Nations Organisation. T **289** and similar horiz designs. Multicoloured. W **105** (sideways). P 13½×14.

764	4c. Type **289**	25	15
765	11c. Arrow-headed ribbons	60	1·25
766	31c. Stylised figures	1·40	3·25
764/766 *Set of 3*		2·00	4·25

(Des R. Pitré)

1985 (3 Oct). Celebrities Anniversaries. T **290** and similar vert design. Multicoloured. W **105** (sideways) P 14

767	8c. Type **290**	75	35
768	12c. Pietru Caxaru (poet and administrator) (400th death anniversary)	1·25	2·50

291 The Three Wise Men

292 John XXIII Peace Laboratory and Statue of St Francis of Assisi

(Des G. Bonnici)

1985 (10 Oct). Christmas. T **291** and similar vert designs showing details of terracotta relief by Ganni Bonnici. Multicoloured. W **105** (sideways). P 14.

769	2c. +1c. Type **291**	45	60
770	8c. +2c. Virgin and Child	1·00	1·50
771	20c. +3c. Angels	2·00	3·50
769/771 *Set of 3*		3·00	5·00

(Des N. Attard)

1985 (27 Nov). Maltese Ships (3rd series). Steamships. Horiz designs as T **271**. Multicoloured. W **105**. P 14.

772	3c. *Scotia* (paddle-steamer), 1844	85	20
773	7c. *Tagliaferro* (screw steamer), 1882	1·00	75
774	15c. *Gleneagles* (screw steamer), 1885	1·25	2·75
775	23c. *L'Isle Adam* (screw steamer), 1886	1·75	3·75
772/775 *Set of 4*		4·25	6·75

(Des A. Agiuus. (8c.). T. Bugeja (11, 27c.))

1986 (28 Jan). International Peace Year. T **292** and, similar horiz designs. Multicoloured. W **105** (sideways). P 14 (8, 27c.) or 13½×14 (11c.).

776	8c. Type **292**	1·00	40
777	11c. Dove and hands holding Olive branch 40×19 mm	1·10	1·75
778	27c. Map of Africa, Dove and two heads	2·75	4·75
776/778 *Set of 3*		4·25	6·25

293 Symbolic Plant and *Cynthia cardui*, *Vanessa atalanta* and *Polyommatus icarus* (Butterflies)

294 Heading the Ball

(Des M. Burló)

1986 (3 Apr). Europa. Environmental Conservation. T **293** and similar vert design. Multicoloured. W **105**. P 14.

779	8c. Type **293**	1·00	50
780	35c. Island, Neolithic frieze, sea and sun	1·50	4·00

Nos. 779/780 were each printed in sheets including two *se-tenant* stamp-size labels.

(Des T. Bugeja)

1986 (30 May). World Cup Football Championship, Mexico. T **294** and similar horiz designs. Multicoloured. W **105**. P 14.

781	3c. Type **294**	50	20
782	7c. Saving a goal	1·00	75
783	23c. Controlling the ball	3·00	5·75
781/783	*Set of 3*	4·00	6·00
MS784	125×90 mm. Nos. 781/783. Wmk sideways	7·00	8·50

295 Father Diegu

296 *Nativity*

(Des L. Micallef)

1986 (28 Aug). Maltese Philanthropists. T **295** and similar vert designs. Multicoloured. W **105**. P 14.

785	2c. Type **295**	30	30
786	3c. Adelaide Cini	40	30
787	8c. Alfonso Maria Galea	70	60
788	27c. Vincenzo Bugeja	2·50	5·50
785/788	*Set of 4*	3·50	6·00

(Des L. Micallef)

1986 (10 Oct). Christmas. T **296** and similar multicoloured designs showing paintings by Giuseppe d'Arena. W **105** (sideways on horiz designs). P 14.

789	2c. +1c. Type **296**	1·25	1·75
790	8c. +2c. *Nativity* (detail) (*vert*)	2·75	3·50
791	20c. +3c. *Epiphany*	3·75	7·00
789/791	*Set of 3*	7·00	11·00

(Des N. Attard)

1986 (19 Nov). Maltese Ships (4th series). Horiz designs as T **271**. Multicoloured. W **105**. P 14.

792	7c. *San Paul* (freighter), 1921	1·25	50
793	10c. *Knight of Malta* (mail steamer), 1930	1·50	1·75
794	12c. *Valetta City* (freighter), 1948	1·75	2·75
795	20c. *Saver* (freighter), 1959	2·75	4·50
792/795	*Set of 4*	6·50	8·50

297 European Robin

(Des R. Caruana)

1987 (26 Jan). 25th Anniversary of Malta Ornithological Society. T **297** and similar multicoloured designs. W **105** (sideways on 3, 23c.). P 14.

796	3c. Type **297**	1·25	50
797	8c. Peregrine Falcon (*vert*)	2·50	1·00
798	13c. Hoopoe (*vert*)	3·25	4·00
799	23c. Cory's Shearwater	3·75	6·00
796/799	*Set of 4*	9·75	10·50

298 Aquasun Lido

299 16th-century Pikeman

(Des R. England)

1987 (15 Apr). Europa. Modern Architecture. T **298** and similar vert design. Multicoloured. W **105**. P 14.

800	8c. Type **298**	60	60
801	35c. Church of St Joseph, Manikata	1·40	3·00

Nos. 800/801 were each printed in sheets including two *se-tenant* stamp-size labels.

(Des L. Micallef)

1987 (10 June). Maltese Uniforms (1st series). T **299** and similar vert designs. Multicoloured. W **105** (sideways). P 14.

802	3c. Type **299**	85	40
803	7c. 16th-century officer	1·60	90
804	10c. 18th-century standard bearer	1·75	2·25
805	27c. 18th-century General of the Galleys	3·75	4·75
802/805	*Set of 4*	7·25	7·50

See also Nos. 832/835, 851/854, 880/883 and 893/896.

300 Maltese Scenes, Wheat Ears and Sun (European Environment Year)

(Des A. Camilleri)

1987 (18 Aug). Anniversaries and Events. T **300** and similar horiz designs. Multicoloured. W **105** (sideways). P 14.

806	5c. Type **300**	1·25	50
807	8c. Esperanto star as comet (Centenary of Esperanto)	2·00	60
808	23c. Family at house door (International Year of Shelter for the Homeless)	3·00	3·00
806/808	*Set of 3*	5·50	3·75

(Des N. Attard)

1987 (16 Oct). Maltese Ships (5th series). Horiz designs as T **271**. Multicoloured. W **105**. P 14.

809	2c. *Medina* (freighter), 1969	70	60
810	11c. *Rabat* (container ship), 1974	2·50	2·50
811	13c. *Ghawdex* (passenger ferry), 1979	2·75	2·75
812	20c. *Pinto* (car ferry), 1987	3·75	4·75
809/812	*Set of 4*	8·75	9·50

301 The Visitation

306 Globe and Red Cross
Emblems (125th Anniversary
of International Red Cross)

307 Athletics

(Des R. Caruana)

1987 (6 Nov). Christmas. T **301** and similar horiz designs, each showing illuminated illustration, score and text from 16th-century choral manuscript. Multicoloured. W **105** (sideways). P 14.

813	2c. +1c. Type **301**	50	65
814	8c. +2c. The Nativity	1·75	2·50
815	20c. +3c. The Adoration of the Magi	3·25	4·50
813/815 *Set of 3*		5·00	7·00

302 Dr. Arvid Pardo
(UN representative)

303 Ven. Nazju Falzon
(Catholic catechist)

(Des S. Mallia)

1987 (18 Dec). 20th Anniversary of United Nations Resolution on Peaceful Use of the Seabed. T **302** and similar vert design. Multicoloured. W **105**. P 14.

816	8c. Type **302**	75	60
817	12c. UN emblem and sea	1·25	2·40
MS818 125×90 mm. Nos. 816/817. Wmk sideways. P 13×13½.		3·00	4·50

(Des E. Barthet)

1988 (23 Jan). Maltese Personalities. T **303** and similar vert designs. Multicoloured. W **105**. P 14.

819	2c. Type **303**	30	30
820	3c. Mgr. Sidor Formosa (philanthropist)	30	30
821	4c. Sir Luigi Preziosi (ophthalmologist)	60	30
822	10c. Fr. Anastasju Cuschieri (poet)	80	85
823	25c. Mgr. Pietro Pawl Saydon (Bible translator)	2·00	3·25
819/823 *Set of 5*		3·50	4·50

304 St John Bosco
with Youth (statue)
(Death Centenary)

305 Bus, Ferry and
Airliner

(Des F. Portelli)

1988 (5 Mar). Religious Anniversaries. T **304** and similar vert designs. Multicoloured. W **105** (sideways). P 14.

824	10c. Type **304**	1·00	75
825	12c. *Assumption of Our Lady* (altarpiece by Perugino, Ta' Pinu, Gozo) (Marian Year)	1·25	1·25
826	14c. *Christ the King* (statue by Sciortino) (75th Anniversary of International Eucharistic Congress, Valletta)	1·50	2·00
824/826 *Set of 3*		3·25	3·50

(Des F. Fenech)

1988 (9 Apr). Europa. Transport and Communications. T **305** and similar vert design. Multicoloured. W **105** (sideways). P 13½.

827	10c. Type **305**	1·25	75
828	35c. Control panel, dish aerial and pylons	2·00	3·75

Nos. 827/828 were each printed in sheets including two *se-tenant* stamp-size labels.

(Des M. Cremona)

1988 (28 May). Anniversaries and Events. T **306** and similar horiz designs. Multicoloured. W **105**. P 13½.

829	4c. Type **306**	50	50
830	18c. Divided globe (Campaign for North South Interdependence and Solidarity)	1·25	2·25
831	19c. Globe and symbol (40th Anniversary of World Health Organisation)	1·25	2·25
829/831 *Set of 3*		2·75	4·50

(Des L. Micallef)

1988 (23 July). Maltese Uniforms (2nd issue). Vert designs as T **299**. Multicoloured. W **105** (sideways). P 14.

832	3c. Private, Maltese Light Infantry, 1800	50	30
833	4c. Gunner, Malta Coast Artillery, 1802	55	35
834	10c. Field Officer, 1st Maltese Provincial Battalion, 1805	1·40	1·25
835	25c. Subaltern, Royal Malta Regiment, 1809	2·75	4·25
832/835 *Set of 4*		4·75	5·50

(Des R. Gauci)

1988 (17 Sept). Olympic Games, Seoul. T **307** and similar vert designs. Multicoloured. W **105** (sideways). P 14×13½.

836	4c. Type **307**	20	20
837	10c. Diving	50	60
838	35c. Basketball	2·00	2·75
836/838 *Set of 3*		2·40	3·25

308 Shepherd with
Flock

309 Commonwealth
Emblem

(Des R. Gauci)

1988 (5 Nov). Christmas. T **308** and similar vert designs. Multicoloured. W **105**. P 14.

839	3c. +1c. Type **308**	30	30
840	10c. +2c. The Nativity	75	1·00
841	25c. +3c. Three Wise Men	1·75	2·50
839/841 *Set of 3*		2·50	3·50

(Des F. Portelli)

1989 (28 Jan). 25th Anniversary of Independence. T **309** and similar multicoloured designs. W **105** (sideways). P 14 (25c.) or 13½ (others).

842	2c. Type **309**	20	30
843	3c. Council of Europe flag	20	30
844	4c. UN flag	25	30
845	10c. Workers hands gripping ring and National Flag	70	80
846	12c. Scales and allegorical figure of Justice	75	1·10
847	25c. Prime Minister Borg Olivier with Independence constitution (42×28 *mm*)	1·10	3·00
842/847 *Set of 6*		3·00	5·00

310 New State Arms

(Des F. Portelli)

1989 (25 Mar). W **105**. P 14.
848   **310**   £1 multicoloured .... 3·00   4·00

311 Two Boys flying Kite   **312** Human Figures and Buildings

(Des R. Gauci)

1989 (6 May). Europa. Children's Games. T **311** and similar vert design. Multicoloured. W **105** (sideways). P 13½.
849   10c. Type **311**... 60   60
850   35c. Two girls with dolls .... 1·50   3·50
Nos. 849/850 were each printed in sheets including two *se-tenant* stamp-size labels.

(Des L. Micallef)

1989 (24 June). Maltese Uniforms (3rd series). Vert designs as T **299**. Multicoloured. W **105** (sideways). P 14.
851   3c. Officer, Maltese Veterans, 1815 45   45
852   4c. Subaltern, Royal Malta Fencibles, 1839.... 50   50
853   10c. Private, alta Militia, 1856......................... 1·25   1·50
854   25c. Colonel, Royal Malta Fencible Artillery, 1875.. 2·50   3·75
851/854 *Set of 4*.. 4·25   5·50

(Des L. Casha)

1989 (17 Oct). Anniversaries and Commemorations. T **312** and similar horiz designs showing logo and stylised human figures. Multicoloured. W **105** (sideways). P 14.
855   3c. Type **312** (20th Anniversary of UN Declaration on Social Progress and Development)... 30   30
856   4c. Workers and figure in wheelchair (Malta's Ratification of European Social Charter)... 35   35
857   10c. Family (40th Anniversary of Council of Europe)... 50   80
858   14c. Teacher and children (70th Anniversary of Malta Union of Teachers) 65   1·25
859   25c. Symbolic knights (Knights of the Sovereign Military Order of Malta Assembly)... 1·40   3·00
855/859 *Set of 5*.. 3·00   5·00

313 Angel and Cherub

(Des J. Mallia)

1989 (11 Nov). Christmas. T **313** and similar horiz designs showing vault paintings by Mattia Preti from St John's Co-Cathedral. Valletta. Multicoloured. W **105**. P 13½.
860   3c. +1c. Type **313**..................................... 60   60
861   10c. +2c. Two Angels................................... 1·40   1·90
862   20c. +3c. Angel blowing trumpet................ 2·00   4·00
860/862 *Set of 3*.. 3·50   6·00

314 Presidents George H. Bush and Mikhail Gorbachev   **315** General Post Office, Auberge d'Italie, Valletta

1989 (2 Dec). USA–USSR Summit Meeting, Malta. W **105**. P 14.
863   **314**   10c. multicoloured .... 1·00   1·25

(Des R. Caruana)

1990 (9 Feb). Europa. Post Office Buildings. T **315** and similar multicoloured design. W **105** (sideways on 10c.). P 14.
864   10c. Type **315**... 75   50
865   35c. Branch Post Office, Zebbug (*horiz*)........... 1·50   3·25
Nos. 864/865 were each printed in sheets including two *se-tenant* stamp-size labels.

316 Open Book and Letters from Different Alphabets (International Literacy Year)   **317** Samuel Taylor Coleridge (poet) and Government House

(Des T. Bugeja)

1990 (7 Apr). Anniversaries and Events. T **316** and similar multicoloured designs. W **105** (sideways on 4, 19c.). P 14.
866   3c. Type **316**... 25   15
867   4c. Count Roger of Sicily and Norman soldiers (900th Anniversary of Sicilian rule) (*horiz*)... 50   25
868   19c. Communications satellite (25th Anniversary of International Telecommunication Union membership) (*horiz*)... 1·60   2·00
869   20c. Football and map of Malta (Union of European Football Associations 20th Ordinary Congress, Malta)........................... 1·60   2·00
866/869 *Set of 4*.. 3·50   4·00

(Des A. Grech)

1990 (3 May). British Authors. T **317** and similar horiz designs. Multicoloured. W **105** (sideways). P 13½.
870   4c. Type **317**... 50   30
871   10c. Lord Byron (poet) and map of Valletta..... 90   70
872   12c. Sir Walter Scott (novelist) and Great Siege.. 1·00   95
873   25c. William Makepeace Thackeray (novelist) and Naval Arsenal....................................... 2·00   2·25
870/873 *Set of 4*.. 4·00   3·75

318 St Paul   **319** Flags and Football

(Des N. Bason)

1990 (25 May). Visit of Pope John Paul II. T **318** and similar vert design showing bronze bas-reliefs. W **105** (sideways). P 14.
874   4c. brownish black, flesh and carmine 50   1·50
        a. Pair. Nos. 874/875 .... 2·00   3·25
875   25c. brownish black, flesh and carmine .... 1·50   1·75
Design: 4c. T **318**; 25c. Pope John Paul II.
Nos. 874/875 were printed together in a sheet of 12 (4×3) containing ten stamps, *se-tenant* horizontally or vertically, and two stamp-size labels on R. 2/1 and 2/4.

(Des T. Bugeja)

1990 (8 June). World Cup Football Championship, Italy. T **319** and similar horiz designs. Multicoloured. W **105**. P 14.
876   5c. Type **319**... 35   30
877   10c. Football in net...................................... 65   1·00
878   14c. Scoreboard and football .... 1·00   1·75
876/878 *Set of 3*.. 1·75   2·75
MS879 123×90 mm. Nos. 876/878. Wmk sideways .... 3·00   4·25

(Des L. Micallef)

1990 (25 Aug). Maltese Uniforms (4th series). Vert designs as T **299**. Multicoloured. W **105** (sideways). P 14.

880	3c. Captain, Royal Malta Militia, 1889	1·25	55
881	4c. Field officer, Royal Malta Artillery, 1905 ..	1·40	60
882	10c. Labourer, Malta Labour Corps, 1915	2·50	1·50
883	25c. Lieutenant, King's Own Malta Regiment of Militia, 1918	3·75	5·75
880/883	Set of 4	8·00	7·50

320 Innkeeper

321 1919 10s. Stamp under Magnifying Glass

(Des J. Smith)

1990 (10 Nov). Christmas. Figures from Crib by Austin Galea, Marco Bartolo and Rosario Zammit. T **320** and similar multicoloured designs. W **105** (sideways). P 14×14½ (10c.) or 13½×14 (others).

884	3c. +1c. Type **320**	30	50
885	10c. +2c. Nativity (41×28 mm)	70	1·25
886	25c. +3c. Shepherd with sheep	1·60	2·50
884/886	Set of 3	2·40	3·75

(Des J. Mallia)

1991 (6 Mar). 25th Anniversary of Philatelic Society of Malta. W **105** (sideways). P 14.

887	**321** 10c. multicoloured	60	70

322 Eurostar Satellite and VDU Screen

323 St Ignatius Loyola (founder of Jesuits) (500th birth anniversary)

(Des R. Caruana)

1991 (16 Mar). Europa. Europe in Space. T **322** and similar vert design. Multicoloured. W **105** (sideways). P 14.

888	10c. Type **322**	75	70
889	35c. Ariane 4 rocket and projected HOTOL aerospaceplane	1·25	2·75

Nos. 888/889 were each printed in sheets including two se-tenant stamp-size labels.

(Des J. Mallia)

1991 (29 Apr). Religious Commemorations. T **323** and similar multicoloured designs. W **105** (sideways on 3, 30c.). P 14.

890	3c. Type **323**	30	20
891	4c. Abbess Venerable Maria Adeodata Pisani (185th birth anniversary) (vert).....	35	25
892	30c. St John of the Cross (400th death anniversary)	1·60	2·75
890/892	Set of 3	2·00	3·00

(Des L. Micallef)

1991 (13 Aug). Maltese Uniforms (5th series). Vert designs as T **299**. Multicoloured. W **105** (sideways). P 14.

893	3c. Officer with colour, Royal Malta Fencibles, 1860	55	25
894	10c. Officer with colour, Royal Malta Regiment of Militia, 1903	1·10	60
895	19c. Officer with Queen's colour, King's Own Malta Regiment, 1968	2·00	1·75
896	25c. Officer with colour, Malta Armed Forces, 1991	2·50	2·00
893/896	Set of 4	5·50	4·25

324 Interlocking Arrows   **325** Honey Buzzard

(Des N. Attard)

1991 (23 Sept). 25th Anniversary of Union Haddiema Maghqudin (public services union). W **105** (sideways). P 13½.

897	**324** 4c. multicoloured	30	30

(Des H. Borg)

1991 (3 Oct). Endangered Species. Birds. T **325** and similar vert designs. Multicoloured. W **105**. P 14.

898	4c. Type **325**	2·50	2·75
	a. Horiz strip of 4. Nos. 898/901 ...	9·00	10·00
899	4c. Marsh Harrier	2·50	2·75
900	10c. Eleonora's Falcon	2·50	2·75
901	10c. Lesser Kestrel	2·50	2·75
898/901	Set of 4	9·00	10·00

Nos. 898/901 were printed together, se-tenant, in horizontal strips of four throughout the sheet.

326 Three Wise Men   **327** Ta' Hagrat Neolithic Temple

(Des H. Borg)

1991 (6 Nov). Christmas. T **326** and similar vert designs. Multicoloured. W **105**. P 14.

902	3c. +1c. Type **326**...............	55	50
903	10c. +2c. Holy Family............	1·00	1·40
904	25c. +3c. Two shepherds.........	2·00	3·25
902/904	Set of 3	3·25	4·75

(Des F. Portelli)

1991 (9 Dec). National Heritage of the Maltese Islands. T **327** and similar multicoloured designs. W **105** (sideways on £2). P 13½.

905	1c. Type **327**	35	50
906	2c. Cottoner Gate	35	50
907	3c. St Michael's Bastion, Valletta	40	50
908	4c. Spinola Palace, St Julian's.........	50	15
909	5c. Birkirkara Church	60	20
910	10c. Mellieha Bay	1·25	35
911	12c. Wied iz-Zurrieq	1·40	40
912	14c. Mgarr harbour, Gaza	2·00	45
913	20c. Yacht marina	2·50	65
914	50c. Gaza Channel	3·75	1·60
915	£1 Arab Horses (sculpture by Antonio Sciortino)	6·00	3·25
916	£2 Independence Monument (Ganni Bonnici) (vert)	11·00	8·00
905/916	Set of 12	27·00	15·00

328 Aircraft Tailfins and Terminal

(Des. H. Borg)

1992 (8 Feb). Opening of International Air Terminal. T **328** and similar horiz design. W **105** (sideways). P 14.

917	4c. Type **328**...................	75	30
918	10c. National Flags and terminal	1·25	70

329 Ships of Columbus

330 George Cross and Anti-aircraft Gun Crew

(Des H. Borg)

1992 (20 Feb). Europa. 500th Anniversary of discovery of America by Columbus. T **329** and similar horiz design. W **105** (sideways). P 14.

919	10c. Type **329**	1·25	55
920	35c. Columbus and map of Americas	2·50	2·25

Nos. 919/920 were each printed in sheets including two *se-tenant* stamp-size labels.

(Des H. Borg)

1992 (15 Apr). 50th Anniversary of Award of George Cross to Malta. T **330** and similar vert designs. Multicoloured. W **105**. P 14.

921	4c. Type **330**	1·00	30
922	10c. George Cross and memorial bell	1·50	1·00
923	50c. Tanker *Ohio* entering Grand Harbour	7·00	8·50
921/923 Set of 3		8·50	9·00

331 Running

332 Church of the Flight into Egypt

(Des H. Borg)

1992 (24 June). Olympic Games, Barcelona. T **331** and similar horiz designs. Multicoloured. W **105** (sideways). P 14.

924	3c. Type **331**	55	20
925	10c. High jumping	80	75
926	30c. Swimming	2·00	4·00
924/926 Set of 3		3·00	4·50

(Des N. Attard)

1992 (5 Aug). Rehabilitation of Historical Buildings. T **332** and similar designs. W **105** (sideways on 4, 25c.). P 14.

927	3c. black, pale stone and bluish grey	45	30
928	4c. black, pale stone and flesh	45	30
929	19c. black, pale stone and pale rose-lilac	2·25	3·75
930	25c. black, pale stone and pale grey-olive	2·50	3·75
927/930 Set of 4		5·00	7·25

Designs: Horiz—4c. St John's Co-Cathedral; 25c. Auberge de Provence. Vert—3c. T **332**; 19c. Church of Madonna del Pillar.

333 The Nativity (Giuseppe Cali)

334 Malta College Building, Valletta

(Des L. Buttigieg)

1992 (22 Oct). Christmas. Religious Paintings by Giuseppe Cali from Mosta Church. T **333** and similar horiz designs. Multicoloured. W **105** (sideways). P 14.

931	3c. +1c. Type **333**	75	1·10
932	10c. +2c. *Adoration of the Magi*	1·75	2·50
933	25c. +3c. *Christ with the Elders in the Temple*	3·00	4·50
931/933 Set of 3		5·00	7·25

(Des L. Buttigieg)

1992 (12 Nov). 400th Anniversary of University of Malta. T **334** and similar multicoloured design. W **105** (sideways on 30c.). P 14.

934	4c. Type **334**	75	25
935	30c. Modern University complex, Tal-Qroqq (*horiz*)	2·50	4·25

335 Lions Club Emblem

336 Untitled Painting by Paul Carbonaro

(Des H. Borg)

1993 (4 Feb). 75th Anniversary of International Association of Lions Club. T **335** and similar horiz design. Multicoloured. W **105**. P 13½.

936	4c. Type **335**	50	25
937	50c. Eye (Sight First Campaign)	2·75	4·00

1993 (7 Apr). Europa. Contemporary Art. T **336** and similar multicoloured design. W **105** (sideways on 35c.). P 14.

938	10c. Type **336**	1·00	50
939	35c. Untitled painting by Alfred Chircop (*horiz*)	1·75	3·50

Nos. 938/939 were each printed in sheets including two stamp-size labels.

337 Mascot holding Flame

(Des R. Caruana)

1993 (4 May). Fifth Small States of Europe Games. T **337** and similar horiz designs. Multicoloured. W **105**. P 13½×14.

940	3c. Type **337**	20	20
941	4c. Cycling	1·75	30
942	10c. Tennis	1·25	1·00
943	35c. Yachting	2·00	3·50
940/943 Set of 4		4·75	4·00
MS944 120×80 mm. Nos. 940/943. Wmk sideways		4·50	5·50

338 Learning First Aid

339 Papilio machaon

(Des L. Micallef)

1993 (21 July). 50th Anniversary of Award of Bronze Cross to Maltese Scouts and Guides. T **338** and similar vert designs. Multicoloured. W **105**. P 14.

945	3c. Type **338**	50	20
946	4c. Bronze Cross	50	20
947	10c. Scout building camp fire	1·10	90
948	35c. Governor Lord Gort presenting Bronze Cross, 1943	2·75	4·00
945/948 Set of 4		4·25	4·75

Nos. 945/948 are known imperforate. These are believed to come from proof sheets.

(Des M. Burlò)

1993 (23 Sept). European Year of the Elderly. Butterflies. T **339** and similar vert design. Multicoloured. W **105**. P 14.

949	5c. Type **339**	35	20
950	35c. *Vanessa atalanta*	1·75	2·25

340 GWU Badge and Interlocking '50'

341 Child Jesus and Star

(Des H. Borg)

1993 (5 Oct). 50th Anniversary of General Workers Union. W **105** (sideways). P 13½.

951	**340**	4c. multicoloured	35	40

(Des H. Borg)

1993 (5 Nov). Christmas. T **341** and similar vert designs. Multicoloured. W **105**. P 14.

952	3c. +1c. Type **341**	30	35
953	10c. +2c. Christmas tree	85	1·25
954	25c. +3c. Star in traditional window	1·60	2·75
952/954 Set of 3		2·50	4·00

342 Council Arms (face value top left)

(Des J. Mizzi)

1993 (20 Nov). Inauguration of Local Community Councils. Sheet 110×93 mm. containing T **342** and similar horiz designs showing different Council Arms. Multicoloured. W **105** (sideways). P 14.

MS955 5c. Type **342** 5c. Face value top right; 5c. Face value bottom left; 5c. Face value bottom right		1·50	2·25

343 Symbolic Tooth and Probe

344 Sir Themistocles Zammit (discoverer of Brucella microbe)

(Des F. Ancilleri)

1994 (12 Feb). 50th Anniversary of Maltese Dental Association. T **343** and similar vert design. Multicoloured. W **105**. P 14.

956	5c. Type **343**	35	30
957	44c. Symbolic mouth and dental mirror	2·00	2·50

(Des H. Borg)

1994 (29 Mar). Europa. Discoveries. T **344** and similar vert design. Multicoloured. W **105**. P 14.

958	14c. Type **344**	50	30
959	30c. Bilingually inscribed candelabrum of 2nd-century BC (deciphering of ancient Phoenician language)	1·90	3·25

Nos. 958/959 were each printed in sheets including two *se-tenant* stamp-size labels.

345 Family in Silhouette (International Year of the Family)

346 Football and Map

(Des F. Ancilleri)

1994 (10 May). Anniversaries and Events. T **345** and similar multicoloured designs. W **105** (sideways on 25c.). P 14.

960	5c. Type **345**	30	20
961	9c. Stylised Red Cross (International Recognition of Malta Red Cross Society)	60	50
962	14c. Animals and crops (150th Anniversary of Agrarian Society)	90	80
963	20c. Worker in silhouette (75th Anniversary of International Labour Organisation)	1·25	1·60
964	25c. St Paul's Anglican Cathedral (155th Anniversary) (vert)	1·40	1·75
960/964 Set of 5		4·00	4·25

(Des F. Ancilleri)

1994 (9 June). World Cup Football Championship, USA T **346** and similar horiz designs. Multicoloured. W **105**. P 14.

965	5c. Type **346**	30	20
966	14c. Ball and goal	70	80
967	30c. Ball and pitch superimposed on map	1·75	4·25
965/967 Set of 3		2·50	4·75
MS968 123×88 mm. Nos. 965/967. Wmk sideways		3·75	5·00

347 Falcon Trophy, Twin Comanche and Auster (25th Anniversary of Malta International Rally)

348 National Flags and Astronaut on Moon

(Des R. Caruana)

1994 (2 July). Aviation Anniversaries and Events. T **347** and similar horiz designs. Multicoloured. W **105** (sideways). P 14.

969	5c. Type **347**	50	25
970	14c. Alouette helicopter, display teams and logo (Malta International Airshow)	1·75	1·00
971	20c. de Havilland Dove City of Valetta and Avro York aircraft with logo (50th Anniversary of International Civil Aviation Organisation)	1·90	2·00
972	25c. Airbus 320 Nicolas Cottoner and de Havilland Comet aircraft with logo (50th Anniversary of ICAO)	1·90	2·25
969/972 Set of 4		5·50	5·00

After printing it was found that all examples of the 20c. were inscribed 'Anniverarju' in error. These were withdrawn before issue and replaced by stock showing the word correctly spelt as 'Anniversarju'. It is reported that all sheets of the incorrect printing were destroyed.

(Des R. Caruana)

1994 (20 July). 25th Anniversary of First Moon Landing. W **105**. P 14.

973	**348**	14c. multicoloured	1·10	1·25

349 Virgin Mary and Child with Angels

350 Helmet-shaped Ewer

(Des H. Borg)

1994 (26 Oct). Christmas. T **349** and similar multicoloured designs. W **105** (sideways on 5c.). P 13½ (5c.) or 14 (others).

974	5c. Type **349**	20	10
975	9c. +2c. Angel in pink (vert)	50	70
976	14c. +3c. Virgin Mary and Child (vert)	80	1·25
977	20c. +3c. Angel in green (vert)	1·25	2·50
974/977 Set of 4		2·50	4·00

Nos. 975/977 are larger, 28×41 mm, and depict details from T **349**.

(Des M. Burlò)

1994 (12 Dec). Maltese Antique Silver Exhibition. T **350** and similar vert designs. Multicoloured. W **105**. P 14.

978	5c. Type **350**	50	20
979	14c. Balsamina	1·10	80
980	20c. Coffee pot	1·50	2·00
981	25c. Sugar box	1·75	2·75
978/981 Set of 4		4·25	5·25

351 '60 plus' and Hands touching

352 Hand holding Leaf and Rainbow

(Des Anna Grima)

1995 (27 Feb). Anniversaries and Events. T **351** and similar vert designs. Multicoloured. W **105** (sideways). P 14.

982	2c. Type **351** (25th Anniversary of National Association of Pensioners)	15	25
983	5c. Child's drawing (Tenth Anniversary of National Youth Council)	25	20
984	14c. Conference emblem (Fourth World Conference on Women, Peking, China)	50	60
985	20c. Nurse and thermometer (50th Anniversary of Malta Memorial District Nursing Association)	1·25	1·40
986	25c. Louis Pasteur (biologist) (death centenary)	1·50	1·75
982/986 Set of 5		3·25	3·75

(Des Harry Borg)

1995 (29 Mar). Europa. Peace and Freedom. T **352** and similar multicoloured design. W **105** (sideways on 30c.). P 14.

987	14c. Type **352**	1·00	55
988	30c. Peace Doves (horiz)	1·50	2·50

Nos. 987/988 were each printed in sheets including two stamp-size labels.

353 Junkers Ju 87B Stuka Dive Bombers over Valletta and Anti-aircraft Gun

354 Light Bulb

(Des Frank Ancilleri)

1995 (21 Apr). Anniversaries. T **353** and similar multicoloured designs. W **105** (sideways on horiz designs). P 14.

989	5c. Type **353** (50th Anniversary of end of Second World War)	25	25
990	14c. Silhouetted people holding hands (50th Anniversary of United Nations)	55	60
991	35c. Hands holding bowl of wheat (50th Anniversary of Food and Agriculture Organisation) (vert)	1·60	2·25
989/991 Set of 3		2·25	2·75

(Des Maurice Tanti Burlò)

1995 (15 June). Maltese Electricity and Telecommunications. T **354** and similar vert designs. Multicoloured. W **105** (sideways). P 13½.

992	2c. Type **354**	15	25
993	5c. Symbolic Owl and binary codes	25	15
994	9c. Dish aerial	35	50
995	14c. Sun and rainbow over trees	50	65
996	20c. Early telephone, satellite and Moon's surface	1·00	1·50
992/996 Set of 5		2·00	2·75

355 Rock Wall and Girna

356 Pinto's Turret Clock

(Des Maurice Tanti Burlò)

1995 (26 July). European Nature Conservation Year. T **355** and similar horiz designs. W **105** (sideways). P 14.

997	5c. Type **355**	75	25
998	14c. Maltese Wall Lizards	2·25	80
999	44c. Aleppo Pine	3·50	3·00
997/999 Set of 3		5·75	3·50

(Des Frank Ancilleri)

1995 (5 Oct). Treasures of Malta. Antique Maltese Clocks. T **356** and similar vert designs. Multicoloured. W **105**. P 14.

1000	1c. Type **356**	15	60
1001	5c. Michelangelo Sapiano (horologist) and clocks	50	25
1002	14c. Arlogg tal-lira clock	1·50	80
1003	25c. Sundials	2·50	3·50
1000/1003 Set of 4		4·25	4·75

357 Children's Christmas Eve Procession

(Des Harry Borg)

1995 (15 Nov). Christmas. T **357** and similar multicoloured designs. W **105** (sideways on 5c.). P 14×13½.

1004	5c. Type **357**	25	10
1005	5c. +2c. Children with crib (vert)	30	50
1006	14c. +3c. Children with lanterns (vert)	1·00	1·25
1007	25c. +3c. Boy with lantern and balustrade (vert)	1·75	2·75
1004/1007 Set of 4		3·00	4·25

Nos. 1005/1007 are 27×32 mm and depict details from T **357**.

358 Silhouetted Children and President's Palace, San Anton

(Des Frank Ancilleri)

1996 (29 Feb). Anniversaries. T **358** and similar horiz designs. Multicoloured. W **105** (sideways). P 14.

1008	5c. Type **358** (35th Anniversary of the President's Award)	20	15
1009	14c. Father Nazzareno Camilleri and St Patrick's Church, Salesjani (90th birth anniversary)	50	50
1010	20c. St Mary Euphrasia and convent (Birth bicentenary)	80	1·10
1011	25c. Silhouetted children and fountain (50th Anniversary of UNICEF)	95	1·60
1008/1011 Set of 4		2·25	3·00

359 Carved Figures from Skorba

(Des Harry Borg)

1996 (29 Mar). Maltese Prehistoric Art Exhibition. T **359** and similar multicoloured designs. W **105** (sideways on horiz designs). P 14.

1012	5c. Type **359**	25	15
1013	14c. Temple carving, Gozo	60	65
1014	20c. Carved figure of a woman, Skorba (*vert*)	80	1·00
1015	35c. Ghar Dalam pot (*vert*)	1·50	3·00
1012/1015 *Set of 4*		2·75	4·25

360 Mabel Strickland (politician and journalist)

361 Face and Emblem (United Nations Decade against Drug Abuse)

(Des Catherine Cavallo)

1996 (24 Apr). Europa. Famous Women. T **360** and similar vert design. Multicoloured. W **105**. P 14.

1016	14c. Type **360**	60	55
1017	30c. Inez Sole, (artist, musician and writer)	1·40	2·00

(Des Damian Borg Nicolas)

1996 (5 June). Anniversaries and Events. T **361** and similar vert designs. Multicoloured. W **105**. P 14.

1018	5c. Type **361**	20	20
1019	5c. 'Fi' and emblem (50th Anniversary of Malta Federation of Industry)	20	20
1020	14c. Commemorative plaque and National Flag (75th Anniversary of Self-government)	60	60
1021	44c. Guglielmo Marconi and early radio equipment (Centenary of radio)	1·50	2·50
1018/1021 *Set of 4*		2·25	3·25

362 Judo

(Des Luciano Micallef)

1996 (10 July). Olympic Games Atlanta. T **362** and similar horiz designs. Multicoloured. W **105** (sideways). P 14.

1022	2c. Type **362**	10	20
1023	5c. Athletics	30	15
1024	14c. Diving	70	80
1025	25c. Rifle-shooting	1·10	1·60
1022/1025 *Set of 4*		2·00	2·50

363 Harvest Time (Cali)

(Des Debbie Caruana Dingli)

1996 (22 Aug). 150th Birth Anniversary of Guiseppe Cali (painter). T **363** and similar multicoloured designs. W **105** (sideways on 5, 14c.). P 14.

1026	5c. Type **363**	30	25
1027	14c. *Dog* (Cali)	70	70
1028	20c. *Countrywoman in a Field* (Cali) (*vert*)	90	1·10
1029	25c. *Cali at his Easel* (Edward Dingli) (*vert*)	1·00	1·25
1026/1029 *Set of 4*		2·50	3·00

364 Bus No. 1990 *Diamond Star*, 1920s

(Des Richard J. Caruana)

1996 (26 Sept). Buses. T **364** and similar horiz designs. Multicoloured. W **105** (sideways). P 14.

1030	2c. Type **364**	40	20
1031	5c. No. 434 *Tom Mix*, 1930s	70	25
1032	14c. No. 1764 *Verdala*, 1940s	1·40	1·00
1033	30c. No. 3495, 1960s	2·00	2·75
1030/1033 *Set of 4*		4·00	3·75

365 Stained Glass Window

(Des Harry Borg)

1996 (17 Nov). Christmas. T **365** and similar multicoloured designs. W **105** (sideways on 5c.). P 14×13½.

1034	5c. Type **365**	35	10
1035	5c. +2c. Madonna and Child (29×35 *mm*)	40	60
1036	14c. +3c. Angel facing right (29×35 *mm*)	80	1·40
1037	25c. +3c. Angel facing left (29×35 *mm*)	1·25	2·50
1034/1037 *Set of 4*		2·50	4·25

Nos. 1035/1037 show details from T **365**.

366 Hompesch Arch and Arms, Zabbar

367 Captain-General of the Galleys' Sedan Chair

(Des Richard Caruana)

1997 (20 Feb). Bicentenary of Maltese Cities. T **366** and similar vert designs. Multicoloured. W **105**. P 14.

1038	6c. Type **366**	30	25
1039	16c. Statue, church and Arms, Siggiewi	70	70
1040	26c. Seated statue and Arms, Zejtun	1·10	1·25
1038/1040 *Set of 3*		1·90	1·75
MS1041 125×90 mm. As Nos. 1038/1040. Wmk sideways		5·50	5·50

1997 (11 Apr). Treasures of Malta. Sedan Chairs. T **367** and similar multicoloured designs. W **105** (sideways on horiz designs). P 14.

1042	2c. Type **367**	15	15
1043	6c. Cotoner Grandmasters' chair	30	30
1044	16c. Chair from Cathedral Museum, Mdina (*vert*)	70	70
1045	27c. Chevalier D'Arezzo's chair (*vert*)	1·10	1·10
1042/1045 *Set of 4*		2·00	2·00

368 Gahan carrying Door

369 Modern Sculpture (Antonio Sciortino)

(Des J. Mallia)

1997 (5 May). Europa. Tales and Legends. T **368** and similar vert design. Multicoloured. W **105** (sideways). P 14.

1046	16c. Type **368**	1·00	75
1047	35c. St Dimitrius appearing from painting	1·75	2·50

Nos. 1046/1047 were each printed in sheets of ten and two stamp-size labels.

1997 (10 July). Anniversaries. T **369** and similar multicoloured designs. W **105** (sideways on horiz designs). P 14.

1048	1c. Type **369**	10	15
1049	6c. Joseph Calleia and film reel (*horiz*)	40	40
1050	6c. Gozo Cathedral (*horiz*)	40	40
1051	11c. City of Gozo (*horiz*)	60	50
1052	16c. Sculpture of head (Sciortino)	80	70
1053	22c. Joseph Calleia and film camera (*horiz*)	1·00	1·00
1048/1053 *Set of 6*		3·00	2·75

Anniversaries; 1c., 16c. 50th death anniversary of Antonio Sciortino (sculptor); 6c. (No. 1049), 22c., Birth centenary of Joseph Calleia (actor); 6c. (No. 1050), 11c. 300th anniversary of construction of Gozo Cathedral.

370 Dr. Albert Laferla

371 The Nativity

(Des Debbie Caruana Dingli)

1997 (24 Sept). Pioneers of Education. T **370** and similar vert designs. Multicoloured. W **105**. P 14.

1054	6c. Type **370**	30	25
1055	16c. Sister Emilie de Vialar	70	70
1056	19c. Mgr. Paolo Pullicino	80	80
1057	26c. Mgr. Tommaso Gargallo	1·00	1·10
1054/1057 *Set of 4*		2·50	2·50

(Des Harry Borg)

1997 (12 Nov). Christmas. T **371** and similar multicoloured designs. W **105** (sideways on 6c.). P 14.

1058	6c. Type **371**	30	10
1059	6c. +2c. Mary and baby Jesus (*vert*)	35	50
1060	16c. +3c. Joseph with Donkey (*vert*)	1·00	1·40
1061	26c. +3c. Shepherd with Lamb (*vert*)	1·50	2·50
1058/1061 *Set of 4*		2·75	4·00

Nos. 1059/1061 show details from T **371**.

372 Plan of Fort and Soldiers in Victoria Lines

373 *Maria Amelia Grognet* (Antoine de Favray)

1997 (5 Dec). Anniversaries. T **372** and similar horiz designs. Multicoloured (except 6c.). W **105** (sideways). P 14.

1062	2c. Type **372**	20	10
1063	6c. Sir Paul Boffa making speech (black and scarlet)	30	25
1064	16c. Plan of fort and gun crew	90	65
1065	37c. Queue of voters	1·50	2·00
1062/1065 *Set of 4*		2·50	2·75

Anniversaries; 2c. 16c. Centenary of Victoria Lines; 6c., 37c. 50th anniversary of 1947 Self-Government Constitution.

(Des Frank Ancilleri)

1998 (26 Feb). Treasures of Malta. Costumes and Paintings. T **373** and similar vert designs. W **105**. P 14.

1066	6c. Type **373**	60	50
1067	6c. Gentleman's waistcoat, *c.* 1790–1810	60	50
1068	16c. Lady's dinner dress, *c.* 1880	75	90
1069	16c. *Veneranda, Baroness Abela, and her Grandson* (de Favray)	75	90
1066/1069 *Set of 4*		2·40	2·50

MS1070 123×88 mm. 26c. City of Valletta from old print (39×47 *mm*). Wmk sideways. P 13×13½ .... 1·60 1·60

374 Grand Master Ferdinand von Hompesch

375 Racing Two-man Luzzus

(Des Joseph Mizzi)

1998 (28 Mar). Bicentenary of Napoleon's Capture of Malta. T **374** and similar horiz designs. Multicoloured. W **105**. P 14.

1071	6c. Type **374**	60	80
	a. Vert pair. Nos. 1071/1072	1·10	1·60
1072	6c. French fleet	60	80
1073	16c. French landing	1·10	1·60
	a. Vert pair. Nos. 1073/1074	2·10	3·00
1074	16c. General Napoleon Bonaparte	1·10	1·60
1071/1074 *Set of 4*		3·00	4·25

Nos. 1071/1072 and 1073/1074 were each printed together, *se-tenant*, in horizontal pairs throughout the sheets.

(Des Frank Ancilleri and Richard Caruana)

1998 (22 Apr). Europa. Sailing Regatta, Grand Harbour. T **375** and similar horiz design. Multicoloured. W **51**. P 14.

1075	16c. Type **375**	75	55
1076	35c. Racing four-man luzzus	1·25	2·25

376 Dolphin and Diver

377 Goalkeeper saving Goal

(Des Isabelle Borg)

1998 (27 May). International Year of the Ocean. T **376** and similar multicoloured designs. W **105** (sideways on 16 and 27c.). P 14.

1077	2c. Type **376**	25	25
1078	6c. Diver and Sea-urchin	40	25
1079	16c. Jacques Cousteau and diver (*horiz*)	90	80
1080	27c. Two divers (*horiz*)	1·40	2·25
1077/1080 *Set of 4*		2·75	3·25

(Des Richard Caruana)

1998 (10 June). World Cup Football Championship, France. T **377** and similar horiz designs showing players and flags. Multicoloured. W **105**. P 14.

1081	6c. Type **377**	55	25
1082	16c. Two players and referee	1·00	70
1083	22c. Two footballers	1·40	2·00
1081/1083 *Set of 3*		2·75	2·75

MS1084 122×87 mm. Nos. 1081/1083. Wmk sideways ... 3·50 3·25

378 Ships' Wheels
(50th Anniversary
of International
Maritime
Organisation)

379 *Rest on the Flight to Egypt*

(Des Harry Borg)

1998 (17 Sept). Anniversaries. T **378** and similar horiz designs. Multicoloured. W **105** (sideways). P 14.

1085	1c. Type **378**	10	30
1086	6c. Symbolic family (50th Anniversary of Universal Declaration of Human Rights).	30	25
1087	11c. 'GRTU' and cogwheels (50th Anniversary of General Retailers and Traders Union)	45	40
1088	19c. Mercury (50th Anniversary of Chamber of Commerce)	80	1·40
1089	26c. Aircraft tailfins (25th Anniversary of Air Malta)	2·00	2·50
1085/1089 *Set of 5*		3·25	4·25

1998 (19 Nov). Christmas. Paintings by Mattia Preti. T **379** and similar vert designs. Multicoloured. W **105**. P 14.

1090	6c. Type **379**	40	10
1091	6c. +2c. *Virgin and Child with Sts Anthony and John the Baptist*	50	70
1092	16c. +3c. *Virgin and Child with Sts Raphael, Nicholas and Gregory*	1·25	1·75
1093	26c. +3c. *Virgin and Child with Sts. John the Baptist and Nicholas*	1·75	3·00
1090/1093 *Set of 4*		4·50	5·00

PRINTERS. All stamps between Nos. 1094 and 1383 were printed in lithography by German State Printing Works, Berlin.

380 Fort St Angelo

(Des Frank Ancilleri)

1999 (26 Feb). 900th Anniversary of the Sovereign Military Order of Malta. T **380** and similar multicoloured designs. P 14.

1094	2c. Type **380**	35	10
1095	6c. Grand Master de l'Isle Adam (*vert*)	60	25
1096	16c. Grand Master La Valette (*vert*)	1·10	65
1097	27c. Auberge de Castille et León	1·60	3·00
1094/1097 *Set of 4*		3·25	3·50

381 Little Ringed Plover, Ghadira Nature Reserve

(Des Richard J. Caruana)

1999 (6 Apr). Europa. Parks and Gardens. T **381** and similar horiz design. Multicoloured. P 14.

1098	16c. Type **381**	2·00	55
1099	35c. Common Kingfisher, Simar Nature Reserve	2·50	3·00

382 Council of Europe Assembly

(Des Richard J. Caruana)

1999 (6 Apr). 50th Anniversary of the Council of Europe. T **382** and similar horiz design. Multicoloured. P 14.

1100	6c. Type **382**	60	25
1101	16c. Council of Europe Headquarters, Strasbourg	1·00	1·25

383 UPU Emblem and Marsamxett Harbour, Valletta

384 Couple in Luzzu

(Des Ansgar Spratte)

1999 (2 June). 125th Anniversary of Universal Postal Union. T **383** and similar horiz designs. Multicoloured. P 13½.

1102	6c. Type **363**	1·25	1·50
	a. Horiz strip of 5. Nos. 1102/1106	7·25	8·75
1103	16c. Nuremberg and IBRA '99 International Stamp Exhibition emblem	1·50	1·75
1104	22c. Paris and Philexfrance '99 International Stamp Exhibition emblem	1·60	1·90
1105	27c. Peking and China'99 International Stamp Exhibition emblem	1·75	2·00
1106	37c. Melbourne and Australia '99 International Stamp Exhibition emblem	1·90	2·50
1102/1106 *Set of 5*		7·25	8·75

Nos. 1102/1106 were printed together, *se-tenant*, as horizontal strips of five in sheets of tne.

(Des Gorg Mallia)

1999 (16 June). Tourism. T **384** and similar multicoloured designs. P 14.

1107	6c. Type **384**	40	25
1108	16c. Tourist taking photograph	75	55
1109	22c. Man sunbathing (*horiz*)	1·00	1·00
1110	27c. Couple with horse-drawn carriage (*horiz*)	1·75	1·40
1111	37c. Caveman at Ta' Hagrat Neolithic temple (*horiz*)	2·00	3·25
1107/1111 *Set of 5*		5·50	5·75

385 Common Jellyfish

(Des Andrew Micallef)

1999 (25 Aug). Marine Life of the Mediterranean. T **385** and similar square designs. Multicoloured. P 13½.

1112	6c. Type **385**	70	75
	a. Sheetlet of 16. Nos. 1112/1127	10·00	11·00
1113	6c. Peacock Wrasse	70	75
1114	6c. Common Cuttlefish	70	75
1115	6c. Violet Sea-urchin	70	75
1116	6c. Dusky Grouper	70	75
1117	6c. Common Two-banded Seabream	70	75
1118	6c. Star-coral	70	75
1119	6c. Spiny Spider Crab	70	75

1120	6c. Rainbow Wrasse	70	75
1121	6c. Octopus	70	75
1122	6c. Atlantic Trumpet Triton	70	75
1123	6c. Mediterranean Parrotfish	70	75
1124	6c. Long-snouted Seahorse	70	75
1125	6c. Deep-water Hermit Crab	70	75
1126	6c. Mediterranean Moray	70	75
1127	6c. Common Starfish	70	75
1112/1127	*Set of 16*	10·00	11·00

Nos. 1112/1127 were printed together, *se-tenant*, in sheetlets of 16, forming a composite design.

386 Father Mikiel Scerri

(Des Joseph Mizzi)

1999 (6 Oct). Bicentenary of Maltese Uprising against the French. T **386** and similar horiz designs. Multicoloured. P 14.

1128	6c. Type **386**	75	90
	a. Pair. Nos. 1128/1129	1·50	1·75
1129	6c. *L-Eroj Maltin* (statue)	75	90
1130	16c. General Belgrand de Vaubois (French commander)	1·25	1·75
	a. Pair. Nos. 1130/1131	2·50	3·50
1131	16c. Captain Alexander Ball RN	1·25	1·75
1128/1131	*Set of 4*	3·75	4·75

Nos. 1128/1129 and 1130/1131 were each printed together, *se-tenant*, as horizontal or vertical pairs in sheets of ten.

387 *Wolfgang Philip Guttenberg interceding with The Virgin* (votive painting)

(Des Joseph Mizzi)

1999 (6 Oct). Mellieha Sanctuary Commemoration. T **387** and similar multicoloured design. P 14.

1132	35c. Type **387**	1·40	1·75
MS1133	123×88 mm. 6c. *Mellieha Virgin and Child* (rock painting) (*vert*)	1·00	1·10

388 Sea Daffodil   **389** Madonna and Child

(Des Maurice Tanti Burlò)

1999 (20 Oct)–**2003**. Maltese Flowers. T **388** and similar square designs. Multicoloured. P 14.

1134	1c. *Helichrysum melitense* (13.9.00)	10	20
1135	2c. Type **388**	10	30
1136	3c. *Cistus creticus* (13.9.00)	10	50
1137	4c. Southern Dwarf Iris	15	35
1138	5c. *Papaver thoeas* (20.9.01)	1·50	60
1139	6c. French Daffodil	25	25
1139a	7c. *Vitex angus-castus* (30.1.03)	50	65
1140	10c. *Rosa sempervirens* (13.9.00)	40	35
1141	11c. *Silene colorata* (20.9.01)	1·75	1·00
1142	12c. *Cynara cardunculus* (13.9.00)	50	45
1143	16c. Yellow-throated Crocus	65	55
1144	19c. *Anthemis arvensis* (20.9.01)	2·25	1·00
1145	20c. *Anacamptis pyramidalis* (13.9.00)	1·00	70
1145a	22c. *Spartium junceum* (30.1.03)	1·75	75
1146	25c. Large Star of Bethlehem	1·10	85

1147	27c. *Borago officinalis* (20.9.01)	3·00	1·25
1147a	28c. *Crataegus azalorus* (30.1.03)	1·75	1·50
1147b	37c. *Cercis siliquastrum* (30.1.03)	2·25	1·40
1147c	45c. *Myrtus communis*	2·25	1·75
1148	46c. Wild Tulip (30.1.03)	2·25	1·75
1149	50c. *Chrysanthemum coronarium* (20.9.01)	3·75	1·90
1149a	76c. *Pistacia lentiscus* (30.1.03)	5·00	3·25
1150	£1 *Malva sylvestris* (20.9.01)	6·00	4·25
1151	£2 *Adonis microcarpa* (13.9.00)	8·00	8·50
1134/1151	*Set of 24*	40·00	30·00

For Nos. 1139a and 1143 in smaller size and self-adhesive, see Nos. 1335/1336.

See also Nos. 1430/1431 and 1503a.

(Des Harry Borg)

1999 (27 Nov). Christmas. T **389** and similar square designs. Multicoloured. P 14.

1152	6c. Type **389**	60	10
1153	6c. +3c. Carol singers	65	80
1154	16c. +3c. Santa Claus	1·60	2·00
1155	26c. +3c. Christmas decorations	2·00	3·50
1152/1155	*Set of 4*	4·25	5·75

390 Parliament Chamber and Symbolic Luzzu

(Des Richard J. Caruana)

1999 (10 Dec). 25th Anniversary of Republic. T **390** and similar horiz designs. Multicoloured. P 14.

1156	6c. Type **390**	40	25
1157	11c. Parliament in session and Council of Europe emblem	60	35
1158	16c. Church and Central Bank of Malta building	80	55
1159	19c. Aerial view of Gozo and emblems	1·10	1·00
1160	26c. Computer and shipyard	1·40	1·60
1156/1160	*Set of 5*	3·75	3·25

391 Gift and Flowers

(Des Harry Borg)

2000 (9 Feb). Greetings Stamps. T **391** and similar horiz designs. Multicoloured. P 14.

1161	3c. Type **391**	30	15
1162	6c. Photograph envelope and Rose	50	25
1163	16c. Flowers and silver heart	1·00	55
1164	20c. Champagne and pocket watch	1·25	1·00
1165	22c. Wedding rings and Roses	1·25	1·00
1161/1165	*Set of 5*	3·75	3·00

Nos. 1161/1165 were printed with greetings labels on the vertical sheet margins.

392 Luzzu and Cruise Liner

(Des Frank X. Ancilleri)

2000 (7 Mar). Malta during the 20th-century. T **392** and similar horiz designs. Multicoloured. P 14.

1166	6c. Type **392**	65	25
1167	16c. Street musicians and modern street carnival	90	65
1168	22c. Family in 1900 and illuminated quayside	1·25	1·50
1169	27c. Rural occupations and Citadel, Victoria	1·75	2·75
1166/1169	*Set of 4*	4·00	4·75

393 Footballers and Trophy (Centenary of Malta Football Association)

394 Building Europe

(Des Ludwig Flask)

2000 (28 Mar). Sporting Events. T **393** and similar horiz designs. Multicoloured. P 14.
1170	6c. Type **393**	45	25
1171	16c. Swimming and sailing (Olympic Games, Sydney)	75	55
1172	26c. Judo, shooting and running (Olympic Games, Sydney)	1·10	1·10
1173	37c. Football (European Championship)	1·60	2·50
1170/1173 Set of 4		3·50	4·00

(Des Jean Paul Cousin)

2000 (9 May). Europa. P 14.
1174	**394** 16c. multicoloured	1·00	65
1175	46c. multicoloured	2·25	3·25

395 DH.66 Hercules, 1928

(Des Richard J. Caruana)

2000 (28 June). Century of Air Transport, 1900–2000. T **395** and similar horiz designs. Multicoloured. P 14.
1176	6c. Type **395**	85	1·10
	a. Horiz pair. Nos. 1176/1177	1·60	2·10
1177	6c. LZ 127 Graf Zeppelin, 1933	85	1·10
1178	16c. Douglas DC 3 Dakota of Air Malta Ltd, 1949	1·60	1·90
	a. Horiz pair. Nos. 1178/1179	3·00	3·75
1179	16c. Airbus A320 of Air Malta	1·60	1·90
1176/1179 Set of 4		4·50	5·50
MS1180 122×87 mm. Nos. 1176/1179		4·75	5·50

Nos. 1176/1177 and 1178/1179 were each printed together, se-tenant, as horizontal pairs in sheets of ten, with the backgrounds forming composite designs.

396 Catherine Wheel and Fireworks

(Des Martin Bonavia)

2000 (19 July). Fireworks. T **396** and similar horiz designs. Multicoloured. P 14.
1181	2c. Type **396**	20	10
1182	6c. Exploding multicoloured fireworks	40	20
1183	16c. Catherine wheel	70	40
1184	20c. Exploding green fireworks	80	80
1185	50c. Numbered rockets in rack	1·75	4·50
1181/1185 Set of 5		3·50	5·50

397 Boy walking Dog

398 Boy's Sermon, Nativity Play and Girl with Doll

(Jean Paul Zammit)

2000 (18 Oct). Stampin' the Future (children's stamp design competition winners). T **397** and similar horiz designs. Multicoloured. P 14.
1186	6c. Type **397**	55	65
1187	6c. Stars and Woman in Megalithic Temple (Chiara Borg)	55	65
1188	6c. Sunny Day (Bettina Paris)	55	65
1189	6c. Hands holding Heart (Roxana Caruana)	55	65
1186/1189 Set of 4		2·00	2·40

See also No. **MS**1489 and **MS**1509.

(Des Gorg Mallia)

2000 (18 Nov). Christmas. T **398** and similar multicoloured designs. P 13½.
1190	6c. Type **398**	65	10
1191	6c. +3c. Three Wise Men (23×27 mm)	75	85
1192	16c. +3c. Family with Father Christmas	1·75	2·25
1193	26c. +3c. Christmas tree, church and family	2·25	3·50
1190/1193 Set of 4		4·75	6·00
MS1194 174×45 mm. Nos. 1190/1193		4·75	6·50

399 Crocodile Float

(Des Francis X. Ancilleri)

2001 (23 Feb). Maltese Carnival. T **399** and similar multicoloured designs. P 14.
1195	6c. Type **399**	40	25
1196	11c. King Karnival in procession (vert)	60	40
1197	16c. Woman and children in costumes (vert)	75	55
1198	19c. Horseman carnival float (vert)	85	1·40
1199	27c. Carnival procession	1·25	2·00
1195/1199 Set of 5		3·50	4·25
MS1200 127×92 mm. 12c. Old-fashioned clowns; 37c. Women dressed as clowns (both 32×32 mm) P 13½		2·25	3·50

400 St Elmo Lighthouse

401 The Chicken Seller (E. Caruana Dingli)

(Des Richard J. Caruana)

2001 (21 Mar). Maltese Lighthouses. T **400** and similar vert designs. Multicoloured. P 14.
1201	6c. Type **400**	65	25
1202	16c. Gurdan Lighthouse	1·25	70
1203	22c. Delimara Lighthouse	1·75	2·25
1201/1203 Set of 3		3·25	3·00

(Des Harry Borg)

2001 (18 Apr). Edward Caruana Dingli (painter) Commemoration. T **401** and similar vert designs. Multicoloured. P 14.
1204	2c. Type **401**	20	30
1205	4c. The Village Beau	30	15
1206	6c. The Faldetta	40	25

1207	10c. *The Guitar Player*	65	60
1208	26c. *Wayside Orange Seller*	1·50	2·75
1204/1208 *Set of 5*		2·75	3·75

402 Nazju Falzon, Gorg Preca and Adeodata Pisani (candidates for Beatification)

(Des Joseph Mizzi)

2001 (4 May). Visit of Pope John Paul II. T **402** and similar horiz designs. Multicoloured. P 14.

1209	6c. Type **402**	1·00	25
1210	16c. Pope John Paul II and statue of St Paul	1·50	1·50
MS1211	123×87 mm. 75c. Pope John Paul with Nazju Falzon, Gorg Preca and Adeodata Pisani	5·00	5·50

403 Painted Frog

(Des Trevor Zahra)

2001 (23 May). Europa. Pond Life. T **403** and similar horiz design. Multicoloured. P 14.

1212	16c. Type **403**	1·00	65
1213	46c. Red-veined Darter (Dragonfly)	2·00	3·50

404 Yellow-legged Gull (*Larus cachinnans*)   **405** Whistle Flute

(Des. Andrew Micallef)

2001 (22 June). Maltese Birds. T **404** and similar square designs. Multicoloured. P 13½.

1214	6c. Type **404**	85	85
	a. Sheetlet of 16. Nos. 1214/1229	12·00	12·00
1215	6c. Common Kestrel (*Falco tinnunculus*)	85	85
1216	6c. Golden Oriole (*Oriolus oriolus*)	85	85
1217	6c. Chaffinch (*Fringilla coelebs*) and Eurasian Goldfinch (*Carduelis carduelis*)	85	85
1218	6c. Blue Rock Thrush (*Monticola solitarius*)	85	85
1219	6c. European Bee-eater (*Merops apiaster*)	85	85
1220	6c. Common House Martin (*Delichon urbica*) and Swallow (*Hirundo rustica*)	85	85
1221	6c. Spanish Sparrow (*Passer hispaniolensis*)	85	85
1222	6c. Spectacled Warbler (*Sylvia conspicillata*)	85	85
1223	6c. Turtle Dove (*Streptopelia turtur*)	85	85
1224	6c. Northern Pintail (*Anas acuta*)	85	85
1225	6c. Little Bittern (*Ixobrychus minutus*)	85	85
1226	6c. Eurasian Woodcock (*Scolopax rusticola*)	85	85
1227	6c. Short-eared Owl (*Asio flammeus*)	85	85
1228	6c. Northern Lapwing (*Vanellus vanellus*)	85	85
1229	6c. Moorhen (*Gallinula chloropus*)	85	85
1214/1229 *Set of 16*		12·00	12·00

Nos 1214/1229 were printed together, *se-tenant*, in sheetlets of 16 with the backgrounds forming a composite design.

(Des Gorg Mallia)

2001 (22 Aug). Traditional Maltese Musical Instruments. T **405** and similar square designs. Multicoloured. P 13½.

1230	1c. Type **405**	15	50
1231	3c. Reed pipe	25	40
1232	14c. Maltese bagpipe	60	40
1233	20c. Friction drum	85	1·25
1234	25c. Frame drum	1·00	1·75
1230/1234 *Set of 5*		2·50	3·75

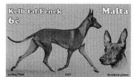

406 Kelb tal-Fenek (Pharaoh Hound)   **407** Man with Net chasing Star

(Des Ludwig Flask)

2001 (20 Oct). Maltese Dogs. T **406** and similar horiz designs. Multicoloured. P 14.

1235	6c. Type **406**	75	25
1236	16c. Kelb tal-Kacca	1·60	55
1237	19c. Maltese	1·75	1·25
1238	35c. Kelb tal-But	2·50	4·00
1235/1238 *Set of 4*		6·00	5·50

(Des Gattaldo)

2001 (29 Nov). Christmas. T **407** and similar square designs. Multicoloured. P 14.

1239	6c. +2c. Type **407**	70	45
1240	15c. +2c. Father and children	1·25	1·75
1241	16c. +2c. Mother and daughter	1·25	1·75
1242	19c. +3c. Young woman with shopping bags	1·50	2·50
1239/1242 *Set of 4*		4·25	5·75

The 6c.+2c. incorporates greetings labels into the vertical margins of the sheets.

408 *Hippocampus guttulatus*   **409** Sideboard

(Des Martin Bonavia)

2002 (30 Jan). Endangered Species. Mediterranean Seahorses. T **408** and similar vert designs. Multicoloured. P 14.

1243	6c. Type **408**	60	80
1244	6c. *Hippocampus hippocampus*	60	80
1245	16c. Close-up of *Hippocampus guttulatus*	90	1·75
1246	16c. *Hippocampus hippocampus* on seabed	90	1·75
1243/1246 *Set of 4*		2·75	4·50

(Des F. Ancilleri)

2002 (5 Apr). Antique Furniture. T **409** and similar multicoloured designs. P 14.

1247	2c. Type **409**	25	40
1248	4c. Bureau (*vert*)	45	30
1249	11c. Inlaid table (*vert*)	70	40
1250	26c. Cabinet (*vert*)	1·25	85
1251	60c. Carved chest	2·50	5·00
1247/1251 *Set of 5*		4·75	6·25

410 Child's Face painted as Clown   **411** *Hyles sammuti*

(Des Roberta Zahra)

2002 (9 May). Europa. Circus. P 14.

1252	**410**	16c. multicoloured	1·25	1·00

(Des Maurice Tanti Burlò)

2002 (26 June). Moths and Butterflies. T **411** and similar square designs. Multicoloured. P 13½.

1253	6c. Type **411**	55	65
	a. Sheetlet of 16. Nos. 1253/1268	8·00	9·50
1254	6c. *Utetheisa pulchella*	55	65
1255	6c. *Ophiusa tirhaca*	55	65
1256	6c. *Phragmatobia fulginosa melitensis*	55	65
1257	6c. *Vanessa cardui*	55	65
1258	6c. *Polyommatus icarus*	55	65
1259	6c. *Gonepteryx Cleopatra*	55	65
1260	6c. *Vanessa Atlanta*	55	65
1261	6c. *Eucrostes indigenata*	55	65
1262	6c. *Macroglossum stellatarum*	55	65
1263	6c. *Lasiocampa quercus*	55	65
1264	6c. *Catocala electa*	55	65
1265	6c. *Maniola jurtina hyperhispulla*	55	65
1266	6c. *Pieris brassicae*	55	65
1267	6c. *Papilio machaon melitensis*	55	65
1268	6c. *Danaus chrysippus*	55	65
1253/1268 *Set of 16*		8·00	9·50

Nos. 1253/1268 were printed together, *se-tenant*, in sheetlets of 16. No. 1260 is inscribed 'atalania' and No. 1264 'elocata', both in error.

412 'Kusksu Bil-ful' (bean stew)

413 *Yavia cryptocarpa* (Cactus)

(Des J. Smith)

2002 (13 Aug). Maltese Cookery. T **412** and similar horiz designs. Multicoloured. P 14.

1269	7c. Type **412**	45	25
1270	12c. 'Qaqocc mimli' (stuffed Artichoke)	70	50
1271	16c. 'Lampuki' (Dorada with Aubergines)	80	75
1272	27c. 'Qaghqd Tal-kavatelli' (Chestnut dessert)	1·40	2·75
1269/1272 *Set of 4*		3·00	3·75
MS1273 125×90 mm. 75c. 'Stuffat Tal-fenek' (Rabbit stew)		4·00	5·50

(Des A. Micallef)

2002 (25 Sept). Cacti and Succulents. T **413** and similar multicoloured designs. P 14.

1274	1c. Type **413**	15	50
1275	7c. *Aztekium hintonii* (Cactus) (vert)	55	25
1276	28c. *Pseudolithos migiurtinus* (Succulent)	1·25	70
1277	37c. *Pierrebraunia brauniorum* (Cactus) (vert)	1·75	1·50
1278	76c. *Euphorbia turbiniformis* (Succulent)	3·00	6·00
1274/1278 *Set of 5*		6·00	8·00

414 Chief Justice Adrian Dingli

415 Mary and Joseph in Donkey Cart

(Des H. Borg)

2002 (18 Oct). Personalities. T **414** and similar vert designs. P 14.

1279	3c. bright green and greenish black	25	40
1280	7c. brown-olive and brownish black	70	35
	a. No dot over 'c'	6·00	6·00
1281	15c. reddish brown and agate	1·25	75
	a. No dot over 'c'	9·00	9·00
1282	35c. grey-brown and sepia	1·50	2·00
1283	50c. light blue and deep turquoise-blue	2·50	4·25
1279/1283 *Set of 5*		5·75	7·00

Designs: 3c. T **414**; 7c. Oreste Kirkop (opera singer); 15c. Athanasius Kircher (Jesuit scholar); 35c. Archpriest Saverio Cassar; 50c. Emmanuele Vitali (notary).

The No dot over 'c' variety occurred on R. 2/4-1 on the 7c. and 15c. values.

(Des Debbie Dingli)

2002 (20 Nov). Christmas. T **415** and similar horiz designs. Multicoloured. P 14.

1284	7c. Type **415**	70	25
1285	16c. Shepherds and Kings on a bus	1·25	55
1286	22c. Holy Family and Angels in luzzu (boat)	1·60	75
1287	37c. Holy Family in horse-drawn carriage	2·00	1·50
1288	75c. Nativity on Maltese fishing boat	3·75	6·00
1284/1288 *Set of 5*		8·25	8·00

416 Vanden Plas Princess Landaulette, 1965

(Des Joe P. Smith)

2003 (26 Feb). Vintage Cars. T **416** and similar horiz designs. Multicoloured. P 14.

1289	2c. Type **416**	25	60
1290	7c. Allard M type, 1948	55	25
1291	10c. Cadillac Model B, 1904	70	35
1292	26c. Fiat Cinquecento Model A Topolino, 1936	1·25	1·60
1293	35c. Ford Anglia Super, 1965	1·75	3·00
1289/1293 *Set of 5*		4·00	5·25

417 Fort St Elmo

418 St George on Horseback

(Des S. Spiteri)

2003 (21 Mar)–03. Maltese Military Architecture. T **417** and similar horiz designs. Multicoloured. P 14.

1294	1c. Type **417**	15	40
1295	4c. Rinella Battery	30	30
1296	11c. Fort St Angelo	65	40
1297	16c. Section through Reserve Post R15	1·00	60
	a. Booklet pane. No. 1297×6 (16.4.03)	9·00	
1298	44c. Fort Tigne	2·25	4·25
1294/1298 *Set of 5*		4·00	5·50

No. 1297a was available from 96c. stamp booklets, No. SB7.

(Des J. Mizzi)

2003 (23 Apr). Paintings of St George. T **418** and similar vert designs. P 14.

1299	**418**	3c. multicoloured	25	30
1300	–	7c. multicoloured	50	30
1301	–	14c. multicoloured	75	60
1302	–	19c. multicoloured	1·10	1·40
1303	–	27c. multicoloured	1·50	2·25
1299/1303 *Set of 5*			3·50	4·25

419 'CISKBEER'

420 Games Mascot with Javelin

(Des Debbie Dingli)

2003 (9 May). Europa. Poster Art. T **419** and similar vert design. Multicoloured. P 14.

1304	16c. Type **419**	60	55
1305	46c. 'CARNIVAL 1939'	1·75	3·25

(Des R. Caruana)

2003 (26 May). Games of Small European States, Malta. T **420** and similar horiz designs. Multicoloured. P 14.

1306	25c. Type **420**	1·25	85
1307	50c. Mascot with gun	2·25	1·75
1308	75c. Mascot with ball and net	3·75	2·75
1309	£3 Mascot with rubber ring at poolside	14·00	17·00
1306/1309 *Set of 4*		19·00	20·00

421 Princess Elizabeth in Malta, c. 1950

422 Valletta Bastions at Night

(Des F. Attard and G. Theuma)

2003 (3 June). 50th Anniversary of Coronation. T **421** and similar horiz designs. P 14.

1310	12c. black, brownish grey and cinnamon	60	35
1311	15c. multicoloured	65	40
1312	22c. black, brownish grey and grey	80	65
1313	60c. black, olive-grey and deep ultramarine	2·00	3·00
1310/1313 *Set of 4*		3·50	4·00
MS1314 100×72 mm. £1 multicoloured		5·50	7·50

Designs: 12c. T **421**; 15c. Princess Elizabeth with crowd of children, Malta, c. 1950; 22c. Queen Elizabeth II in evening dress with Duke of Edinburgh, Malta; 60c. Queen Elizabeth II (receiving book) and Duke of Edinburgh, Malta; £1 Queen on walkabout with crowd.

(Des jp advertising)

2003 (1 July). Elton John, The Granaries, Floriana. Sheet 125×90 mm. P 14.

MS1315 **422** £1·50 multicoloured	8·00	10·00

No. **MS**1315 also contains four labels showing different portraits of Elton John.

423 *Chlamys pesfelis*

424 Racing Yachts, Malta–Syracuse Race

(Des A. Micallef)

2003 (20 Aug). Sea Shells. T **423** and similar square designs. Multicoloured. P 13½.

1316	7c. Type **423**	50	55
	a. Sheetlet of 16. Nos. 1316/1331	7·25	8·00
1317	7c. *Gyroscala lamellose*	50	55
1318	7c. *Phalium granulatum*	50	55
1319	7c. *Fusiturris similes*	50	55
1320	7c. *Luria lurida*	50	55
1321	7c. *Bolinus brandaris*	50	55
1322	7c. *Charonia tritonis variegate*	50	55
1323	7c. *Clanculus corallinus*	50	55
1324	7c. *Fusinus syracusanus*	50	55
1325	7c. *Pinna nobilis*	50	55
1326	7c. *Acanthocardia tuberculata*	50	55
1327	7c. *Aporrhais pespelecani*	50	55
1328	7c. *Haliotis tuberculata lamellose*	50	55
1329	7c. *Tonna galea*	50	55
1330	7c. *Spondylus gaederopus*	50	55
1331	7c. *Mitra zonata*	50	55
1316/1331 *Set of 16*		7·25	8·00

Nos. 1316/1331 were printed together, *se-tenant*, in sheetlets of 16.

(Des F. Ancilleri)

2003 (30 Sept). Yachting. T **424** and similar multicoloured designs. P 14.

1332	8c. Type **424**	60	35
1333	22c. Yacht, Middle Sea Race (*vert*)	1·25	1·00
1334	35c. Racing yachts, Royal Malta Yacht Club (*vert*)	2·00	3·00
1332/1334 *Set of 3*		3·50	4·00

(Litho Cartor)

2003 (22 Oct). Self-adhesive booklet stamps. As Nos. 1139a and 1143 but smaller, 23×23 mm, printer's imprint omitted and imprint date at right instead of centre. P 12½ die-cut.

1335	7c. *Vitex agnus-castus*	70	60
	a. Booklet pane. No. 1335×12	7·00	

1336	16c. *Crocus longiflorus*	1·50	1·75
	a. Booklet pane. No. 1336×6	8·00	

Booklet panes Nos. 1335a and 1336a have imperforate edges, giving stamps imperforate on either two or three sides.

425 Is-Sur ta' San Mikiel, Valletta

426 The Annunciation

(Des M. Vella)

2003 (29 Oct). Windmills. T **425** and similar black designs. P 14.

1337	11c. Type **425**	85	40
1338	27c. Ta'Kola, Xaghra (*vert*)	2·00	1·25
1339	45c. Tax-Xarolla, Zurrieq (*vert*)	2·75	4·50
1337/1339 *Set of 3*		5·00	5·50

(Des Harry Borg)

2003 (12 Nov). Christmas. T **426** and similar multicoloured designs. P 14.

1340	7c. Type **426**	70	30
1341	16c. Holy Family	1·00	35
1342	22c. The Shepherds following the Star (*horiz*)	1·40	85
1343	50c. The Three Kings with gifts (*horiz*)	2·75	4·50
1340/1343 *Set of 4*		5·25	5·50

427 Pillar Box on Seafront

428 Tortoiseshell Cat

(Des Alfred Caruana Ruggier)

2004 (12 Mar). Letter Boxes. T **427** and similar vert designs. Multicoloured. P 14.

1344	1c. Type **427**	10	30
1345	16c. Pillar box on pavement	1·50	55
1346	22c. Wall pillar boxes	1·75	90
1347	37c. Pillar box inside post office	2·50	1·75
1348	76c. Square pillar box and statue	6·00	8·00
1344/1348 *Set of 5*		10·50	10·50

(Des H. Borg)

2004 (26 Mar). Cats. T **428** and similar square designs. Multicoloured. P 13½.

1349	7c. Type **428**	70	30
1350	27c. Tabby	1·90	1·25
1351	28c. Silver tabby	1·90	1·25
1352	50c. Ginger tabby	3·50	4·00
1353	60c. Black and white cat	3·75	4·75
1349/1353 *Set of 5*		10·50	10·50

429 St John Bosco

(Des Paul Camilleri-Cauchi)

2004 (7 Apr). Centenary of Salesians in Malta. Sheet 124×89 mm. P 14.

MS1354 **429** 75c. multicoloured	3·50	5·00

430 Pipistrelle (*Pipistrellus pygmaeus*)

431 New Members Flags inside EU Stars

(Des Andrew Micallef)

2004 (21 Apr). Mammals and Reptiles. T **430** and similar square designs. Multicoloured. P 14.

1355	16c. Type **430**	85	90
	a. Sheetlet of 16. Nos. 1355/1370	12·00	13·00
1356	16c. Lesser Mouse-eared Bat (*Myotis blythi punicus*)	85	90
1357	16c. Weasel (*Mustela nivalis*)	85	90
1358	16c. Algerian Hedgehog (*Atelerix algirus fallax*)	85	90
1359	16c. Mediterranean Chameleon (*Chamaeleo chamaeleon*)	85	90
1360	16c. Sicilian Shrew (*Crocidura sicula*)	85	90
1361	16c. Ocellated Skink (*Chalcides ocellatus*)	85	90
1362	16c. Filfla Maltese Wall Lizard (*Podarcis filfolensis filfolensis*)	85	90
1363	16c. Moorish Gecko (*Tarentola mauritanica*)	85	90
1364	16c. Turkish Gecko (*Hemidactylus turcicus*)	85	90
1365	16c. Leopard Snake (*Elaphe situla*)	85	90
1366	16c. Western Whip Snake (*Coluber viridiflavus*)	85	90
1367	16c. Common Dolphin (*Delphinus delphis*)	85	90
1368	16c. Striped Dolphin (*Stenella coeruleoalba*)	85	90
1369	16c. Mediterranean Monk Seal (*Monachus monachus*)	85	90
1370	16c. Green Turtle (*Chelonia mydas*)	85	90
1355/1370	Set of 16	12·00	13·00

Nos. 1355/1370 were printed together, *se-tenant*, in sheetlets of 16 with the background of each horizontal pair (1355/1356, 1357/1358, 1359/1360, 1361/1362, 1363/1364, 1365/1366, 1367/1368, and 1369/1370) forming a composite design.

(Des Jean Pierre Mizzi)

2004 (1 May). Accession to European Union. T **471** and similar horiz design. Multicoloured. P 14.

1371	16c. Type **431**	1·00	55
1372	28c. Former Prime Minister Eddie Fenech Adami and former Foreign Minister Joe Borg signing Accession Treaty	1·50	2·00

432 Children Jumping into Water

(Des Joe P. Smith)

2004 (19 May). Europa. Holidays. T **432** and similar horiz design. Multicoloured. P 14.

1373	16c. Type **432**	1·00	55
1374	51c. Hagar Qim prehistoric temples	2·75	3·50

433 Hal Millieri Chapel, Zurrieq

434 Tram

(Des R. Sacco)

2004 (16 June). Chapels. T **433** and similar horiz designs. Multicoloured. P 14×14½.

1375	3c. Type **433**	30	30
1376	7c. San Basilju, Mqabba	60	30
1377	39c. San cir, Rabat	2·25	1·75
1378	48c. Santa Lucija, Mtarfa	2·50	2·75
1379	66c. Ta' Santa Marija, Kemmuna	4·25	6·00
1375/1379	Set of 5	9·00	10·00

(Des Debbie Caruana Dingli)

2004 (14 July). Trams. T **434** and similar designs. P 13½ (19c, 75c) or 14 (37c, 50c).

1380	19c. bright yellow-green and black	1·25	65
1381	37c. orange and black	2·25	1·40
1382	50c. greenish yellow and black	3·25	3·50
1383	75c. bright new blue and black	4·50	6·00
1380/1383	Set of 4	10·00	10·50

Designs: (25×42 *mm*)—37c. Tram driver; 50c. Ticket. (As T **434**)—19c. T **434**; 75c. Tram under bridge.

PRINTERS. All stamps from No. 1384 onwards were printed in lithography by Printex Ltd., Malta.

435 Discus Thrower

(Des. M. Tanti Burlò)

2004 (13 Aug). Olympic Games, Athens. T **435** and similar square designs. Multicoloured. W **105**. P 14½.

1384	11c. Type **435**	80	40
1385	16c. Greek column and Laurel wreath	1·10	55
1386	76c. Javelin thrower	5·00	6·50
1384/1386	Set of 3	6·25	6·75

436 Children playing on Ascension Day (Luigi Brocktorff painting) (Lapsi)

(Des Francis X. Ancilleri)

2004 (15 Sept). Festivals. T **436** and similar multicoloured designs. W **105**. P 14.

1387	5c. Type **436**	45	30
1388	15c. Votive Penitentiary General Procession, Zejtun (San Girgor)	1·25	50
1389	27c. Pilgrimage in front of the Sanctuary of Our Lady of Graces, Zabbar (painting, Italo Horatio Serge) (Hadd In-Nies)	2·00	1·00
1390	51c. Children with St Martin's Bags of nuts (Michele Bellanti lithograph) (San Martin) (*vert*)	3·50	3·75
1391	£1 Peasants in traditional costumes singing and dancing (painting, Antoine Favray) (Mnarja) (*vert*)	6·50	8·50
1387/1391	Set of 5	12·00	12·50

437 Church of St Mary, Attard

(Des Joseph Casha)

2004 (13 Oct). Art. T **437** and similar multicoloured designs. W **105**. P 14.

1392	2c. Type **437**	30	35
1393	20c. Mdina Cathedral organ and music score (*vert*)	1·40	70
1394	57c. Statue of St Agatha (*vert*)	4·00	5·00
1395	62c. Il-Gifen Tork (poem) and books (*vert*)	4·25	6·00
1392/1395	Set of 4	9·00	11·00
MS1396	93×100 mm. 72c. Medieval painting of St Paul (*vert*)	3·50	5·50

438 Papier mache Bambino on rocks, Lecce

(Des Richard J. Caruana)

2004 (10 Nov). Christmas. Bambino Models. T **438** and similar multicoloured designs. W **105**. P 14.

1397	7c. Type **438**	55	25
1398	16c. Wax Bambino inside glass dome (*vert*)....	1·10	55
1399	22c. Wax Bambino on back, Lija (*vert*)............	1 50	75
1400	50c. Beeswax Bambino under tree (*vert*)	3·25	5·00
1397/1400 *Set of 4*		5·75	6·00

439 Quintinus Map

(Des Alfred Caruana Ruggier)

2005 (19 Jan). Old Maps. T **439** and similar horiz designs. W **105**. P 14×14½.

1401	1c. black and scarlet	15	40
1402	12c. multicoloured	90	50
1403	37c. multicoloured	2·75	2·00
1404	£1 multicoloured	6·50	8·25
1401/1404 *Set of 4*		9·25	10·00

Designs: 1c. T **439**; 12c. Copper-engraved map; 37c. Fresco map; £1 Map of Gozo.

440 Dar il-Kaptan (Respite Home)

(Des Martin Bonavia)

2005 (23 Feb). Centenary of Rotary International (humanitarian organisation). T **440** and similar horiz designs. Multicoloured. W **105**. P 14×14½.

1405	27c. Type **440**	1·00	90
1406	76c. Outline of Malta and Gozo and 'CELEBRATE ROTARY'	3·50	6·00

441 Hans Christian Andersen **442** Pope John Paul II

(Des Mette and Eric Mourier del.)

2005 (3 Mar). Birth Bicentenary of Hans Christian Andersen (artist and children's writer). T **441** and similar designs. W **105**. P 14.

1407	7c. black and silver	40	20
1408	22c. multicoloured	1·00	55
1409	60c. multicoloured	2·50	4·00
1410	75c. multicoloured	3·75	5·25
1407/1410 *Set of 4*		7·00	9·00

Designs: 7c. T **441**; 20×38 mm—22c. Scissors and paper cutting; 60c. Ugly Duckling, pen and inkwell; 75c. Moroccan travelling boots and drawing of Villa Borghese, Rome.

2005 (15 Apr). Pope John Paul II Commemoration. W **105**. P 14½×14.

1411	**442**	51c. multicoloured	4·25	4·00

443 Coccinella septempunctata

444 Cayenne Pepper, Baked, Stuffed Courgettes and Stuffed Eggplant

(Des Andrew Micallef)

2005 (20 Apr). Insects. T **443** and similar square designs. Multicoloured. W **105**. P 14½.

1412	16c. Type **443**	1·10	1·25
	a. Sheetlet of 16. Nos. 1412/1427	16·00	18·00
1413	16c. Chrysoperla carnea	1·10	1·25
1414	16c. Apis mellifera	1·10	1·25
1415	16c. Crocothemis erythraea	1·10	1·25
1416	16c. Anax imperator	1·10	1·25
1417	16c. Lampyris pallida	1·10	1·25
1418	16c. Henosepilachna elaterii	1·10	1·25
1419	16c. Forficula decipiens	1·10	1·25
1420	16c. Mantis religiosa	1·10	1·25
1421	16c. Eumenes lunulatus	1·10	1·25
1422	16c. Cerambyx cerdo	1·10	1·25
1423	16c. Gryllus bimaculatus	1·10	1·25
1424	16c. Xylocopa violacea	1·10	1·25
1425	16c. Cicada orni	1·10	1·25
1426	16c. Acrida ungarica	1·10	1·25
1427	16c. Oryctes nasicornis	1·10	1·25
1412/1427 *Set of 16*		16·00	18·00

Nos. 1412/1427 were printed together, *se-tenant*, in sheetlets of 16 stamps.

(Des Joseph P. Smith)

2005 (9 May). Europa. Gastronomy. T **444** and similar vert design. Multicoloured. W **105**. P 14.

1428	16c. Type **444**	1·00	60
1429	51c. Roast Rabbit	3·00	3·75

2005 (24 May). Flowers. Personalised Stamps. Designs as Nos. 1139*a* and 1143 but printed by Printex and with imprint date '2005'. Multicoloured. W **105**. P 14½.

1430	7c. *Vitex agnus-castus*	45	15
1431	16c. Yellow-throated Crocus	80	55

Nos. 1430/1431 were each printed with a *se-tenant* stamp-size label attached at right advertising the 25th anniversary of Sliema Stamp Shop. These labels could be personalised with the addition of a photograph or, in the case of businesses, advertisments.

446 The Beheading of St Catherine **447** Mons. Mikiel Azzopardi (philanthropist)

(Des Francis X. Ancilleri)

2005 (8 June). St Catherine in Art. T **446** and similar multicoloured designs. W **105**. P 14×14½ (horiz) or 14½×14 (vert).

1432	28c. Type **446**	1·40	1·40
1433	28c. *Martyrdom of St Catherine* (Mattia Preti) (*vert*)	1·40	1·40
1434	45c. *Mystic Marriage* (Francesco Zahra) (*vert*).	2·00	2·75
1435	45c. *St Catherine Disputing the Philosophers* (Francesco Zahra)	2·00	2·75
1432/1435 *Set of 4*		6·00	7·50

(Des Maurice Tanti Burlò)

2005 (13 July). Personalities. T **447** and similar square designs. Multicoloured. W **105**. P 14½.

1436	3c. Type **447**	30	20
1437	19c. Egidio Lapira (professor of dental surgery)	1·00	70

1438	20c. Letter and Shield of Order of the Knights (Guzeppi Callus, doctor)	1·00	70
1439	46c. Hand writing musical score (Geronimo Abos, composer)	2·00	2·50
1440	76c. Gann Frangisk Abela (historian)	3·25	5·00
1436/1440	Set of 5	6·75	8·25

448 Horse-drawn Hearse

(Des Damian Borg Nicholas)

2005 (19 Aug). Equines in Malta. T **448** and similar horiz designs. Multicoloured. W **105** (sideways). P 14×14½.

1441	11c. Type **448**	1·00	40
1442	15c. Mule pulling traditional wooden plough	1·25	50
1443	62c. Mule on treadmill grinding flour	3·75	4·50
1444	66c. Horse-drawn water sprinkler cart	3·75	4·50
1441/1444	Set of 4	8·75	9·00

449 Queue outside 'Victory Kitchen' and Ruins of Royal Opera House, Valletta

(Des Richard J. Caruana)

2005 (23 Sept). 60th Anniversary of End of Second World War. Battle of Malta. T **449** and similar horiz designs, all showing George Cross. Multicoloured. W **105** (sideways). P 14×14½.

1445	2c. Type **449**	60	30
1446	5c. Royal Navy convoy under air attack	85	25
1447	25c. Anti aircraft guns and St Publius Church, Floriana	2·25	95
1448	51c. Pilots scrambling, Hurricane, Spitfire and Sea Gladiators	4·00	4·00
1449	£1 Tanker *Ohio* and unloading of supplies at Grand Harbour, August 1943	7·50	9·00
1445/1449	Set of 5	13·50	13·00

450 *The Nativity*

(Des Paul Camilleri Cauchi)

2005 (12 Oct). Christmas. Paintings by Emvin Cremona from Sanctuary of Our Lady of Ta' Pinu, Gozo. T **450** and similar multicoloured designs. W **105** (sideways on 7, 22, 50c.). P 14×14½ (7, 22c.), 14½×14 (16c.) or 14 (50c.).

1450	7c. Type **450**	60	25
1451	16c. *The Annunciation* (*vert*)	1·10	55
1452	22c. *The Adoration of the Magi*	1·50	75
1453	50c. *The Flight to Egypt* (69×30 *mm*)	3·50	6·00
1450/1453	Set of 4	6·00	6·75

451 Maltese, Commonwealth and CHOGM Flags

452 1986 8c. Butterflies Stamp

(Des Harry Borg)

2005 (23 Nov). Commonwealth Heads of Government Meeting (CHOGM), Valletta. T **451** and similar horiz designs, each showing Maltese and Commonwealth flags. Multicoloured. W **105**. P 14×14½.

MS1454 Four sheets, each 75×63 mm. (a) 14c. Type **451**. (b) 28c. Peace Doves. (c) 37c. Maltese Cross. (d) 75c. Silhouettes shaking hands *Set of 4 sheets* .... 5·00 7·50

(Des Martin Bonavia)

2006 (3 Jan). 50th Anniversary of Europa Stamps. T **452** and similar horiz designs showing Maltese Europa stamps. W **105** (sideways). P 14.

MS1455 120×85 mm. 5c. Type **452**; 13c. 1983 30c. Fort St Angelo stamp; 23c. 1977 20c. Is-Salini stamp; 24c. 1989 35c. Girls with dolls stamp .... 3·00 4·50
No. **MS**1455 has a composite background design.

453 Female Terracotta Figurine, *c.* 4100 BC

454 Shetland Pony

(Des Alfred Caruana Ruggier)

2006 (25 Feb). Ceramics in Maltese Collections. T **453** and similar horiz designs. Multicoloured. W **105**. P 14½×14.

1456	7c. Type **453**	50	25
1457	16c. Roman terracotta head, *c.* 1st/3rd-century BC	1·00	55
1458	28c. Terracotta oil lamp holder, 14th/15th-century AD	1·25	1·40
1459	37c. Sicilian maiolica display plate, 18th-century	2·25	2·40
1460	60c. Modern stylised figure in Maltese costume (Ianni Wennici)	2·00	1·75
1456/1460	Set of 5	7·25	8·50

(Des Andrew Micallef)

2006 (14 Mar). Pets. T **454** and similar square designs. Multicoloured. W **105** (sideways). P 14½.

1461	7c. Type **454**	85	90
	a. Sheetlet of 16. Nos. 1461/1476	12·00	13·00
1462	7c. Kelb tal-But (Maltese pocket dog)	85	90
1463	7c. Goldfish	85	90
1464	7c. Siamese cat	85	90
1465	7c. Siamese Fighting Fish	85	90
1466	7c. Ferret	85	90
1467	7c. Canary	85	90
1468	7c. Terrapin	85	90
1469	22c. Chinchilla	85	90
1470	22c. Budgerigar	85	90
1471	22c. Rabbit	85	90
1472	22c. Zebra Finch	85	90
1473	22c. Kelb tal-Kacca (Maltese hunting dog)	85	90
1474	22c. Pigeon	85	90
1475	22c. Guinea Pig	85	90
1476	22c. Cat	85	90
1461/1476	Set of 16	12·00	13·00

Nos. 1461/1476 were printed together, *se-tenant*, in sheetlets of 16 stamps.

455 Penitents carrying Crosses

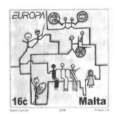

456 Circuit of Linked People

(Des Joseph P. Smith)

2006 (12 Apr). Holy Week. T **455** and similar vert designs. Multicoloured. W **105**. P 14.

| 1477 | 7c. Type **455** | 50 | 15 |
| 1478 | 15c. Crucifixion tableau in procession | 1·00 | 30 |

1479	22c. Burial of Christ tableau in procession	1·25	75
1480	27c. Statue of the Risen Christ paraded on Easter Sunday	1·50	1·10
1481	82c. Altar of Repose, Collegiate Church of St Lawrence, Vittoriosa	4·50	6·50
1477/1481 *Set of 5*		8·00	8·00

(Des Astrid Zammit)

2006 (9 May). Europa. Integration. T **456** and similar multicoloured design. W **105**. P 14½ (16c.) or 14½×14 (51c.).

1482	16c. Type **456**	1·00	50
1483	51c. Four rows of linked people (30×43 *mm*).	2·50	3·50

457 Bobby Charlton

458 *Santa Anna* ('Gran Caracca di Rodi'), 1530

(Des Maurice Tanti Burlò)

2006 (2 June). World Cup Football Championship, Germany. T **457** and similar vert designs. Multicoloured. W **105**. P 14.

1484	7c. Type **457**	45	15
1485	16c. Pelè	70	30
1486	27c. Franz Beckenbauer	1·00	60
1487	76c. Dino Zoff	2·75	5·00
1484/1487 *Set of 4*		4·50	5·50
MS1488 160×86 mm. Nos. 1484/1487. Wmk sideways...		4·25	5·50

(Des 26th Frame)

2006 (5 June). Sting Concert, Luxol Grounds. Sheet 121×86 mm containing design as No. 1188. W **105** (sideways). P 14.

MS1489 £1·50 Sunny Day (Bettina Paris)	4·50	5·50

(Des Francis X. Ancilleri)

2006 (18 Aug). Naval Vessels. T **458** and similar horiz designs. Multicoloured. W **105** (sideways). P 14.

1490	8c. Type **458**	80	20
1491	29c. *Guillaume Tell* (French) dismasted by HMS *Penelope, Lion* and *Foudroyant*, Malta, 1800 (Edwin Galea)	2·00	1·10
1492	51c. USS *Constitution*, 1837 (J. G. Evans)	3·25	3·00
1493	76c. HMS *Dreadnought* leaving Grand Harbour, November 1913	5·00	6·00
1494	£1 USS *Belknap* (frigate) and *Slava* (Soviet cruiser) providing communications support for Malta Summit, December 1989	6·00	7·50
1490/1494 *Set of 5*		15·00	16·00

459 Candles ('Happy Birthday')

460 Wignacourt Tower

(Des Jean Pierre Mizzi)

2006 (18 Sept). Occasions. T **459** and similar square designs. Multicoloured. W **105**. P 14½.

1495	8c. Type **459**	45	15
1496	16c. Heart ('Happy Anniversary')	80	35
1497	27c. Stars holding parcel, balloon and candle ('Congratulations')	1·25	1·25
1498	37c. Balloons ('Best Wishes')	1·75	2·75
1495/1498 *Set of 4*		3·75	4·00

(Des Anouschka Grech)

2006 (29 Sept). Maltese Castles and Towers. T **460** and similar horiz designs. Multicoloured. W **105** (sideways). P 14×14½.

1499	7c. Type **460**	65	15
1500	16c. Verdala Castle	1·25	35
1501	27c. San Lucjan Tower	1·90	1·10
1502	37c. Kemmuna Tower	2·50	1·75
1503	£1 Selmun Castle	6·00	9·00
1499/1503 *Set of 5*		11·00	11·00

2006 (13 Oct). As No. 1134 but W **105** (sideways) and printed in lithography by Printex Ltd. P 14½. Imprint date '2006'.

1503*a*	1c. *Helichrysum melitense* 40	50

461 Paolino Vassallo, *Inno per Natale* and Nativity

(Des George Vella)

2006 (5 Nov). Christmas Music. T **461** and similar horiz designs showing composer and score. Multicoloured. W **105** (sideways). P 14×14½.

1504	8c. Type **461**	55	15
1505	16c. Carmelo Pace, *They Heard the Angels and Three Magi*	1·00	30
1506	22c. Paul Nani, *Maltese Christmas* and *Angels*	1·40	1·40
1507	27c. Carlo Diacono, *Notte di Natale*, Shepherds and Angel	1·60	2·40
1504/1507 *Set of 4*		4·00	3·75
MS1508 120×86 mm. 50c. Wolfgang Amadeus Mozart (250th birth anniversary) and *Alma di Creatoris*. P 14...		3·25	3·50

(Des Jean Pierre Mizzi)

2006 (22 Dec). Bob Geldof Concert for YMCA, Manoel Island. Sheet 121×86 mm containing design as No. 1189. W **105** (sideways). P 14.

MS1509 £1·50 Hands holding Heart (Roxana Caruana)..	7·50	8·50

462 Wrought Iron Work

(Des Richard Caruana)

2006 (29 Dec). Crafts. T **462** and similar horiz designs. Multicoloured. W **105** (sideways). P 14×14½.

1510	8c. Type **462**	55	15
1511	16c. Glass making	1·00	35
1512	22c. Filigree work	1·40	70
1513	37c. Pottery	2·00	1·75
1514	60c. Reed basketwork	3·75	5·50
1510/1514 *Set of 5*		8·00	7·75

463 Stone Head

464 *Opuntia ficus-indica* (Prickly Pear)

(Des Josian Bonello)

2007 (28 Feb). Prehistoric Sculptures, *c.* 3000–2500 BC. T **463** and similar multicoloured designs. W **105** (sideways on horiz designs). P 14½×14 (vert) or 14×14½ (horiz).

1515	15c. Type **463**	1·00	30
1516	29c. Stone bas-relief of animals (*horiz*)	1·75	1·10
1517	60c. Stone-carved spiral pattern (*horiz*)	3·75	4·25
1518	£1·50 Clay statuette of female figure	7·50	10·00
1515/1518 *Set of 4*		12·50	14·00

(Des Andrew Micallef)

2007 (16 Apr). Maltese Fruits. T **464** and similar square designs. Multicoloured. W **105** (sideways). P 14½.

1519	8c. Type **464**	60	70
	a. Sheetlet of 16. Nos. 1519/1534	8·50	10·00

1520	8c. *Vitis vinifera* (Grapes)	60	70
1521	8c. *Eriobotrya japonica* (Loquat)	60	70
1522	8c. *Morus nigra* (Black Mulberry)	60	70
1523	8c. *Ficus carica* (Figs)	60	70
1524	8c. *Citrus limonum* (Lemons)	60	70
1525	8c. *Pyrus communis* (Pear)	60	70
1526	8c. *Prunus persica* (Peaches)	60	70
1527	8c. *Punica granatum* (Pomegranate)	60	70
1528	8c. *Prunus salicina* (Japanese Plum)	60	70
1529	8c. *Citrullus vulgaris* (Watermelon)	60	70
1530	8c. *Citrus sinensis* (Orange)	60	70
1531	8c. *Olea europaea* (Olives)	60	70
1532	8c. *Lycopersicon esculentum* (Tomatoes)	60	70
1533	8c. *Malus domestica* (Apples)	60	70
1534	8c. *Cucumis melo* (Melon)	60	70
1519/1534 *Set of 16*		8·50	10·00

Nos. 1519/1534 were printed together, *se-tenant*, in sheetlets of 16 stamps.

See also No. **MS**1568.

465 Wrought-iron Balcony

466 Lord Baden-Powell (founder) and District Commissioner Captain J. V. Abela, Malta, 1937

(Des Alfred Caruana Ruggier)

2007 (28 Apr). Maltese Balconies. T **465** and similar multicoloured designs. W **105**. P 14.

1535	8c. Type **465**	50	40
1536	22c. Ornate open stone balcony and recessed doorway, Gozo	1·25	1·10
1537	27c. Balustraded balcony, National Library of Malta	1·60	1·60
1538	29c. Carved stone balcony with glazed timber enclosure, Gozo	1·75	1·75
1539	46c. Two balconies on Art Deco 1930's building	2·75	4·00
1535/1539 *Set of 5*		7·00	8·00
MS1540 123×86 mm. 51c. Detail of balcony on Hostel de Verdelin, Valletta (*horiz*). Wmk sideways		3·00	3·75

(Des Mark Anthony Vella)

2007 (9 May). Europa. Centenary of Scouting. T **466** and similar square design. Multicoloured. W **105**. P 14½.

1541	16c. Type **466**	1·00	60
	a. Wmk sideways	1·40	1·40
	ab. Booklet pane. No. 1541a×5	6·00	
1542	51c. Malta scouts marching, Golden Jubilee Jamboree, near Birmingham, 1957	3·00	4·00

No. 1541a was only issued in 80c. booklets, No. SB11.

467 St Gorg Preca

468 Rocking Horse, Tricycle and Car, all Triang (1950s)

(Des Edward Pirotta)

2007 (28 May). Canonisation of Dun Gorg Preca. T **467** and similar square design. Multicoloured. W **105**. P 14½.

1543	8c. Type **467**	50	30
1544	£1 As Type **467** but sun rising behind Basilica	5·50	7·00

(Des Richard Caruana)

2007 (11 July). Toys from Days Gone By. T **468** and similar vert designs. Multicoloured. W **105**. P 14.

1545	2c. Type **468**	10	20
1546	3c. Pedigree dolls pram (1950s), drums and skipping rope	15	20
1547	16c. Japanese tin cabin cruiser (1960s), sand pails, spade and Triang sailing boat	90	80
1548	22c. Lenci doll, Pedigree doll and 1930s Armand Marseille doll	1·25	1·10
1549	50c. Alps clockwork racing car (1950s), P.N. motorcycle (1950s) and Chad Valley delivery van (1930s)	3·25	4·50
1545/1549 *Set of 5*		5·00	6·00

469 *St Jerome* (Caravaggio)

2007 (20 July). 400th Anniversary of the Arrival of Michelangelo Merisi (Caravaggio) in Malta. T **469** and similar multicoloured designs showing his paintings. W **105** (sideways). P 14.

1550	5c. Type **469**	50	35
1551	29c. *The Beheading of St John the Baptist* (detail)	2·25	2·25
MS1552 130×86 mm. £2 *The Beheading of St John the Baptist* (*vert*)		15·00	18·00

MS1552 was reissued in limited quantities on 30 July 2010 embossed in gold.

470 Malta GPO Royal Enfield Motorcycle, 1954

(Des Joe P. Smith)

2007 (12 Sept). Motorcycles. T **470** and similar horiz designs. Multicoloured. W **105** (sideways). P 14.

1553	1c. Type **470**	15	30
1554	16c. Malta Garrison Matchless G3/L, 1941	1·25	85
1555	27c. Civilian Minerva, 1903	2·00	1·40
1556	50c. Malta Police Triumph Speed Twin, 1965	4·00	5·00
1553/1556 *Set of 4*		6·75	6·75

471 Heart and 'LOVE'

(Des Harry Borg)

2007 (28 Sept). Occasions Greetings Stamps. T **471** and similar square designs. Multicoloured. W **105** (sideways). P 14½.

1557	8c. Type **471**	55	60
1558	8c. Teddy bears	55	60
1559	8c. Star decorations ('Congratulations!')	55	60
1560	8c. Pink Roses ('GREETINGS')	55	60
1561	8c. Balloons	55	60
1562	8c. Champagne glasses	55	60
1557/1562 *Set of 6*		3·00	3·25

472 Mdina Skyline seen from Mtarfa

(Des John Martin Borg)

2007 (1 Oct). Maltese Scenery. T **472** and similar horiz designs showing watercolours by John Martin Borg. W **105** (sideways). P 14.

1563	11c. Type **472**	1·00	65
1564	16c. Windmill, farmhouse and church, Qrendi	1·40	85
1565	37c. Vittoriosa waterfront	2·75	2·25
1566	46c. Mgarr Harbour, Gozo	3·25	3·50
1567	76c. Xlendi Bay, Gozo	5·50	7·50
1563/1567	Set of 5	12·50	13·00

No. 1564 is inscr 'sepac'.

2007 (18 Oct). 34U (Tree for You) Campaign. Sheet 100×66 mm containing design as No. 1531. W **105** (sideways). P 14.

MS1568	75c. *Olea europaea* (Olives)	4·25	5·50

473 Military Band

474 Madonna and Baby Jesus

(Des Joe Mark Micallef)

2007 (13 Nov). Maltese Bands. T **473** and similar square designs. Multicoloured. W **105**. P 14½.

1569	4c. Type **473**	55	40
1570	15c. Police band	2·00	1·00
1571	21c. Band playing at carnival	2·00	1·50
1572	22c. Band playing at Christmas	2·00	1·50
1573	£1 Band and conductor	8·00	10·00
1569/1573	Set of 5	13·00	13·00

2007 (20 Nov). Christmas. T **474** and similar square designs showing details from painting *The Nativity* by Giuseppe Cali in St Andrew's parish church, Luqa. Multicoloured. W **105**. P 14½.

1574	8c. Type **474**	70	30
1575	16c. Holy Family with two countrywomen and young girl	1·25	85
1576	27c. Baby Jesus and young girl	2·25	3·00
1574/1576	Set of 3	3·75	3·75

Similar stamps were issued by the Vatican City.

475 Boys playing Football

476 Malta £1 Coin

(Des Harry Borg)

2007 (29 Dec). Anniversaries and Personalities. T **475** and similar multicoloured designs. W **105**. P 14.

1577	4mils Type **475** (25th Anniversary of Youth Football Association)	10	10
1578	9c. Children receiving religious instruction (centenary of Society of Christian Doctrine)	70	30
1579	16c. Canon Monsignor Professor Francesco Bonnici (founder of St Joseph Institute for orphan boys)	1·25	85
1580	43c. Father Manwel Magri (ethnographer, archaeologist and educator)	3·25	3·25

1581	86c. Carolina Cauchi (founder of Dominican order at Lunzjata Monastery, Gozo)	6·00	8·50
1577/1581	Set of 5	10·00	11·50
MS1582	100×70 mm. 76c. Signatories (50th Anniversary of Treaty of Rome) (*horiz*). Wmk sideways	4·50	6·00

(Des Frank X. Ancilleri)

2007 (31 Dec). Coins of Malta 1972–2007. Sheet 100×66 mm. W **105** (sideways). P 14½.

MS1583	**476** £1 multicoloured	6·00	7·00

(New Currency: 100 cents = 1 euro)

(Des Frank X. Ancilleri)

2008 (1 Jan). Adoption of the Euro Currency (1st issue). Sheet 100×66 mm containing square design as T **476**. Multicoloured. W **105** (sideways). P 14½.

MS1584	€1 Obverse and reverse of one euro coin	3·50	4·25

477 *Aphrodite* Statue of Cyprus

478 Door Knocker from Ministry of Finance, Valletta

2008 (1 Jan). Adoption of the Euro Currency (2nd issue). Sheet 100×62 mm containing T **477** and similar square design. Multicoloured. W **105** (sideways). P 14½.

MS1585	€1 Type **477**; €1 *Sleeping Lady* statuette, Malta	6·00	8·00

A similar miniature sheet was issued by Cyprus.

(Des Frank X. Ancilleri)

2008 (5 Mar). Door Knockers. T **478** and similar vert designs. Multicoloured. W **105**. P 14.

1586	26c. Type **478**	1·25	65
1587	51c. Fish door knocker from Museum of Fine Arts, Valletta	2·00	1·25
1588	63c. Door knocker from Department of Industrial and Employment Relations, Valletta	2·25	2·50
1589	€1.77 Door knocker from Museum of Archaeology, Valletta	5·50	8·00
1586/1589	Set of 4	10·00	11·00

479 Shooting

(Des Darren Duncan)

2008 (7 Mar). Olympic Games, Beijing. T **479** and similar horiz designs. Multicoloured. W **105** (sideways). P 14.

1590	5c. Type **479**	15	10
1591	12c. Swimming	30	20
1592	€1.57 Running	4·75	6·50
1590/2	Set of 3	4·75	6·50

480 Postman and Mail Room (in sepia)

481 Woodcarving by Xandru Farrugia, Conversion of St Paul Church, Hal Safi

(Des Edward D. Pirotta)

2008 (9 May). Europa. The Letter. Multicoloured. W **105** (sideways). P 14½.

1593	37c.	Type **480**	1·75	85
	a.	Booklet pane. No. 1593×5	7·50	
1594	€1.19	As Type **480** (in monochrome)	4·50	5·00

(Des Paul Psaila)

2008 (28 June). Annus Paulinus 2008–2009 (2000th Birth Anniversary of St Paul). T **481** and similar vert designs showing statues of St Paul. Multicoloured. W **105**. P 14.

1595	19c.	Type **481**	1·00	30
1596	68c.	Pápier maché statue by Agostino Camilleri, St Paul's Shipwreck Church, Munxar, Gozo	2·75	3·00
1597	€1.08	Wooden statue by Giovanni Caruana, St Paul's Shipwreck Church, Rabat	4·25	6·00
1595/1597 *Set of 3*			7·25	8·50
MS1598	120×86 mm. €3 Wooden statue by Melchiorre Gafà, St Paul's Shipwreck Church, Valletta. Wmk sideways		9·50	11·00

482 Sand Dunes

(Des Paul Psaila)

2008 (11 Aug). International Year of Planet Earth. T **482** and similar horiz designs. Multicoloured. W **105** (sideways). P 14.

1599	7c.	Type **482**	50	20
1600	86c.	Single tree growing in field	3·50	3·25
1601	€1	Globe	3·75	4·00
1602	€1.77	Rocky coast	6·50	8·00
1599/1602 *Set of 4*			12·50	14·00

483 MSC *Musica*

(Des Daniel Mangini)

2000 (10 Nov). Cruise Liners (1st series). T **483** and similar horiz designs. Multicoloured. W **105** (sideways). P 14.

1603	63c.	Type **483**	3·00	1·50
1604	€1.16	MS *Voyager of the Seas*	4·50	4·50
1605	€1.40	MS *Westerdam*	5·00	5·00
1606	€3	RMS *Queen Elizabeth II*	11·00	14·00
1603/1606 *Set of 4*			21·00	22·00

See also Nos. 1627/1630.

484 *Madonna and Child with Infant St John the Baptist* (detail) (Francesco Trevisani)

(Des Daniel Mangini)

2008 (27 Nov). Christmas. Nativity Paintings from the National Museum of Fine Arts, Valletta. T **484** and similar horiz designs. Multicoloured. W **105** (sideways). P 14.

1607	19c.	Type **484**	70	30
1608	26c.	*Nativity* (detail of Virgin and Christ Child from panel by Maestro Alberto)	1·00	60
1609	37c.	*Virgin and Child with Infant St John the Baptist* (Carlo Maratta)	1·25	1·90
1607/1609 *Set of 3*			2·75	2·50

485 *Laetiorus sulphureus*

486 Dornier Wal SANA Seaplane

(Des Stephen Mifsud)

2009 (27 Mar). Fungi. T **485** and similar square designs. Multicoloured. W **105** (sideways). P 14.

1610	5c.	Type **485**	25	15
1611	12c.	*Montagnea arenaria*	55	30
1612	19c.	*Pleurotus eryngii*	80	40
1613	26c.	*Inonotus indicus*	1·10	70
1614	€1.57	*Suillus collinitus*	5·75	7·50
1610/1614 Set of 4			7·75	8·00

2009 (28 Apr). Vintage Postal Transport. T **486** and similar square designs. Multicoloured. W **105** (sideways). P 14.

1615	9c.	Type **486**	75	25
1616	35c.	Postmen on BSA motorcycles	2·75	1·25
1617	€2.50	Postmen with Raleigh bicycles	10·00	12·00
1618	€3	Gozo Mail Boat	10·00	12·00
1615/1618 Set of 4			21·00	23·00

487 Emblem

488 Galileo Galilei, his Sketch of Moon and *Apollo 11* Lunar Module *Eagle*

(Des Edward Pirotta)

2009 (30 Apr). Tenth Anniversary of the Euro. W **105** (sideways). P 14.

1619	**487**	€2 multicoloured	6·00	7·00

(Des Alexei Pace and Gordon Caruana Dingli)

2009 (9 May). Europa. Astronomy. T **488** and similar vert design. Multicoloured. W **105**. P 14.

1620	37c.	Type **488**	1·50	1·10
	a.	Booklet pane. No. 1620×5	7·50	
1621	€1.19	William Lassell's telescope (set up in Malta 1861–1865) and Nebula M42	3·00	4·25

489 Sailing

(Des Daniel Mangani)

2009 (1 June). 13th Games of the Small States of Europe, Nicosia and Limassol, Cyprus. T **489** and similar horiz designs. Multicoloured. W **105** (sideways). P 14.

1622	10c.	Type **489**	35	25
1623	19c.	Judo	65	40
1624	37c.	Shooting	1·40	1·40
1625	67c.	Swimming	2·50	2·75
1626	€1.77	Athletics	5·00	7·00
1622/1626 Set of 5			9·00	10·50

(Des Fabio Agius)

2009 (15 July). Cruise Liners (2nd series). Horiz designs as T **483**. Multicoloured. W **105** (sideways). P 14.

1627	37c.	*Seabourn Pride*	2·50	1·10
1628	68c.	*Brilliance of the Seas*	3·50	2·50

1629	91c. *Costa Magica* and *Costa Atlantica*	4·50	5·00
1630	€2 MSC *Splendida*	7·50	10·00
1627/1630 Set of 4		16·00	16·00

490 Headland

491 *Mater Admirablis* (in the manner of Botticelli)

(Des Stefan Attard)

2009 (16 Sept). Scenery. T **490** and similar horiz designs. Multicoloured. W **105** (sideways). P 14.

1631	2c. Type **490**	15	30
1632	7c. Watchtower of Knights of the Sovereign Military Order of Malta	45	20
1633	37c. Stone salt pans, Qbajjar, Gozo	2·00	70
1634	€1.02 Segment of the Ggantija Temples, Gozo	4·00	6·00
1631/1634 Set of 4		6·00	6·50
No. 1633 is inscr 'sepac'.			

2009 (30 Nov). Christmas. T **491** and similar vert designs. Multicoloured. W **105**. P 14.

1635	19c. Type **491**	75	30
1636	37c. *Madonna and Child* (Corrado Giacquinto)	1·50	45
1637	63c. *The Madonna and Child* (follower of Simone Cantarini)	2·00	3·75
1635/1637 Set of 3		3·75	4·00

492 Skeleton of Prehistoric Animal (Pleistocene Period)

(Des Edward Pirotta and Paul Psaila)

2009 (29 Dec)–**12**. History of Malta. T **492** and similar multicoloured designs. W **105** (sideways on horiz designs). P 14.

1638	1c. Type **492**	15	30
1639	2c. Ruins of stone temple (Early Temple Period)	20	30
1640	5c. Carved stone pattern (Late Temple Period)	30	25
1641	7c. Pair of pots (Bronze Age)	35	25
1642	9c. Gold statue (Phoenician and Punic Period) (*vert*)	40	40
1643	10c. Mosaic (Roman Period)	40	40
1644	19c. Gold coin (Byzantine Period) (*vert*)	65	30
1644a	20c. As No. 1644 (grey background) (*vert*) (7.3.12)	70	40
1645	26c. Fragment of carved stone (Arab Period)	90	60
1646	37c. Painting (Norman and Hohenstaufen Period) (*vert*)	1·25	75
1647	50c. Stone tablet carved with shield (Angevin and Aragonese) (*vert*)	1·75	1·75
1648	51c. Gold pattern with central Maltese Cross (Knights of St John)	1·75	1·75
1649	63c. Painting of officers and crew disembarking in rowing boats from ships (French Period)	1·75	1·75
1650	68c. George Cross (British Period) (*vert*)	2·00	2·00
1650a	69c. As No. 1650 (stone background) (*vert*) (7.3.12)	2·00	2·00
1651	86c. Independence (*vert*)	2·75	2·75
1652	€1 Republic (*vert*)	3·50	3·50
1653	€1.08 EU Accession (*vert*)	3·50	3·50
1654	€5 Arms of Malta (*vert*)	16·00	17·00
1638/1654 *Set of 19*		35·00	32·00
MS1655 169×263 mm. Nos. 1638/1654. Wmk upright....		42·00	45·00

493 100 Ton Gun, Fort Rinella, Malta, 2010

(Des John Batchelor)

2010 (19 Feb). 100 Ton Guns. Sheet 118×102 mm containing T **493** and similar horiz designs. Multicoloured. W **105**. P 13½.

MS1656 75c.×4 Type **493**; 100 ton gun, Fort Rinella, Malta, 1882; 100 ton gun, Napier of Magdala Battery, Gibraltar, 1880; 100 ton gun, Napier of Magdala Battery, Gibraltar, 2010 .... 8·00 9·00

A miniature sheet containing the same designs was issued by Gibraltar.

494 Balloons

(Des Sean Cini)

2010 (17 Mar). Occasions Greetings Stamps. T **494** and similar multicoloured designs. W **105** (sideways on horiz designs). P 14.

1657	19c. Type **494**	65	75
1658	19c. Aerial view of coastline and offshore rocks	65	75
1659	19c. Mortarboard and scroll	65	75
1660	19c. Woman greeting man and crowd (painting)	65	75
1661	19c. Two glasses of champagne and bottle in ice bucket (*vert*)	65	75
1662	19c. St John's Co-Cathedral, Valletta and fireworks (*vert*)	65	75
1663	19c. Hand holding trophy (*vert*)	65	75
1664	37c. Outline map of Malta and Gozo................	1·10	1·10
1657/1664 *Set of 8*...		5·00	5·75

495 Pope Benedict XVI

496 *Puttinu u Toninu* (Dr. Philip Farrugia Randon)

(Des Sean Cimi. Litho Printex Ltd)

2010 (17 Apr). Visit of Pope Benedict XVI to Malta. Sheet 130×85 mm. W **105** (sideways). P 14.

MS1665 **495** €3 multicoloured................................ 12·00 12·00

(Des Edward D. Pirotta. Litho Printex)

2010 (4 May). Europa. Children's Books. T **496** and similar vert design. Multicoloured. W **105**. P 14.

1666	37c. Type **496**..	1·75	75
	a. Booklet pane. No. 1666×5	7·50	
1667	€1.19 *Meta l-Milied ma giex* (Clare Azzopardi)...	3·25	4·50

497 Globe and National Flags

498 Maltese Wall Lizard

(Des Frank Azzopardi. Litho Printex Ltd)

2010 (11 June). World Cup Football Championship, South Africa. T **497** and similar vert design. Multicoloured. W **105**. P 14.

1668	63c. Type **497**	1·75	1·75
1669	€2.50 Zakumi the Leopard mascot	6·25	7·50
MS1669a	131×80 mm. As Nos. 1668/1669. Wmk sideways	8·00	9·25

(Des Maurice Tanti Burlò. Litho Printex Ltd)

2010 (23 Sept). Biodiversity. T **498** and similar horiz designs. Multicoloured. W **105** (sideways on horiz designs). P 14.

1670	19c. Type **498**	1·25	50
1671	68c. Storm Petrel (vert)	3·25	2·25
1672	86c. Maltese Pyramidal Orchid (vert)	4·00	4·25
1673	€1.40 Freshwater Crab	4·00	5·50
1670/1673	Set of 4	11·50	11·50

499 Azure Window, Gozo

(Des Cedric Galea Pirotta. Litho Printex Ltd)

2010 (19 Oct). Natural Treasures. T **499** and similar multicoloured designs. W **105** (sideways on horiz designs). P 14.

1674	37c. Type **499**	1·75	70
1675	51c. Blue Grotto, Zurrieq (vert)	2·50	2·00
1676	67c. Ta' Cenc, Gozo (vert)	3·00	2·75
1677	€1.16 Filfla	4·00	6·00
1674/1677	Set of 4	10·00	10·50

500 The Adoration of the Magi (Valerio Castello)

501 Cancelled Malta 1860 ½d. Buff Stamp

(Litho Printex Ltd)

2010 (9 Nov). Christmas. T **500** and similar multicoloured designs. W **105** (sideways on horiz designs). P 14.

1678	19c. Type **500**	75	30
1679	37c. The Flight into Egypt (Filippo Paladini)	1·50	55
1680	63c. Madonna di Maggio (Pierre Guillemin) (vert)	2·25	3·75
1678/1680	Set of 3	4·00	4·25

(Des Joseph Said. Litho Printex Ltd)

2010 (1 Dec). 150th Anniversary of the First Malta Stamp. Sheet 130×85 mm. W **105** (sideways). P 14.

MS1681	**501** €2.80 multicoloured	10·00	11·00

502 Valletta

(Des Edward Said. Litho Printex Ltd)

2011 (9 Mar). Treasures of Malta. Landscapes. T **502** and similar horiz designs showing oil paintings by Edward Said. Multicoloured. W **105** (sideways). P 14.

1682	19c. Type **502**	80	30
1683	37c. Manoel Island	1·75	60
1684	€1.57 Cittadella (Gozo)	5·50	8·00
1682/1684	Set of 3	7·25	8·00

503 Chimaera monstrosa (Rabbitfish)

504 Trees, Pine Cones, Flowers and Butterfly (Nicole Sciberras)

(Litho Printex Ltd)

2011 (29 Apr). 50th Anniversary of WWF (Worldwide Fund for Nature). Chimaera monstrosa (Rabbitfish). Sheet 130×85 mm containing T **503** and similar horiz designs. Multicoloured. W **105**. P 13½.

MS1685	51c. Type **503**; 63c. Rabbitfish (swimming towards top right; 67c. Rabbitfish (seen from front); 97c. Rabbitfish (with fins outstretched)	10·00	11·00

(Litho Printex Ltd)

2011 (9 May). Europa. Forests. T **504** and similar vert design. Multicoloured. W **105**. P 14.

1686	37c. Type **504**	1·75	1·00
	a. Booklet pane. No. 1686×5	7·50	
1687	€1.19 Trees, fallen tree and fungi	3·25	4·25

505 Reo Bus, Birkirkara

(Des Cedric Galea Pirotta. Litho Printex Ltd)

2011 (2 July). Malta Buses. The End of an Era (1st series). Buses of the 1950s and 1960s. Make of Bus and Route given. T **505** and similar horiz designs. Multicoloured. W **105** (sideways). P 14.

1688	20c. Type **505**	1·50	1·50
	a. Sheetlet of 10. Nos. 1688/1697	13·00	13·00
1689	20c. Dodge T110L, Zabbar	1·50	1·50
1690	20c. Leyland Comet, Zurrieq	1·50	1·50
1691	20c. Ford V8, Zebbug–Siggiewi	1·50	1·50
1692	20c. Bedford SLD, Gudja–Ghaxaq	1·50	1·50
1693	20c. Gozo mail bus	1·50	1·50
1694	20c. Federal bus, Kalafrana	1·50	1·50
1695	20c. Dodge T110L, Siggiewi	1·50	1·50
1696	20c. Indiana bus, Rabat	1·50	1·50
1697	20c. Austin CXD, Zejtun	1·50	1·50
1698	69c. Ford V8, Sliema	3·25	3·25
	a. Sheetlet of 10. Nos. 1698/1707	29·00	29·00
1699	69c. Commer Q4, Lija	3·25	3·25
1700	69c. Fordson BB, Mosta–Naxxar	3·25	3·25
1701	69c. Thorneycroft Sturdy ZE, Mellieha	3·25	3·25
1702	69c. Bedford QL, Cospicua	3·25	3·25
1703	69c. Magirus Deutz, all routes	3·25	3·25
1704	69c. Commer Q4, Naxxar	3·25	3·25
1705	69c. Bedford SB8, Gozo	3·25	3·25
1706	69c. Thames ET7, Birkirkara–St Julians	3·25	3·25
1707	69c. Bedford QL, private hire	3·25	3·25
1688/1707	Set of 20	42·00	42·00

See also Nos. 1842/1847.

506 MV Ta' Pinu (Gozo Channel Company passenger and car ferry)

(Litho Printex Ltd)

2011 (10 Aug). Maritime Malta (1st series). T **506** and similar horiz designs. Multicoloured. W **105** (sideways). P 14.

1708	26c. Type **506**	1·40	65

1709	37c. MV *Jean De La Valette* (Virtu Ferries catamaran)	2·25	80
1710	67c. P23 (Maritime Squadron patrol boat)	3·25	3·50
1711	91c. MV *Spinola* (Tug Malta Bollard Pull Terminal/Escort VSP tractor tug)	4·25	6·00
1708/1711 Set of 4		10·00	10·00

See also Nos. 1857/1860, 1922/1924, **MS**1951, 1994/1996 and 2012/2014.

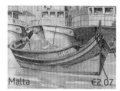

507 Mgarr, Gozo

(Des Cedric Galea Pirotta. Litho Printex Ltd)

2011 (15 Sept). Fishing Villages. Sheet 120×81 mm. W **105** (sideways). P 13½.

| **MS**1712 | **507** | €2.07 multicoloured | 7·00 | 7·50 |

A similar design showing the Icelandic fishing village of Húsavik was issued by Iceland.

508 The Holy Family in an Interior (follower of Marcello Venusti, 1510–1579)

509 Malta 1922 £1 Stamp

(Litho Printex Ltd)

2011 (15 Nov). Christmas. T **508** and similar vert designs. Multicoloured. W **105**. P 14.

1713	20c. Type **508**	70	30
1714	37c. *The Madonna and Child with Infant St John the Baptist* (Tuscan school, c. 1600)	1·25	50
1715	63c. *The Rest on the Flight into Egypt* (16th-century Flemish)	1·90	3·00
1713/1715 Set of 3		3·50	3·50

(Litho Printex Ltd)

2011 (2 Dec). 90th Anniversary of Malta Senate and Legislative Assembly. Sheet 130×85 mm. W **105** (sideways). P 14.

| **MS**1716 | **509** | €4.16 multicoloured | 12·00 | 13·00 |

510 *Marsalforn* (H. M. Bateman)

(Litho Printex Ltd)

2012 (23 Mar). International Artists and Malta. Paintings of Maltese Landscapes by H. M. Bateman and Edward Lear. T **510** and similar horiz designs. Multicoloured. W **105** (sideways on horiz designs). P 14.

1717	20c. Type **510**	65	30
1718	26c. *Qala* (H. M. Bateman)	75	35
1719	37c. *Ghajnsielem* (H. M. Bateman) (vert)	1·10	50
1720	67c. *Inquisitor's Palace* (Edward Lear)	1·90	2·00
1721	97c. *Gran Fontana* (Edward Lear)	3·00	4·25
1717/1721 Set of 5		6·75	6·75

511 Champagne Bottle and Glasses

512 George Cross

(Litho Printex Ltd)

2012 (3 Apr). Occasions. I **511** and similar multicoloured designs. W **105** (sideways on horiz designs). P 14.

1722	37c. Type **511**	1·10	1·25
1723	37c. Two gold rings (horiz)	1·10	1·25
1724	37c. Mortarboard and scroll (horiz)	1·10	1·25
1725	37c. Trophy	1·10	1·25
1726	37c. Christmas baubles and gold ribbon (horiz)	1·10	1·25
1727	37c. Fireworks behind St John's Co-Cathedral, Valletta	1·10	1·25
1728	37c. Comino coastline (horiz)	1·10	1·25
1729	37c. *Auberge de Castille* (Charles Frederick de Brocktorff) (horiz)	1·10	1·25
1722/1729 Set of 8		8·00	9·00

(Litho Printex Ltd)

2012 (15 Apr). 70th Anniversary of the Award of the George Cross to Malta. Sheet 120×81 mm. W **105** (sideways). P 14.

| **MS**1730 | **512** | €4.16 multicoloured | 12·00 | 13·00 |

513 Saluting Battery, Harbour and Fort St Angelo

(Des Sean Cini. Litho Printex Ltd)

2012 (9 May). Europa. Visit Malta. T **513** and similar horiz design. Multicoloured. W **105** (sideways). P 14.

1731	37c. Type **513**	1·25	60
	a. Horiz pair. Nos. 1731/1732	4·75	4·75
	b. Booklet pane. No. 1731×5, with margins all round	5·50	
1732	€1.19 Saluting Battery, harbour and Fort St Elmo	3·50	4·25

Nos. 1731/1732 were printed together, *se-tenant*, as horizontal pairs in sheetlets of ten, each pair forming a composite design showing the Grand Harbour, Valletta, seen from the Upper Barakka Gardens.

514 Official London Olympic Games Logo

515 SS *Almeria Lykes*

(Des Sean Cini. Litho Printex Ltd)

2012 (27 July). Olympic Games, London. Sheet 120×80 mm containing T **514** and similar vert design. Multicoloured. W **105** (sideways). P 14.

| **MS**1733 | Type **514**; €2.11 Official mascot Wenlock | 6·50 | 7·50 |

(Des Cedric Galea Pirotta. Litho Printex Ltd)

2012 (10 Aug). 70th Anniversary of Operation Pedestal (Second World War Malta supply convoy). T **515** and similar horiz designs. Multicoloured. W **105** (sideways). P 14.

1734	26c. Type **515**	1·25	1·25
	a. Sheetlet of 8. Nos. 1734/1741 and two labels	9·00	9·00
1735	26c. HMS *Amazon*	1·25	1·25
1736	26c. HMS *Antelope*	1·25	1·25
1737	26c. HMS *Ashanti*	1·25	1·25
1738	26c. HMS *Badsworth*	1·25	1·25
1739	26c. HMS *Bicester*	1·25	1·25
1740	26c. HMS *Bramham*	1·25	1·25
1741	26c. MV *Brisbane Star*	1·25	1·25
1742	26c. RFA *Brown Ranger*	1·25	1·25
	a. Sheetlet of 8. Nos. 1742/1749 and two labels	9·00	9·00
1743	26c. HMS *Cairo*	1·25	1·25
1744	26c. HMS *Charybdis*	1·25	1·25
1745	26c. MV *Clan Ferguson*	1·25	1·25
1746	26c. HMS *Coltsfoot*	1·25	1·25
1747	26c. HMS *Derwent*	1·25	1·25
1748	26c. MV *Deucalion*	1·25	1·25
1749	26c. RFA *Dingledale*	1·25	1·25
1750	26c. MV *Dorset*	1·25	1·25
	a. Sheetlet of 8. Nos. 1750/1757 and two labels	9·00	9·00
1751	26c. HMS *Eagle*	1·25	1·25
1752	26c. MV *Empire Hope*	1·25	1·25
1753	26c. HMS *Eskimo*	1·25	1·25
1754	26c. HMS *Foresight*	1·25	1·25
1755	26c. HMS *Furious*	1·25	1·25
1756	26c. HMS *Fury*	1·25	1·25
1757	26c. HMS *Geranium*	1·25	1·25
1758	26c. MV *Glenorchy*	1·25	1·25
	a. Sheetlet of 8. Nos. 1758/1765 and two labels	9·00	9·00
1759	26c. HMS *Hebe*	1·25	1·25
1760	26c. HMS *Hythe*	1·25	1·25
1761	26c. HMS *Icarus*	1·25	1·25
1762	26c. HMS *Indomitable*	1·25	1·25
1763	26c. HMS *Intrepid*	1·25	1·25
1764	26c. HMS *Ithuriel*	1·25	1·25
1765	26c. HMS *Jaunty*	1·25	1·25
1766	26c. HMS *Jonquil*	1·25	1·25
	a. Sheetlet of 8. Nos. 1766/1773 and two labels	9·00	9·00
1767	26c. HMS *Kenya*	1·25	1·25
1768	26c. HMS *Keppel*	1·25	1·25
1769	26c. HMS *Laforey*	1·25	1·25
1770	26c. HMS *Ledbury*	1·25	1·25
1771	26c. HMS *Lightning*	1·25	1·25
1772	26c. HMS *Lookout*	1·25	1·25
1773	26c. HMS *Malcolm*	1·25	1·25
1774	26c. HMS *Manchester*	1·25	1·25
	a. Sheetlet of 8. Nos. 1774/1781 and two labels	9·00	9·00
1775	26c. HMS *Matchless*	1·25	1·25
1776	26c. MV *Melbourne Star*	1·25	1·25
1777	26c. HMS *Nelson*	1·25	1·25
1778	26c. HMS *Nigeria*	1·25	1·25
1779	26c. SS *Ohio* (tanker)	1·25	1·25
1780	26c. HMS *Pathfinder*	1·25	1·25
1781	26c. HMS *Penn*	1·25	1·25
1782	26c. HMS *Phoebe*	1·25	1·25
	a. Sheetlet of 8. Nos. 1782/1789 and two labels	9·00	9·00
1783	26c. MV *Port Chalmers*	1·25	1·25
1784	26c. HMS *Quentin*	1·25	1·25
1785	26c. MV *Rochester Castle*	1·25	1·25
1786	26c. HMS *Rodney*	1·25	1·25
1787	26c. HMS *Rye*	1·25	1·25
1788	26c. HMS *Salvonia*	1·25	1·25
1789	26c. SS *Santa Elisa*	1·25	1·25
1790	26c. HMS *Sirius*	1·25	1·25
	a. Sheetlet of 8. Nos. 1790/1797 and two labels	9·00	9·00
1791	26c. HMS *Somali*	1·25	1·25
1792	26c. HMS *Speedy*	1·25	1·25
1793	26c. HMS *Spirea*	1·25	1·25
1794	26c. HMS *Tartar*	1·25	1·25
1795	26c. HMS *Una*	1·25	1·25
1796	26c. HMS *Utmost*	1·25	1·25
1797	26c. HMS *Vansittart*	1·25	1·25
1798	26c. HMS *Venomous*	1·25	1·25
	a. Sheetlet of 8. Nos. 1798/1805 and two labels	9·00	9·00
1799	26c. HMS *Victorious*	1·25	1·25
1800	26c. HMS *Vidette*	1·25	1·25
1801	26c. SS *Waimarama*	1·25	1·25
1802	26c. MV *Wairangi*	1·25	1·25
1803	26c. HMS *Westcott*	1·25	1·25
1804	26c. HMS *Wilton*	1·25	1·25
1805	26c. HMS *Wishart*	1·25	1·25
1806	26c. HMS *Wolverine*	1·25	1·25
	a. Sheetlet of 8. Nos. 1806/1813 and two labels	9·00	9·00
1807	26c. HMS *Wrestler*	1·25	1·25
1808	26c. HMS *Zetland*	1·25	1·25
1809	26c. HMS *P.34*	1·25	1·25
1810	26c. HMS *P.42*	1·25	1·25
1811	26c. HMS *P.44*	1·25	1·25
1812	26c. HMS *P.46*	1·25	1·25
1813	26c. ML121	1·25	1·25
1814	26c. ML126	1·25	1·25
	a. Sheetlet of 8. Nos. 1814/1821 and two labels	9·00	9·00
1815	26c. ML134	1·25	1·25
1816	26c. ML135	1·25	1·25
1817	26c. ML168	1·25	1·25
1818	26c. HMS *P.211*	1·25	1·25
1819	26c. HMS *P.222*	1·25	1·25
1820	26c. ML459	1·25	1·25
1821	26c. ML462	1·25	1·25
1734/1821	*Set of 88*	90·00	90·00

Nos. 1734/1741, 1742/1749, 1750/1757, 1758/1765, 1766/1773, 1774/1781, 1782/1789, 1790/1797, 1798/1805, 1806/1813 and 1814/1821 were each printed together, *se-tenant*, in sheetlets of eight stamps and two stamp-size labels inscribed '70TH ANNIVERSARY OPERATION PEDESTAL 1942–2012' and 'CONVOY TA' SANTA MARIJA'.

516 Notre Dame Gate, Zabbar, 1675   **517** *The Adoration of the Magi* (German follower of Rubens)

(Des Cedric Galea Pirotta. Litho Printex Ltd)

2012 (26 Sept). Treasures of Malta. Historic Gates. T **516** and similar multicoloured designs. W **105** (sideways on horiz designs). P 14.

1822	20c. Type **516**	65	30
1823	37c. Couvre Port Gate, Vittoriosa, 1723 (*vert*)	1·10	40
1824	67c. Lunzjata Valley Gate, Victoria, Gozo, c. 1698 (*vert*)	1·90	2·50
1825	69c. Fort Chambray Gate, Ghajnsielem, Gozo	1·90	2·50
1822/1825	*Set of 4*	5·00	5·25

(Litho Printex Ltd)

2012 (31 Oct). Christmas. T **517** and similar vert designs. Multicoloured. W **105**. P 14.

1826	20c. Type **517**	65	30
1827	37c. *The Holy Family* (circle of Denys Calvaert)	1·10	40
1828	63c. *Holy Family* (Dutch School)	1·90	3·00
1826/1828	*Set of 3*	3·25	3·25

518 Blessed Gerard (founder) receiving Deed of Donation from Godfrey de Bouillon (detail) (Antoine Favray)   **519** *The Baptism of Christ*

(Des Edward D. Pirotta. Litho Printex Ltd)

2013 (15 Feb). 900th Anniversary of Papal Bull by Pope Paschal II to Blessed Gerard (founder of Hospital of St John of Jerusalem, now the Sovereign Military Hospitaller Order of St John of Jerusalem of Rhodes and of Malta (Order of Malta)). Sheet 120×80 mm. W **105** (sideways). P 14.

MS1829	**518** €2.47 multicoloured	8·00	8·50

(Des Edward D. Pirotta. Litho Printex Ltd)

2013 (23 Feb). 400th Birth Anniversary of Mattia Preti (artist). Sheet 120×81 mm containing T **519** and similar multicoloured design. W **105** (sideways). P 14.

MS1830 Type **519**; €1.87 Self-portrait (31×44 *mm*).......... 9·50   10·50

520 Vilhena Fountain, Floriana, 1728

521 Ford Transit Mark 1 Van passing former General Post Office at Auberge d'Italie, Merchant's Street, Valletta

(Des Cedric Galea Pirotta. Litho Printex Ltd)

2013 (27 Mar). Treasures of Malta. Fountains (1st series). T **520** and similar multicoloured designs. W **105** (sideways on 32c.). P 14.

1831	6c. Type **520**...	35	15
1832	32c. Triton Fountain, Floriana, 1959 (*horiz*)	1·50	35
1833	€2.62 Spinola Fountain, Valletta, late 19th-century	10·50	12·00
1831/1833 *Set of 3*		11·00	12·00

See also Nos. 1853/1855 and 1912/1913.

(Des Cedric Galea Pirotta. Litho Printex Ltd)

2013 (9 May). Europa. Postal Vehicles. T **521** and similar square design. Multicoloured. W **105** (sideways). P 14×13½.

1834	37c. Type **521**...	1·25	30
	a. Booklet pane. No. 1834×5, with margins all round........................	5·50	
1835	€1.19 Lambretta three wheeler, Dingli Street, Sliema	4·00	4·50

522 Riviera

(Litho Printex Ltd)

2013 (20 May). European Maritime Day. Cruise Liners. T **522** and similar horiz designs. Multicoloured. W **105** (sideways). P 14.

1836	26c. Type **522**...	1·25	65
1837	51c. *Costa Deliziosa*	2·50	2·25
1838	97c. *Ryndam*	5·00	6·50
1836/1838 *Set of 3*		8·00	8·50

523 Rabbit

(Des Cedric Galea Pirotta. Litho Printex Ltd)

2013 (20 June). Wild and Domestic Fauna of the Maltese Islands. T **523** and similar horiz design. W **105** (sideways). P 14.

1839	37c. Type **523**...	1·40	30
1840	€2.25 Maltese Ox	8·00	9·00

524 Grand Harbour, Malta

(Des Cedric Galea Pirotta. Litho Printex Ltd)

2013 (20 Aug). Harbours. Sheet 121×80 mm . W **105** (sideways). P 13½.

MS1841 **524** €4.51 multicoloured..................................... 13·00   14·00

No. **MS**1841 was a joint issue with Curaçao which issued a miniature sheet showing Schottegat Harbour.

525 Airport Bus, 1950s

(Des Cedric Galea Pirotta. Litho Printex Ltd)

2013 (27 Aug). Malta Buses. The End of an Era (2nd series). T **525** and similar horiz designs. Multicoloured. W **105** (sideways). P 14.

1842	6c. Type **525**	45	25
1843	10c. Double-deck bus, Valletta–St Julian's Route, c. 1903........................	60	40
1844	37c. Victoria Hire Service bus, 1925–1934.......	2·00	60
1845	52c. Royal Navy Bedford SB bus, 1950s–1960s ('Royal Armed Forces Bus')	3·25	2·25
1846	€1.16 Malta Police Bus, 1970s	6·50	6·50
1847	€2.25 Magirus-Deutz 03500	9·00	10·00
1842/1847 *Set of 6*		19·00	18·00

526 Red Cross

(Litho Printex Ltd)

2013 (29 Oct). 150th Anniversary of the International Red Cross. Sheet 120×80 mm. W **105** (sideways). P 13.

MS1848 **526** €4.57 multicoloured.................................. 13·00   14·00

527 Crib Scene

(Litho Printex Ltd)

2013 (18 Nov). Christmas. Scenes from Mechanical Nativity Crib at Jesus of Nazareth Institute, Zejtun. T **527** and similar horiz designs. Multicoloured. W **105** (sideways on MS1852). P 13½×14.

1849	26c. Type **527**....................................	75	30
1850	37c. Crib scene with Palm trees and Angels flying over city walls........................	1·10	40
1851	63c. Crib scene with flour mill...................	1·90	3·00
1849/1851 *Set of 3*		3·25	3·25
MS1852 105×68 mm. €1 Flying Angels over city walls, Palm trees and flour mill; €1 Nativity (*both* 76×20 *mm*)..........................		6·00	6·50

(Des Cedric Galea Pirotta. Litho Printex Ltd)

2014 (3 Jan). Treasures of Malta. Fountains (2nd series). Multicoloured designs as T **520**. W **105** (sideways on 59c.). P 14.

1853	42c. Fountain under arch, The Mall, Floriana	1·40	70
1854	59c. Fountain in front of wall, San Anton Gardens, Attard (*horiz*)................	1·75	1·75
1855	€1.25 Fountain in wall niche, Kercem, Gozo......	3·50	4·75
1853/1855 *Set of 3*		6·00	6·50

528 Halls of the Knights Hospitallers in Valletta, Malta and Acre, Israel

(Des Ronen Goldberg. Litho Printex Ltd)

2014 (28 Jan). The Halls of the Knights Hospitallers. W **105** (sideways). P 13½.

1856	**528**	51c. multicoloured	2·00	2·00

529 Police Boat, Marsamxett Harbour, Valletta

530 Pope John XXIII

(Des Cedric Galea Pirotta. Litho Printex Ltd)

2014 (18 Mar). Maritime Malta (2nd series). Bicentenary of the Malta Police Force (26c.) and 35th Anniversary of the End of Military Facilities Agreement (€1.55). T **529** and similar horiz designs. Multicoloured. W **105** (sideways). P 14.

1857	26c. Type **529**	1·50	1·25
1858	26c. Police Boat at Sliema Ferries	1·50	1·25
1859	€1.55 HMS *Alexander* off Fort St Angelo, 1800..	7·50	7·50
1860	€1.55 HMS *London* (off Fort St Michael) leaving Malta, 1 April 1979	7·50	7·50
1857/1860 *Set of 4*		16·00	16·00

Nos. 1857/1858 and 1859/1860 were each printed together in sheets of eight stamps containing two vertical strips of four stamps separated by a vertical gutter.

(Litho Printex Ltd)

2014 (26 Apr). Canonisation of Pope John XXIII and Pope John Paul II. Sheet 121×80 mm containing T **530** and similar vert design. Multicoloured. W **105** (sideways). P 14.

MS1861 Type **530**; €1.85 Pope John Paul II .... 8·50   8·50

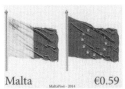

531 Flags of Malta and EU

(Litho Printex Ltd)

2014 (30 Apr). Tenth Anniversary of Malta's Accession to the European Union. W **105** (sideways). P 14.

1862	**531**	59c. multicoloured	2·00	2·00

532 Musician playing Maltese Bagpipe

533 Dove and EU Emblem

(Litho Printex Ltd)

2014 (9 May). Europa. National Musical Instruments. Details from 19th-century oil painting by Girolamo Gianni showing bagpipe and drum musicians performing at Porta Reale, Valletta. T **532** and similar vert design. Multicoloured. W **105**. P 13½.

1863	59c. Type **532**	1·75	60
	a. Wmk sideways	1·75	1·75
	b. Booklet pane. No. 1863a×5 with margins all round	8·00	
1864	€2.19 Drummer	6·00	7·00

(Litho Printex Ltd)

2014 (15 May). Anniversaries. 50th Anniversary of Independence and 40th Anniversary of the Republic of Malta. Sheet 95×86 mm containing T **533** and similar design, based on Nos. 324 and 537 but revalued. Multicoloured. W **105**. P 14.

MS1865 Type **533**; €3 As 1974 5c. Inauguration of Republic stamp but with '40TH ANNIVERSARY 1974–2014' inscription (44×31 *mm*) .... 11·00   12·00

T **533** is based on No. 324 but has the Crown at top left replaced by the EU emblem and the inscription '50TH ANNIVERSARY 1964–2014'.

534 Emblem

535 *Gladiolus italicus*

(Des Sean Cini. Litho Printex Ltd)

2014 (12 June). World Cup Football Championship, Brazil. Sheet 120×87 mm containing T **534** and similar square design. Multicoloured. W **105** (sideways). P 14.

MS1866 Type **534**; €1.55 Mascot Fuleco .... 5·50   6·00

(Litho Printex Ltd)

2014 (27 June). Maltese Flora (1st series). T **535** and similar vert designs. Multicoloured. W **105** (sideways). P 14×13½.

1867	26c. Type **535**	60	20
1868	59c. *Verbascum sinuatum*	1·50	75
1869	€1.16 *Orchis conica*	4·00	5·00
1867/1869 *Set of 3*		5·50	5·50

See also No. 1909/1911, 1932/1934 and 1960/1962.

536 Globe showing Mediterranean Sea

537 Fra' Philippe de Villiers de L'Isle-Adam (1521)

(Des Amany Ahmed Ali, Egypt Post Litho Printex Ltd)

2014 (9 July). Euromed Postal (Postal Union for the Mediterranean). The Mediterranean Sea. W **105** (sideways). P 13½.

1870	**536** €1.85 multicoloured	4·75	5·50

Similar designs were issued by Cyprus, Egypt, France, Greece, Jordan, Lebanon, Libya, Morocco, Palestine, Slovenia and Syria.

(Des Cedric Galea Pirotta (No. 1894/1898). Litho Printex Ltd)

2014 (30 Sept). Grandmasters of the Sovereign Military Order of Malta, 1530–1798. T **537** and similar vert designs. Multicoloured. W **105**. P 14.

1871	26c. Type **537**	70	00
	a. Sheetlet of 8. Nos. 1871/1878 and two stamp-size labels	5·00	
1872	26c. Fra' Pierino del Ponte (1534)	70	80
1873	26c. Fra' Didier de Saint-Jaille (1535)	70	80
1874	26c. Fra' Jean de Homedes (1536)	70	80
1875	26c. Fra' Claude de la Sengle (1553)	70	80
1876	26c. Fra' Jean de la Valette-Parisot (1557)	70	80
1877	26c. Fra' Pierre de Monte (1568)	70	80
1878	26c. Fra' Jean L'Evesque de la Cassière (1572)	70	80
1879	26c. Fra' Hugues Loubenx de Verdala (1582)..	70	80
	a. Sheetlet of 10. Nos. 1879/1888	6·25	

1880	26c. Fra' Martin Garzez (1595)	70	80
1881	26c. Fra' Alof de Wignacourt (1601)	70	80
1882	26c. Fra' Luis Mandez de Vasconcellos (1622).	70	80
1883	26c. Fra' Antoine de Paule (1623)	70	80
1884	26c. Fra' Jean-Paul de Lascaris-Castellar (1636)	70	80
1885	26c. Fra' Martin de Redin (1657)	70	80
1886	26c. Fra' Annet de Clermont-Gessant (1660) ..	70	80
1887	26c. Fra' Raphael Cotoner (1660)	70	80
1888	26c. Fra' Nicolas Cotoner (1663)	70	80
1889	26c. Fra' Gregorio Carafa (1680)	70	80
	a. Sheetlet of 10. Nos. 1889/1898	6·25	
1890	26c. Fra' Adrien de Wignacourt (1690)	70	80
1891	26c. Fra' Ramon Perellos y Roccaful (1697)	70	80
1892	26c. Fra' Marc' Antonio Zondadari (1720)	70	80
1893	26c. Fra' Antonio Manoel de Vilhena (1722)....	70	80
1894	26c. Fra' Raymond Despuig (1735)	70	80
1895	26c. Fra' Manuel Pinto de Fonseca (1741)	70	80
1896	26c. Fra' Francisco Ximenes de Texada (1773)	70	80
1897	26c. Fra' Emmanuel de Rohan-Polduc (1775) .	70	80
1898	26c. Fra' Ferdinand von Hompesch zu Bolheim (1797)	70	80
1871/1898	Set of 28	17·00	19·00

Nos. 1871/1878 were printed together, *se-tenant*, as sheetlets of eight stamps and two stamp-size labels.

Nos. 1879/1888 and 1889/1898 were each printed together, *se-tenant*, as sheetlets of ten stamps (5×2).

The portraits on Nos. 1871/1893 were from *Histoire de L'Ordre de Malte* by René Aubert de Vertot.

538 Bighi Hospital

539 Mary and Joseph with Newborn Jesus

(Des Paul Psaila. Litho Printex Ltd)

2014 (7 Nov). Centenary of World War I. Nurse of the Mediterranean. Military Hospitals. T **538** and similar horiz designs. Multicoloured. W **105** (sideways). P 14.

1899	10c. Type **538**	30	20
1900	59c. Floriana Hospital	1·75	1·25
1901	€2 HMHS *Rewa*	5·50	6·50
1899/1901	Set of 3	6·75	7·25

(Litho Printex Ltd)

2014 (17 Nov). Christmas. Scenes from *Bethlehem f'Ghajnsielem* (re-enactment of the Nativity by people of Ghajnsielem, Gozo). T **539** and similar multicoloured designs. W **105** (sideways on horiz designs). P 14.

1902	26c. Type **539**	70	25
1903	59c. Visit of the Three Kings to the Holy Family (*horiz*)	1·40	80
1904	63c. Two shepherds by fire, Gchurch in background (*horiz*)	1·60	1·25
1905	€1.16 The Holy Family in the stable	3·00	4·00
1902/1905	Set of 4	6·00	5·75

540 US President Franklin D. Roosevelt and Winston Churchill, Malta Conference, 1945 ("No more let us falter")

541 Red Cross Nurse, Wounded Soldier and Other Soldiers

(Des Joseph Said. Litho Printex Ltd)

2015 (4 Feb). 70th Anniversary of the Yalta Conference. T **540** and similar square designs showing quotations from Winston Churchill's correspondence with President Roosevelt. Multicoloured. W **105**. P 14.

1906	€1 Type **540**	2·50	2·75
	a. Horiz strip of 3. Nos. 1906/1908	6·75	7·50

1907	€1 Montgomery House, Floriana (venue of Malta Conference) ("From Malta to Yalta!")	2·50	2·75
1908	€1 Winston Churchill, President Roosevelt and Stalin at Yalta Conference ("Let nobody alter!")	2·50	2·75
1906/1908	Set of 3	6·75	7·50

Nos. 1906/1908 were printed together, *se-tenant*, as horizontal strips of three stamps in sheetlets of nine.

(Litho Printex Ltd)

2015 (14 Feb). Maltese Flora (2nd series). Vert designs as T **535**. Multicoloured. W **105** (sideways). P 14×13½.

1909	26c. *Tragopogon hybridus* (Smooth Goatsbeard)	60	20
1910	59c. *Anemone coronaria* (Crown Anemone) ...	1·25	75
1911	€1.16 *Arisarum vulgare* (Friar's Cowl)	2·50	3·25
1909/1911	Set of 3	4·00	3·75

(Des Cedric Galea Pirotta. Litho Printex Ltd)

2015 (21 Apr). Treasures of Malta (3rd series). 400th Anniversary of Construction of Wignacourt Aqueduct. Multicoloured designs as T **520**. W **105** (sideways on 42c.). P 14.

1912	42c. Wignacourt Arch, Fleur-de-lys (*horiz*)	1·00	70
1913	€1.55 Wignacourt Water Tower, Floriana (inscr 'Wignacourt')	3·50	4·00

(Litho Printex Ltd)

2015 (25 Apr). ANZAC Centenary. Sheet 120×75 mm. W **105** (sideways). P 13½.

MS1914	**541** €3.59 multicoloured	7·50	8·00

542 Penny Black

543 Boys with Cart

(Litho Printex Ltd)

2015 (2 May). 175th Anniversary of the Penny Black. Multicoloured. W **105** (sideways). P 13½.

MS1915	123×80 mm. €1.21 Type **542**×3	7·50	8·00

(Des Joe Mark Micallef. Litho Printex Ltd)

2015 (9 May). Europa. Old Toys. T **543** and similar vert design. Multicoloured. W **105** (sideways). P 13½.

1916	59c. Type **543**	1·25	75
	a. Booklet pane. No. 1916×5 with margins all round	5·00	
1917	€2.19 Girl running with hoop	4·50	5·00

544 Feast of St George, Victoria, Gozo ('The Festa')

545 Firilla

(Litho Printex Ltd)

2015 (16 June). Culture. T **544** and similar vert designs. Multicoloured. W **105**. P 14.

1918	26c. Type **544**	60	20
1919	59c. Annual Regatta, Grand Harbour	1·25	75
1920	€1.16 Statue of the Risen Christ carried in procession, Easter Sunday, Zebbug	2·50	3·25
1918/1920	Set of 3	4·00	3·75

No. 1919 was inscr 'sepac'.

(Des Sean Cini. Litho Printex Ltd)

2015 (9 July). Euromed Postal (Postal Union for the Mediterranean). Boats of the Mediterranean. W **105** (sideways). P 13½.

1921	**545**	€3.59 multicoloured	7·50	8·00

546 Brigantine *Concezione* in Shallow Water during Storm, 18 December 1835

547 St John Bosco

(Litho Printex Ltd)

2015 (29 July). Maritime Malta (3rd series). Ex-Voto Paintings from the Sanctuary of Our Lady, Mellieha. T **546** and similar horiz designs. Multicoloured. W **105** (sideways). P 14.

1922	51c. Type **546**...	1·00	60
1923	82c. Barque *Matutina* blown sideways onto shallow banks, 17 January 1839.................	2·00	2·25
1924	€1 *Speronara* (sailing coaster) S. Francesco di Paula with broken rudder, 9 December 1843	2·25	2·50
1922/1924 *Set of 3*	4·75	4·75

(Des Austin Camilleri. Litho Printex Ltd)

2015 (14 Aug). Birth Bicentenary of St John Bosco. W **105**. P 14.

1925	**547**	€2 multicoloured	4·00	4·25

548 *The Allegory of the Triumph of the Order* (Mattia Preti), from St John's Co-Cathedral, Valletta

549 Anniversary Emblem

(Litho Printex Ltd)

2015 (7 Sept). 450th Anniversary of the Great Siege. Sheet 120×80 mm. W **105** (sideways). P 13.

MS1926	**548**	€4.25 multicoloured	9·00	9·50

(Des Sean Cini. Litho Printex Ltd)

2015 (24 Oct). 70th Anniversary of the United Nations. Sheet 120×80 mm. W **105** (sideways). P 14.

MS1927	**549**	€3.51 multicoloured	7·00	7·50

550 *The Flight into Egypt*

551 Emblem

(Litho Printex Ltd)

2015 (14 Nov). Christmas. Woodcuts from series *Life of the Virgin* by Albrecht Dürer. T **550** and similar vert designs. Multicoloured. W **105**. P 14.

1928	26c. Type **550**...	60	20
1929	59c. *The Nativity of the Lord*	1·40	65
1930	63c. *The Adoration of the Magi*	1·60	2·00
1928/1930 *Set of 3*	3·25	2·50

(Des Sean Cini. Litho Printex Ltd)

2015 (27 Nov). Commonwealth Heads of Government Meeting (CHOGM), Valletta. Sheet 84×84 mm. W **105** (sideways). P 14.

MS1931	**551**	€3 multicoloured	6·00	6·50

(Litho Printex Ltd)

2016 (22 Jan). Maltese Flora (3rd series).Vert designs as T **535**. Multicoloured. W **105** (sideways). P 14×13½.

1932	26c. *Asphodelus aestivus* (Branched Asphodel)...	60	20
1933	59c. *Anacamptis pyramidalis* (Common Pyramidal Orchid)...................................	1·25	75
1934	€1.16 *Ophrys melitensis* (Maltese Spider Orchid)...	2·50	3·25
1932/1934 *Set of 3*	4·00	3·75

552 Coin of 1566

553 Shearwater

(Des Sean Cini. Litho Printex Ltd)

2016 (28 Mar). 450th Anniversary of the Foundation of Valletta. Sheet 120×80 mm. W **105** (sideways). P 14.

MS1935	**552**	€4.25 multicoloured	9·00	9·50

(Litho Printex Ltd)

2016 (15 Apr). Endangered Species. Shearwater. Sheet 120×80 mm containing T **553** and similar square designs. Multicoloured. W **105**. P 14.

MS1936	75c. Type **553**; 75c. Shearwater flying to left; 75c. Shearwater on the sea; 75c. Four shearwaters on the sea	6·50	6·50

554 Painting Contaminated Landscape Green

555 *Dulber* (Yalta Historical and Literature Museum)

(Des Doxia Sergidou (59c.), Sean Cini (€2.19). Litho Printex Ltd)

2016 (9 May). Europa. Think Green. T **554** and similar horiz design. Multicoloured. W **105** (sideways). P 14.

1937	59c. Type **554**...	1·25	75
	a. Booklet pane. No. 1937×5 with stamp-size label at top left...	5·00	
1938	€2.19 Human profiles containing polluted and green environments................................	4·50	5·00

(Des Marka, Russian Post. Litho Printex Ltd)

2016 (24 May). Paintings by Nicholas Krassnoff. T **555** and similar vert design. Multicoloured. W **105** (sideways). P 14.

1939	€1 Type **555**	2·25	2·50
	a. Pair. Nos. 1939/1940	4·50	5·00
1940	€1 *View from Vittoriosa Gate* (Malta National Museum of Fine Arts).................	2·25	2·50

Nos. 1939/1940 were printed together, *se-tenant*, as horizontal and vertical pairs in sheetlets of ten (4×3) with stamp-size labels at top left and bottom right, giving three horizontal pairs (two centre columns of the sheetlet) and two vertical pairs (left and right columns of sheetlet). Similar designs were issued by Russia.

556 Woman in Maltese Costume, Landscape with Flowers and Gozo's Cittadella (Spring)

557 Dorado (Lampuka – *Coryphaena hippurus*)

(Des Tony Calleja. Litho Printex Ltd)

2016 (21 June). Seasons. T **556** and similar multicoloured designs. Multicoloured. W **105**. P 14.

1941	26c. Type **556**	60	25
1942	51c. Sunbathers and swimmers on sandy beach of Ghajn Tuffieha (Summer) (*horiz*)	1·10	60
1943	59c. Woman, autumn trees and Verdala Palace (Autumn)	1·25	80
1944	€2 Woman on shore on stormy day, Ghar-id-Dud, Sliema (Winter) (*horiz*)	4·75	5·50
1941/1944 *Set of 4*		7·00	6·50

No. 1943 was inscr 'sepac'.

(Des Richard J. Caruana. Litho Printex Ltd)

2016 (9 July). Euromed Postal (Postal Union for the Mediterranean). Fish in the Mediterranean. W **105**. P 14.

1945	**557** €3.59 multicoloured	7·50	8·00

558 Shooting

559 Dom Mintoff

(Des Sean Cini. Litho Printex Ltd)

2016 (5 Aug). Olympic Games, Rio de Janeiro, Brazil. T **558** and similar square designs. Multicoloured. W **105**. P 14.

1946	42c. Type **558**	90	60
1947	62c. Swimming	1·40	1·00
1948	90c. Weightlifting	2·25	1·75
1949	€1.55 Relay runner with baton	3·75	4·75
1946/1949 *Set of 4*		7·50	7·50

(Litho Printex Ltd)

2016 (6 Aug). Birth Centenary of Dominic ('Dom') Mintoff (1916–2012, Prime Minister of Malta 1955–1958, 1971–1984). W **105**. P 14.

1950	**559** €3 multicoloured	6·50	6·50

560 HMS *Hastings* in Valletta Grand Harbour, 30 November 1838 (lithograph of drawing by Charles von Brocktorff)

561 Balcony Corbel

(Litho Printex Ltd)

2016 (15 Sept). Maritime Malta (4th series). Arrival of HMS *Hastings* carrying Queen Adelaide, Valletta, 1838. W **105**. P 13.

MS1951 120×80 mm. **560** €3.59 multicoloured		7·50	7·50

(Des Cedric Galea Pirotta. Litho Printex Ltd)

2016 (15 Oct). Balcony Corbels (1st series). T **561** and similar vert designs. Multicoloured. W **105**. P 14.

1952	26c. Type **561**	60	25
1953	€1 Balcony corbel with carved head	2·50	2·75
1954	€1.16 Balcony corbel with carved mask	2·75	3·00
1952/1954 *Set of 3*		5·25	5·50

See also Nos. 1963/1965.

562 Cittadella, Ghawdex

563 Mary, Joseph and Jesus

(Des Cedric Galea Pirotta (illustration) and Sean Cini. Litho Printex Ltd)

2016 (18 Oct). Fortifications. Multicoloured. P 13½.

MS1955 120×80 mm. 59c. Type **562**; €3 First Tower, San Marino		8·00	8·00

A similar miniature sheet was issued by San Marino.

(Des Joseph Pulo. Litho Printex Ltd)

2016 (18 Nov). Christmas. Paintings by Joseph Pulo. T **563** and similar vert designs. Multicoloured. W **105**. P 13½.

1956	26c. Type **563**	60	20
1957	59c. Stable with Mary, Joseph and baby Jesus in manger and Star of Bethlehem above	1·25	1·00
1958	63c. Three Wise Men giving gifts	1·75	2·25
1956/1958 *Set of 3*		3·25	3·00

564 Emblem

565 St Agatha Tower, Mellieha, Malta

(Des Sean Cini. Litho Printex Ltd)

2017 (12 Jan). Maltese Presidency of the Council of the European Union. W **105** (sideways). P 14.

MS1959 85×85 mm. **564** €3.59 multicoloured		8·00	8·00

(Litho Printex Ltd)

2017 (24 Feb). Maltese Flora (4th series). Vert designs as T **535**. Multicoloured. W **105** (sideways). P 14×13½.

1960	26c. *Orchis collina* (Fan-lipped Orchid)	70	20
1961	42c. *Ophrys lutea* (Yellow Bee-orchid)	1·00	60
1962	€1.25 *Serapias parviflora* (Small-flowered Tongue-orchid)	3·00	3·50
1960/1962 *Set of 3*		4·25	4·00

(Des Cedric Galea Pirotta. Litho Printex Ltd)

2017 (30 Mar). Balcony Corbels (2nd series). Vert designs as T **561**. Multicoloured. W **105**. P 14.

1963	51c. Two balcony corbels	1·50	90
1964	€1.32 Square balcony with scroll corbel	3·25	3·50
1965	€1.55 Round balcony with scroll corbel	3·75	4·25
1963/1965 *Set of 3*		7·75	7·75

(Des Cedric Galea Pirotta. Litho Printex Ltd)

2017 (9 May). Europa. Castles. T **565** and similar horiz design. Multicoloured. W **105** (sideways). P 14.

1966	59c. Type **565**	1·25	75
	a. Booklet pane. No. 1966×5 with stamp-size label at top left	5·00	
1967	€2.19 Gourgion Tower, Xewkija, Gozo	5·00	5·50

566 Peppi Pustier Mascot in Modern Uniform

567 Boat Builder

(Des Fabio Aguis (illustration) and Sean Cini. Litho Printex Ltd)

2017 (31 May). Postal Uniforms. T **566** and similar square designs. Multicoloured. W **105** (sideways). P 14.

1968	26c. Type **566**	70	30
1969	59c. Peppi Pustier (MaltaPost mascot) in uniform of early 2000s	1·50	80
1970	€1 Peppi Pustier on motorcycle wearing 1980s uniform with grey jacket	2·75	3·00
1971	€2 Peppi Pustier in early 1900s uniform	4·75	5·50
1968/1971	Set of 4	8·75	8·75

(Des Tony Calleja. Litho Printex Ltd)

2017 (28 June). Traditional Handicrafts. T **567** and similar horiz designs. Multicoloured. W **105** (sideways). P 14.

1972	26c. Type **567**	70	30
1973	59c. Man making Bamboo fish trap	1·50	80
1974	€1 Weaving	2·75	3·00
1975	€3.51 Tberfil artist decorating wheels of horse-drawn carriage	8·50	9·50
1972/1975	Set of 4	12·00	12·00

568 *Tetraclinis articulata* Tree at Mellieha

569 Siege Bell War Memorial, Valletta

(Des Richard J. Caruana. Litho Printex Ltd)

2017 (10 July). Euromed Postal (Postal Union for the Mediterranean). Trees of the Mediterranean. Araar or Sandarac Tree (*Tetraclinis articulata*). T **568** and similar horiz design. Multicoloured. W **105** (sideways). P 14.

1976	10c. Type **568**	40	25
1977	€3.63 *Tetraclinis articulata* tree at Qrendi	8·50	9·00

(Des Cedric Galea Pirotta. Litho Printex Ltd)

2017 (10 Aug). 75th Anniversary of Operation Pedestal. W **105** (sideways). P 14.

MS1978	120×80 mm. **569** €3 multicoloured	7·25	7·50

570 Bone China Virgin Mary Statue, sculpted by Rafl Ignaz, 1874, Attard Parish Church

571 *La Gloria Di Santa Rosa Di Lima*

(Litho Printex Ltd)

2017 (14 Aug). Maltese Festivals (1st series). The Feast of the Assumption of Our Lady. T **570** and similar vert designs. Multicoloured. W **105**. P 14.

1979	26c. Type **570**	70	70
	a. Sheetlet of 10. Nos. 1979/1988	6·25	6·25

1980	26c. Wooden Virgin Mary statue, sculpted by Mastru Anton Busuttil and Son, 1861, Dingli Parish Church	70	70
1981	26c. Wooden Virgin Mary statue, sculpted by Marjanu Gerada, 1808, Ghaxaq Parish Church	70	70
1982	26c. Virgin Mary statue, sculpted by Vincenzo Dimech, 1807, Gudja Parish Church	70	70
1983	26c. Virgin Mary statue, Mgarr Parish Church	70	70
1984	26c. Virgin Mary statue, sculpted by Salvatore Dimech, 1868, Mosta Sanctuary	70	70
1985	26c. Virgin Mary statue, sculpted by Xandru Farrugia, 1836, Mqabba Parish Church	70	70
1986	26c. Wooden Virgin Mary statue, sculpted by Antonio Chircop, 1837, Qrendi Parish Church	70	70
1987	26c. Virgin Mary statue, Victoria Cathedral, Gozo	70	70
1988	26c. Virgin Mary statue, made by Gallard et Fils in Marseilles, 1863, Zebbug Parish Church, Gozo	70	70
1979/1988	Set of 10	6·25	6·25

Nos. 1979/1988 were printed together, *se-tenant*, in sheetlets of ten stamps (5×2).
See also Nos. 2030/2039.

(Des Sean Cini. Litho Printex Ltd)

2017 (4 Sept). 350th Death Anniversary of Melchiorre Gafá (1636–1667, Maltese sculptor). T **571** and similar vert designs. Multicoloured. W **105**. P 14.

1989	20c. Type **571**	70	30
1990	42c. *La Gloria Di Santa Caterina Di Siena*	1·00	60
1991	51c. *L'Annunciazione*	1·25	80
1992	€1 *L'Adorazione dei Pastori*	2·50	2·75
1993	€1.16 *La Nativita*	2·75	3·25
1989/1993	Set of 5	7·50	7·00

572 Model of Third Rate Ship-of-the-line

573 Infant Jesus Figurine, Church of the Nativity of the Virgin Mary, Naxxar

(Des Sean Cini. Litho Printex Ltd)

2017 (29 Sept). Maritime Malta (5th series). Vessels of the Order of St John. T **572** and similar horiz designs. Multicoloured. W **105** (sideways). P 14.

1994	63c. Type **572**	1·60	1·10
1995	€1.85 Model of carrack *Sant' Anna*	4·75	5·00
1996	€3.59 Model of third rate ship-of-the-line (*different*)	9·00	10·00
1994/1996	Set of 3	14·00	14·50

(Litho Printex Ltd)

2017 (17 Nov). Christmas. Baby Jesus Figurines. T **573** and similar vert designs. Multicoloured. W **105**. P 14.

1997	26c. Type **573**	70	20
1998	51c. Baby Jesus, Church of the Immaculate Conception, Cospicua	1·25	60
1999	59c. Baby Jesus, Basilica of St Peter and St Paul, Nadur	1·50	1·40
2000	63c. Baby Jesus, Sanctuary of Our Lady of Grace, Zabbar	1·75	2·25
1997/2000	Set of 4	4·75	4·00

574 Tile Pattern of Green and Claret Flowers (top left portion)

575 White Shirt, Trousers held up by Sash, Waistcoat and Cap

(Des Stephanie Borg. Litho Printex Ltd)

2017 (12 Dec). Traditional Floor Tile Patterns. T **574** and similar square designs. Multicoloured. W **105**. P 14.

2001	25c. Type **574**	70	70
	a. Sheetlet of 4. Nos. 2001/2004	2·50	2·50
2002	25c. Pattern of green and claret flowers (top right portion)	70	70
2003	25c. Pattern of green and claret flowers (bottom left portion)	70	70
2004	25c. Pattern of green and claret flowers (bottom right portion)	70	70
2005	29c. Pattern of four red flowers	80	80
2006	59c. Pattern with Maltese Cross	1·50	1·50
2007	75c. Pattern with green flowers and brown, red and white triangles (top left and lowe right portion)	2·25	2·25
	a. Sheetlet of 4. Nos. 2007/2008, each×2	8·00	
2008	75c. Pattern with green flowers and brown, red and white triangles (top right and lower left portion)	2·25	2·25
2001/2008 Set of 8		9·00	9·00

Nos. 2001/2004 were printed together, *se-tenant*, in sheetlets of four stamps, each sheetlet forming a composite design.

Nos. 2005/2006 were each printed in separate sheetlets of four stamps.

Nos. 2007/2008 were printed together, *se-tenant*, in sheetlets of four containing two of each design, the whole sheetlet forming a composite design.

(Litho Printex Ltd)

2018 (9 Feb). Traditional Costumes. T **575** and similar vert designs. Multicoloured. W **105**. P 14.

2009	26c. Type **575**	70	30
2010	59c. White shirt, trousers held up by sash, waistcoat and cap, with addition of horga (cloth pouch slung over shoulder)	1·40	1·00
2011	€1.16 Kabozza (hooded winter overcoat)	2·75	3·00
2009/2011 Set of 3		4·25	4·00

576 Sensile (common galley)

(Des Sean Cini. Litho Printex Ltd)

2018 (23 Mar). Maritime Malta (6th series). Vessels of the Order of St John. Models from Malta Maritime Museum. T **576** and similar horiz designs. Multicoloured. W **105** (sideways). P 14.

2012	26c. Type **576**	70	30
2013	42c. Demi galley or half galley	1·00	70
2014	€1 Brigantine (ceremonial barge of Portuguese Grand Master Antonio Manoel de Vilhena)	2·25	2·50
2012/2014 Set of 3		3·50	3·25

577 Grand Harbour Breakwater Bridge (St Elmo Bridge), Valletta

578 Painting by Joseph Pulo

(Des David P. Attard. Litho Printex Ltd)

2018 (3 May). Europa. Bridges. T **577** and similar horiz design. Multicoloured. W **105** (sideways). P 14.

2015	59c. Type **577**	1·25	1·50
	a. Booklet pane. No. 2015x5 with label	5·75	
2016	€2.19 Madliena or Wied id-Dis Bridge	4·50	5·00

(Des Joseph Pulo. Litho Printex Ltd)

2018 (22 May). Valletta 2018. European Capital of Culture. T **578** and similar multicoloured designs. W **105** (sideways on 63c., €2). P 14.

2017	26c. Type **578**	55	40

2018	63c. Valletta skyline with St Paul's Anglican Pro-Cathedral and Basilica of Our Lady of Mount Carmel (*horiz*)	1·25	1·50
2019	€2 Portrait and montage of buildings (*horiz*)	4·25	4·75
2017/2019 Set of 3		5·50	6·00

579 Zabivaka (wolf mascot)　　**580** Medieval Façade

(Des Sean Cini. Litho Printex Ltd)

2018 (14 June). World Cup Football Championship, Russia. W **105**. P 14.

MS2020 84×85 mm. **579** €3 multicoloured | 6·25 | 6·75

(Litho Printex Ltd)

2018 (9 July). Euromed Postal (Postal Union for the Mediterranean). Houses in the Mediterranean. T **580** and similar multicoloured designs. W **105** (sideways on 90c.). P 14.

2021	20c. Type **580**	40	30
2022	90c. Townhouse (*horiz*)	1·90	2·10

581 General Eisenhower inspects the Soldiers under the Command of General Oxley

(Litho Printex Ltd)

2018 (10 July). 75th Anniversary of Operation Husky (Allied invasion of Sicily). T **581** and similar square designs. Multicoloured. W **105**. P 14.

2023	€1 Type **581**	2·10	2·40
	a. Horiz strip of 3. Nos. 2023/2025	5·75	6·50
2024	€1 British Commanders of Operation Husky Major General F. W. de Guingand, Air Commodore C. B. R. Pelly, Air Vice Marshal H. Broadhurst, General Montgomery and Admiral Sir Bertram Ramsey planning their operations in Malta, 1943	2·10	2·40
2025	€1 General Eisenhower, Governor Lord Gort and Air Chief Marshal Sir Arthur Tedder	2·10	2·40
2023/2025 Set of 3		5·75	6·50

Nos. 2023/2025 were printed together, *se-tenant*, as horizontal strips of three stamps in sheetlets of nine.

582 Church of St John the Baptist, Xewkija, Gozo

(Litho Printex Ltd)

2018 (27 July). Sepac. Spectacular Views. T **582** and similar horiz designs. Multicoloured. W **105** (sideways). P 14.

2026	26c. Type **582**	55	40
2027	42c. Ghajn Tuffieha	90	80
2028	59c. Gozo Aqueduct	1·25	1·50
2029	€1.25 Dwejra Bay, Gozo	2·75	3·25
2026/2029 Set of 4		5·00	5·25

(Litho Printex Ltd)

2018 (14 Aug). Maltese Festivals (2nd series). Processional Statues of Patron Saints of Villages. Vert designs as T **570**. Multicoloured. W **105**. P 14.

2030	26c. Wooden statue of St Paul by Melchiorre Gafa', brought from Rome, 1659 (Valletta)	55	40
	a. Sheetlet of 10. Nos. 2030/2039	5·00	3·50
2031	26c. Statue of St Peter and St Paul, 1882 (Nadur)	55	40
2032	26c. Papier-mâché statue of the Immaculate Conception (Hamrun)	55	40
2033	26c. Wooden statue of Our Lady of Mount Carmel by Andrea Imbroll, 1761 (Mdina)	55	40
2034	26c. Papier-mâché statue of St Gaetan by Karlu Darmanin, 1885–8 (Hamrun)	55	40
2035	26c. Wooden statue of St Dominic attributed to Melchiorre Gafa', pre-1687 (Valletta)	55	40
2036	26c. Papier-mâché statue of St Julian by Karlu Darmanin, 1893 (St Julian's)	55	40
2037	26c. Wooden statue of St Catherine of Alexandria by Mariano Gerarda, 1818 (Zurrieq)	55	40
2038	26c. Statue of the Nativity of the Blessed Virgin (Maria Bambina), 1618 (Senglea)	55	40
2039	26c. Statue of Our Lady of Consolation (Gudja)	55	40
2030/2039 Set of 10		5·00	3·50

Nos. 2030/2039 were printed together, *se-tenant*, in sheetlets of ten stamps (5×2).

583 Padre Pio (Patri Krispin)

(Litho Printex Ltd)

2018 (22 Sept). 50th Death Anniversary of Padre Pio (1887–1968). W **105** (sideways). P 14.

MS2040 120×80 mm. **583** €3 multicoloured		6·25	6·75

584 German Pointer

(Des Andrew Micallef. Litho Printex Ltd)

2018 (23 Oct). Dogs. T **584** and similar square designs. Multicoloured. W **105** (sideways). P 14.

2041	59c. Type **584**	1·25	1·50
	a. Sheetlet of 16. Nos. 2041/2056	18·00	22·00
2042	59c. Labrador	1·25	1·50
2043	59c. French Bulldog	1·25	1·50
2044	59c. Irish Setter	1·25	1·50
2045	59c. Chow Chow	1·25	1·50
2046	59c. Boxer	1·25	1·50
2047	59c. Golden Retriever	1·25	1·50
2048	59c. Pharoah's Hound	1·25	1·50
2049	59c. Cavalier King Charles Spaniel	1·25	1·50
2050	59c. Scottish Terriers	1·25	1·50
2051	59c. Maltese Dog	1·25	1·50
2052	59c. Border Collie	1·25	1·50
2053	59c. Pug	1·25	1·50
2054	59c. Yorkshire Terrier	1·25	1·50
2055	59c. Bernese Mountain Dog	1·25	1·50
2056	59c. Chihuahua	1·25	1·50
2041/2056 Set of 16		18·00	22·00

Nos. 2041/2056 were printed together, *se-tenant*, in sheetlets of 16 stamps.

585 Baby Jesus Figurine, St Helen's Basilica, Birkirkara

(Litho Printex Ltd)

2018 (16 Nov). Christmas. T **585** and similar vert designs. Multicoloured. W **105**. P 14.

2057	26c. Type **585**	55	40
2058	59c. Baby Jesus figurine, St Catherine's Parish Church, Zejtun	1·25	1·50
2059	63c. Baby Jesus figurine, Basilica of the Nativity of Our Lady, Xaghra, Gozo	1·25	1·50
2057/2059 Set of 3		2·75	3·00

586 Valletta Skyline

(Litho Printex Ltd)

2018 (23 Nov). UNESCO World Heritage Sites. T **586** and similar horiz design. Multicoloured. W **105** (sideways). P 13½×14.

2060	€1.16 Type **586**	2·40	2·75
	a. Vert pair, Nos. 2060/2061	4·75	5·50
2061	€1.16 Burana Tower, Kyrgyzstan	2·40	2·75

Nos. 2060/2061 were printed together, *se-tenant*, as vertical pairs in sheetlets of ten stamps (1×10).

Similar designs were issued on the same date by Kyrgyzstan.

MACHINE LABELS. From 9 January 2002 gummed 6c. labels in four different designs showing Maltese scenes were available from vending machines, at Malta International Airport.

STAMP BOOKLETS

B **1** General Post Office, Palazzo Parisio, Valletta

1970 (16 May). Brownish black on brownish grey cover as T B **1** depicting GPO Palazzo Parisio, Valletta. Stitched.
SB1   2s.6d. booklet containing 6×1d. and 12×2d. (Nos. 331, 333) in blocks of 6 .... 5·50

B **1a** Magisterial Palace, Valletta

1970 (18 May). Black on pink cover as T B **1a** depicting Magisterial Palace, Valletta. Stitched.
SB2   2s.6d. booklets containing 6×1d. and 12×2d. (Nos. 331, 333) in blocks of 6 .... 4·00

B **1b** Auberge d'Aragon, Valletta

1971 (29 May). Black on green cover, 92×49 mm, as T B **1b** depicting Auberge d'Aragon, Valletta. Stitched.
SB3   2s.6d. booklet containing 6×1d. and 12×2d. (Nos. 331, 333) in blocks of 6 .... 11·00

B **2**

1994 (2 Nov). Multicoloured covers, 100×75 mm, as T B **2**. Stamps attached by selvedge.
SB5   50c. booklet containing 5c. (No. 909) in block of 10, (cover showing Malta 1926 2s. Mdina (Notabile) stamp) .... 5·50
SB6   70c. booklet containing 14c. (No. 912) in strip of 5 with 6 airmail labels (cover showing Malta 1926 1s. Valleta Harbour stamp) .... 7·00

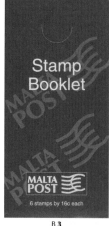

B **3**   B **4**

2003 (16 Apr). Ultramarine and lemon cover, 55×117 mm, as T B **3**. Stamps attached by selvedge.
SB7   96c. booklet containing pane No. 1297a .... 9·00

2003 (22 Oct). Ultramarine and chrome-yellow covers as T B **4**. Self-adhesive.
SB8   84c. booklet containing pane No. 1335a (48×80 mm) .... 7·00
SB9   96c. booklet containing pane No. 1336a (48×73 mm) .... 8·00

B **5**   B **6**

2006 (9 May). Europa. Integration. Orange-yellow, dull violet-blue and royal blue cover, 50×80 mm, as T B **5**. Stamps attached by selvedge.
SB10   80c. booklet containing 16c. (No. 1482) in strip of 5 .... 6·00

2007 (9 May). Europa. Centenary of Scouting. Chrome-yellow and bright ultramarine cover, 75×79 mm, as T B **6**. Stamps attached by selvedge.
SB11   80c. booklet containing pane No. 1541ab .... 6·00

B **1c** Fort St Angelo

1971 (3 July). Black on white cover, 92×49 mm, as T B **1c** depicting Fort St Angelo. Stitched.
SB4   5s. booklet containing 12×5d. (No. 337b) in blocks of 6 .... 9·50

B **7**

B **10**

2008 (9 May). Europa. The Letter. Orange-yellow, bright blue and bright ultramarine cover, 79×86 mm, as T B **7**. Stamps attached by selvedge.
SB12 €1.85 booklet containing pane No. 1593a .... 7·50

2009 (9 May). Europa. Astronomy. Ultramarine, bright ultramarine and orange-yellow cover, 77×85 mm, as T B **7** but cover inscr. 'ASTRONOMY'. Stamps attached by selvedge.
SB13 €1.85 booklet containing pane No. 1620a .... 7·50

2014 (9 May). Europa. National Musical Instruments. Grey, red and black cover, 78×85 mm, as T B **10**. Stamps attached by selvedge.
SB18 €2.95 booklet containing pane No. 1863b .... 8·00

2015 (9 May). Europa. Old Toys. Grey and red cover, 77×85 mm, as T B **10** but inscr EUROPA 2015 'OLD TOYS'. Stamps attached by selvedge.
SB19 €2.95 booklet containing pane No. 1916a .... 5·00

B **8**

B **11**

2010 (4 May). Europa. Children's Books. Ultramarine, bright ultramarine and orange-yellow cover, 77×85 mm, as T B **8**. Stamps attached by the selvedge.
SB14 €1.85 booklet containing pane No. 1666a .... 7·50

2016 (9 May). Europa. Think Green. Multicoloured cover, 100×100 mm, as T B **11**. Pane loose within sachet.
SB20 €2.95 booklet containing pane No. 1937a .... 5·00

B **9**

B **12** St Agatha Tower, Mellieħa, Malta

2011 (9 May). Europa. Forests. Grey, red and black cover, 78×85 mm, as T B **9**. Stamps attached by selvedge.
SB15 €1.85 booklet containing pane No. 1686a .... 7·50

2012 (9 May). Europa. Visit Malta. Grey and black cover, 78×85 mm, as T B **9** but cover inscr 'VISIT MALTA'. Stamps attached by selvedge.
SB16 €1.85 booklet containing pane No. 1731b .... 5·50

2013 (9 May). Europa. Postman Van. Grey, red and black cover, 78×85 mm, as T B **9** but cover inscr 'POSTMAN VAN'. Stamps attached by selvedge.
SB17 €1.85 booklet containing pane No. 1834a .... 5·50

2017 (9 May). Europa. Castles. Multicoloured cover, 100×100 mm, as T B **12**. Pane loose within sachet.
SB21 €2.95 booklet containing pane No. 1966a .... 5·00

B **13** Grand Harbour Breakwater
Bridge (St Elmo Bridge), Valletta

2018 (3 May). Europa. Bridges. Multicoloured cover as T B **13**.
SB22 €2.95 booklet containing pane No. 2015a .... 5·75

POSTAGE DUE STAMPS

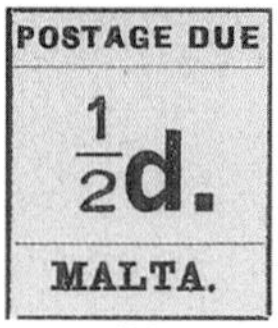

D **1**

1925 (16 Apr). Typeset by Govt Printing Office, Valletta. Imperf.

D1	D **1**	½d. black		1·25	11·00
		a. *Tête-bêche* (horiz pair)		5·00	24·00
D2		1d. black		3·25	4·75
		a. *Tête-bêche* (horiz pair)		10·00	13·00
D3		1½d. black		3·00	3·75
		a. *Tête-bêche* (horiz pair)		10·00	15·00
D4		2d. black		15·00	26·00
		a. *Tête-bêche* (horiz pair)		32·00	65·00
D5		2½d. black		2·75	2·75
		a. '2' of '½' omitted		£900	£1300
		b. *Tête-bêche* (horiz pair)		12·00	15·00
D6		3d. black/*grey*		9·00	15·00
		a. *Tête-bêche* (horiz pair)		30·00	48·00
D7		4d. black/*buff*		5·00	9·50
		a. *Tête-bêche* (horiz pair)		17·00	38·00
D8		6d. black/*buff*		5·00	32·00
		a. *Tête-bêche* (horiz pair)		17·00	70·00
D9		1s. black/*buff*		6·50	35·00
		a. *Tête-bêche* (horiz pair)		25·00	70·00
D10		1s.6d. black/*buff*		20·00	75·00
		a. *Tête-bêche* (horiz pair)		42·00	£150
D1/D10 *Set of 10*				60·00	£190

Nos. D1/D10 were each issued in sheets containing four panes (6×7) printed separately, the impressions in the two left-hand panes being inverted. 14 horizontal *tête-bêche* pairs occur from the junction of the left and right-hand panes.

No. D5a occurred on R. 4/4 of the last 2½d. pane position to be printed. Forgeries exist, but can be detected by comparison with a normal example under ultra-violet light. They are often found in pair with normal, showing forged cancellations of 'VALLETTA AP 20 25' or 'G.P.O. MY 7 25'.

D **2**

(Typo B.W.)

1925 (20 July). Wmk Mult Script CA (sideways). P 12.

D11	D **2**	½d. green		1·25	60
D12		1d. violet		1·25	45
D13		1½d. brown		1·50	80
D14		2d. grey		6·50	1·00
D15		2½d. orange		2·00	1·25
		x. Wmk reversed		£160	
D16		3d. blue		4·00	1·25
D17		4d. olive-green		8·00	16·00
D18		6d. purple		3·50	8·00
D19		1s. black		5·00	18·00
D20		1s.6d. carmine		7·50	50·00
D11/D20 *Set of 10*				35·00	85·00
D11s/D20s Optd 'SPECIMEN.' *Set of 10*				£275	

1953–63. Chalk-surfaced paper. Wmk Mult Script CA (sideways). P 12.

D21	D **2**	½d. emerald		70	4·00
D22		1d. purple		70	1·25
		a. Deep purple (17.9.63)		75	3·75
D23		1½d. yellow-brown		2·50	18·00
D24		2d. grey-brown (20.3.57)		6·00	9·50
		a. Blackish brown (3.4.62)		29·00	13·00
D25		3d. deep slate-blue		1·00	2·00
D26		4d. yellow-olive		2·50	4·25
D21/D26 *Set of 6*				12·00	35·00

1966 (1 Oct). As No. D24, but wmk w **12** (sideways).

D27	D **2**	2d. grey-brown		10·00	20·00

1967–70. Ordinary paper. W **105** (sideways).

(a) P 12, line (9.11.67)

D28	D **2**	½d. emerald		4·00	9·00
D29		1d. purple		4·00	9·00
D30		2d. blackish brown		6·50	9·00
D31		4d. yellow-olive		45·00	£110
D28/D31 *Set of 4*				55·00	£120

(b) P 12½, comb (30.5.68–1970)

D32	D **2**	½d. emerald		35	2·00
D33		1d. purple		30	1·50

D34		1½d. yellow-brown		35	3·25
		a. *Orange-brown* (23.10.70)		1·25	3·00
D35		2d. blackish brown		85	70
		a. *Brownish black* (23.10.70)		3·25	3·00
D36		2½d. yellow-orange		60	70
D37		3d. deep slate-blue		60	60
D38		4d. yellow-olive		1·00	80
D39		6d. purple		75	1·75
D40		1s. black		90	1·50
D41		1s.6d. carmine		2·75	7·50
D32/D41 *Set of 10*				7·00	18·00

The above are the local release dates. In the 12½ perforation the London release dates were 21 May for the ½d. to 4d. and 4 June for the 6d. to 1s.6d. Nos. D34a and D35a are on glazed paper.

D **3** Maltese Lace

(Des G. Pace. Litho Printex Ltd, Malta)

1973 (28 Apr). W **105**. P 13×13½.

D42	D **3**	2m. grey-brown and reddish brown		10	10
D43		3m. dull orange and Indian red		10	15
D44		5m. rose and bright scarlet		15	20
D45		1c. turquoise and bottle green		30	35
D46		2c. slate and black		40	35
D47		3c. light yellow-brown and red-brown		40	35
D48		5c. dull blue and royal blue		65	70
D49		10c. reddish lilac and plum		85	1·00
D42/D49 *Set of 8*				2·50	2·75

D **4**

(Des M. Bonavia. Litho Printex Ltd, Malta)

1993 (4 Jan). W **105** (sideways). P 14.

D50	D **4**	1c. magenta and pale magenta		20	40
D51		2c. new blue and pale blue		25	50
D52		5c. blue-green and pale turquoise-green		35	45
D53		10c. yellow-orange and greenish yellow		55	60
D50/D53 *Set of 4*				1·25	1·75

Cyprus, Gibraltar & Malta Order Form

STANLEY GIBBONS
Est 1856

YOUR ORDER

Stanley Gibbons account number ☐ ☐ ☐ ☐ ☐ ☐

Condition (mint/UM/ used)	Country	SG No.	Description	Price	Office use only
			POSTAGE & PACKING	£3.60	
			TOTAL		

The lowest price charged for individual stamps or sets purchased from Stanley Gibbons Ltd, is £1.

Payment & address details

Name

Address (We cannot deliver to PO Boxes)

Postcode

Tel No.

Email

PLEASE NOTE Overseas customers MUST quote a telephone number or the order cannot be dispatched. Please complete ALL sections of this form to allow us to process the order.

☐ Cheque (made payable to Stanley Gibbons)

☐ I authorise you to charge my

☐ Mastercard ☐ Visa ☐ Diners ☐ Amex ☐ Maestro

Card No. ☐☐☐☐ ☐☐☐☐ ☐☐☐☐ ☐☐☐☐ (Maestro only)

Valid from ☐☐ ☐☐ Expiry date ☐☐ ☐☐ Issue No. (Maestro only) ☐☐ CVC No. (4 if Amex) ☐☐☐☐

CVC No. is the last three digits on the back of your card (4 if Amex)

Signature

Date

4 EASY WAYS TO ORDER

Post to
Mark Pegg,
Stamp Mail Order
Department,
Stanley Gibbons Ltd,
399 Strand, London,
WC2R 0LX, England

Call
020 7836 8444
+44 (0)20 7836 8444

Fax
020 7557 4499
+44 (0)20 7557 4499

Click
mpegg@
stanleygibbons.com